Linear Time–Varying Systems:

Analysis and Synthesis

This book is part of
The ALLYN AND BACON series
in Electrical Engineering

Consulting Editor
Norman Balabanian
Syracuse University

LINEAR TIME–VARYING SYSTEMS:

ANALYSIS AND SYNTHESIS

Henry D'Angelo

Chairman, Department of Electrical Engineering
Michigan Technological University

Allyn and Bacon, Boston

Dedicated to the memory of my father

AGOSTINO D'ANGELO

LIBRARY OF CONGRESS CATALOG CARD NUMBER: 69-17546

PRINTED IN THE UNITED STATES OF AMERICA

TABLE OF CONTENTS

PREFACE

The main purpose of this book is to provide a unified treatment of the main techniques for the analysis and synthesis of linear time-varying systems. It represents, insofar as the author knows, the first comprehensive work on the analysis and synthesis of linear time-varying systems. The theory is developed essentially from scratch for general multivariable systems using state variables. Until this time the theory of linear time-varying systems has been widely scattered throughout the technical literature. It has thus been extremely difficult for both the student and the interested investigator to obtain proper perspective in this field of rapidly increasing importance. Hopefully this book will fill the needs of both.

This book is primarily the result of class notes developed during four years of teaching a graduate course on the analysis and synthesis of linear time-varying systems. Thus the book has a strong pedagogical flavor resulting from trying to provide the reader with a "feel" for fundamental properties of these systems through a study of simple examples and special cases before proceeding to the development of a general theory. Such an approach can be objectionable to a reader already quite familiar with linear time-varying systems who might prefer a more direct treatment. Affirmatively, the approach used has proved to be very effective with graduate students relatively new to the subject. In addition, extreme care has been taken to ensure that the fine cause of pedagogy is not blasphemed by either the substituting of important issues with trivia or the emasculating of the real problems associated with the analysis and synthesis of linear time-varying systems.

The level of the book is such that it can be read by graduate students in engineering, science, or mathematics. A typical undergraduate background of calculus, differential equations and the elements of matrix algebra has proved to be sufficient. Thus the book might be used for advanced undergraduates.

The first three chapters present the basic properties of linear time-varying systems including an introduction to state variables. Of fundamental importance are the existence and uniqueness theorems and the development of the superposition integrals in terms of the Wronskian matrix, the transition matrix and the impulsive-response matrix; application of these results to discrete linear time-varying systems is detailed. An operational algebra for combining scalar systems, useful for synthesis, is developed.

Chapters 4, 5, and 6 develop the important notions, and their interrelations, of controllability and observability, canonical structures, minimal realizations, and equivalence transformations. These lead to a development of algorithms for reducing systems, transforming systems to desired forms and, most importantly, for synthesizing systems from their impulsive-response matrices.

Chapter 7, starting with Floquet theory, develops the special properties associated with systems having periodically varying parameters. Practical procedures for analyzing periodic systems are detailed. A useful canonic form for second-order systems is introduced and utilized in developing methods for approximating solutions.

Chapter 8 presents stability concepts peculiar to linear time-varying systems: emphasis is placed on the important distinction between the stability of forced and unforced systems. The notions of relative stability and short-time stability are presented in detail. Methods for extending frequency-domain methods to time-varying systems are developed.

Chapters 9 and 10 present the subject of integral transforms in terms of general linear time-varying systems and the notion of a compatible transform. The usefulness and relative merits of compatible and noncompatible integral transforms are detailed.

My very special thanks go to my students who served as laboratory subjects through the first "rough" drafts and made innumerable valuable suggestions which have been incorporated in the book. I especially thank S. M. Barrager, T. D. Dicken, J. W. Dickenson, C. M. Glass, N. A. Osborne, J. P. Portasik and Bhangwant Singh. I am indebted to Dean David A. Day and Professor Arlie E. Paige of the University of Denver for their major efforts in securing funds to partially cover the expense of having the class notes typed. My special gratitude to Mrs. Joan Hart, who did an outstanding job of typing and editing the entire manuscript. I sincerely thank and acknowledge Professor Thomas J. Higgins of the University of Wisconsin, whose methods for inspiring students I *now* fully appreciate and endorse (to those as hardy), for initially motivating me in this area. To my wife, Gail, who understands, and to my sons, Gus, Jim, Peter, and Paul, who will, my love as always.

Denver, Colorado H. D'A.

ACKNOWLEDGMENT

Although the organization and presentation of the material included in this text are unique, it is generally based on the original contributions of others. The exceptions to this are noted.

References are included at the end of each chapter to acknowledge contributions which either directly or indirectly influenced the material in that particular chapter. However, the large number of references cited may often cause unjust deemphasis of a specific contribution on which a major part of a chapter may be based. The purpose here is to acknowledge the more influential contributions and thus place them in a more proper perspective insofar as this text is concerned. It is often difficult to determine exactly who is responsible for a given idea and little attempt is made to do so here; this acknowledgment simply represents the citing of works heavily utilized during the writing of this text.

In chapter 2 the existence theorem proofs generally follow K. S. Miller's works. The ideas and results on operator algebra are from the works of A. Stubberud.

Section 3.6 is influenced primarily by the work of S. Mal'chikov.

In Chapter 4 the strong motivating force is obviously the creative work of R. Kalman on controllability and observability. The concept of the controllability and observability matrices for linear time-varying systems appears to have been advanced by several: A. Chang, G. Haynes, R. Herman, L. Silverman and H. Meadows, and A. Stubberud. However, the development given here is primarily influenced by the work of G. Haynes. The introduction of the important concepts of uniform controllability and observability is due to L. Silverman and H. Meadows.

Again in Chapter 5 the motivating idea is that of Kalman, i.e., the idea of relating the minimal realization of a system's impulsive-response matrix to its controllable and observable part. The section on reduced systems is suggested by and to a large degree follows the work of D. Youla. However, the work contained herein represents a significant extension of Youla's work in that the problem of nonanticipatory systems is considered. In particular, Theorems 5.3, 5.4, and 5.6 are original.

In Chapter 6, the motivating ideas and the results contained are almost exclusively from the excellent works of L. Silverman and H. Meadows.

Most of Chapter 7 is based on the significant nineteenth century contribution of M. Floquet. However, the work of I. Lee and L. Pipes provided much of the background for the interpretation given, as well as many of the specific details.

In Chapter 8 the emphasis on the difference between stable systems and nonresonant systems was motivated by the work of W. Kaplan. The works of R. Bellman and T. Bridgeland are freely drawn upon in the section on relative stability. The results of P. Dorato, used in the sections on short-time stability and nonresonance, motivated the results on short-time boundedness developed by J. Portasik and myself. The work of I. Sandberg forms the foundation for the section on frequency-domain stability.

In Chapter 9, the work of H. Davis was used in formulating the central ideas on a compatible transform. The work of Zadeh provides the foundation for extending the Laplace transform to linear time-varying systems in the form of a useful noncompatible transform.

In Chapter 10, the works of J. Cruz and L. Weiss were used in exploiting the idea of a separable system function. Results from the works of J. Cruz, E. Gilbert, and A. Stubberud provided much of the methodology for approximating system functions in separable form.

Certainly, exposure and familiarity with many works not specifically referenced markedly influenced the outcome of this text. For such unintentional omissions I apologize.

Linear Time–Varying Systems:

Analysis and Synthesis

1

Introduction

1.1. TIME-VARYING SYSTEMS

Most methods used in the analysis and synthesis of engineering systems require that the system be well characterized by a model that is:

1. *Causal*: The quiescent system does not respond before an input is applied.
2. *Lumped*: The dimensions of the system components are small compared to the wavelengths of the significant frequencies of the system signals.
3. *Time-invariant*: None of the system components has parameters that vary with time.
4. *Linear*: Superposition applies between any input/output pair for an initially quiescent system, e.g., doubling the input doubles the output.

This book deals primarily with systems that are not necessarily time-invariant. Thus attention is focused on the infinitely larger class of systems which are causal, lumped, and linear, i.e., *linear time-varying systems*. The equations characterizing linear time-varying systems are similar to those characterizing linear time-invariant systems with the exception that the coefficients can be functions of time. Thus linear time-varying systems are characterized by either, in the case of a scalar system,

$$\alpha_0(t)\frac{d^n x(t)}{dt^n} + \cdots + \alpha_n(t)x(t) = \beta_0(t)\frac{d^m r(t)}{dt^m} + \cdots + \beta_m(t)r(t) \quad (1.1)$$

or, in the case of a multivariable system,

$$\frac{dx_1(t)}{dt} = a_{11}(t)x_1(t) + \cdots + a_{1n}(t)x_n(t) + b_{11}(t)u_1(t) + \cdots + b_{1m}(t)u_m(t)$$

$$\vdots \tag{1.2a}$$

$$\frac{dx_n(t)}{dt} = a_{n1}(t)x_1(t) + \cdots + a_{nn}(t)x_n(t) + b_{n1}(t)u_1(t) + \cdots + b_{nm}(t)u_m(t) \; .$$

$$y_1(t) = c_{11}(t)x_1(t) + \cdots + c_{1n}(t)x_n(t) + d_{11}(t)u_1(t) + \cdots + d_{1m}(t)u_m(t)$$

$$\vdots \tag{1.2b}$$

$$y_r(t) = c_{r1}(t)x_1(t) + \cdots + c_{rn}(t)x_n(t) + d_{r1}(t)u_1(t) + \cdots + d_{rm}(t)u_m(t)$$

However, unlike the situation for linear time-invariant systems, general methods for obtaining the response of any linear time-varying systems do not exist.

1.2. EXAMPLES OF LINEAR TIME-VARYING SYSTEMS

Frequently cited older classical examples of linear time-varying systems include the microphone transmitter containing a variable resistor, the condensor microphone containing a variable capacitor, and the induction generator in which the mutual inductance between the primary and secondary windings is variable. These are less complex in nature than such recent examples as communication channels consisting of various media which are subject to cyclic and random variations and parametric amplifiers which derive their gain from variable-reactance circuit elements.

Carrier-frequency control systems, of both continuous and sampled-data or digital types, typically comprise modulators (multipliers), a-c amplifiers, and demodulators (multipliers). The product-type modulator, which multiplies the input signal by the carrier signal, is often treated as a periodically time-varying gain or parameter. Examples typical of some mechanical devices which are "carrier-frequency" type systems in their basic aspects are a pendulum suspended on a spring, coupled pendulums with oscillating supports, and a pair of spring-coupled masses contained in an orbital space satellite.

The rapid development of adaptive control systems, where the parameters of the controller are adjusted to compensate for changes in process dynamics stemming from changes in environment, has focused considerable interest on automatic control systems with time-varying parameters. For example, if the "plant" dynamics are characterized by linear differential equations, a "model-reference" adaptive control system can be represented adequately, over appropriate time intervals, by a linear time-varying system.

Largely responsible for this increasing interest in adaptive control systems is the great emphasis that is being placed on supresonic aircraft and space flight. Thus in the study of the flight control of ordinary aircraft, the pertinent equations of motion have coefficients dependent on flight speed. In the past it has been the conventional practice to consider the speed as constant, resulting in linear differential equations with constant coefficients. The relatively small accelerations experienced by subsonic aircraft rendered the assumption a reasonable one in that good results were obtained. With the much increased accelerations and velocities that attend modern supersonic aircraft and missiles, however, the parameters dependent on flight velocity change at a significantly rapid rate. Further, the high rates of fuel consumption cause the mass, center of gravity, and moments of inertia of a vehicle to alter to a significant degree during the characteristic response times of the controlled motions. In addition, variations of flight conditions in rapid ascent through the atmosphere introduce time-varying parameter variations. Consequently, modern automatic flight-control analysis of aircraft and missiles requires including these time-varying parameters, such that the responses are characterized by linear differential equations with variable coefficients.

Space flight introduces variations of a yet different nature. Of great current interest are problems of transferring a space vehicle from one orbit to another, rendezvous, and interplanetary guidance. The development of the rigid-body equations of motion of artificial satellites requires accounting for cyclic variations of inertial torques that occur as the vehicle progresses in its orbit. Similarly, successful solution of the satellite rendezvous problem requires dealing with the combined complexity of both mass and orbital variations. For with both the target and interceptor in orbit, the interceptor must expend fuel-mass in maneuvering; further, the kinematics of intercept-quidance introduces additional time-varying parameters, whence the characterizing differential equations have both periodic and aperiodic coefficients. Also of interest is a class of problems which relate to the gyroscopic stabilization of orbiting satellites. It is shown that these situations lead to a study of the damped Mathieu equation.

1.3. LINEAR TIME-INVARIANT SYSTEMS

Any causal, lumped, time-invariant, linear system is denoted as a *linear time-invariant system* or often loosely as a *linear system*. Such a system can be characterized by the ordinary n-order linear differential equations with constant coefficients:

$$\alpha_0 \frac{d^n x(t)}{dt^n} + \cdots + \alpha_n x(t) = \beta_0 \frac{d^m r(t)}{dt^m} + \cdots + \beta_m r(t) \tag{1.3}$$

Equation 1.3 suggests a *scalar system*, i.e., a system having a single input

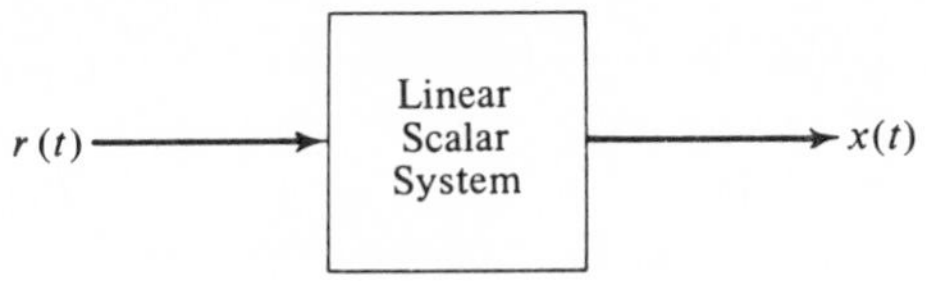

Fig. 1.1. Single-input, single-output system.

$r(t)$ and a single output $x(t)$, as shown in Fig. 1.1. Alternatively, and perhaps more generally, such a system can also be characterized by the n ordinary first-order linear differential equations with constant coefficients

$$\begin{aligned}\frac{dx_1(t)}{dt} &= a_{11}x_1(t) + \cdots + a_{1n}x_n(t) + b_{11}u_1(t) + \cdots + b_{1m}u_m(t)\\ &\vdots\\ \frac{dx_n(t)}{dt} &= a_{n1}x_1(t) + \cdots + a_{nn}x_n(t) + b_{n1}u_1(t) + \cdots + b_{nm}u_m(t)\end{aligned} \tag{1.4}$$

For the sake of compactness, Eq. 1.4 can be equivalently written, using matrix notation, in the *state-variable* form as

$$\frac{d\mathbf{x}(t)}{dt} = \mathbf{A}\mathbf{x}(t) + \mathbf{B}\mathbf{u}(t) \tag{1.5}$$

where $\mathbf{A}$ is a constant $n \times n$ matrix, $\mathbf{B}$ is a constant $n \times m$ matrix, $\mathbf{x}(t)$ is an n-vector termed the *state-variable*, and $\mathbf{u}(t)$ is an m-vector termed the *input*. Equations 1.4 and 1.5 suggest a *multivariable* system, i.e., a system having m inputs $u_1(t), \cdots, u_m(t)$ and, considering each of the state variables as an output variable, n outputs $x_1(t), \cdots, x_n(t)$. Such a multivariable system is represented in Fig. 1.2. Initial conditions $x_1(t_0), \cdots, x_n(t_0)$ are represented as shown.

In general, however, the number of outputs is independent of the number of states. For these cases the outputs can be defined as linear combinations of the state variables and the inputs. Thus

$$\begin{aligned}y_1(t) &= c_{11}x_1(t) + \cdots + c_{1n}x_n(t) + d_{11}u_1(t) + \cdots + d_{1m}u_m(t)\\ &\vdots\\ y_r(t) &= c_{r1}x_1(t) + \cdots + c_{rn}x_n(t) + d_{r1}u_1(t) + \cdots + d_{rm}u_m(t)\end{aligned} \tag{1.6}$$

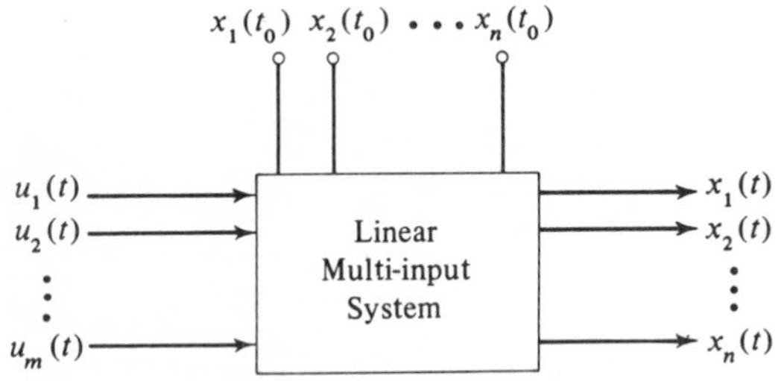

Fig. 1.2. Multi-input, n-state system.

or, using matrix notation,

$$\mathbf{y}(t) = \mathbf{C}\mathbf{x}(t) + \mathbf{D}\mathbf{u}(t) \tag{1.7}$$

where **C** is a $r \times n$ matrix and **D** is a $r \times m$ matrix. Clearly, the number of state variables is determined by the order of the system—an nth-order system has n state variables—while the number of outputs possible is not restricted. The number of outputs is generally determined by physical needs and considerations. Such a system is depicted in Fig. 1.3.

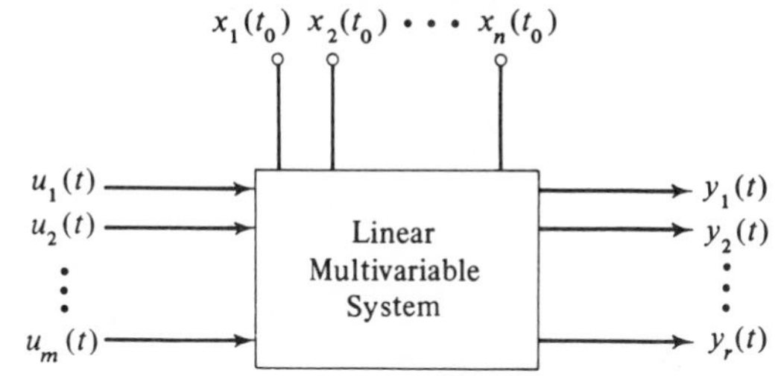

Fig. 1.3. Multi-input, multi-output system.

Simplification in drawing block diagrams is obtained by using a double line to represent a vector. Thus the systems of Figs. 1.2 and 1.3 can be represented as in Figs. 1.4 and 1.5 respectively.

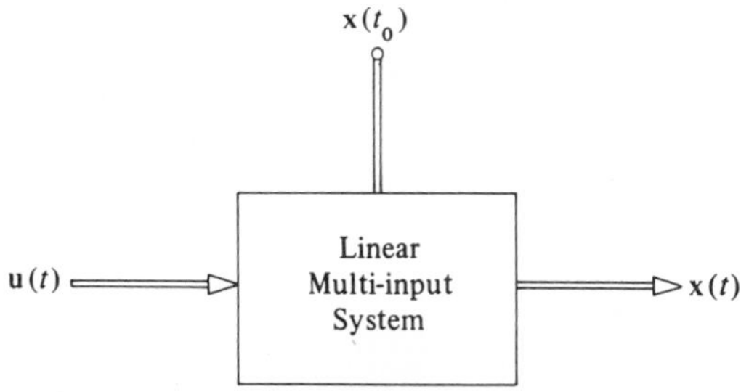

Fig. 1.4. Multi-input, n-state system.

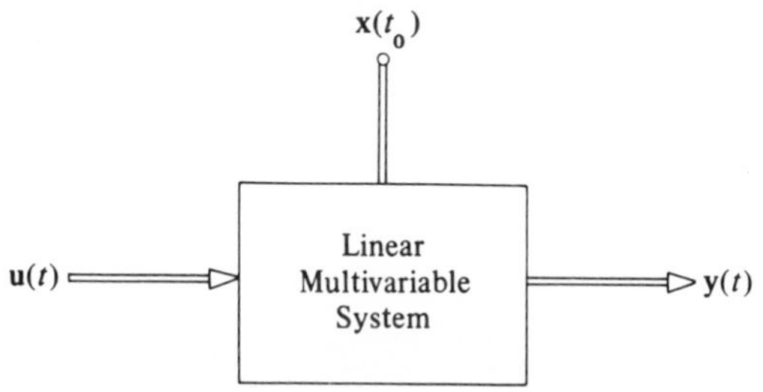

Fig. 1.5. Multi-input, multi-output system.

General methods of analysis for determining the response of any linear time-invariant system to arbitrary inputs are well known and, excepting pathological numerical cases, easily applied.

Example 1.1. The state-variable equations are to be written for the circuit shown in Fig. 1.6. The state-variable equations are obtained by

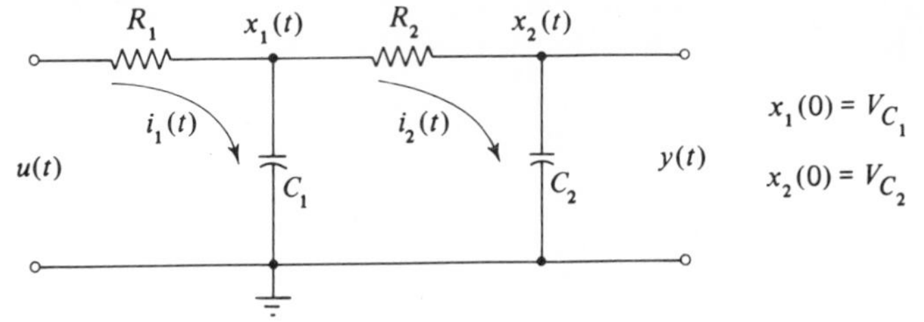

Fig. 1.6. *R-C* circuit analyzed in Example 1.1.

taking the two states of the system to be the voltages across the capacitors and writing the current-voltage relations for each of the capacitors:

$$i_1(t) - i_2(t) = C_1 \frac{dx_1(t)}{dt}$$

$$i_2(t) = C_2 \frac{dx_2(t)}{dt}$$

The currents $i_1(t)$ and $i_2(t)$ are expressed in terms of voltages by application of Ohm's law to each of the resistors:

$$i_1(t) = \frac{1}{R_1}[u(t) - x_1(t)]$$

$$i_2(t) = \frac{1}{R_2}[x_1(t) - x_2(t)]$$

Thus

$$\dot{x}_1(t) = -\left(\frac{1}{C_1R_1} + \frac{1}{C_1R_2}\right)x_1(t) + \frac{1}{C_1R_2}x_2(t) + \frac{1}{C_1R_1}u(t)$$

$$\dot{x}_2(t) = \frac{1}{C_2R_2}x_1(t) - \frac{1}{C_2R_2}x_2(t)$$

and

$$y(t) = x_2(t)$$

In matrix form, this is

$$\begin{bmatrix} \dot{x}_1(t) \\ \dot{x}_2(t) \end{bmatrix} = \begin{bmatrix} -\left(\frac{1}{C_1R_1} + \frac{1}{C_1R_2}\right) & \frac{1}{C_1R_2} \\ \frac{1}{C_2R_2} & -\frac{1}{C_2R_2} \end{bmatrix} \begin{bmatrix} x_1(t) \\ x_2(t) \end{bmatrix} + \begin{bmatrix} \frac{1}{C_1R_1} \\ 0 \end{bmatrix} u(t)$$

$$y(t) = [0 \quad 1]\begin{bmatrix} x_1(t) \\ x_2(t) \end{bmatrix}$$

or simply

$$\dot{\mathbf{x}}(t) = \mathbf{A}\mathbf{x}(t) + \mathbf{B}u(t)$$
$$y(t) = \mathbf{C}\mathbf{x}(t)$$

Example 1.2. The following third-order differential equation is to be put into state-variable form:

$$\frac{d^3x(t)}{dt^3} + 2\frac{d^2x(t)}{dt^2} + 3\frac{dx(t)}{dx} + 4x(t) = r(t)$$

The following procedure can always be used to obtain the state-variable equations for linear differential equations which do not involve derivatives of the forcing function $r(t)$..

Define the state variables by

$$x_1(t) \equiv x(t)$$
$$x_2(t) \equiv \dot{x}_1(t) = \dot{x}(t)$$
$$x_3(t) = \dot{x}_2(t) = \ddot{x}(t)$$

Therefore

$$\dot{x}_3(t) = \frac{d^3x(t)}{dt^3} = -4x(t) - 3\frac{dx(t)}{dt} - 2\frac{d^2x(t)}{dt^2} + r(t)$$
$$= -4x_1(t) - 3x_2(t) - 2x_3(t) + r(t)$$

Thus the state-variable equation in matrix form is

$$\begin{bmatrix} \dot{x}_1(t) \\ \dot{x}_2(t) \\ \dot{x}_3(t) \end{bmatrix} = \begin{bmatrix} 0 & 1 & 0 \\ 0 & 0 & 1 \\ -4 & -3 & -2 \end{bmatrix} \begin{bmatrix} x_1(t) \\ x_2(t) \\ x_3(t) \end{bmatrix} + \begin{bmatrix} 0 \\ 0 \\ 1 \end{bmatrix} r(t)$$

A *state-variable diagram* for this system, in which each state variable is represented as the output of an integrator, is shown in Fig. 1.7.

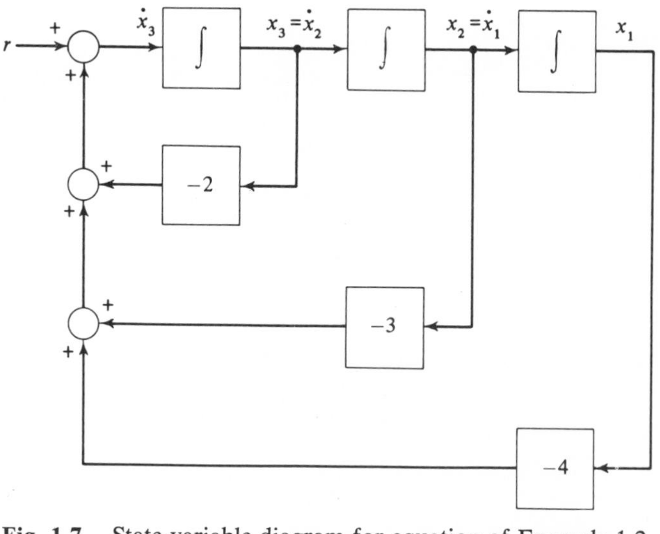

Fig. 1.7. State-variable diagram for equation of Example 1.2.

Example 1.3. The following third-order differential equation, involving derivatives of the forcing function, is to be put into state-variable form:

$$\frac{d^3y(t)}{dt^3} + 2\frac{d^2y(t)}{dt^2} + 3\frac{dy(t)}{dt} + 4y(t) = 5\frac{d^3r(t)}{dt^2} + \\ + 6\frac{d^2r(t)}{dt^2} + 7\frac{dr(t)}{dt} + 8r(t)$$

The state variables $x_1(t)$, $x_2(t)$, $x_3(t)$ are defined such that

$$\begin{bmatrix} \dot{x}_1(t) \\ \dot{x}_2(t) \\ \dot{x}_3(t) \end{bmatrix} = \begin{bmatrix} 0 & 1 & 0 \\ 0 & 0 & 1 \\ -4 & -3 & -2 \end{bmatrix} \begin{bmatrix} x_1(t) \\ x_2(t) \\ x_3(t) \end{bmatrix} + \begin{bmatrix} b_1 \\ b_2 \\ b_3 \end{bmatrix} r(t)$$

$$y(t) = [1 \quad 0 \quad 0] \begin{bmatrix} x_1(t) \\ x_2(t) \\ x_3(t) \end{bmatrix} + b_0 r(t)$$

where b_0, b_1, b_2, b_3 are to be determined. Differentiating $y(t)$ and substituting for $\dot{x}_1(t)$ gives

$$\begin{aligned} \dot{y}(t) &= \dot{x}_1(t) + b_0\dot{r}(t) \\ &= x_2(t) + b_1 r(t) + b_0\dot{r}(t) \end{aligned}$$

Repeating in a similar manner results in

$$\begin{aligned} \ddot{y}(t) &= \dot{x}_2(t) + b_1\dot{r}(t) + b_0\ddot{r}(t) \\ &= x_3(t) + b_2 r(t) + b_1\dot{r}(t) + b_0\ddot{r}(t) \end{aligned}$$

and

$$\begin{aligned} \dddot{y}(t) &= \dot{x}_3(t) + b_2\dot{r}(t) + b_1\ddot{r}(t) + b_0\dddot{r}(t) \\ &= -4x_1(t) - 3x_2(t) - 2x_3(t) \\ &\qquad + b_3 r(t) + b_2\dot{r}(t) + b_1\ddot{r}(t) + b_0\dddot{r}(t) \end{aligned}$$

Substituting in for $x_1(t)$, $x_2(t)$, $x_3(t)$ gives

$$\begin{aligned} \dddot{y}(t) = &-4y(t) - 3\dot{y}(t) - 2\ddot{y}(t) \\ &+ (4b_0 + 3b_1 + 2b_2 + b_3)r(t) \\ &+ (3b_0 + 2b_1 + b_2)\dot{r}(t) \\ &+ (2b_0 + b_1)\ddot{r}(t) + b_0\dddot{r}(t) \end{aligned}$$

Solving the original differential equation for $\dddot{y}(t)$ gives

$$\dddot{y}(t) = -4y(t) - 3\dot{y}(t) - 2\ddot{y}(t) + 8r(t) + 7\dot{r}(t) + 6\ddot{r}(t) + 5\dddot{r}(t)$$

Comparing the coefficients of $r(t)$ and its derivatives in the last two equa-

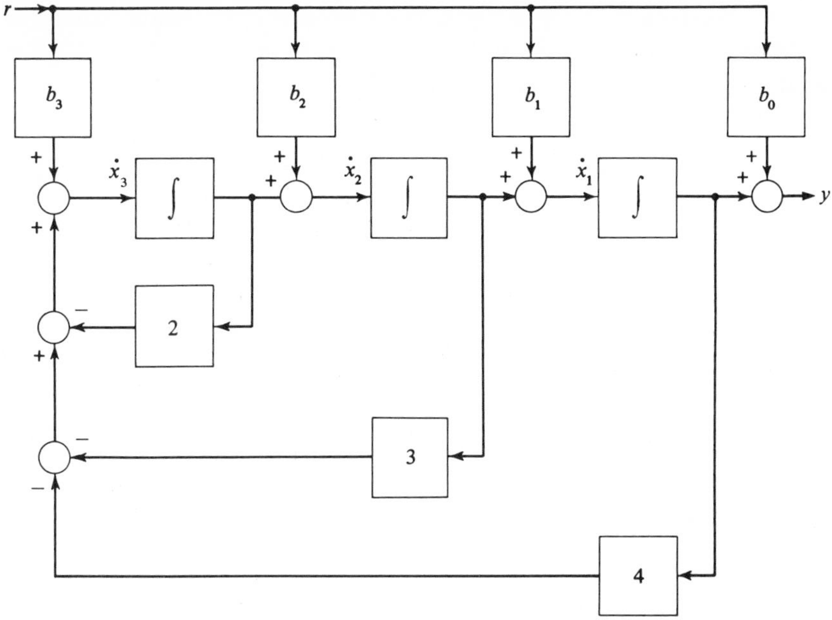

Fig. 1.8. State-variable diagram for equation of Example 1.3.

tions gives the four equations from which b_0, b_1, b_2, b_3 can be obtained:

$$\begin{bmatrix} 4 & 3 & 2 & 1 \\ 3 & 2 & 1 & 0 \\ 2 & 1 & 0 & 0 \\ 1 & 0 & 0 & 0 \end{bmatrix} \begin{bmatrix} b_0 \\ b_1 \\ b_2 \\ b_3 \end{bmatrix} = \begin{bmatrix} 8 \\ 7 \\ 6 \\ 5 \end{bmatrix}$$

A state-variable diagram for this system is shown in Fig. 1.8. Note the similarity between this simulation and the one of Fig. 1.7. The minimum number of integrators are used in this simulation.

Example 1.4. Given a state-variable diagram, the equations can be written by a step-by-step procedure. This is done for the system shown in Fig. 1.9 as follows:

$$\dot{x}_1 = x_2$$
$$\dot{x}_2 = -3x_2 - 2x_3 + u_1$$
$$\dot{x}_3 = x_4$$
$$\dot{x}_4 = -x_2 - x_3 + u_2$$
$$y_1 = x_1$$
$$y_2 = x_3$$

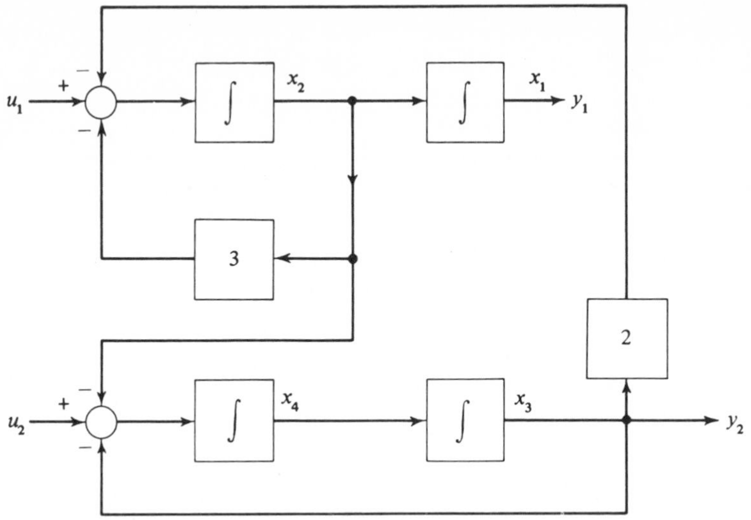

Fig. 1.9. State-variable diagram for Example 1.4.

or in matrix form,

$$\begin{bmatrix} \dot{x}_1 \\ \dot{x}_2 \\ \dot{x}_3 \\ \dot{x}_4 \end{bmatrix} = \begin{bmatrix} 0 & 1 & 0 & 0 \\ 0 & -3 & -2 & 0 \\ 0 & 0 & 0 & 1 \\ 0 & -1 & -1 & 0 \end{bmatrix} \begin{bmatrix} x_1 \\ x_2 \\ x_3 \\ x_4 \end{bmatrix} + \begin{bmatrix} 0 & 0 \\ 1 & 0 \\ 0 & 0 \\ 0 & 1 \end{bmatrix} \begin{bmatrix} u_1 \\ u_2 \end{bmatrix}$$

$$\begin{bmatrix} y_1 \\ y_2 \end{bmatrix} = \begin{bmatrix} 1 & 0 & 0 & 0 \\ 0 & 0 & 1 & 0 \end{bmatrix} \begin{bmatrix} x_1 \\ x_2 \\ x_3 \\ x_4 \end{bmatrix}$$

1.4. DIFFICULTY WITH METHODS FOR EXACT ANALYSIS OF LINEAR TIME-VARYING SYSTEMS

Methods for exact analysis of linear time-varying systems are relatively few and tend to be either extremely difficult to apply or limited in application to a small class of systems. The fundamental difficulty underlying the analysis of linear time-varying systems becomes apparent when one reviews some of the common methods for exact analysis.

1.4.1. Classical Analysis. The classical approach to the analysis problem hinges on the determination of the *basis functions*, and then use of an integration procedure based on superposition to determine the response of the system to particular inputs. The basis functions, which comprise n independent solutions to the homogeneous n-order linear differential equation characterizing the system, are generally difficult to determine; no general procedure exists for determining a set of basis functions for an arbitrary linear differential equation with time-varying coefficients.

For linear time-varying systems characterized by a single n-order differential equation, the classical approach has involved determining the basis functions as infinite polynomials and then using the method of variation of parameters to determine a specific response. This method has been applied successfully to only a small class of systems. As a result, systems characterized by the following equations have basis functions that are well known and extensively tabulated:

a. Bessel equations
b. Mathieu equations
c. Legendre equations
d. Laguerre equations
e. Weber equations
f. Hypergeometric equations
g. Airy equations

Clearly these equations represent an infinitesmal fraction of the infinite number of linear time-varying differential equations possible. Determination of the basis functions for significantly different equations is a difficult matter.

For linear time-varying systems characterized by state-variable equations, a method involving an infinite number of iterative integrations can be used to generate the *matrizant*, or the *fundamental matrix* as it has been termed recently. The fundamental matrix is implicitly related to the basis functions.

However, the various methods for obtaining exact solutions are not complementary to each other and difficulty in obtaining exact solutions with one method is usually sufficient indication that difficulty will be encountered with another.

1.4.2. Operational Methods: Compatible Transforms. The use of integral transforms in analyzing linear time-varying systems is attractive, since it can transform a differential equation into an algebraic equation. Thus the transform defined by

$$\mathscr{L}[x(t)] \equiv X(s) \equiv \int_a^b x(t)K(x, t)\, dt$$

$$\mathscr{L}^{-1}[X(s)] \equiv x(t) \equiv \frac{1}{2\pi i}\int_C X(s)k(t, s)\, ds \tag{1.8}$$

$$\int_C k(t, s)K(s, \tau)\, ds = \delta(t - \tau) \equiv \text{unit impulse}$$

is useful when the differential equation

$$L[x(t)] \equiv \alpha_0(t)\frac{d^n x(t)}{dt^n} + \cdots + \alpha_n(t)x(t) = f(t) \tag{1.9}$$

is transformed into an algebraic equation. Thus when

$$\mathscr{L}\{L[x(t)] = f(t)\} \tag{1.10}$$

results in an algebraic equation of the form

$$A(s)X(s) = F(s) \tag{1.11}$$

the solution to differential equation 1.8 is

$$x(t) = \mathscr{L}^{-1}[F(s)/A(s)] \tag{1.12}$$

As might be expected, not all transformation kernels $K(s,t)$ transform all differential equations into algebraic equations. A kernel $K(s,t)$ is termed compatible with a differential operator L if transformations of $L[x(t)]=f(t)$ result in algebraic equations. As is well known, the kernel $K(s, t) = e^{-st}$ is compatible with the linear time-invariant operator $L = \alpha_0 \dfrac{d^n}{dt^n} + \cdots + \alpha_n$ and leads to the Laplace transform.

The general theory of compatible transforms is well developed. In this context the Laplace transform, the Mellin transform, and the Hankel transform are easily derived and put in proper perspective. Other compatible transforms can be similarly developed. Due to the great amount of work that has been done in the analysis and synthesis of linear time-invariant systems using the "s-domain," it is desirable to extend these works to linear time-varying systems. This appears to be quite possible through the theory of compatible transforms.

Determination of a kernel that is compatible with an arbitrary linear time-varying operator is generally a difficult matter. In fact, determination of the kernel compatible with an n-order linear time-varying differential operator requires than an n-order linear differential equation with time-varying coefficients be solved. One could now complete the cycle and revert back to classical methods of analysis in an attempt to solve the resulting differential equation for the compatible kernel.

Thus it is seen that in using operational methods the problem of determining basis functions is not avoided. Similar investigation of other methods of exact analysis would lead to a similar conclusion: The inherent difficulty involved in the determination of the basis functions cannot be avoided.

1.4.3. Operational Methods: Noncompatible Transforms. A noncompatible transform that has proved useful with time-varying systems utilizes a kernel somewhat similar to that used for the Laplace transform. Thus this noncompatible transform parallels the Laplace transform allowing one to make use of the extensive tables of Laplace transforms. Introducing the kernel $K(s, \tau) = e^{-s(t-\tau)}$ the *system function* is defined by

$$G(s, t) = \int_{-\infty}^{t} \Omega(t, \tau) e^{-s(t-\tau)}\, d\tau \tag{1.13}$$

where $\Omega(t, \tau)$ is the response of the system to a unit impulse applied at $t = \tau$. The system function is analogous to the (Laplace) transfer function of a linear time-invariant system which is

$$G(s) = \int_{0}^{\infty} \Omega(t)\, e^{-st} dt \tag{1.14}$$

The motivation is to obtain a system function which when multiplied by the Laplace transform of the input function gives the Laplace transform of the output function. The difficulty in determining the system function lies in determining the impulsive response $\Omega(t, \tau)$; the impulsive response is easily determined from the basis functions, and vice versa.

REFERENCES

[1] Athans, M., "The Status of Optimal Control Theory and Applications for Deterministic Systems," *IEEE International Convention Record*, part 6 (March 1966), pp. 100–124.

[2] Athans, M., and P. Falb, *Optimal Control*, McGraw-Hill, New York, 1966.

[3] Bongroino, J., *Computer Controlled Adaptive Feedback Control Systems*, Report No. PIBMRI-1039-62, Polytechnic Institute of Brooklyn, Microwave Research Institute, Sept. 6, 1962.

[4] Brocket, R., "The Status of Stability Theory for Deterministic Systems," *IEEE International Convention Record*, part 6 (March 1966), pp. 125–142.

[5] Collar, A., "On the Stability of Accelerated Motion: Some Thoughts on Linear Differential Equations with Variable Coefficients," *Aeronautical Quarterly*, Vol. 8 (1957), pp. 309–330.

[6] DeRusso, P., R. Roy, and C. Close, *State Variables for Engineers*, Wiley, New York, 1965.

[7] Graham, D., E. Brunnelle, W. Johnson, and H. Passmore, *Engineering Analysis Methods for Linear Time-Varying Systems*, Technical Documentary Report ASD-TDR-62-362, ASTIA, January 1963.

[8] Narendra, K., "Integral Transforms for a Class of Time-Varying Linear Systems," *IRE Trans. on Automatic Control*, vol. AC-6 (1961), pp. 311–319.

[9] Schwarz, R., and B. Friedland, *Linear Systems*, McGraw-Hill, New York, 1965.

[10] Zadeh, L., and C. Desoer, *Linear System Theory: The State Space Approach*, McGraw-Hill, New York, 1963.

PROBLEMS

1.1 Write a single differential equation and the state-variable equations for the mechanical system shown in Fig. Pl.1.

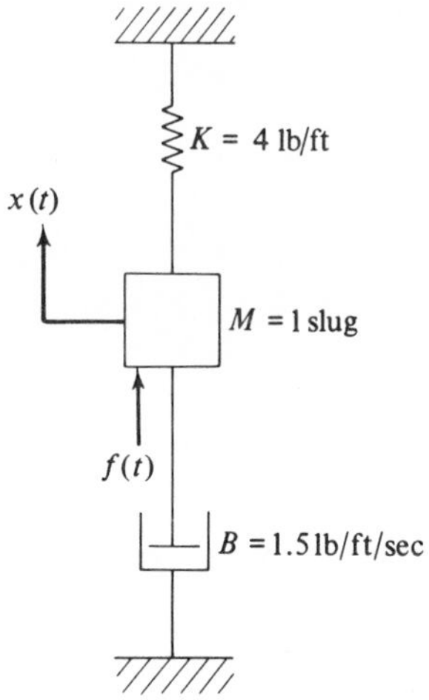

Fig. P1.1. System for Prob. 1.1.

1.2 For the system shown in Fig. Pl.2 write a single differential equation relating $r(t)$ and $x(t)$. Write the state-variable differential equations taking $x(t)$ and $y(t)$ as the state variables; repeat with a second input $g(t)$ (shown dotted) added in at the second integrator.

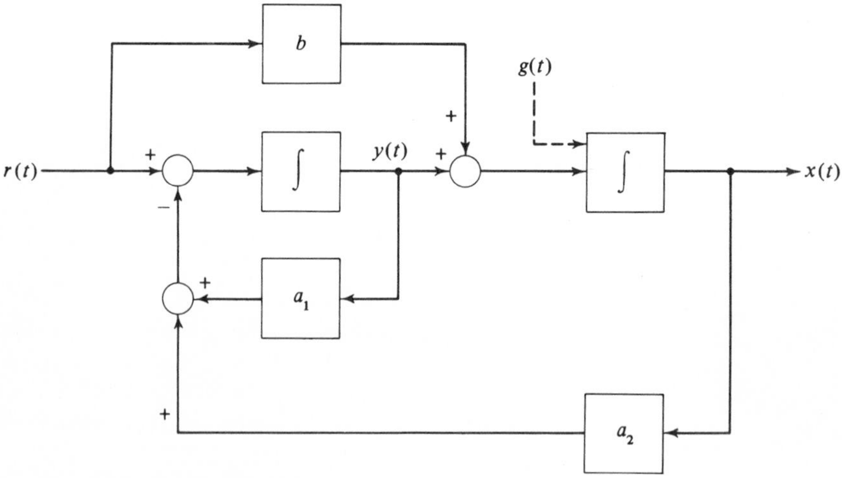

Fig. P1.2. System for Prob. 1.2.

1.3 Write the state-variable equations corresponding to the following second-order differential equation

$$\ddot{y}(t) + \dot{y}(t) + y(t) = \dot{r}(t) + r(t)$$

Sketch the associated state-variable diagram.

2

Fundamental Properties of Linear Systems

2.1. FIRST-ORDER SYSTEMS

A certain measure of insight in the analysis of time varying systems is obtained by analyzing a first-order system, i.e., a system characterized by the ordinary first-order linear differential equation

$$\begin{aligned} \alpha_0(t)\dot{x}(t) + \alpha_1(t)x(t) &= u(t) \\ x(t_0) &= x_0 \end{aligned} \tag{2.1}$$

where $\dot{x}(t) \equiv \dfrac{dx(t)}{dt}$

It is assumed that $\alpha_0(t)$, $\alpha_1(t)$ and $u(t)$ are continuous on the closed interval $[a, b]$ and that the initial condition is $x(t_0) = x_0$ for some t_0 on $[a, b]$. By noting that

$$\frac{d}{dt} \ln x(t) = \frac{1}{x(t)} \frac{dx(t)}{dt} \tag{2.2}$$

the homogeneous equation

$$\begin{aligned} \alpha_0(t)\dot{x}(t) + \alpha_1(t)x(t) &= 0 \\ x(t_0) &= x_0 \end{aligned} \tag{2.3}$$

can be written as

$$\frac{d}{dt} \ln x(t) + \frac{\alpha_1(t)}{\alpha_0(t)} = 0 \tag{2.4}$$

provided that $x(t)$ and $\alpha_0(t)$ do not vanish. Integration of Eq. 2.4 gives

$$\ln\left[\frac{x(t)}{x_0}\right] + \int_{t_0}^{t} \frac{\alpha_1(\eta)}{\alpha_0(\eta)}\, d\eta = 0 \tag{2.5}$$

Thus exponentiating and multiplying by x_0 gives the solution to the first-order homogeneous equation 2.3.

$$x(t) = \exp\left[-\int_{t_0}^{t} \frac{\alpha_1(\eta)}{\alpha_0(\eta)}\, d\eta\right] x_0 \tag{2.6}$$

Defining $\phi(t, t_0)$ as

$$\phi(t, t_0) \equiv \exp\left[-\int_{t_0}^{t} \frac{\alpha_1(\eta)}{\alpha_0(\eta)}\, d\eta\right] \tag{2.7}$$

results in

$$x(t) = \phi(t, t_0)x_0 \tag{2.8}$$

The solution to the nonhomogeneous equation 2.1 is found in a straightforward manner with the introduction of the *adjoint equation* of Eq. 2.3:

$$\dot{x}^*(t) - \frac{\alpha_1(t)}{\alpha_0(t)}\, x^*(t) = 0 \tag{2.9}$$

For convenience, the initial condition is taken as

$$x^*(t_0) = 1 \tag{2.10}$$

From Eqs. 2.6 and 2.7, it is determined that the solution to Eq. 2.9 is

$$x^*(t) = \exp\left[\int_{t_0}^{t} \frac{\alpha_1(\eta)}{\alpha_0(\eta)}\, d\eta\right] = \phi(t_0, t) \tag{2.11}$$

The solution to Eq. 2.1 is now found by noting that the product $x(t)x^*(t)$ satisfies the linear differential equation

$$\frac{d[x(t)x^*(t)]}{dt} = x^*(t)\, \frac{u(t)}{\alpha^0(t)} \tag{2.12}$$

Therefore integrating Eq. 2.12 gives

$$x(t)x^*(t) = x(t_0)x^*(t_0) + \int_{t_0}^{t} x^*(\tau)\, \frac{u(\tau)}{\alpha_0(\tau)}\, d\tau \tag{2.13}$$

Dividing through by $x^*(t)$ and substituting from Eq. 2.11 gives the general solution to the first-order differential equation 2.1:

$$\begin{aligned} x(t) &= \exp\left[-\int_{t_0}^{t} \frac{\alpha_1(\eta)}{\alpha_0(\eta)}\, d\eta\right] x_0 \\ &\quad + \exp\left[-\int_{t_0}^{t} \frac{\alpha_1(\eta)}{\alpha_0(\eta)}\, d\eta\right] \int_{t_0}^{t} \exp\left[\int_{t_0}^{\tau} \frac{\alpha_1(\eta)}{\alpha_0(\eta)}\, d\eta\right] \frac{u(\tau)}{\alpha_0(\tau)}\, d\tau \\ &= \phi(t, t_0)x_0 + \phi(t, t_0) \int_{t_0}^{t} \phi(t_0, \tau)\, \frac{u(\tau)}{\alpha_0(\tau)}\, d\tau \end{aligned} \tag{2.14}$$

From the definition of $\phi(t, t_0)$ given in Eq. 2.7, it is observed that

$$\phi(t, t_0)\,\phi(t_0, \tau) = \phi(t, \tau) \tag{2.15}$$

Thus the solution given by Eq. 2.14 simplifies to

$$x(t) = \phi(t, t_0)x_0 + \int_{t_0}^{t} \phi(t, \tau)\,\frac{u(\tau)}{\alpha_0(\tau)}\,d\tau \tag{2.16}$$

Example 2.1. Find the solution to

$$t\dot{x}(t) - 2x(t) = 0$$

with the initial value $x(t_0) = 1$.

Using Eq. 2.6 the solution is seen to be

$$x(t) = \exp\left[+\int_{t_0}^{t} 2\eta^{-1}\,d\eta\right]$$

or, after integration,

$$x(t) = (t/t_0)^2$$

Clearly, the solution does not exist for $t_0 = 0$ as this would imply a division by zero. It is easily shown that this difficulty arises whenever $\alpha_0(t)$ vanishes.

The results of this section are summarized in the following existence and uniqueness theorem.

Theorem 2.1. The differential equation 2.1, with $\alpha_0(t)$, $\alpha_1(t)$ and $u(t)$ continuous on the interval $[a, b]$ has the unique continuously differentiable solution given by Eq. 2.14 on $[a, b]$ provided that t_0 is on $[a, b]$ and $\alpha_0(t)$ does not vanish on $[a, b]$.

In the interest of simplifying subsequent comparisons with higher-order systems, Eq. 2.1 is written as

$$\begin{aligned} \dot{x}(t) &= A(t)x(t) + B(t)u(t) \\ x(t_0) &= x_0 \end{aligned} \tag{2.17}$$

where

$$A(t) = -\frac{\alpha_1(t)}{\alpha_0(t)}, \qquad B(t) = \frac{1}{\alpha_0(t)} \tag{2.18}$$

As $A(t)$ and $B(t)$ are discontinuous for values of t at which $\alpha_0(t)$ vanishes, existence and uniqueness are established by requiring that $A(t)$ and $B(t)$ be continuous in the interval of interest. Thus an alternate to Theorem 2.1 is

Theorem 2.2. The differential equation 2.17, with $A(t)$, $B(t)$ and $u(t)$ continuous on the interval $[a,b]$ has the unique continuously differentiable solution

$$x(t) = \exp\left[+\int_{t_0}^{t} A(\eta)\,d\eta\right]x_0$$

$$+ \exp\left[+\int_{t_0}^{t} A(\eta)\,d\eta\right]\int_{t_0}^{t} \exp\left[-\int_{t_0}^{\tau} A(\eta)\,d\eta\right]B(\tau)u(\tau)\,d\tau \quad (2.19)$$

$$= \phi(t, t_0)x_0 + \int_{t_0}^{t} \phi(t, \tau)B(\tau)u(\tau)\,d\tau$$

on $[a, b]$ provided that t_0 is in $[a, b]$.

Note that for the system in which the output is transformed by multiplication of a time-varying gain, i.e., the system characterized by

$$\begin{aligned} \dot{x}(t) &= A(t)x(t) + B(t)u(t),\; x(t_0) = x_0 \\ y(t) &= C(t)x(t) \end{aligned} \quad (2.20)$$

the solution $y(t)$ is

$$y(t) = C(t)\phi(t, t_0)x_0 + \int_{t_0}^{t} C(t)\phi(t, \tau)B(\tau)u(\tau)\,d\tau \quad (2.21)$$

Defining the quantity $\Omega(t, \tau)$ by

$$\Omega(t, \tau) \equiv C(t)\phi(t, \tau)B(\tau) \quad (2.22)$$

gives

$$y(t) = C(t)\phi(t, t_0)x_0 + \int_{t_0}^{t} \Omega(t, \tau)u(\tau)\,d\tau \quad (2.23)$$

Clearly, knowledge of the functions $\phi(t, \tau)$ and $\Omega(t, \tau)$ is valuable in determining the response of a system, characterized by Eqs. 2.20, to arbitrary inputs and initial conditions. As seen in the sequel, the functions $\phi(t, \tau)$ and $\Omega(t, \tau)$ are the first-order, scalar system *transition matrix* and the *impulsive-response matrix* respectively. The properties of these important matrix functions are studied in great detail.

2.2. HIGHER-ORDER SYSTEMS

Theorem 2.1 provides the existence and uniqueness statement for first-order linear time-varying differential equations; it does, in fact, provide the actual solution by *quadratures*, i.e., by a finite number of algebraic operations and integrations. For higher-order equations an explicit solution, such as those given by Eqs. 2.6, 2.19, and 2.23, cannot be obtained by quadratures. Each specific equation must be analyzed separately in obtaining solutions to the homogeneous equations, and techniques that prove successful in solving one equation are generally not useful in solving others.

However, for higher-order equations existence and uniqueness theorems comparable to those of the first-order equation do exist. Further, once the solution to the homogeneous equation has been found, analysis of the nonhomogeneous equation can proceed in a manner analogous to that used for first-order equations.

2.2.1. Notation. The most general nth-order linear time-varying system can always be characterized by a set of n ordinary first-order linear differential equations:

$$\begin{aligned}\dot{x}_1(t) &= a_{11}(t)x_1(t) + \cdots + a_{1n}(t)x_n(t) + b_{11}(t)u_1(t)\\ &\qquad + \cdots + b_{1m}(t)u_m(t)\\ &\vdots\\ \dot{x}_n(t) &= a_{n1}(t)x_1(t) + \cdots + a_{nn}(t)x_n(t) + b_{n1}(t)u_1(t)\\ &\qquad + \cdots + b_{nm}(t)u_m(t)\end{aligned} \tag{2.24}$$

with the outputs defined by

$$\begin{aligned}y_1(t) &= c_{11}(t)x_1(t) + \cdots + c_{1n}(t)x_n(t) + d_{11}(t)u_1(t)\\ &\qquad + \cdots + d_{1m}(t)u_m(t)\\ &\vdots\\ y_r(t) &= c_{r1}(t)x_1(t) + \cdots + c_{rn}(t)x_n(t) + d_{r1}(t)u_1(t)\\ &\qquad + \cdots + d_{rm}(t)u_m(t)\end{aligned} \tag{2.25}$$

or in matrix form,

$$\begin{aligned}\dot{\mathbf{x}}(t) &= \mathbf{A}(t)\mathbf{x}(t) + \mathbf{B}(t)\mathbf{u}(t)\\ \mathbf{y}(t) &= \mathbf{C}(t)\mathbf{x}(t) + \mathbf{D}(t)\mathbf{u}(t)\end{aligned} \tag{2.26}$$

where $\mathbf{A}(t)$, $\mathbf{B}(t)$, $\mathbf{C}(t)$, and $\mathbf{D}(t)$ are $n \times n$, $n \times m$, $r \times n$, and $r \times m$ matrices and $\mathbf{x}(t)$, $\mathbf{u}(t)$, and $\mathbf{y}(t)$ are n-, m-, and r-vectors. Such a system with multiple inputs and multiple outputs, namely m imputs and r outputs, is referred to as a *multivariable* system. Writing $\mathbf{B}(t)\mathbf{u}(t)$ as the single n-vector $\mathbf{f}(t)$ results in the equivalently general form

$$\begin{aligned}\dot{\mathbf{x}}(t) &= \mathbf{A}(t)\mathbf{x}(t) + \mathbf{f}(t)\\ \mathbf{y}(t) &= \mathbf{C}(t)\mathbf{x}(t) + \mathbf{D}(t)\mathbf{u}(t)\end{aligned} \tag{2.27}$$

In much of the recent control work $\mathbf{x}(t)$ is denoted as the *state-variable* vector, the n components being the *state variables*, and Eqs. 2.26 and 2.27 are said to be in the state-variable formulation.

It is often found that an nth-order single-input single-output system, i.e., a *scalar system*, is characterized by a single nth-order ordinary linear differential equation of the type

$$\begin{aligned}\alpha_0(t)y^{(n)}(t) + \alpha_1(t)y^{(n-1)}(t) + \cdots + \alpha_n(t)y(t)\\ = \beta_0(t)r^{(n)}(t) + \cdots + \beta_n(t)r(t)\end{aligned} \tag{2.28}$$

where $y(t)$ is the scalar output, $r(t)$ is the scalar input and $y^{(i)}(t)$ denotes the ith derivative of $y(t)$ with respect to time. Insofar as analysis is concerned, the entire right-hand side of Eq. 2.28 can be viewed as the single known forcing function $u(t)$. Thus the scalar differential equation becomes

$$\alpha_0(t)y^{(n)}(t) + \alpha_1(t)y^{(n-1)}(t) + \cdots + \alpha_n(t)y(t) = u(t) \tag{2.29}$$

By defining the linear differential operator

$$L \equiv \alpha_0(t)\frac{d^n}{dt^n} + \alpha_1(t)\frac{d^{n-1}}{dt^{n-1}} + \cdots + \alpha_n(t) \tag{2.30}$$

Eq. 2.29 is written simply as

$$L[y(t)] = u(t) \tag{2.31}$$

It is desirable to show for what follows that Eq. 2.29 is a special case of the state variable formulation given by Eqs. 2.27. This is done by introducing the n variables defined by

$$x_i(t) \equiv y^{(i-1)}(t), \qquad i = 1, 2, \cdots, n \tag{2.32}$$

Combining Eqs. 2.29 and 2.32 results in the n first-order linear differential equations

$$\begin{aligned} \dot{x}_1(t) &= x_2(t) \\ \dot{x}_2(t) &= x_3(t) \\ &\vdots \\ \dot{x}_{n-1}(t) &= x_n(t) \\ \dot{x}_n(t) &= -\frac{\alpha_n(t)}{\alpha_0(t)}x_1(t) - \cdots - \frac{\alpha_1(t)}{\alpha_0(t)}x_n(t) + \frac{u(t)}{\alpha_0(t)} \end{aligned} \tag{2.33a}$$

where

$$y(t) = x_1(t) \tag{2.33b}$$

Writing Eqs. 2.33 using matrix notation results in the state-variable equation[1]

[1]In this formulation it is necessary to obtain $u(t)$ which is the sum of derivatives of the actual input r(t):

$$u(t) = \beta_0(t)r^{(n)}(t) + \cdots + \beta_n(t)r(t) \tag{2.33A}$$

In terms of a physical realization, this implies that n differentiators are required to obtain $u(t)$ in addition to the n integrators normally required for the simulation of an nth-order system. Further, if one is interested in solving a control problem using this formulation, one is in the unfortunate position of seeking a control function $u(t)$ constrained to be of the form of Eq. 2.33A, since $r(t)$ is the actual input. Both difficulties are alleviated by seeking an alternate, more useful state-variable formulation of the form

$$\begin{aligned} \dot{\mathbf{x}}(t) &= \mathbf{A}(t)\mathbf{x}(t) + \hat{\mathbf{b}}(t)r(t) \\ y(t) &= \mathbf{c}(t)\mathbf{x}(t) + d(t)r(t) \end{aligned} \tag{2.33B}$$

It is shown (see Prob. 2.16) that in this formulation $\mathbf{A}(t)$ and $\mathbf{c}(t)$ are as given in Eq. 2.35 while

$$\hat{\mathbf{b}}(t) = \begin{bmatrix} \hat{b}_1(t) \\ \hat{b}_2(t) \\ \vdots \\ \hat{b}_n(t) \end{bmatrix} \tag{2.33C}$$

with

$$\hat{b}_0(t) = \frac{\beta_0(t)}{\alpha_0(t)} \tag{2.33D}$$

$$\hat{b}_i(t) = \frac{1}{\alpha_0(t)}\left[\beta_i(t) - \sum_{j=0}^{i-1}\sum_{k=0}^{i-j}\binom{n+k-i}{n-1}\alpha_{i-j-k}(t)\,\frac{d^k\hat{b}_j(t)}{dt^k}\right] \tag{2.33E}$$

and

$$d(t) = \hat{b}_0(t) \tag{2.33}$$

$$\dot{\mathbf{x}}(t) = \mathbf{A}(t)\mathbf{x}(t) + \mathbf{b}(t)u(t)$$
$$y(t) = \mathbf{c}(t)\mathbf{x}(t) \tag{2.34}$$

where

$$\mathbf{A}(t) = \begin{bmatrix} 0 & 1 & 0 & \cdots & 0 \\ 0 & 0 & 1 & \cdots & 0 \\ \vdots & \vdots & \vdots & & \vdots \\ 0 & 0 & 0 & \cdots & 1 \\ -\dfrac{\alpha_n(t)}{\alpha_0(t)} & -\dfrac{\alpha_{n-1}(t)}{\alpha_0(t)} & -\dfrac{\alpha_{n-2}(t)}{\alpha_0(t)} & \cdots & -\dfrac{\alpha_1(t)}{\alpha_0(t)} \end{bmatrix} \tag{2.35a}$$

$$\mathbf{b}(t) = \begin{bmatrix} 0 \\ 0 \\ \vdots \\ \dfrac{1}{\alpha_0(t)} \end{bmatrix} \tag{2.35b}$$

$$\mathbf{c}(t) = [1 \quad 0 \cdots 0 \quad 0] \tag{2.35c}$$

and

$$\mathbf{x}(t) = \begin{bmatrix} x_1(t) \\ x_2(t) \\ \vdots \\ x_{n-1}(t) \\ x_n(t) \end{bmatrix} \tag{2.36}$$

A state-variable equation having an $\mathbf{A}(t)$ matrix of the form of Eq 2.35a is said to be in the *phase-variable* canonical form. Clearly, Eq. 2.28 is equivalent to Eqs. 2.33B and 2.34, which, in turn, are special cases of the state-variable equation 2.27. Therefore any results shown to be true for the state-variable equations 2.27 are also true for Eqs. 2.33B and 2.34 and thus also for its scalar equivalent, Eq. 2.28.

2.2.2. Existence and Uniqueness for the Homogeneous System [6]. An existence and uniqueness theorem can be established for general nonhomogeneous higher-order systems characterized by

$$\dot{\mathbf{x}}(t) = \mathbf{A}(t)\mathbf{x}(t) + \mathbf{f}(t)$$
$$\mathbf{x}(t_0) = \mathbf{x}_0 \tag{2.37}$$

that is analogous to Thorem 2.2 for first-order systems.[2] The proof of this

[2]It would be desirable if the results obtained for the *first-order scalar* differential equation

$$\dot{x}(t) = \mathbf{A}(t)x(t), \; x(t_0) = x_0 \tag{2.38A}$$

could be extended to the *first-order matrix* differential equation 2.38. Since it

theorem, however, is greatly simplified if an existence and uniqueness theorem is established for the homogeneous system characterized by

$$\begin{aligned} \dot{\mathbf{x}}(t) &= \mathbf{A}(t)\mathbf{x}(t) \\ \mathbf{x}_0(t) &= \mathbf{x}_0 \end{aligned} \tag{2.38}$$

Therefore the general existence and uniqueness theorem for nonhomogeneous systems is deferred until existence and uniqueness of solutions is proved for the homogeneous systems and the properties of the homogeneous solutions are studied.

Theorem 2.3. Let $\mathbf{A}(t)$ be an $n \times n$ matrix with all elements $a_{ij}(t)$, $i, j = 1, 2, \cdots, n$, continuous on the interval $[a, b]$. Then there exists on $[a, b]$ a unique continuously differentiable n-vector $\mathbf{x}(t)$ satisfying Eq. (2.38), provided that t_0 is on $[a, b]$.

Proof. Assuming that $\mathbf{x}(t)$ exists as per Theorem 2.3, Eq. 2.38 can be writen as

$$\mathbf{x}(t) = \mathbf{x}_0 + \int_{t_0}^{t} \mathbf{A}(\tau)\mathbf{x}(\tau)\, d\tau \tag{2.39}$$

As $\mathbf{A}(t)$ and $\mathbf{x}(t)$ are continuous, $\int_{t_0}^{t} \mathbf{A}(\tau)\mathbf{x}(\tau) d\tau$ is differentiable and thus $\mathbf{x}(t)$ given by Eq. 2.39 is differentiable. Setting $t = t_0$ in Eq. 2.39 it is seen that $x(t_0) = x_0$ as required. Thus a vector $\mathbf{x}(t)$ satisfying Eq. 2.39 is a solution to Eq. 2.38 satisfying the initial conditions.

---

is established in Theorem 2.2 that the solution to the first-order scalar equation 2.38A is

$$x(t) = \exp\left[\int_{t_0}^{t} \mathrm{A}(\eta)\, d\eta\right] x_0 \tag{2.38B}$$

one might hope that the solution to the first-order matrix equation 2.38 would analogously be

$$\mathbf{x}(t) = \exp\left[\int_{t_0}^{t} \mathbf{A}(\eta)\, d\eta\right] \mathbf{x}_0 \tag{2.38C}$$

Unfortunately, this is true for only the extremely limited class of systems where [10]

(i) $\mathbf{A}(t)$ is a constant matrix

or more generally, where

$$\text{(ii)} \quad \mathbf{A}(t) = \sum_k \mathbf{A}_k a_k(t) \tag{2.38D}$$

where $a_i(t) \neq a_j(t)$ for $i \neq j$ and $\mathbf{A}_i\mathbf{A}_j = \mathbf{A}_j\mathbf{A}_i$ for all i and j

or equivalently

$$\text{(iii)} \quad \mathbf{B}(t)\dot{\mathbf{B}}(t) = \dot{\mathbf{B}}(t)\mathbf{B}(t) \tag{2.38E}$$

where $\mathbf{B}(t) = \int \mathbf{A}(t) dt$

For notational convenience define

$$|\mathbf{A}(t)| \equiv \max_i \sum_{j=1}^{n} |a_{ij}(t)|,\ t \in [a, b] \tag{2.40}$$

$$\|\mathbf{A}(t)\| \equiv \underset{t\in[a,b]}{\text{l.u.b.}}\ |\mathbf{A}(t)| \tag{2.41}$$

$$|\mathbf{x}(t)| \equiv \max_i |x_i(t)|,\ t \in [a, b] \tag{2.42}$$

$$\|\mathbf{x}(t)\| \equiv \underset{t\in[a,b]}{\text{l.u.b.}}\ |e^{-\alpha|t-t_0|}\mathbf{x}(t)|,\ \alpha > 0 \tag{2.43}$$

Note that $|\mathbf{A}(t)|$ and $|\mathbf{x}(t)|$ are scalar functions of t while $\|\mathbf{A}(t)\|$ and $\|\mathbf{x}(t)\|$ are scalar constants. From Eq. 2.40 and 2.42 it can be shown that

$$|\mathbf{A}(t)\mathbf{x}(t)| \le |\mathbf{A}(t)|\,|\mathbf{x}(t)| \tag{2.44}$$

Also from Eqs. 2.41 and 2.43 it can be shown that

$$\|\mathbf{A}(t)\mathbf{x}(t)\| \le \|\mathbf{A}(t)\|\,\|\mathbf{x}(t)\| \tag{2.45}$$

Equation 2.42 is used to establish the integral inequality

$$\left|\int_{t_0}^{t} \mathbf{x}(\tau)d\tau\right| \le \int_{t_0}^{t} |\mathbf{x}(\tau)|\, d\tau \tag{2.46}$$

Define the integral operator $\mathbf{\Gamma}$ by

$$\mathbf{\Gamma x}(t) \equiv \int_{t_0}^{t} \mathbf{A}(\tau)\mathbf{x}(\tau)\, d\tau \tag{2.47}$$

Let t_1 be any point on $[a, b]$ such that $t_1 > t_0$. Thus

$$\begin{aligned}|\mathbf{\Gamma x}(t_1)| &= \left|\int_{t_0}^{t_1} \mathbf{A}(\tau)\mathbf{x}(\tau)d\tau\right| \le \int_{t_0}^{t_1} |\mathbf{A}(\tau)\mathbf{x}(\tau)|\,d\tau \\ &\le \int_{t_0}^{t_1} |\mathbf{A}(\tau)|\,|\mathbf{x}(\tau)|\,d\tau\end{aligned} \tag{2.48}$$

Multiplying inequality 2.48 by the positive quantity $e^{-\alpha|t_1-t_0|}$ gives

$$\begin{aligned}&|\mathbf{\Gamma x}(t_1)|\,e^{-\alpha|t_1-t_0|} \\ &\quad\le \int_{t_0}^{t_1} |\mathbf{A}(\tau)|\ |e^{-\alpha|\tau-t_0|}\mathbf{x}(\tau)|\,e^{-\alpha|t_1-t_0|}e^{\alpha|\tau-t_0|}\ d\tau\end{aligned} \tag{2.49}$$

In accordance with Eqs. 2.41 and 2.43 and the fact that $t_0 < \tau < t_1$, inequality 2.49 can be replaced by

$$|\mathbf{\Gamma x}(t_1)|\,e^{-\alpha|t_1-t_0|} \le \|\mathbf{A}(t)\|\,\|\mathbf{x}(t)\| \int_{t_0}^{t_1} e^{-\alpha(t_1-\tau)}\,d\tau \tag{2.50}$$

where $(t_1 - \tau) > 0$. Since

$$\int_{t_0}^{t_1} e^{-\alpha(t_1-\tau)}\,d\tau = \frac{1}{\alpha}\,[1 - e^{-\alpha(t_1-t_0)}] \le \frac{1}{\alpha} \tag{2.51}$$

Eq. 2.50 becomes

$$|\mathbf{\Gamma x}(t_1)|e^{-\alpha|t_1-t_0|} \le \frac{1}{\alpha}\|\mathbf{A}(t)\|\,\|\mathbf{x}(t)\| \tag{2.52}$$

Applying Eq. 2.43 gives

$$\|\mathbf{\Gamma x}(t_1)\| = \underset{t\in[a,b]}{\text{l.u.b.}}\,|\mathbf{\Gamma x}(t_1)e^{-\alpha|t_1-t_0|}| = |\mathbf{\Gamma x}(t_1)|e^{-\alpha|t_1-t_0|} \tag{2.53}$$

$$\|\mathbf{\Gamma x}(t_1)\| = |\mathbf{\Gamma x}(t_1)|e^{-\alpha|t_1-t_0|} \le \frac{1}{\alpha}\|\mathbf{A}(t)\|\,\|\mathbf{x}(t)\| \tag{2.54}$$

or simply

$$\|\mathbf{\Gamma x}(t)\| \le \frac{1}{\alpha}\|\mathbf{A}(t)\|\,\|\mathbf{x}(t)\| \tag{2.55}$$

As Eq. 2.55 is valid for any $\alpha > 0$, select

$$\alpha > \frac{1}{k}\|\mathbf{A}(t)\|,\ 0 < k < 1 \tag{2.56}$$

Thus

$$k > \frac{1}{\alpha}\|\mathbf{A}(t)\| \tag{2.57}$$

Combining inequalities 2.55 and 2.57 gives

$$\|\mathbf{\Gamma x}(t)\| \le k\|\mathbf{x}(t)\| \tag{2.58}$$

In a similar manner it can be shown that

$$\|\mathbf{\Gamma}^n\mathbf{x}(t)\| \le k^n\|\mathbf{x}(t)\| \tag{2.59}$$

and thus

$$\|\sum_{i=0}^{n}\mathbf{\Gamma}^i\mathbf{x}(t)\| \le \sum_{i=1}^{n}\|\mathbf{\Gamma}^i\mathbf{x}(t)\| \le \sum_{i=1}^{n}k^i\|\mathbf{x}(t)\| \tag{2.60}$$

Using the results obtained thus far, it is possible to construct a sequence of vectors

$$\mathbf{x}_0(t),\ \mathbf{x}_1(t),\ \cdots,\ \mathbf{x}_n(t),\ \cdots \tag{2.61}$$

that converge uniformly on $[a,b]$ to the solution of Eq. 2.38, i.e.,

$$\lim_{n\to\infty}|\mathbf{x}(t) - \mathbf{x}_n(t)| = 0 \tag{2.62}$$

If this is done $\lim_{n\to\infty}\mathbf{x}_n(t)$ satisfies Eq. 2.39 and is thus a solution to the homogeneous equation 2.38. The sequence of vectors defined by

$$\mathbf{x}_0(t) \equiv \mathbf{x}_0 \tag{2.63}$$

and

$$\mathbf{x}_n(t) \equiv \mathbf{x}_0 + \mathbf{\Gamma x}_{n-1}(t),\ n = 1, 2, \cdots \tag{2.64}$$

are introduced as such a set of vectors. Therefore

$$\mathbf{x}_1(t) = \mathbf{x}_0 + \mathbf{\Gamma x}_0 = (\mathbf{I} + \mathbf{\Gamma})\mathbf{x}_0 \tag{2.65}$$

$$\mathbf{x}_2(t) = \mathbf{x}_0 + \mathbf{\Gamma x}_1 = (\mathbf{I} + \mathbf{\Gamma}^1 + \mathbf{\Gamma}^2)\mathbf{x}_0 \tag{2.66}$$

and by induction

$$\mathbf{x}_n(t) = (\mathbf{I} + \mathbf{\Gamma} + \cdots \mathbf{\Gamma}^n)\mathbf{x}_0 \tag{2.67}$$

Clearly, for $m < n$,

$$\mathbf{x}_n(t) - \mathbf{x}_m(t) = (\mathbf{\Gamma}^{m+1} + \mathbf{\Gamma}^{m+2} + \cdots + \mathbf{\Gamma}^n)\mathbf{x}_0 \tag{2.68}$$

Use of inequality 2.60 in Eq. 2.68 gives

$$\|\mathbf{x}_n(t) - \mathbf{x}_m(t)\| \leq (k^{m+1} + k^{m+2} + \cdots + k_n)\|\mathbf{x}_0\| \tag{2.69}$$

For k defined in Eq. 2.56

$$\frac{k^{m+1}}{1-k} = k^{m+1} + k^{m+2} + \cdots + k^n + \cdots \tag{2.70}$$

Thus

$$k^{m+1} + k^{m+2} + \cdots + k^n < \frac{k^{m+1}}{1-k} \tag{2.71}$$

and

$$\|\mathbf{x}_n(t) - \mathbf{x}_m(t)\| < \frac{k^{m+1}}{1-k}\|\mathbf{x}_0\| \tag{2.72}$$

Therefore in the limit $m \to \infty$, and thus $n \to \infty$,

$$\lim_{m\to\infty} \|\mathbf{x}_n(t) - \mathbf{x}_m(t)\| = 0 \tag{2.73}$$

and thus

$$\lim_{m\to\infty} |\mathbf{x}_n(t) - \mathbf{x}_m(t)| = 0 \tag{2.74}$$

Hence the sequence equation 2.61 converges uniformly on $[a, b]$ to some continuous vector to be denoted by $\hat{\mathbf{x}}(t)$. Thus in accordance with Eq. 2.67,

$$\hat{\mathbf{x}}(t) = \lim_{n\to\infty} \mathbf{x}_n(t) = \sum_{i=0}^{\infty} \mathbf{\Gamma}^i \mathbf{x}_0 \tag{2.75}$$

Taking Eq. 2.64 in the limit $n \to \infty$ gives

$$\lim_{n\to\infty} \mathbf{x}_n(t) = \lim_{n\to\infty} \mathbf{x}_0 + \lim_{n\to\infty} \mathbf{\Gamma}\, \mathbf{x}_{n-1}(t) \tag{2.76}$$

As $\mathbf{\Gamma}$ is independent of the limit operation,

$$\mathbf{x}(t) = \mathbf{x}_0 + \mathbf{\Gamma x}(t) \tag{2.77}$$

which, by the definition of $\mathbf{\Gamma}$, can be written as

$$\mathbf{x}(t) = \mathbf{x}_0 + \int_{t_0}^{t} \mathbf{A}(\tau)\mathbf{x}(\tau)d\tau \tag{2.78}$$

Thus $\mathbf{x}(t)$ satisfies Eq. 2.39 and is a desired solution $\mathbf{x}(t)$ to the homogeneous Eq. 2.38. Therefore a solution to Eq. 2.38 is:

$$\mathbf{x}(t) = \sum_{i=0}^{\infty} \mathbf{\Gamma}^i \mathbf{x}_0 \tag{2.79}$$

Equation 2.79 can be used to obtain the solution of the linear homogeneous differential equation 2.38 in the form of a uniformly convergent infinite series. Thus the existence of solutions is established.

The following example illustrates an application of Eq. 2.79.

Example 2.2. Determine the solution of the linear homogeneous equation

$$\begin{bmatrix} \dot{x}_1(t) \\ \dot{x}_2(t) \end{bmatrix} = \begin{bmatrix} 0 & t \\ 1 & 0 \end{bmatrix} \begin{bmatrix} x_1(t) \\ x_2(t) \end{bmatrix}, \qquad \begin{bmatrix} x_1(0) \\ x_2(0) \end{bmatrix} = \begin{bmatrix} 1 \\ 0 \end{bmatrix}$$

Use is made of Eq. 2.79 where

$$\mathbf{\Gamma}^0 \mathbf{x}_0 = \begin{bmatrix} 1 \\ 0 \end{bmatrix}$$

$$\mathbf{\Gamma}^1 \mathbf{x}_0 = \int_0^t \begin{bmatrix} 0 & \tau \\ 1 & 0 \end{bmatrix} \begin{bmatrix} 1 \\ 0 \end{bmatrix} d\tau = \int_0^t \begin{bmatrix} 0 \\ 1 \end{bmatrix} d\tau = \begin{bmatrix} 0 \\ t \end{bmatrix}$$

$$\mathbf{\Gamma}^2 \mathbf{x}_0 = \int_0^t \begin{bmatrix} 0 & \tau \\ 1 & 0 \end{bmatrix} \begin{bmatrix} 0 \\ \tau \end{bmatrix} d\tau = \int_0^t \begin{bmatrix} \tau^2 \\ 0 \end{bmatrix} d\tau = \begin{bmatrix} \frac{1}{3} t^3 \\ 0 \end{bmatrix}$$

$$\mathbf{\Gamma}^3 \mathbf{x}_0 = \int_0^t \begin{bmatrix} 0 & \tau \\ 1 & 0 \end{bmatrix} \begin{bmatrix} \frac{1}{3}\tau^3 \\ 0 \end{bmatrix} d\tau = \int_0^t \begin{bmatrix} 0 \\ \frac{1}{3}\tau^3 \end{bmatrix} d\tau = \begin{bmatrix} 0 \\ \frac{1}{12} t^4 \end{bmatrix}$$

Therefore

$$\mathbf{x}(t) = \sum_{i=0}^{\infty} \mathbf{\Gamma}^i \mathbf{x}_0 = \begin{bmatrix} 1 + \frac{1}{3} t^3 + \cdots \\ t + \frac{1}{12} t^4 + \cdots \end{bmatrix}$$

For a few special cases the infinite series can be expressed in closed form.

Example 2.3. Determine the solution of the linear homogeneous equation

$$\begin{bmatrix} \dot{x}_1(t) \\ \dot{x}_2(t) \end{bmatrix} = \begin{bmatrix} 0 & 1 \\ -2 & -3 \end{bmatrix} \begin{bmatrix} x_1(t) \\ x_2(t) \end{bmatrix}, \qquad \begin{bmatrix} x_1(t_0) \\ x_2(t_0) \end{bmatrix} = \begin{bmatrix} 1 \\ 0 \end{bmatrix}$$

Use is made of Eq 2.79 where

$$\mathbf{\Gamma}^0 \mathbf{x}_0 = \begin{bmatrix} 1 \\ 0 \end{bmatrix}$$

$$\Gamma^1\mathbf{x}_0 = \int_{t_0}^{t}\begin{bmatrix}0 & 1\\-2 & -3\end{bmatrix}\begin{bmatrix}1\\0\end{bmatrix}d\tau = \begin{bmatrix}0 & 1\\-2 & -3\end{bmatrix}\begin{bmatrix}1\\0\end{bmatrix}(t - t_0)$$

$$\Gamma^2\mathbf{x}_0 = \int_{t_0}^{t}\begin{bmatrix}0 & 1\\-2 & -3\end{bmatrix}\begin{bmatrix}0 & 1\\-2 & -3\end{bmatrix}\begin{bmatrix}1\\0\end{bmatrix}(\tau - t_0)d\tau$$

$$= \begin{bmatrix}0 & 1\\-2 & -3\end{bmatrix}^2\begin{bmatrix}1\\0\end{bmatrix}\frac{(t - t_0)^2}{2}$$

$$\vdots$$

$$\Gamma^n\mathbf{x}_0 = \begin{bmatrix}0 & 1\\-2 & -3\end{bmatrix}^n\begin{bmatrix}1\\0\end{bmatrix}\frac{(t - t_0)_n}{n!}$$

Therefore

$$\mathbf{x}(t) = \sum_{i=0}^{\infty}\begin{bmatrix}0 & 1\\-2 & -3\end{bmatrix}^i\frac{(t - t_0)^i}{i!}\begin{bmatrix}1\\0\end{bmatrix}$$

Noting that the infinite series defines the matrix exponential[3] gives the solution

$$\mathbf{x}(t) = \exp\begin{bmatrix}0 & 1\\-2 & -3\end{bmatrix}(t - t_0)\begin{bmatrix}1\\0\end{bmatrix}$$

Use of Sylvester's theorem[3] gives

[3]**Summary of Pertinent Relationships in the Calculus of Matrices.**

(a) Differentiation of a matrix:

$$d\mathbf{M}/dt = \{dm_{ij}/dt\} \tag{2.79A}$$

(b) Integration of a matrix:

$$\int \mathbf{M}\,dt = \left\{\int m_{ij}dt\right\} \tag{2.79B}$$

(c) Polynomial of a matrix:

$$P(\mathbf{M}) = \mathbf{C}_0\mathbf{M}^k + \mathbf{C}_1\mathbf{M}^{k-1} + \cdots + \mathbf{C}_{k-1}\mathbf{M} + \mathbf{C}_k\mathbf{I} \tag{2.79C}$$

where $\mathbf{I}$ is the unit matrix.

(d) Functions of a matrix:

If a function of a scalar variable $f(z)$ is defined by the power series in z,

$$f(z) = \sum_{n=0}^{\infty} c_n z^n \tag{2.79D}$$

the matrix function $f(\mathbf{M})$ is defined as

$$f(\mathbf{M}) = \sum_{n=0}^{\infty} c_n \mathbf{M}^n \tag{2.79E}$$

Example:

$$\exp \mathbf{M} = \mathbf{I} + \mathbf{M} + \mathbf{M}^2/2! + \mathbf{M}^3/3! + \cdots \tag{2.79F}$$

(e) Representing a function of a matrix by a polynomial:

$$f(\mathbf{M}) = (D_{n-1}/D)\mathbf{M}^{n-1} + \cdots + (D_1/D)\mathbf{M} + (D_0/D)\mathbf{I} \tag{2.79G}$$

where

$$\mathbf{x}(t) = \begin{bmatrix} 2e^{-(t-t_0)} - e^{-2(t-t_0)} \\ -2e^{-(t-t_0)} + 2e^{-2(t-t_0)} \end{bmatrix}$$

To complete the proof of Theorem 2.3, uniqueness of the solution $\mathbf{x}(t)$ must be shown. Denote any solution of Eq. 2.38 by $\mathbf{v}(t)$. As a solution $\mathbf{v}(t)$ must satisfy Eq. 2.39,

$$\mathbf{v}(t) = \mathbf{x}_0 + \mathbf{\Gamma v}(t) \tag{2.80}$$

Applying Eqs. 2.64 and 2.67 to Eq. 2.80 results in

$$\mathbf{v}(t) - \mathbf{x}_n(t) = \mathbf{\Gamma}^{n+1}\mathbf{v}(t) \tag{2.81}$$

which in accordance with Eq. 2.59 gives

$$\|\mathbf{v}(t) - \mathbf{x}_n(t)\| \leq k^{n+1}\|\mathbf{v}(t)\| \tag{2.82}$$

Therefore in the limit $n \to \infty$,

$$\lim_{n\to\infty} \|\mathbf{v}(t) - \mathbf{x}_n(t)\| = 0 \tag{2.83}$$

and thus the sequence 2.61 converges uniformly on $[a, b]$ to $\mathbf{v}(t)$, and the solution is unique. Q.E.D.

2.2.3. Properties of Solutions of the Homogeneous System. Important properties of the solutions of linear systems are obtained by a detailed study of the general homogeneous system characterized by

$$\dot{\mathbf{x}}(t) = \mathbf{A}(t)\mathbf{x}(t) \tag{2.84}$$

$$D = \begin{bmatrix} 1 & 1 & \cdots & 1 \\ \lambda_1 & \lambda_2 & \cdots & \lambda_n \\ \vdots & \vdots & & \vdots \\ \lambda_1^{n-1} & \lambda_2^{n-1} & \cdots & \lambda_n^{n-1} \end{bmatrix}; \ \lambda_i \text{ are eigenvalues of } \mathbf{M} \tag{2.79H}$$

and

$$D_1 = \begin{bmatrix} 1 & f(\lambda_1) & \cdots & 1 \\ \lambda_1 & f(\lambda_2) & \cdots & \lambda_n \\ \vdots & \vdots & & \vdots \\ \lambda_1^{n-1} & f(\lambda_n) & \cdots & \lambda_n^{n-1} \end{bmatrix} \tag{2.79I}$$

(f) Sylvester's theorem:
If the eigenvalues of $\mathbf{M}$ are distinct,

$$f(\mathbf{M}) = \sum_{r=1}^{n} f(\lambda_r)\mathbf{Z}_r \tag{2.79J}$$

where

$$\mathbf{Z}_r = \prod_{\substack{s=1 \\ s\neq r}}^{n} (\lambda_s\mathbf{I} - \mathbf{M}) / \prod_{\substack{s=1 \\ s\neq r}}^{n} (\lambda_s - \lambda_r) \tag{2.79K}$$

and

$$\mathbf{Z}_r\mathbf{Z}_s = 0.\ r \neq s \tag{2.79La}$$
$$\mathbf{Z}_r^m = \mathbf{Z}_r,\ r = 1, \cdots, n \tag{2.79Lb}$$

Several fundamental results pertaining to the properties of the solutions of the homogeneous system are developed here.

A set of n solutions of the homogeneous equation 2.84 on the interval $[a,b]$ are denoted by

$$\mathbf{x}_i(t) \equiv \begin{bmatrix} x_{1i}(t) \\ x_{2i}(t) \\ \vdots \\ x_{ni}(t) \end{bmatrix}, \qquad i = 1, \cdots, n \tag{2.85}$$

and the matrix of these n solutions $\mathbf{x}_i(t)$, $i = 1, \cdots, n$ written as columns is termed the *Wronskian matrix* (or the *solution matrix*):

$$\begin{aligned} \mathbf{W}(t) &\equiv [\mathbf{x}_1(t), \mathbf{x}_2(t), \cdots, \mathbf{x}_n(t)] \\ &= \begin{bmatrix} x_{11}(t) & x_{12}(t) & \cdots & x_{1n}(t) \\ x_{21}(t) & x_{22}(t) & \cdots & x_{2n}(t) \\ \vdots & \vdots & & \vdots \\ x_{n1}(t) & x_{n2}(t) & \cdots & x_{nn}(t) \end{bmatrix} \end{aligned} \tag{2.86}$$

The determinant of the Wronskian matrix $\det \mathbf{W}(t)$ is termed the *Wronskian*.

Theorem 2.4. A linear combination of solutions to the homogeneous system 2.84 is also a solution to the system.

Proof. Assume that $\mathbf{x}_1(t), \cdots, \mathbf{x}_k(t)$ are solutions of the homogeneous equation 2.84. Then

$$\hat{\mathbf{x}}(t) = \sum_{i=1}^{k} c_i \mathbf{x}_i(t) \tag{2.87}$$

is also a solution as is seen by substituting $\hat{\mathbf{x}}(t)$ in Eq. 2.84 and noting that

$$c_i \dot{\mathbf{x}}_i(t) = \mathbf{A}(t) c_i \mathbf{x}_i(t)\,, \qquad i = 1, \cdots, k \tag{2.88}$$

Q.E.D.

Theorem 2.5. If the Wronskian $\det \mathbf{W}(t)$ corresponding to solutions 2.85 vanishes at any point t_1 in the interval $[a, b]$, then the solutions are linearly dependent.

Proof. If $\det \mathbf{W}(t_1) = 0$, then the constant vectors $\mathbf{x}_1(t_1), \cdots, \mathbf{x}_n(t_1)$ corresponding to columns of $\mathbf{W}(t)$, and thus the solutions of the system, are linearly dependent. Thus constants $c_1, \cdots, c_n$ can be found, not all zero, such that

$$\sum_{i=1}^{n} c_i \mathbf{x}_i(t_1) = \mathbf{0} \tag{2.89}$$

By Theorem 2.4,

$$\hat{\mathbf{x}}(t) = \sum_{i=1}^{n} c_i \mathbf{x}_i(t) \tag{2.90}$$

is also a solution of the homogeneous equation 2.84. Thus a solution $\hat{\mathbf{x}}(t)$ satisfying the boundary condition $\hat{\mathbf{x}}(t_1) = 0$ is the vanishing solution $\hat{\mathbf{x}}(t) = 0$. However, by the uniqueness Theorem 2.3 there can only be one solution satisfying Eq. 2.84 and vanishing at $t = t_1$. Therefore

$$\sum_{i=1}^{n} c_i \mathbf{x}_i(t) = \mathbf{0} \tag{2.91}$$

and the $\mathbf{x}_i(t)$, $i = 1, \cdots, n$ are linearly dependent. Thus by Theorem 2.4, $\det \mathbf{W}(t) = 0$. Q.E.D.

Corollary 2.5a. If the functions 2.85 are linearly dependent, then their Wronskian $\det \mathbf{W}(t)$ vanishes identically on the interval $[a, b]$.

Corollary 2.5b. If the Wronskian formed from the solutions 2.85 vanishes at a single point, then it vanishes identically on the interval $[a,b]$.

A *fundamental matrix* $\mathbf{W}_f(t)$ is defined as a Wronskian matrix for which $\det \mathbf{W}_f(t) \neq 0$, i.e., the n columns of a fundamental matrix are composed of linearly independent solutions of the homogeneous equation 2.84. Note that in the sequel a fundamental Wronskian matrix will often be denoted without the subscript f.

Theorem 2.6. The product of a constant nonsingular $n \times n$ matrix $\mathbf{K}$ with a fundamental matrix $\mathbf{W}_f(t)$ is also a fundamental matrix; any fundamental matrix can be formed from a given fundamental matrix $\mathbf{W}_f(t)$ and some nonsingular $\mathbf{K}$.

Proof. (i) *Sufficiency*: Since $\mathbf{W}_f(t)$ is a fundamental matrix, it satisfies the homogeneous equation 2.84:

$$\dot{\mathbf{W}}_f(t) = \mathbf{A}(t)\mathbf{W}_f(t) \tag{2.92}$$

Postmultiplying both sides of Eq. 2.92 by the nonsingular matrix $\mathbf{K}$ gives

$$\dot{\mathbf{W}}_f(t)\mathbf{K} = \mathbf{A}(t)\mathbf{W}_f(t)\mathbf{K} \tag{2.93}$$

Defining the matrix $\mathbf{W}_{ff}(t)$ by $\mathbf{W}_{ff}(t) \equiv \mathbf{W}_f(t)\mathbf{K}$ and substituting into Eq. 2.93 shows that $\mathbf{W}_{ff}(t)$ is also a fundamental matrix.

(ii) *Necessity*: Consider the two fundamental matrices $\mathbf{W}_f(t)$ and $\mathbf{W}_{ff}(t)$ and define the product $\mathbf{K}(t) = \mathbf{W}_f^{-1}(t)\mathbf{W}_{ff}(t)$. Taking the derivative of $\mathbf{K}(t)$ it is established that $\dot{\mathbf{K}}(t) = 0$ and thus $\mathbf{K}(t) = \mathbf{K}$ is a constant. Q.E.D.

Corollary 2.6. If Eqs. 2.85 represent n linearly independent solutions to the homogeneous system 2.84, then every solution $\mathbf{x}(t)$ can be expressed as a linear combination of these solutions, i.e.,

$$\mathbf{x}(t) = \sum_{i=1}^{n} c_i \mathbf{x}_i(t) \tag{2.94}$$

A set of n linearly independent solutions 2.87 to the homogeneous system 2.84, satisfying no particular set of boundary conditions, are termed a *basis* or a *fundamental* set of solutions. Thus forming the Wronskian matrix from a basis results in a fundamental matrix.

Theorem 2.7. A basis of the homogeneous system 2.84 exists.

Proof. Select any nonsingular $n \times n$ matrix $\mathbf{K}$ and n sets of initial conditions $\mathbf{x}_i(t_0)$, $i = 1, \cdots, n$ corresponding to the columns of $\mathbf{K}$. Therefore $\mathbf{W}(t_0) = \mathbf{K}$ and det $\mathbf{W}(t_0) \neq 0$. Thus, by Corollary 2.5a, the set of solutions $\mathbf{x}_i(t)$, $i = 1, \cdots, n$ corresponding to this specified set of initial conditions are linearly independent and thus comprise a basis Q.E.D.

Most of the definitions and results relating to the state-variable formulation of an nth-order system characterized by Eq. 2.84 also apply to the scalar nth-order system

$$\alpha_0(t)\frac{d^n y(t)}{dt^n} + \cdots + \alpha_n(t)y(t) = 0 \tag{2.95}$$

However, certain difficulties can be avoided by precisely specifying what is intended when terminology, defined for the state-variable situation, is used in describing the scalar system.

The basis, or fundamental set, for the nth-order scalar system is n scalar functions rather than n-vector functions. In particular, any set of n linearly independent functions $x_1(t), x_2(t), \cdots, x_n(t)$ satisfying the homogeneous system 2.95, but not necessarily any particular boundary conditions, is termed a *basis*. The *Wronskian matrix* is defined in terms of the basis and the first $n - 1$ derivatives of the basis. Specifically,

$$\mathbf{W}(t) = \begin{bmatrix} x_1(t) & x_2(t) & \cdots & x_n(t) \\ x_1^{(1)}(t) & x_2^{(1)}(t) & \cdots & x_n^{(1)}(t) \\ \vdots & \vdots & & \vdots \\ x_1^{(n-1)}(t) & x_2^{(n-1)}(t) & \cdots & x_n^{(n-1)}(t) \end{bmatrix} \tag{2.96}$$

It is noted that by putting the nth-order system in the phase-variable canonical form of Eq. 2.34, a basis for the state-variable formulation is obtained by differentiating each member of the scalar basis $n - 1$ times, i.e., the scalar basis member $x_i(t)$ is used to generate the vector basis member $\mathbf{x}_i(t) = [x_i(t), x_i^{(1)}(t), \cdots, \mathbf{x}_i^{(n-1)}(t)]'$. When the scalar basis and the state-variable basis are so related, the Wronskians for both the scalar system and the state-variable systems are identical.

2.2.4. Existence and uniqueness for the nonhomogeneous system. The existence and uniqueness theorem for the solutions of the nth-order nonhomogeneous system

$$\begin{aligned} \dot{\mathbf{x}}(t) &= \mathbf{A}(t)\mathbf{x}(t) + \mathbf{f}(t) \\ \mathbf{x}(t_0) &= \mathbf{x}_0 \end{aligned} \tag{2.97}$$

analogous to Theorem 2.2 for a first-order system is:

Theorem 2.8. Let $\mathbf{A}(t)$ be an $n \times n$ matrix with all elements $a_{ij}(t)$, $i, j = 1, 2, \cdots, n$, continuous on the interval $[a, b]$. Further, let $\mathbf{f}(t)$ be an n-vector with all components $f_i(t)$, $i = 1, 2, \cdots, n$, also continuous on $[a, b]$. Then there exists on $[a, b]$ a unique continuously differentiable n-vector $\mathbf{x}(t)$ satisfying Eq. 2.97 provided that t_0 is in $[a, b]$.

Proof. The proof of this theorem involves showing that existence and uniqueness of a solution to the homogeneous equation 2.38, as established in Theorem 2.3, implies existence and uniqueness of a solution to the nonhomogeneous equation 2.97. The method for obtaining the solution to the higher-order nonhomogeneous equation proceeds in a manner similar to that used for the first-order system in Sec. 2.1.

For a higher-order system characterized by Eq. 2.84, the *adjoint equation* is defined as

$$\dot{\mathbf{x}}^*(t) = -\mathbf{A}'(t)\mathbf{x}^*(t) \tag{2.98}$$

where $\mathbf{A}'(t)$ denotes the transpose of $\mathbf{A}(t)$. In accordance with Theorem 2.3, for a given initial condition $\mathbf{x}_i^*(t_0) = \mathbf{x}_{i0}^*$, a unique solution exists to the adjoint equation (2.98).

Let a basis of the adjoint equation 2.98 be denoted by

$$\mathbf{x}_i^*(t) = \begin{bmatrix} x_{1i}^*(t) \\ x_{2i}^*(t) \\ \vdots \\ x_{ni}^*(t) \end{bmatrix}, \qquad i = 1, \cdots, n \tag{2.99}$$

Assuming that n independent solutions $\mathbf{x}_i^*(t)$, $i = 1, \cdots, n$, to the adjoint equation are known, it can be seen that the scalar product of these solutions with the desired solution to the nonhomogeneous equation 2.97 satisfies the scalar differential equation

$$\frac{d}{dt}[\mathbf{x}_i^{*\prime}(t)\mathbf{x}(t)] = \mathbf{x}_i^{*\prime}(t)\mathbf{f}(t), \qquad i = 1, \cdots, n \tag{2.100}$$

Denoting the fundamental Wronskian matrix of the adjoint system by

$$\mathbf{W}^*(t) \equiv [\mathbf{x}_1^*(t), \mathbf{x}_2^*(t), \cdots, \mathbf{x}_n^*(t)] \tag{2.101}$$

and defining

$$\mathbf{\Phi}^*(t) \equiv \mathbf{W}^{*\prime}(t) \tag{2.102}$$

allows the n scalar equations 2.100 to be written as the single matrix equation

$$\frac{d}{dt}[\mathbf{\Phi}^*(t)\mathbf{x}(t)] = \mathbf{\Phi}^*(t)\mathbf{f}(t) \tag{2.103}$$

Integrating Eq. 2.103 results in

$$\mathbf{\Phi}^*(t)\mathbf{x}(t) = \mathbf{\Phi}^*(t_0)\mathbf{x}_0 + \int_{t_0}^{t} \mathbf{\Phi}^*(\tau)\mathbf{f}(\tau)\, d\tau \tag{2.104}$$

and thus the solution of $\mathbf{x}(t)$ to the nonhomogeneous equation 2.97 is written as

$$\mathbf{x}(t) = \mathbf{\Phi}^{*-1}(t)\mathbf{\Phi}^*(t_0)\mathbf{x}_0 + \int_{t_0}^{t} \mathbf{\Phi}^{*-1}(t)\mathbf{\Phi}^*(\tau)\mathbf{f}(\tau)\, d\tau \tag{2.105}$$

Since $\mathbf{\Phi}^{*-1}(t)$ exists for all t on $[a, b]$, the solution to the nonhomogeneous equation 2.97 is explicitly given by Eq. 2.105. Q.E.D.

2.2.5. Properties of Solutions of the Nonhomogeneous System. The solution to the homogeneous equation 2.97 is intricately related to the solutions of the homogeneous equation 2.84. Properties of the nonhomogeneous solution and its relation to the homogeneous solutions are developed here.

The most important property characterizing linear systems is that of *superposition*:

Theorem 2.9. If the response of the quiescent [zero-state, i.e., $\mathbf{x}(t_0) = \mathbf{0}$] system $\dot{\mathbf{x}}(t) = \mathbf{A}(t)\mathbf{x}(t) + \mathbf{f}_1(t)$ is $\mathbf{x}(t) = \mathbf{\Phi}_1(t)$, and the response of the quiescent system $\dot{\mathbf{x}}(t) = \mathbf{A}(t)\mathbf{x}(t) + \mathbf{f}_2(t)$ is $\mathbf{x}(t) = \mathbf{\Phi}_2(t)$, then the response of the quiescent system $\dot{\mathbf{x}}(t) = \mathbf{A}(t)\mathbf{x}(t) + [\mathbf{f}_1(t) + \mathbf{f}_2(t)]$ is $\mathbf{x}(t) = \mathbf{\Phi}_1(t) + \mathbf{\Phi}_2(t)$.

It is important to note that superposition is a property of linear *quiescent* systems only. Tests for the existence of the superposition property provide perhaps the most direct methods for determining whether or not unknown physical systems are linear.

Any solution $\mathbf{x}_p(t)$ that satisfies the nonhomogeneous system characterized by Eq. 2.97 is termed a *particular* solution (or *forced* solution).

Theorem 2.10. Every solution of the nonhomogeneous system 2.97 can be expressed as the sum

$$\mathbf{x}(t) = \mathbf{x}_c(t) + \mathbf{x}_p(t) \tag{2.106}$$

where $\mathbf{x}_p(t)$ is any particular solution to Eq. 2.97 and $\mathbf{x}_c(t)$, termed the *complementary* solution (or the *free* solution), satisfies the homogeneous system 2.84 and can be expressed as $\mathbf{x}_c(t) = \sum_{i=1}^{n} c_i\mathbf{x}_i(t)$ where $\mathbf{x}_i(t)$, $i = 1, \cdots, n$ is a basis and the c_i, $i = 1, \cdots, n$ are determined by specifying the initial conditions $\mathbf{x}(t_0) = \mathbf{x}_0$. Conversely, every solution of the form of Eq. 2.106 satisfies Eq. 2.97.

Proof. Since $\mathbf{x}_p(t)$ satisfies the nonhomogeneous equation,

$$\dot{\mathbf{x}}_p(t) = \mathbf{A}(t)\mathbf{x}_p(t) + \mathbf{f}(t) \tag{2.107}$$

If $\mathbf{x}(t)$ is an arbitrary solution to the nonhomogeneous equation, then

$$\dot{\mathbf{x}}(t) = \mathbf{A}(t)\mathbf{x}(t) + \mathbf{f}(t) \tag{2.108}$$

Subtracting Eq. 2.107 from Eq. 2.108 gives

$$\frac{d}{dt}[\mathbf{x}(t) - \mathbf{x}_p(t)[= \mathbf{A}(t)[\mathbf{x}(t) - \mathbf{x}_p(t)] \tag{2.109}$$

Denfining $\mathbf{x}_c(t) \equiv \mathbf{x}(t) - \mathbf{x}_p(t)$ and substituting into Eq. 2.109, it is seen that $\mathbf{x}_c(t)$ is always a solution of the homogeneous equation. The converse is proved similarly. Q.E.D.

Thus, corresponding to the solution of the nonhomogeneous equation obtained in Eq. 2.105, there is the complementary solution

$$\mathbf{x}_c(t) = \mathbf{\Phi}^{*-1}(t)\mathbf{\Phi}^*(t_0)\mathbf{x}_0 \tag{2.110}$$

and the particular solution

$$\mathbf{x}_p(t) = \int_{t_0}^{t} \mathbf{\Phi}^{*-1}(t)\mathbf{\Phi}^*(\tau)\mathbf{f}(\tau)d\tau \tag{2.111}$$

The method of *variation of parameters* provides an alternate to the adjoint method in determining a solution to the nonhomogeneous system 2.97. This method, based on Theorem 2.10, requires that a basis $\mathbf{x}_i(t)$, $i = 1, \ldots, n$, to the homogeneous system 2.84 be known. A solution is assumed of the form

$$\mathbf{x}(t) = \sum_{i=1}^{n} v_i(t)\mathbf{x}_i(t) \tag{2.112}$$

where the $v_i(t)$ are arbitrary differentiable functions. Substituting this assumed solution in the nonhomogeneous equation 2.97 which it is to satisfy gives

$$\sum_{i=1}^{n} \dot{v}_i(t)\mathbf{x}_i(t) + \sum_{i=1}^{n} v_i(t)\dot{\mathbf{x}}(t) = \sum_{i=1}^{n} \mathbf{A}(t)v_i(t)\mathbf{x}_i(t) + \mathbf{f}(t) \tag{2.113}$$

As $\dot{\mathbf{x}}_i(t) = \mathbf{A}(t)\mathbf{x}_i(t)$, Eq. 2.113 becomes

$$\sum_{i=1}^{n} \dot{v}_i(t)\mathbf{x}_i(t) = \mathbf{f}(t) \tag{2.114}$$

or in matrix form,

$$\begin{bmatrix} x_{11}(t) & x_{12}(t) & \cdots & x_{1n}(t) \\ x_{21}(t) & x_{22}(t) & \cdots & x_{2n}(t) \\ \vdots & \vdots & & \vdots \\ x_{n1}(t) & x_{n2}(t) & \cdots & x_{nn}(t) \end{bmatrix} \begin{bmatrix} \dot{v}_1(t) \\ \dot{v}_2(t) \\ \vdots \\ \dot{v}_n(t) \end{bmatrix} = \begin{bmatrix} f_1(t) \\ f_2(t) \\ \vdots \\ f_n(t) \end{bmatrix} \tag{2.115}$$

Defining the n-vector $\mathbf{v}(t)$ by

$$\mathbf{v}(t) = \begin{bmatrix} v_1(t) \\ v_2(t) \\ \vdots \\ v_n(t) \end{bmatrix} \tag{2.116}$$

and denoting the fundamental solution matrix by $\mathbf{W}(t)$, Eq. 2.115 is written

$$\mathbf{W}(t)\dot{\mathbf{v}}(t) = \mathbf{f}(t) \tag{2.117}$$

Thus

$$\dot{\mathbf{v}}(t) = \mathbf{W}^{-1}(t)\mathbf{f}(t) \tag{2.118}$$

where the inverse $\mathbf{W}^{-1}(t)$ exists, since $\mathbf{W}(t)$ is a fundamental matrix, i.e., det $W(t)$ is nonvanishing. Integrating Eq. 2.118 gives

$$\mathbf{v}(t) = \mathbf{v}(t_0) + \int_{t_0}^{t} \mathbf{W}^{-1}(\tau)\mathbf{f}(\tau)d\tau \tag{2.119}$$

Since the assumed solution given by Eq. 2.112 can be written in matrix form

$$\mathbf{x}(t) = \mathbf{W}(t)\mathbf{v}(t) \tag{2.120}$$

Eq 2.119 can be written

$$\mathbf{v}(t) = \mathbf{W}^{-1}(t_0)\mathbf{x}(t_0) + \int_{t_0}^{t} \mathbf{W}^{-1}(\tau)\mathbf{f}(\tau)\, d(\tau) \tag{2.121}$$

Combining Eqs. 2.120 and 2.121 gives the general form of the solution

$$\mathbf{x}(t) = \mathbf{W}(t)\mathbf{W}^{-1}(t_0)\mathbf{x}_0 + \int_{t_0}^{t} \mathbf{W}(t)\mathbf{W}^{-1}(\tau)\mathbf{f}(\tau)d\tau \tag{2.122}$$

where the complementary solution is

$$\mathbf{x}_c(t) = \mathbf{W}(t)\mathbf{W}^{-1}(t_0)\mathbf{x}(t_0) \tag{2.123}$$

and the particular solution is

$$\mathbf{x}_p(t) = \int_{t_0}^{t} \mathbf{W}(t)\mathbf{W}^{-1}(\tau)\mathbf{f}(\tau)\, d\tau \tag{2.124}$$

Example 2.4. Determine the solution to the nonhomogeneous equation

$$\begin{bmatrix} \dot{x}_1(t) \\ \dot{x}_2(t) \end{bmatrix} = \begin{bmatrix} 0 & 1 \\ \frac{6}{t^2} & 0 \end{bmatrix} \begin{bmatrix} x_1(t) \\ x_2(t) \end{bmatrix} + \begin{bmatrix} 0 \\ t \ln t \end{bmatrix}, \qquad \begin{bmatrix} x_1(t_0) \\ x_2(t_0) \end{bmatrix} = \begin{bmatrix} x_{10} \\ x_{20} \end{bmatrix}$$

given a basis

$$\mathbf{x}_1(t) = \begin{bmatrix} t^3 \\ 3t^2 \end{bmatrix}, \qquad \mathbf{x}_2(t) = \begin{bmatrix} t^{-2} \\ -2t^{-3} \end{bmatrix}$$

Thus a fundamental Wronskian matrix for this system is

$$\mathbf{W}(t) = \begin{bmatrix} t^3 & t^{-2} \\ 3t^2 & -2t^{-3} \end{bmatrix}$$

Therefore

$$\mathbf{W}^{-1}(t) = \frac{-1}{5} \begin{bmatrix} -2t^{-3} & -t^{-2} \\ -3t^2 & t^3 \end{bmatrix}$$

Thus the solution is obtained by substitution in Eq. 2.122:

$$\begin{bmatrix} x_1(t) \\ x_2(t) \end{bmatrix} = \frac{-1}{5} \begin{bmatrix} -2\frac{t^3}{t_0^3} - 3\frac{t_0^2}{t^2}, & -\left(\frac{t^3}{t_0^2} - \frac{t_0^3}{t^2}\right) \\ -6\left(\frac{t^2}{t_0^3} - \frac{t_0^2}{t^3}\right), & -3\frac{t^2}{t_0^2} - 2\frac{t_0^3}{t^3} \end{bmatrix} \begin{bmatrix} x_{10} \\ x_{20} \end{bmatrix}$$
$$- \frac{1}{5} \begin{bmatrix} t^3 & t^{-2} \\ 3t^2 & -2t^{-3} \end{bmatrix} \int_{t_0}^{t} \begin{bmatrix} -\tau^{-1} \ln \tau \\ \tau^4 \ln \tau \end{bmatrix} d\tau$$

which upon integration gives

$$\begin{bmatrix} x_1(t) \\ x_2(t) \end{bmatrix} = \frac{-1}{5} \begin{bmatrix} -2\frac{t^3}{t_0^3} - 3\frac{t_0^2}{t^2}, & -\left(\frac{t^3}{t_0^2} - \frac{t_0^3}{t^2}\right) \\ -6\left(\frac{t^2}{t_0^3} - \frac{t_0^2}{t^3}\right), & -3\frac{t^2}{t_0^2} - 2\frac{t_0^3}{t^3} \end{bmatrix} \begin{bmatrix} x_{10} \\ x_{20} \end{bmatrix}$$
$$- \frac{1}{5} \begin{bmatrix} t^3 & t^{-2} \\ 3t^2 & -2t^{-3} \end{bmatrix} \begin{bmatrix} -\frac{1}{2}(\ln t_0)^2 + \frac{1}{2}(\ln t)^2 \\ -\frac{t_0^5}{25}(1 - 5\ln t_0) + \frac{t^5}{25}(1 - 5\ln t) \end{bmatrix}$$

2.3. REDUCING THE ORDER OF A SYSTEM

If k, $k < n$, members of a basis of an nth-order system are known, it is possible to determine the remaining $n - k$ members of the basis from the reduced system of order $n - k$. The construction of the *reduced-order* system proceeds as follows.

2.3.1. The scalar System. Assume that the basis function $x_1(t)$ of the basis $x_1(t), x_2(t), \cdots, x_n(t)$ of the scalar system

$$\alpha_0(t)\,\frac{d^n x(t)}{dt^n} + \cdots + \alpha_n(t)x(t) = 0 \tag{2.125}$$

is known. Making the variable substitution

$$x(t) = x_1(t)z(t) \tag{2.126}$$

Eq. 2.125 takes on the form

$$\alpha_0^*(t)\,\frac{d^n z(t)}{dt^n} + \cdots + \alpha_n^*(t)z(t) = 0 \tag{2.127}$$

As $x_1(t)$ is a solution to Eq. 2.125, relation 2.126 requires that $z(t) = 1$ be a solution to Eq. 2.127. This in turn requires that $\alpha_n^*(t) = 0$. Thus defining

$$x^*(t) \equiv \frac{dz(t)}{dt} \tag{2.128}$$

reduces Eq. 2.127 to the $(n - 1)$th-order equation

$$\alpha_0^*(t)\,\frac{d^{n-1} x^*(t)}{dt^n} + \cdots + \alpha_{n-1}^*(t)x^*(t) = 0 \tag{2.129}$$

For the case that k basis functions are known, the process can be repeated until an $(n - k)$th-order system is obtained.

Example 2.5. It is known that the equation

$$\frac{d^2x(t)}{dt^2} + x(t) = 0$$

is satisfied by $x_1(t) = e^{it}$. Taking $x_1(t)$ as a basis function, the other basis function is found from a reduced-order system. The variable substitution

$$x(t) = x_1(t)z(t) = e^{it}z(t)$$

is made. Thus

$$e^{it}\,\frac{d^2z(t)}{dt^2} + 2ie^{it}\,\frac{dz}{dt} = 0$$

Letting $x^*(t) = \dfrac{dz(t)}{dt}$ results in the reduced order system

$$\frac{dx^*(t)}{dt} + 2ix^*(t) = 0$$

Solving gives

$$x^*(t) = e^{-2it}$$

Therefore

$$z(t) = \int x^*(t)dt = \frac{i}{2}\,e^{-2it}$$

and

$$x(t) = x_1(t)z(t) = \frac{i}{2}e^{it}e^{-2it} = \frac{i}{2}e^{-it}$$

Thus a second basis function completing the set is $x_2(t) = e^{-it}$.

2.3.2. The Multivariable System. Assume that the basis vector

$$\mathbf{x}_1(t) = \begin{bmatrix} x_{11}(t) \\ x_{21}(t) \\ \vdots \\ x_{n1}(t) \end{bmatrix} \tag{2.130}$$

for the system

$$\dot{\mathbf{x}}(t) = \mathbf{A}(t)\mathbf{x}(t) \tag{2.131}$$

is known. Make the variable substitution

$$\mathbf{x}(t) = \mathbf{V}(t)\mathbf{z}(t) \tag{2.132}$$

where

$$\mathbf{V}(t) = [\mathbf{e}_1, \cdots, \mathbf{e}_{i-1}, \mathbf{x}_1(t), \mathbf{e}_{i+1}, \cdots, \mathbf{e}_n] \tag{2.133}$$

and $\mathbf{e}_j$ is the jth column of the $n \times n$ identity matrix and $x_{ni}(t)$ is non-vanishing. Thus $\mathbf{V}(t)$ is nonsingular. For simplicity of development, assume that $x_{n1}(t)$ is nonvanishing. Therefore

$$\mathbf{V}(t) = \begin{bmatrix} 1 & 0 & 0 \cdots 0 & x_{11}(t) \\ 0 & 1 & 0 \cdots 0 & x_{21}(t) \\ 0 & 0 & 1 \cdots 0 & x_{31}(t) \\ \vdots & \vdots & \vdots \quad\; \vdots & \vdots \\ 0 & 0 & 0 \cdots 1 & x_{n-1,1}(t) \\ 0 & 0 & 0 \cdots 0 & x_{n1}(t) \end{bmatrix} \tag{2.134}$$

Differentiating Eq. 2.132 and solving for $\dot{\mathbf{z}}(t)$ gives

$$\dot{\mathbf{z}}(t) = \mathbf{V}^{-1}(t)[\dot{\mathbf{x}}(t) - \dot{\mathbf{V}}(t)\mathbf{z}(t)) \tag{2.135}$$

Substituting from Eqs. 2.131 and 2.132 in Eq. 2.135 gives

$$\dot{\mathbf{z}}(t) = \mathbf{V}^{-1}(t)[\mathbf{A}(t)\mathbf{V}(t) - \dot{\mathbf{V}}(t)]\mathbf{z}(t) \tag{2.136}$$

Letting

$$\mathbf{K}(t) \equiv \mathbf{V}^{-1}(t)[\mathbf{A}(t)\mathbf{V}(t) - \dot{\mathbf{V}}(t)] \tag{2.137}$$

results in

$$\dot{\mathbf{z}}(t) = \mathbf{K}(t)\mathbf{z}(t) \tag{2.138}$$

Since the basis vector $\mathbf{x}_1(t)$ is known, a solution to Eq. 2.138 is also known. Specifically,

$$\mathbf{z}_1(t) = \mathbf{V}^{-1}(t)\mathbf{x}_1(t) = \begin{bmatrix} 0 \\ \vdots \\ 0 \\ 1 \end{bmatrix} \tag{2.139}$$

Substituting this known solution into the differential equation 2.138 gives

$$\begin{bmatrix} 0 \\ \vdots \\ 0 \\ 0 \end{bmatrix} = \mathbf{K}(t)\begin{bmatrix} 0 \\ \vdots \\ 0 \\ 1 \end{bmatrix} = \begin{bmatrix} k_{1n}(t) \\ \vdots \\ k_{n-1,n}(t) \\ k_{nn}(t) \end{bmatrix} \tag{2.140}$$

Thus it is seen that

$$k_{in}(t) = 0\,, \qquad i = 1, \cdots, n \tag{2.141}$$

Partitioning Eq. 2.138 in view of Eq. 2.141 results in

$$\begin{bmatrix} z_1(t) \\ \vdots \\ z_{n-1}(t) \\ \hline z_n(t) \end{bmatrix} = \left[\begin{array}{ccc|c} k_{11}(t) & \cdots & k_{1,n-1}(t) & k_{1n}(t) \\ \vdots & & \vdots & \vdots \\ k_{n-1,1}(t) & \cdots & k_{n-1,n-1}(t) & k_{n-1,n}(t) \\ \hline k_{n1}(t) & \cdots & k_{n,n-1}(t) & k_{nn}(t) \end{array}\right] \begin{bmatrix} z_1(t) \\ \vdots \\ z_{n-1}(t) \\ \hline z_n(t) \end{bmatrix} \tag{2.142}$$

or simply

$$\begin{bmatrix} \dot{\mathbf{z}}_a(t) \\ \hline \dot{z}_n(t) \end{bmatrix} = \left[\begin{array}{c|c} \mathbf{K}_a(t) & \mathbf{0} \\ \hline \mathbf{k}_b'(t) & 0 \end{array}\right] \begin{bmatrix} \mathbf{z}_a(t) \\ \hline z_n(t) \end{bmatrix} \tag{2.143}$$

Multiplying out the matrix equation 2.143 gives the $(n-1)$th reduced-order system

$$\dot{\mathbf{z}}_a(t) = \mathbf{K}_a(t)\mathbf{z}_a(t) \tag{2.144}$$

Once this equation is solved for $\mathbf{z}_a(t)$, $z_n(t)$ is obtained from the second of the two equations represented in the partition

$$z_n(t) = \mathbf{k}_b'(t)\mathbf{z}_a(t) \tag{2.145}$$

It can be shown that if k of the basis vectors are known, that the reduction to an $(n-k)$ order system can be obtained in a similar manner by defining

$$\mathbf{V}(t) \equiv \begin{bmatrix} 1 & 0 & 0 \cdots & x_{11}(t) & \cdots & x_{1k}(t) \\ 0 & 1 & 0 \cdots & x_{21}(t) & \cdots & x_{2k}(t) \\ 0 & 0 & 1 \cdots & x_{31}(t) & \cdots & x_{3k}(t) \\ \vdots & \vdots & \vdots & \vdots & & \vdots \\ 0 & 0 & 0 \cdots & x_{n-1,1}(t) & \cdots & x_{n-1,k}(t) \\ 0 & 0 & 0 \cdots & x_{n1}(t) & \cdots & x_{nk}(t) \end{bmatrix} \tag{2.146}$$

2.4. AN OPERATOR ALGEBRA FOR COMBINING DIFFERENTIAL EQUATIONS [11]

In general, combining two differential equations to obtain a third differential equation, as one might wish to do if two systems characterized by known scalar-differential equations are cascaded, is not a trivial matter. In this section the techniques for combining and the rules of manipulation of differential equations are developed in the form of an algebra of linear transformations. It is shown (Prob. 2.22) that when the systems being cascaded are characterized in state-variable form, obtaining the state-variable description of the overall system is a simple matter.

2.4.1. Analysis. Consider the scalar system characterized by the nth-order differential equation

$$\sum_{i=0}^{n} a_i(t) \frac{d^i x(t)}{dt^i} = \sum_{j=0}^{n} b_j(t) \frac{d^j f(t)}{dt^j} \tag{2.147}$$

The following operator notation is introduced:

$$\begin{aligned} z(t) &\equiv \sum_{j=0}^{n} b_j(t) \frac{d^j f(t)}{dt^j} = \sum_{i=0}^{n} a_i(t) \frac{d^i x(t)}{dt^i} \\ &\equiv L_b[f(t)] \equiv L_a[x(t)] \end{aligned} \tag{2.148}$$

where

$$L_b = \sum_{j=0}^{n} b_j(t) \frac{d^j}{dt^j} \tag{2.149a}$$

$$L_a = \sum_{i=0}^{n} a_i(t) \frac{d^i}{dt^i} \tag{2.149b}$$

The system so characterized is graphically represented in Fig. 2.1.

Using this notation a method for cascading scalar systems (i.e., *multiplying* linear differential equations) is developed. Assume that it is desired to determine the single scalar differential equation characterizing the overall system consisting of the following two systems in cascade:

$$\sum_{i=0}^{n} a_i(t) \frac{d^i x(t)}{dt^i} = \sum_{j=0}^{n} b_j(t) \frac{d^j f(t)}{dt^j} \tag{2.150a}$$

$$\sum_{i=0}^{m} c_i(t) \frac{d^i v(t)}{dt^i} = \sum_{j=0}^{m} d^j(t) \frac{d^j g(t)}{dt^j} \tag{2.150b}$$

The effect of cascading is that the output of the first system is the input of the second system, i.e.,

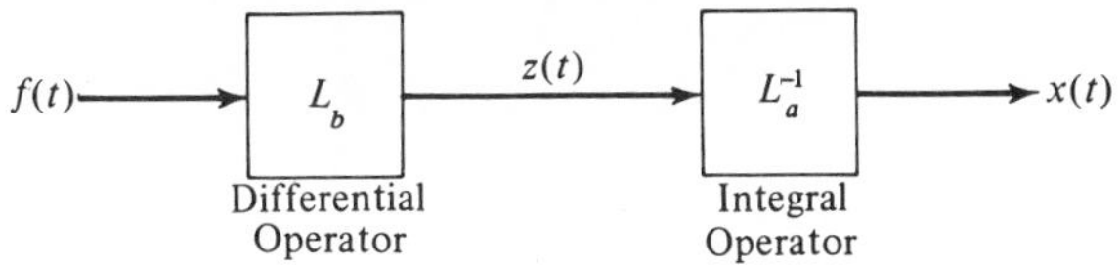

Fig. 2.1. Graphical representation of the linear time-varying system characterized by Eq. 2.148.

$$x(t) = g(t) \tag{2.151}$$

Using the operator notation introduced in Eq. 2.148 the overall system can be represented by

$$z(t) = L_a[x(t)] = L_b[f(t)] \tag{2.152a}$$

$$w(t) = L_c[v(t)] = L_d[x(t)] \tag{2.152b}$$

Such a cascaded system is shown in Fig. 2.2.

Since the single system representation consists of a differential operator cascaded with an integral operator, as in Fig. 2.1, it is assumed that the cascaded systems can be represented by the system of Fig. 2.3. That is, it is assumed that the operators L_δ and L_α can be found such that

$$L_\alpha[w(t)] = y(t) \tag{2.153a}$$

$$L_\delta[z(t)] = y(t) \tag{2.153b}$$

That is, such that

$$L_\alpha[w(t)] = L_\delta[z(t)] \tag{2.154a}$$

Substituting from Eqs. 2.152 in Eq. 2.154a gives

$$L_\alpha[L_d(x)] = L_\delta[L_a(x)] \tag{2.154b}$$

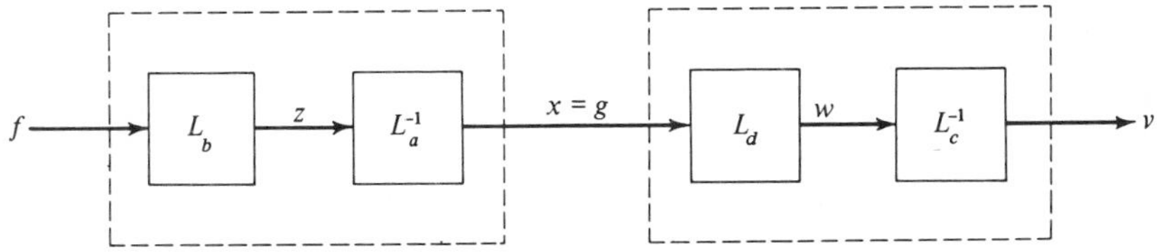

Fig. 2.2. Cascading of the two systems characterized by Eqs. 2.150.

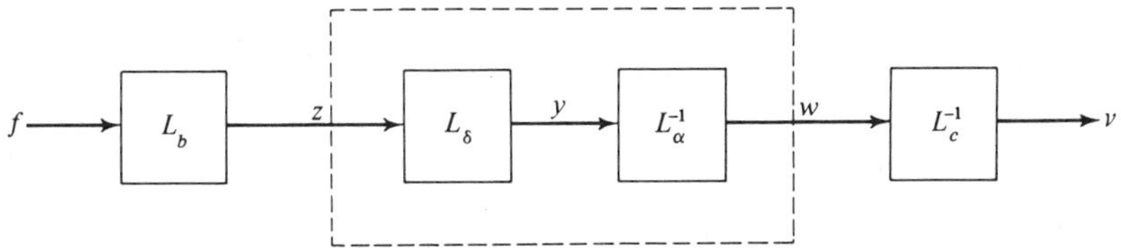

Fig. 2.3. Proposed representation of the two cascaded systems characterized by Eqs. 2.150.

Assume L_α and L_δ of the forms

$$L_\alpha = \sum_{i=0}^{n} \alpha_i(t) \frac{d^i}{dt^i} \tag{2.155a}$$

$$L_\delta = \sum_{j=0}^{m} \delta_j(t) \frac{d^j}{dt^j} \tag{2.155b}$$

Thus substituting from Eqs. 2.150 and 2.155 in Eq. 2.154 gives

$$\begin{aligned} &\sum_{i=0}^{m} \alpha_i(t) \frac{d^i}{dt^i} \left[\sum_{j=0}^{m} d_j(t) \frac{d^j x(t)}{dt^j} \right] \\ &\quad = \sum_{i=0}^{m} \delta_i(t) \frac{d^i}{dt^i} \left[\sum_{j=0}^{n} a_j(t) \frac{d^j x(t)}{dt^j} \right] \end{aligned} \tag{2.156}$$

Equation 2.156 can be manipulated and rearranged to obtain the useful form

$$\begin{aligned} &\sum_{i=0}^{m} \sum_{j=0}^{n} \sum_{k=0}^{i} \binom{i}{k} \delta_i(t) \frac{d^{i-k} a_j(t)}{dt^{i-k}} \frac{d^{j+k} x(t)}{dt^{j+k}} \\ &\quad = \sum_{i=0}^{n} \sum_{j=0}^{m} \sum_{k=0}^{i} \binom{i}{k} \alpha_i(t) \frac{d^{i-k} d_j(t)}{dt^{i-k}} \frac{d^{j+k} x(t)}{dt^{j+k}} \end{aligned} \tag{2.157}$$

Equating coefficients of like derivatives of $x(t)$ gives $m + n + 1$ equations in the $m + n + 2$ unknown coefficients $\alpha_i(t)$, $i = 0, 1, \cdots, n$, $\delta_j(t)$, $j = 0, 1, \cdots, m$. Arbitrarily choosing $\alpha_n(t) = 1$ leaves $m + n + 1$ equations in $m + n + 1$ unknown coefficients. Thus the operators L_α and L_δ are identified in the assumed forms of Eq. 2.155

Defining the differential operators

$$L_{b'} = L_\delta[L_b \tag{2.158a}$$

$$L_{a'} = L_\alpha[L_c \tag{2.158b}$$

results in the representation of the cascaded systems shown in Fig. 2.4. Thus the single scalar differential equation characterizing the two cascaded systems is denoted by

$$L_{a'}[v(t)] = L_{b'}[f(t)] \tag{2.159}$$

or

$$L_\alpha[L_c(v)] = L_\delta[L_b(f)] \tag{2.160}$$

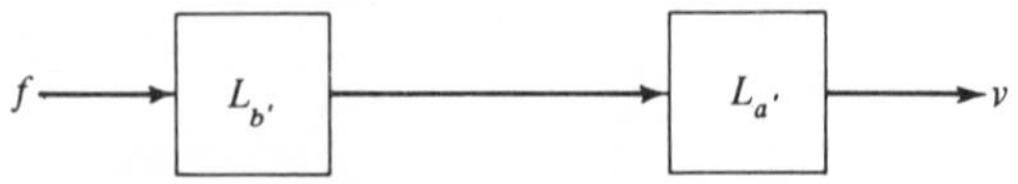

Fig. 2.4. Graphical operator representation of the two cascaded systems characterized by Eqs. 2.150.

or

$$\sum_{i=0}^{n} \alpha_i(t) \frac{d^i}{dt^i} \left[\sum_{j=0}^{m} c_j(t) \frac{d^j v(t)}{dt^j} \right] = \sum_{i=0}^{m} \delta_i(t) \frac{d^i}{dt^i} \left[\sum_{j=0}^{n} b_j(t) \frac{d^j f(t)}{dt^j} \right] \tag{2.161}$$

Equation 2.161 can be manipulated and rearranged to give the general form

$$\sum_{i=0}^{n} \sum_{j=0}^{m} \sum_{k=0}^{i} \binom{i}{k} \alpha_i(t) \frac{d^{i-k} c_j(t)}{dt^{i-k}} \frac{d^{j+k} v(t)}{dt^{j+k}} = \sum_{i=0}^{m} \sum_{j=0}^{n} \sum_{k=0}^{i} \binom{i}{k} \delta_i(t) \frac{d^{i-k} b_j(t)}{dt^{i-k}} \frac{d^{j+k} f(t)}{dt^{j+k}} \tag{2.162}$$

For notational convenience, the cascading of two systems can be represented by the following symbolic multiplication. Consider the two scalar linear time-varying systems cascaded as shown in Fig. 2.5. Let

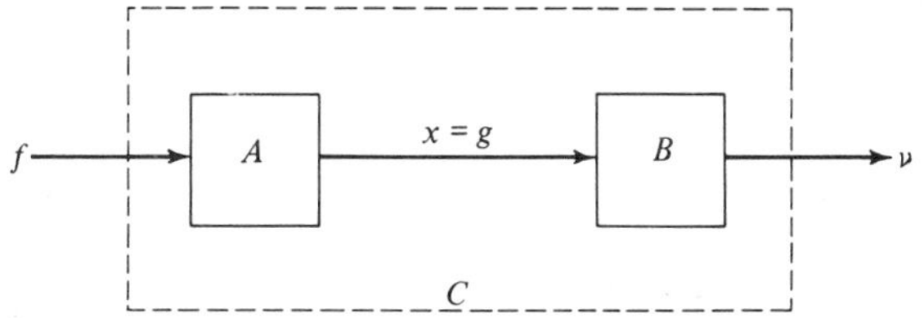

Fig. 2.5. Symbolic representation of the cascading of two systems.

(i) A denote the scalar differential equation 2.150a
(ii) B denote the scalar differential equation 2.150b.

Then the symbolic multiplication of differential equations is denoted by

$$C = BA \tag{2.163}$$

where C denotes the scalar differential equation 2.162.

The *unity element* is defined as that system for which the input and zero-state output are identical. Clearly, the system characterized by Eq. 2.148 is a unity element if $L_a = L_b$, i.e., if the system's differential equation is of the form

$$\sum_{i=0}^{n} a_i(t) \frac{d^i x(t)}{dt^i} = \sum_{i=0}^{n} a_i(t) \frac{d^i f(t)}{dt^i} \tag{2.164}$$

Such a system, shown in Fig. 2.6, is symbolically denoted by I.

A system B is said to be a *multiplicative inverse* of system A if

$$AB = I \tag{2.165}$$

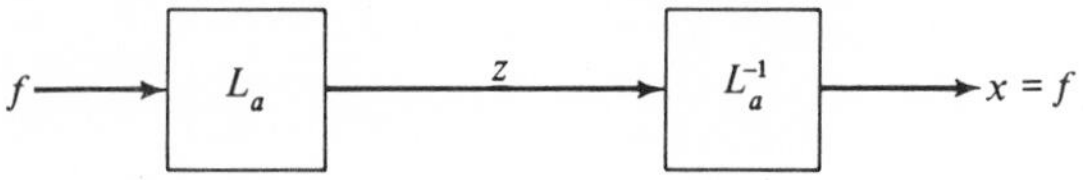

Fig. 2.6. The unity element.

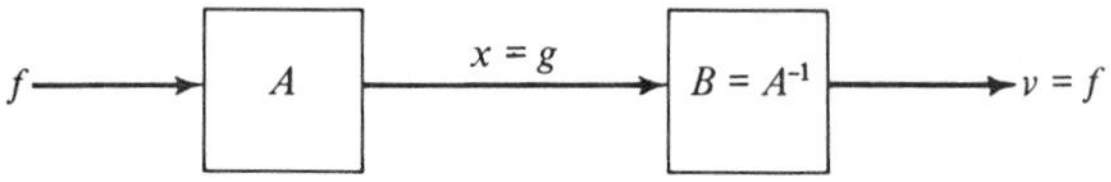

(a)

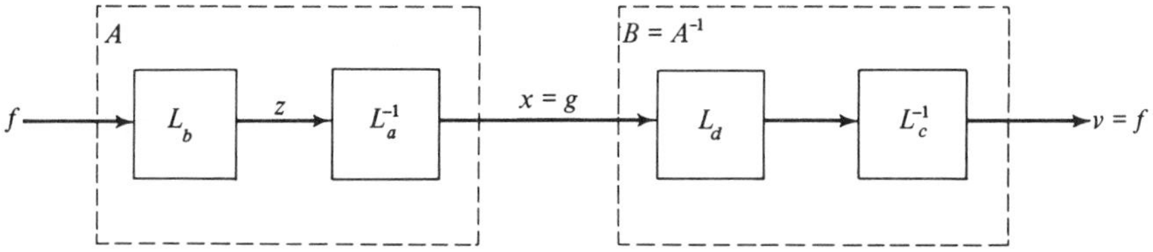

(b)

Fig. 2.7. The multiplicative inverse.

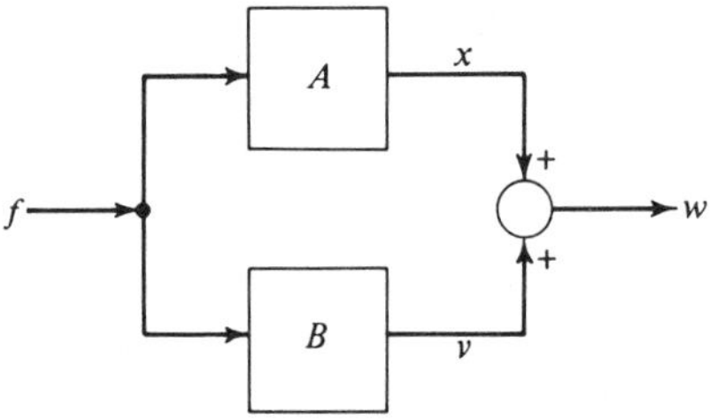

(a)

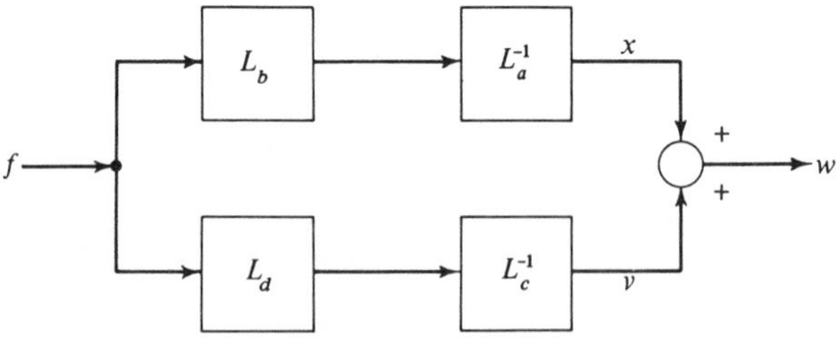

(b)

Fig. 2.8. Step-by-step reduction of addition of two differential equations.

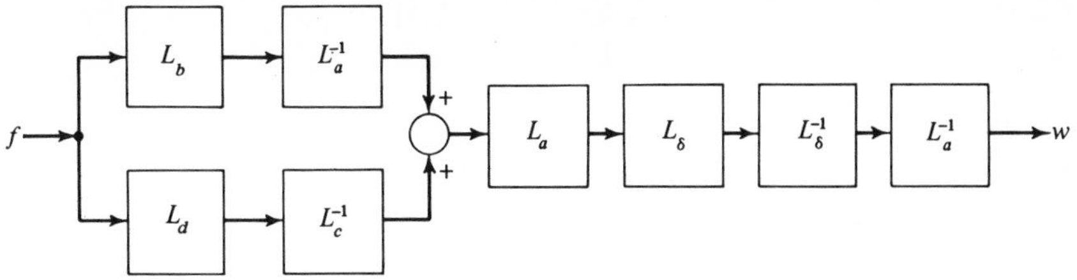

(c)

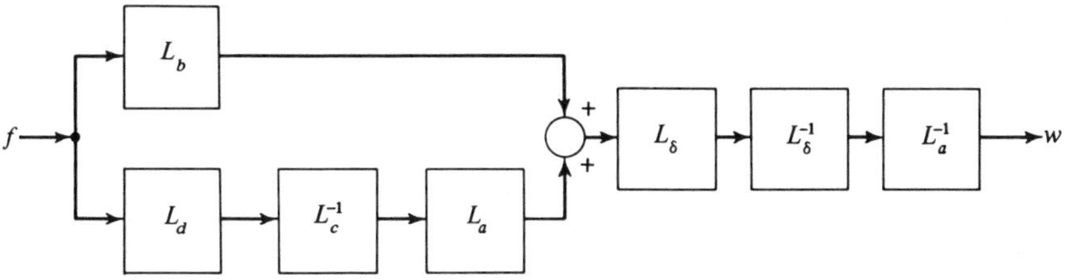

(d)

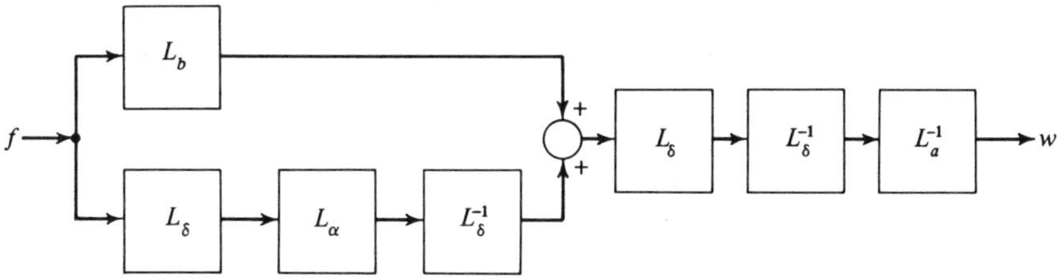

(e)

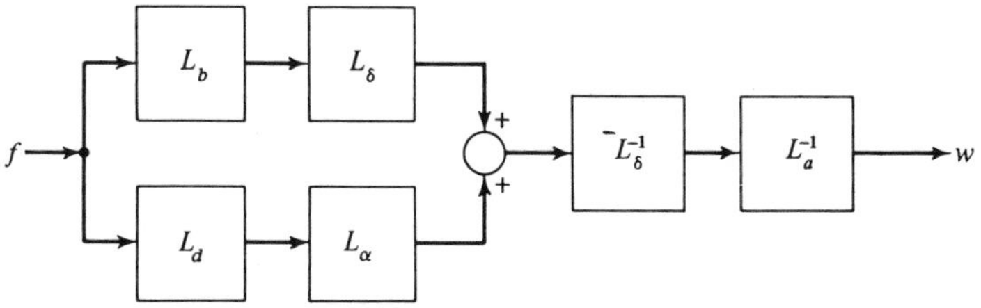

(f)

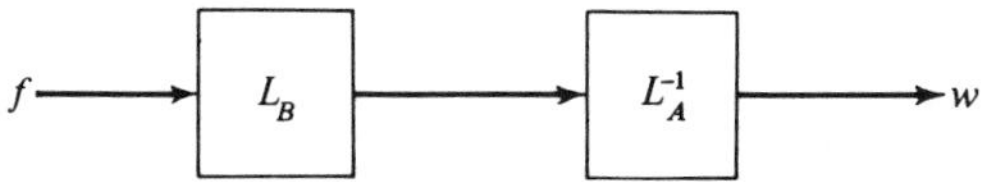

(g)

Fig. 2.8. Continued.

Symbolically, the multiplicative inverse of A is denoted by A^{-1}. The multiplicative inverse is shown in Fig. 2.7. It can be noted from this figure that B is the multiplicative inverse of A when

$$L_d = L_a = \sum_{i=0}^{n} a_i(t) \frac{d^i}{dt^i} \tag{2.166a}$$

$$L_b = L_c = \sum_{i=0}^{n} b_i(t) \frac{d^i}{dt^i} \tag{2.166b}$$

Thus the inverse system is characterized by

$$\sum_{i=0}^{n} b_i(t) \frac{d^i v(t)}{dt^i} = \sum_{j=0}^{n} a_j(t) \frac{d^j g(t)}{dt^j} \tag{2.167}$$

The *addition* of two differential equations is represented symbolically in Fig. 2.8a. The additions is performed step-by-step as shown in Figs. 2.8, b–g. Thus it is seen that by defining an arbitrary operator L_δ, the addition of two differential equations can proceed in a straightforward manner.

2.4.2. Synthesis. The operator algebra introduced in the preceding section, and in particular the concept of the multiplicative inverse, is utilized to provide a method of synthesis. Figure 2.9 is utilized to simplify the statement of the synthesis problem; K and G are the symbolic notations representing the differential equations relating the input and outputs of the individual blocks.

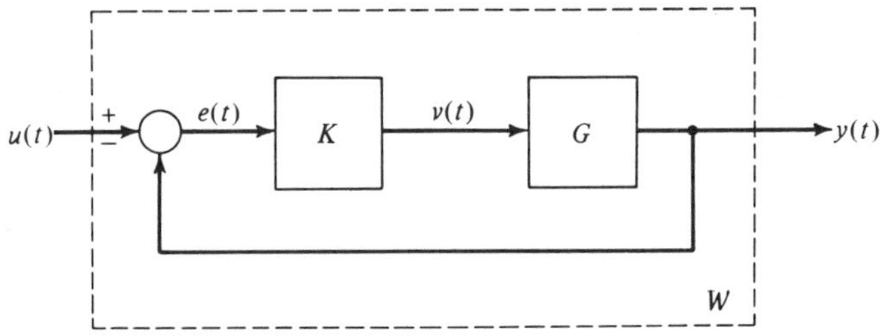

Fig. 2.9. The unity-feedback configuration.

The synthesis problem considered here is that of determining the differential equations characterizing the compensating system K when the differential equation of the plant G is known and the differential equation of the overall system W is specified.

The advantage of applying the operator algebra for combining differential equations to the synthesis problem is that extremely simple straightforward concepts are involved. All the manipulative operations can be performed symbolically and the numerical details carried out only at the end of the process.

For example, by letting the operation $(\cdot)$ represent the operation which a differential equation performs on a variable to produce a new variable, the differential equation of the overall system of Fig. 2.9 is denoted by

$$y(t) = W \cdot u(t) \tag{2.168}$$

Thus it can be easily shown that

$$\begin{aligned} W &= GK(I + GK)^{-1} \\ &= (I + GK)^{-1}GK \end{aligned} \tag{2.169}$$

Therefore knowing W and G the synthesis is completed by solving for differential equation K:

$$\begin{aligned} K &= G^{-1}(I - W)^{-1}W \\ &= G^{-1}W(I - W)^{-1} \end{aligned} \tag{2.170}$$

Example 2.6. This process of synthesis is well illustrated by considering the following problem. Let G in Fig. 2.9 represent the differential equation

$$\frac{d^2y(t)}{dt^2} + \frac{dy(t)}{dt} + e^{-t}y(t) = v(t) \tag{2.171}$$

The differential equation K is to be determined so that the overall differential equation W is

$$\frac{d^2y(t)}{dt^2} + 2\frac{dy(t)}{dt} + y(t) = u(t) \tag{2.172}$$

The differential equation $I - W$ is formed by addition:

$$\frac{d^2z(t)}{dt^2} + 2\frac{dz(t)}{dt} = \frac{d^2y(t)}{dt^2} + 2\frac{dy(t)}{dt} + y(t) \tag{2.173}$$

where $z(t)$ represents the input and $y(t)$ is the output. The differential equation $(I - W)^{-1}W$ is then formed as

$$\frac{d^2y(t)}{dt^2} + 2\frac{dy(t)}{dt} = e(t) \tag{2.174}$$

The differential equation K is then produced in accordance with Eq. 2.170:

$$\begin{aligned} &\frac{d^2e(t)}{dt^2} + \left(\frac{2 + 3e^{-t}}{1 - e^{-t}}\right)\frac{de(t)}{dt} + (1 + e^{-t})e(t) \\ &= \frac{d^2v(t)}{dt^2} + \left(\frac{3 + 4e^{-t}}{1 + e^{-t}}\right)\frac{dv(t)}{dt} + \left(\frac{2 + 3e^{-t}}{1 + e^{-t}}\right)v(t) \end{aligned} \tag{2.175}$$

Thus the compensating system K is completely specified by Eq. 2.175 and is readily synthesized using standard analog computer techniques.

It is pointed out that this technique is essentially a plant-cancellation method whereby the compensator cancels the plant and replaces it with the desired open-loop system. Thus the method suffers all the disadvantages of any plant-cancellation technique; e.g., (1) complex compensation systems result, (2) practical considerations preclude the possibility of perfect cancellation. However, even with these disadvantages the method is a valuable synthesis tool because it is both straightforward and generally practically feasible.

By restricting the choice of the overall differential equation W (the difference in orders of the integral and differential operators of the overall system W are constrained to be equal to or greater than the difference in orders of the integral and differential operators of the fixed plant G) a simple approximation synthesis method can be developed whereby the compensation system does not cancel the fixed plant [11].

REFERENCES

[1] Bellman, R., *Stability Theory of Differential Equations*, McGraw-Hill, New York, 1953.

[2] Birkoff, R., and G. Rota, *Ordinary Differential Equations*, Ginn, Boston, 1962.

[3] Coddington, E., and N. Levinson, *Theory of Ordinary Differential Equations*, McGraw-Hill, New York, 1955.

[4] De Russo, P., R. Roy, and C. Close, *State Variables for Engineers*, Wiley, New York, 1965.

[5] Hockstadt, H., *Differential Equations*, Holt, New York, 1964.

[6] Miller, K., *Linear Differential Equations in the Read Domain*, Copyright (C) 1963 by K. Miller. Norton. New York, pp. 6–12 with permission of publishers.

[7] Petrovski, I. (trans. by R. Silverman), *Ordinary Differential Equations*, Prentice-Hall, Englewood Cliffs, N. J., 1966.

[8] Schwarz, R., and B. Friedland, *Linear Systems*, McGraw-Hill, New York, 1965.

[9] Zadeh, L., and C. Desoer, *Linear System Theory: The State Space Approach*, McGraw-Hill, New York, 1963.

[10] Kinariwala, B., "Analysis of Time-Varying Networks," *IRE International Convention Record*, vol. 9, part 4 (1961), pp. 268–276.

[11] Stubberud, A., "A Technique for the Synthesis of Linear Nonstationary Feedback Systems-Part II: The Synthesis Problem", *IEEE Transactions on Applications in Industry*, vol. 67 (July, 1963), pp. 192–196.

PROBLEMS

2.1 Verify Eq. 2.12.

2.2 Find the solution in terms of an integral expression, to the equation

$$\dot{x}(t) + \cos t x(t) = e^{-\sin t}$$

with the initial condition $x(0) = 1$.

2.3 Show that Eq. 2.6, and thus Eq. 2.16, is valid only when $\alpha_0(t)$ does not vanish on $[a, b]$.

2.4 Prove inequality 2.44.

2.5 Prove inequality 2.45.

2.6 Prove inequality 2.46.

2.7 Use Eq. 2.79 to determine the solution to the homogeneous scalar equation

$$\dot{x}(t) - ax(t) = 0\,, \qquad x(t_0) = x_0$$

2.8 Detail the argument allowing Eq. 2.74 to be written from Eq. 2.73.

2.9 Detail the argument allowing the statement of continuity to be made about $\hat{\mathbf{x}}(t)$ following Eq. 2.58.

2.10 Use Eq. 2.79 to determine the solution to the homogeneous scalar equation

$$\dot{x}(t) - tx - 0\,, \qquad x(0) = 1$$

2.11 Use Eq. 2.79 to determine the solution to the homogeneous equation

$$\begin{bmatrix}\dot{x}_1(t)\\ \dot{x}_2(t)\end{bmatrix} = \begin{bmatrix}-6 & -4\\ 5 & 3\end{bmatrix}\begin{bmatrix}x_1(t)\\ x_2(t)\end{bmatrix}, \qquad \begin{bmatrix}x_1(0)\\ x_2(0)\end{bmatrix} = \begin{bmatrix}1\\ 0\end{bmatrix}$$

2.12 From Theorem 2.3 deduce the restrictions that must be placed on the coefficient $\alpha_0(t)$ of the scalar equation 2.29 in order to establish the existence and uniqueness of solutions.

2.13 Derive Eq. 2.81.

2.14 Using Eq. 2.105 determine the solution to

$$\begin{bmatrix}\dot{x}_1(t)\\ \dot{x}_2(t)\end{bmatrix} = \begin{bmatrix}0 & 1\\ -2 & -3\end{bmatrix}\begin{bmatrix}x_1(t)\\ x_2(t)\end{bmatrix} + \begin{bmatrix}0\\ e^{-3t}\end{bmatrix}, \qquad \begin{bmatrix}x_1(0)\\ x_2(0)\end{bmatrix} = \begin{bmatrix}1\\ 0\end{bmatrix}$$

2.15 Select a set of n initial conditions $\mathbf{x}_i(t_0)$, $i = 1, \ldots, n$ that result in n linearly independent solutions to the homogeneous equation 2.84.

2.16 Derive Eqs. 2.33B through 2.33F.

2.17 Put the scalar system characterized by the equation

$$t_2\frac{d^3y}{dt^3} + \cos t\frac{d^2y}{dt^2} + 2\frac{dy}{dt} + \sin ty = t^3\frac{d^2r}{dt^2} + \cos t\frac{dr}{dt} + r$$

into state-variable form.

2.18 Give an example illustrating that superposition is not a property of nonquiescent systems.

2.19 Use the method of variation of parameters to solve Prob. 2.14.

2.20 For the equation

$$\frac{d^2x}{dt^2} + 3\frac{dx}{dt} + 2x = 0$$

it is known that a basis function is $x_1(t) = e^{-t}$. Determine the second basis function by reducing the order of the system.

2.21 Put the equation of Prob. 2.20 in state-variable form and repeat the problem.

2.22 Systems N_1 and N_2 are characterized by the state-variable equations

$$N_1: \begin{cases} \dot{\mathbf{x}}(t) = \mathbf{A}(t)\mathbf{x}(t) + \mathbf{B}(t)\mathbf{u}(t) \\ \mathbf{y}(t) = \mathbf{C}(t)\mathbf{x}(t) \end{cases}$$

$$N_2: \begin{cases} \dot{\mathbf{v}}(t) = \mathbf{E}(t)\mathbf{v}(t) + \mathbf{F}(t)\mathbf{q}(t) \\ \mathbf{w}(t) = \mathbf{G}(t)\mathbf{v}(t) \end{cases}$$

Assuming that in each case the dimensions are such that compatability is assured, determine the overall state-variable equations for each of the systems shown in Fig. P2.22.

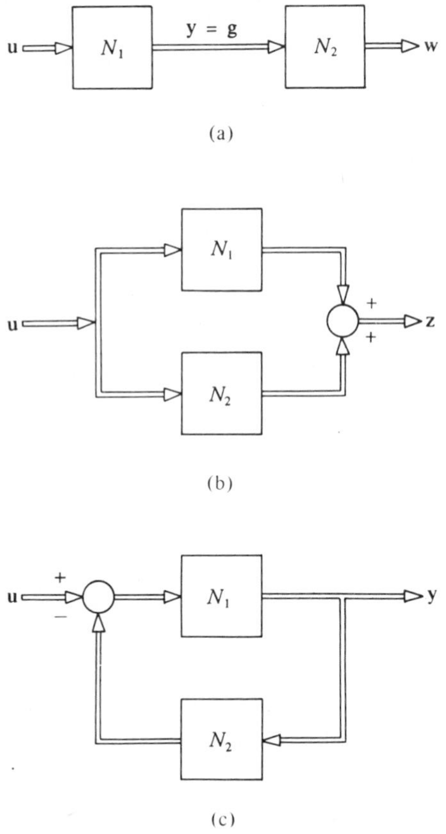

Fig. P2.22. Systems for Prob. 2.21.

The Superposition Integrals

The most important property of linear systems making their analysis and synthesis enormously more tractable than nonlinear systems is the property of superposition (see Theorem 2.10). Simply stated, it is the property of superposition that allows one to infer that a system's output will double when the system's input is doubled, regardless of the input. As a direct consequence of this property, the response of a linear system excited by arbitrary inputs and initial conditions can be determined from knowledge of the system's response to specific inputs and initial conditions. The methods used to determine a linear system's response detailed in this chapter involve the evaluation of integrals known as the *superposition integrals*. The kernels of the superposition integrals are thus important quantities in the study of linear systems. Two often-used kernels investigated in this chapter are the *transition matrix* and the *impulsive-response matrix*.

3.1. THE TRANSITION MATRIX $\phi(t, \tau)$

With results obtained thus far, an obvious approach to determining the response $\mathbf{x}(t)$ to an input $\mathbf{f}(t)$ for a system characterized by the equation

$$\dot{\mathbf{x}}(t) = \mathbf{A}(t)\mathbf{x}(t) + \mathbf{f}(t) \tag{3.1}$$

is to use either Eq. 2.105

$$\mathbf{x}(t) = \mathbf{\Phi}^{*-1}(t)\mathbf{\Phi}^{*}(t_0)\mathbf{x}_0 + \int_{t_0}^{t} \mathbf{\Phi}^{*-1}(t)^{*}\mathbf{\Phi}(\tau)\mathbf{f}(\tau)\, d\tau \tag{3.2}$$

or Eq. 2.122

$$\mathbf{x}(t) = \mathbf{W}(t)\mathbf{W}^{-1}(t_0)\mathbf{x}_0 + \int_{t_0}^{t} \mathbf{W}(t)\mathbf{W}^{-1}(\tau)\mathbf{f}(\tau)\,d\tau \tag{3.3}$$

$\mathbf{\Phi}^*(t)$, as defined in Eq. 2.102, is obtained from a basis of the homogeneous adjoint system and $\mathbf{W}(t)$ is obtained from a basis of the homogeneous system. Clearly then, important quantities in determining the response of a linear system are the products $\mathbf{\Phi}^{*-1}(t)\mathbf{\Phi}^*(\tau)$ and $\mathbf{W}(t)\mathbf{W}^{-1}(\tau)$; comparison of Eq. 3.2 and 3.3 shows that these products are in fact identical. This gives rise to the definition

$$\phi(t, \tau) \equiv \mathbf{\Phi}^{*-1}(t)\mathbf{\Phi}^*(\tau) = \mathbf{W}(t)\mathbf{W}^{-1}(\tau) \tag{3.4}$$

where $\phi(t, \tau)$ is termed the *transition matrix* (or the *fundamental matrix*, or the *characteristic matrix*, or the *matrizant*). Thus Eq. 3.2 and 3.3 can be written as

$$\mathbf{x}(t) = \phi(t, t_0)\mathbf{x}_0 + \int_{t_0}^{t} \phi(t, \tau)\mathbf{f}(\tau)\,d\tau \tag{3.5}$$

For the case that the system is *unforced* ($\mathbf{f}(t) = 0$) the complementary solution, i.e., the solution of the homogeneous equation, is

$$\mathbf{x}_c(t) = \phi(t, t_0)\mathbf{x}_0 \tag{3.6}$$

Thus it is seen that the general element $\phi_{ij}(t, \tau)$ of the transition matrix $\phi(t, \tau)$ represents the unforced response of the ith state $x_i(t)$ due to a unity initial condition on the jth state (i.e., $x_j(t_0) = 1$) for a system that is otherwise quiescent and unforced.

For the case that the system is quiescent ($\mathbf{x}_0 = 0$), Eq. 3.5 reduces to

$$\mathbf{x}_p(t) = \int_{t_0}^{t} \phi(t, \tau)\mathbf{f}(\tau)\,d\tau \tag{3.7}$$

and is termed the *superposition integral*. Thus it is seen that the system's response to arbitrary inputs and initial conditions can be determined from a complete knowledge of its transient response implicit in the transition matrix.

The solution to the homogeneous system is also obtained by the convergent infinite iterative integrations of Eq. 2.79.

$$\mathbf{x}(t) = \sum_{i=0}^{\infty} \mathbf{\Gamma}^i \mathbf{x}_0 \tag{3.8}$$

Nothing that operator $\mathbf{\Gamma}$ is defined by the integral

$$\mathbf{\Gamma}\mathbf{x}(t) = \int_{t_0}^{t} \mathbf{A}(\tau)\mathbf{x}(\tau)\,d\tau \tag{3.9}$$

leads to

$$\mathbf{\Gamma}\mathbf{x}_0 = \int_{t_0}^{t} \mathbf{A}(\tau)\mathbf{x}_0\,d\tau = \mathbf{H}_1(t, t_0)\mathbf{x}_0 \tag{3.10}$$

where

$$\mathbf{H}_1(t, t_0) = \int_{t_0}^{t} \mathbf{A}(\tau)\, d\tau \tag{3.11}$$

Since $\mathbf{x}_0$ is a constant vector one can, in this case, think of the integral operator $\mathbf{\Gamma}$ as a matrix function. Specifically,

$$\mathbf{\Gamma} = \mathbf{H}_1(t, t_0) \tag{3.12}$$

In a similar manner, from the observation that

$$\mathbf{\Gamma}^i \mathbf{x}_0 = \mathbf{H}_i(t, t_0)\mathbf{x}_0 \tag{3.13}$$

where

$$\mathbf{H}_i(t, t_0) = \int_{t_0}^{t} \mathbf{A}(\tau_1)d\tau_1 \int_{t_0}^{\tau_1} \mathbf{A}(\tau_2)d\tau_2 \cdots \int_{t_0}^{\tau_{i-1}} \mathbf{A}(\tau_i)d\tau_i \tag{3.14}$$

it is loosely stated that

$$\mathbf{\Gamma}^i = \mathbf{H}_i(t, t_0) \tag{3.15}$$

Therefore substituting from Eq. 3.15 in Eq. 3.8 results in

$$\mathbf{x}(t) = \mathbf{H}(t, t_0)\mathbf{x}_0 \tag{3.16}$$

where

$$\mathbf{H}(t, t_0) = \sum_{i=0}^{\infty} \mathbf{H}_i(t, t_0) = \sum_{i=0}^{\infty} \mathbf{\Gamma}^i \tag{3.17}$$

Comparison of Eq. 3.6 and 3.16 results in an expression for determining the transition matrix as a uniformly convergent infinite series:

$$\phi(t, t_0) = \sum_{i=0}^{\infty} \mathbf{\Gamma}^i \tag{3.18}$$

The following two examples illustrate application of Eq. 3.18.

Example 3.1. A linear system is characterized by the homogeneous equation

$$\begin{bmatrix} \dot{x}_1(t) \\ \dot{x}_2(t) \end{bmatrix} = \begin{bmatrix} 0 & t \\ 1 & 0 \end{bmatrix} \begin{bmatrix} x_1(t) \\ x_2(t) \end{bmatrix}$$

The transition matrix can be determined from Eq. 3.18:

$$\mathbf{\Gamma}^0 = \begin{bmatrix} 1 & 0 \\ 0 & 1 \end{bmatrix}$$

$$\mathbf{\Gamma}^1 = \int_{t_0}^{t} \begin{bmatrix} 0 & \tau \\ 1 & 0 \end{bmatrix} d\tau = \begin{bmatrix} 0 & \frac{1}{2}t^2 - \frac{1}{2}t_0^2 \\ t - t_0 & 0 \end{bmatrix}$$

$$\mathbf{\Gamma}^2 = \int_{t_0}^{t} \begin{bmatrix} 0 & \tau \\ 1 & 0 \end{bmatrix} \begin{bmatrix} 0 & \frac{1}{2}\tau^2 - \frac{1}{2}t_0^2 \\ \tau - t_0 & 0 \end{bmatrix} d\tau$$

$$= \int_{t_0}^{t} \begin{bmatrix} \tau^2 - t_0\tau & \\ & \frac{1}{2}\tau^2 - \frac{1}{2}t_0^2 \end{bmatrix} d\tau$$

$$= \begin{bmatrix} \frac{1}{3}t^3 - \frac{1}{2}t_0t^2 + \frac{1}{6}t_0^3 & 0 \\ 0 & \frac{1}{6}t^3 - \frac{1}{2}t_0^2t + \frac{1}{3}t_0^3 \end{bmatrix}$$

$$\mathbf{\Gamma}^3 = \int_{t_0}^{t} \begin{bmatrix} 0 & \tau \\ 1 & 0 \end{bmatrix} \begin{bmatrix} \frac{1}{3}\tau^3 - \frac{1}{2}t_0\tau^2 + \frac{1}{6}t_0^3 & 0 \\ 0 & \frac{1}{6}\tau^3 - \frac{1}{2}t_0^2t + \frac{1}{3}t_0^3 \end{bmatrix} d\tau$$

$$= \int_{t}^{t_0} \begin{bmatrix} 0 & \frac{1}{6}\tau^4 - \frac{1}{2}t_0^2\tau^2 + \frac{1}{3}t_0^3\tau \\ \frac{1}{3}\tau^3 - \frac{1}{2}t_0\tau^2 + \frac{1}{6}t_0^3 & 0 \end{bmatrix} d\tau$$

$$= \begin{bmatrix} 0 & \frac{1}{30}t^5 - \frac{1}{6}t_0^2t^3 + \frac{1}{6}t_0^3t^2 - \frac{1}{30}t_0^5 \\ \frac{1}{12}t^4 - \frac{1}{6}t_0t^3 + \frac{1}{6}t_0^3t - \frac{1}{12}t_0^4 & 0 \end{bmatrix}$$

Therefore the transition matrix is

$$\phi(t, t_0) = \mathbf{\Gamma}^0 + \mathbf{\Gamma}^1 + \mathbf{\Gamma}^2 + \mathbf{\Gamma}^3 + \cdots$$

$$= \begin{bmatrix} 1 + \frac{1}{6}t_0^3 - \frac{1}{2}t_0t^2 + \frac{1}{3} + \cdots, & \frac{1}{2}t_0^2 - \frac{1}{30}t_0^5 + \left(\frac{1}{2} + \frac{1}{6}t_0^3\right)t^2 - \frac{1}{6}t_0^2t^3 + \frac{1}{30}t^5 + \cdots \\ -t_0 - \frac{1}{12}t_0^4 + \left(1 + \frac{1}{6}t_0^3\right)t - \frac{1}{6}t_0t^3 + \frac{1}{12}t^4 + \cdots, & 1 + \frac{1}{3}t_0^3 - \frac{1}{2}t_0^2t + \frac{1}{6}t^3 + \cdots \end{bmatrix}$$

Example 3.2. A linear system is characterized by the homogeneous equation $\dot{\mathbf{x}}(t) = \mathbf{A}\mathbf{x}(t)$, i.e.,

$$\begin{bmatrix} \dot{x}_1(t) \\ \dot{x}_2(t) \end{bmatrix} = \begin{bmatrix} -5/2 & 3/2 \\ -1/2 & -1/2 \end{bmatrix} \begin{bmatrix} x_1(t) \\ x_2(t) \end{bmatrix}$$

The transition matrix can be determined from Eq. 3.18:

$$\mathbf{\Gamma}^0 = \begin{bmatrix} 1 & 0 \\ 0 & 1 \end{bmatrix} = \mathbf{A}^0(t - t_0)^0$$

$$\mathbf{\Gamma}^1 = \int_{t_0}^{t} \begin{bmatrix} -5/2 & 3/2 \\ -1/2 & -1/2 \end{bmatrix} d\tau = \begin{bmatrix} -5/2 & 3/2 \\ -1/2 & -1/2 \end{bmatrix} (t - t_0)$$

$$= \mathbf{A}(t - t_0)$$

$$\mathbf{\Gamma}^2 = \int_{t_0}^{t} \begin{bmatrix} -5/2 & 3/2 \\ -1/2 & -1/2 \end{bmatrix} \begin{bmatrix} -5/2 & 3/2 \\ -1/2 & -1/2 \end{bmatrix} (\tau - t_0) d\tau$$

$$= \mathbf{A}^2 \frac{(t - t_0)^2}{2}$$

Continuing in this fashion results in the general term

$$\boldsymbol{\Gamma}^i = \mathbf{A}^i \frac{(t - t_0)^i}{i!}$$

Therefore the transition matrix is

$$\begin{aligned}\phi(t, t_0) &= \sum_{i=0}^{\infty} \frac{\mathbf{A}^i(t - t_0)^i}{i!} \\ &= \exp[\mathbf{A}(t - t_0)]\end{aligned}$$

Use of Sylvester's theorem[1] results in

$$\phi(t, t_0) = \begin{bmatrix} -\frac{1}{2}e^{-(t-t_0)} + \frac{3}{2}e^{-2(t-t_0)}, & \frac{3}{2}e^{-(t-t_0)} - \frac{3}{2}e^{-2(t-t_0)} \\ -\frac{1}{2}e^{-(t-t_0)} + \frac{1}{2}e^{-2(t-t_0)}, & \frac{3}{2}e^{-(t-t_0)} - \frac{1}{2}e^{-2(t-t_0)} \end{bmatrix}$$

For the purposes of comparison, the transition matrix is also determined using the two alternate methods developed thus far. With a knowledge of a basis

$$\mathbf{x}_1(t) = \begin{bmatrix} e^{-t} \\ e^{-t} \end{bmatrix}, \quad \mathbf{x}_2(t) = \begin{bmatrix} 3e^{-2t} \\ e^{-2t} \end{bmatrix}$$

the Wronskian matrix, and its inverse, is determined:

$$\mathbf{W}(t) = \begin{bmatrix} e^{-t} & 3e^{-2t} \\ e^{-t} & e^{-2t} \end{bmatrix}, \qquad \mathbf{W}^{-1}(t) = \begin{bmatrix} -\frac{1}{2}e^{t} & \frac{3}{2}e^{t} \\ \frac{1}{2}e^{2t} & -\frac{1}{2}e^{2t} \end{bmatrix}$$

The transition matrix is determined from Eq. 3.4:

$$\begin{aligned}\phi(t, t_0) &= \mathbf{W}(t)\mathbf{W}^{-1}(t_0) \\ &= \begin{bmatrix} -\frac{1}{2}e^{-(t-t_0)} + \frac{3}{2}e^{-2(t-t_0)}, & \frac{3}{2}e^{-(t-t_0)} - \frac{3}{2}e^{-2(t-t_0)} \\ -\frac{1}{2}e^{-(t-t_0)} + \frac{1}{2}e^{-2(t-t_0)}, & \frac{3}{2}e^{-(t-t_0)} - \frac{1}{2}e^{-2(t-t_0)} \end{bmatrix}\end{aligned}$$

The adjoint system

$$\begin{bmatrix} \dot{x}_1^*(t) \\ \dot{x}_2^*(t) \end{bmatrix} = \begin{bmatrix} \frac{5}{2} & \frac{1}{2} \\ -\frac{3}{2} & \frac{1}{2} \end{bmatrix} \begin{bmatrix} x_1^*(t) \\ x_2^*(t) \end{bmatrix}$$

has the basis

$$\mathbf{x}_1^*(t) = \begin{bmatrix} -e^{t} \\ 3e^{t} \end{bmatrix}, \quad \mathbf{x}_2^*(t) = \begin{bmatrix} e^{2t} \\ -e^{2t} \end{bmatrix}$$

[1]See footnote 2, Chapter 2.

The matrix $\phi^*(t)$, which is defined as the transpose Wronskian matrix of the adjoint system, is formed:

$$\phi^*(t) = \begin{bmatrix} -e^t & 3e^t \\ -e^{2t} & -e^{2t} \end{bmatrix}$$

Thus

$$\phi^{*-1}(t) = \begin{bmatrix} \frac{1}{2}e^{-t} & \frac{3}{2}e^{-2t} \\ \frac{1}{2}e^{-t} & \frac{1}{2}e^{-2t} \end{bmatrix}$$

Again, the transition matrix is determined from Eq. 3.4.

$$\begin{aligned}\phi(t, t_0) &= \Phi^{*-1}(t)\Phi(t_0) \\ &= \begin{bmatrix} -\frac{1}{2}e^{-(t-t_0)} + \frac{3}{2}e^{-2(t-t_0)}, & \frac{3}{2}e^{-(t-t_0)} - \frac{3}{2}e^{-2(t-t_0)} \\ -\frac{1}{2}e^{-(t-t_0)} + \frac{1}{2}e^{-2(t-t_0)}, & \frac{3}{2}e^{-(t-t_0)} - \frac{1}{2}e^{-2(t-t_0)} \end{bmatrix}\end{aligned}$$

It is noted from Example 3.2 that the transition matrix for a time-invariant system can always be written as a function of a single variable $t' = t - t_0$ rather than as a function of two variables. Thus $\phi(t, t_0) = \phi(t - t_0) = \phi(t')$. Such a simplification is not possible for time-varying systems.

3.1.1. Properties of the Transition Matrix. The transition matrix completely characterizes a linear system insofar as relationships between the system input $\mathbf{f}(t)$ and the system state variable $\mathbf{x}(t)$ are concerned. If the transition matrix is known, the system differential equation is easily deduced. Several important properties of the transition matrix are listed:

1. $$\phi(t, t) = \mathbf{I}_n \qquad (3.19)$$

where $\mathbf{I}_n$ is the nth-order identity matrix. Identity 3.19 is deduced by setting $t = t_0$ in Eq. 3.6 and noting that $\mathbf{x}(t_0) = \mathbf{x}_0 = \phi(t_0, t_0)\mathbf{x}_0$. Thus $\phi(t_0, t_0) = \mathbf{I}_n$.

2. $$\phi(t, \tau) = \phi(t, t_1)\phi(t_1, \tau) \qquad (3.20)$$

Substitution of the definition 3.4, $\phi(t, \tau) = \mathbf{W}(t)\mathbf{W}^{-1}(\tau)$, on both sides of 3.20 establishes the identity.

3. $$\phi^{-1}(t, \tau) = \phi(\tau, t) \qquad (3.21)$$

Again use of the definition 3.4, $\phi(t, \tau) = \mathbf{W}(t)\mathbf{W}^{-1}(\tau)$, establishes the identity.

4. $$\frac{d\phi(t, \tau)}{dt} = \mathbf{A}(t)\phi(t, \tau) \qquad (3.22)$$

This identity is established by noting that for the unforced system,

$\dot{\mathbf{x}}(t) = \mathbf{A}(t)\mathbf{x}(t)$ with initial conditions $\mathbf{x}(t_0) = \mathbf{x}_0$, the response is $\mathbf{x}(t) = \phi(t, t_0)\mathbf{x}_0$. Differentiating the response gives $\dot{\mathbf{x}}(t) = \dfrac{d\phi(t, t_0)}{dt}\mathbf{x}_0$ which when compared to the system equation results in $\dfrac{d\phi(t, t_0)}{dt}\mathbf{x}_0 = \mathbf{A}(t)\mathbf{x}(t)$ or $\dfrac{d\phi(t, t_0)}{d\tau}\mathbf{x}_0 = \mathbf{A}(t)\phi(t, t_0)\mathbf{x}_0$.

5. $$\frac{d\phi(t, \tau)}{d\tau} = -\phi(t, \tau)\mathbf{A}(\tau)$$

This identity is established by differentiating the identity $\phi(\tau, t)\phi(t, \tau) = I_n$ with respect to τ:

$$\mathbf{A}(\tau)\phi(\tau, t)\phi(t, \tau) + \phi(\tau, t)\frac{d\phi(t, \tau)}{d\tau} = 0\,. \tag{3.23}$$

6. $\phi(t, \tau)$ is nonsingular for all t.

This is true since $\phi(t, \tau) = \mathbf{W}(t)\mathbf{W}^{-1}(\tau)$ and $\mathbf{W}(t)$ is taken as a fundamental Wronskian matrix.

7. $$\mathbf{x}(t) = \phi(t, t_0)\mathbf{x}_0 \tag{3.24}$$

Equation 3.24 is the response of the unforced system $\dot{\mathbf{x}}(t) = \mathbf{A}(t)\mathbf{x}(t)$ to the initial states $\mathbf{x}(t_0) = \mathbf{x}_0$.

8. $$\mathbf{x}(t) = \int_{t_0}^{t} \phi(t, \tau)\mathbf{f}(\tau)d\tau \tag{3.25}$$

The superposition integral 3.25 is the response of the quiescent system $\dot{\mathbf{x}}(t) = \mathbf{A}(t)\mathbf{x}(t) + \mathbf{f}(t)$, $\mathbf{x}(t_0) = 0$, to an input $\mathbf{f}(t)$.

9. $$\mathbf{x}(t) = \phi(t, t_0)\mathbf{x}_0 + \int_{t_0}^{t} \phi(t, \tau)\mathbf{f}(\tau)d\tau \tag{3.26}$$

Equation 3.26 is the response of the system $\dot{\mathbf{x}}(t) = \mathbf{A}(t)\mathbf{x}(t) + \mathbf{f}(t)$ to the initial states $\mathbf{x}(t_0) = \mathbf{x}_0$ and input $\mathbf{f}(t)$.

3.1.2. An Application of the Transition Matrix in Computation. For the forced system

$$\begin{aligned} \dot{\mathbf{x}}(t) &= \mathbf{A}(t)\mathbf{x}(t) + \mathbf{f}(t) \\ \mathbf{x}(t_0) &= \mathbf{x}_0 \end{aligned} \tag{3.27}$$

the system response $\mathbf{x}(t) = \mathbf{x}[t_0 + (k+1)T]$ at any given time $t = t_0 + (k+1)T$ can always be determined by directly evaluating the integral of an n-vector and knowing the boundary condition $\mathbf{x}(t_s) = \mathbf{x}(t_0 + kT)$ at $t_s = t_0 + kT$. Thus the interval of integration is $t - t_s = T$. Denoting $\mathbf{x}(t_0 + kT)$ by $\mathbf{x}_k$ and $\phi(t, t_s) = \phi[t_0 + (k+1)T, t_0 + kT]$ by $\phi_{k+1,k}$ and substituting in Eq. 3.26 with $t_s = t_0$ gives

$$\mathbf{x}_{k+1} = \phi_{k+1,k}\mathbf{x}_k + \int_{t_0+kT}^{t_0+(k+1)T} \phi[t_0 + (k+1)T, \tau]\mathbf{f}(\tau)\,d\tau \tag{3.28}$$

Choosing T to be a small constant compared to the length of time required for significant variations in $\phi(t, t_0)$ and $\mathbf{f}(t)$ allows Eq. 3.28 to be approximated by

$$\begin{aligned} \mathbf{x}_{k+1} &= \phi_{k+1,k}\mathbf{x}_k + \phi_{k+1,k}\mathbf{f}_k T \\ &= \phi_{k+1,k}(\mathbf{x}_k + \mathbf{f}_k T) \end{aligned} \tag{3.29}$$

where $\mathbf{f}_k = \mathbf{f}(t_0 + kT)$. Equation 3.29 represents a simple recursive computational algorithm for determining the response of a linear system when the transition matrix $\phi(t, \tau)$ is known.

For the case that the linear system is time invariant (i.e., $\dot{\mathbf{x}}(t) = \mathbf{A}\mathbf{x}(t) + \mathbf{f}(t)$, $\mathbf{A}$ = constant $n \times n$ matrix), the transition matrix is $\phi(t, t_0) = \phi(t - t_0) = \exp[\mathbf{A}(t - t_0)]$. Thus $\phi_{k+1,k} = \exp(\mathbf{A}T)$ is a constant independent of k and Eq. 3.29 reduces to

$$\mathbf{x}_{k+1} = \exp(\mathbf{A}T)(\mathbf{x}_k + \mathbf{f}_k T) \tag{3.30}$$

It should be noted that the algorithm given by Eqs. 3.29 and 3.30 are not predictive in nature; if, in any particular situation, greater numerical accuracy is required than can be obtained with a proper choice of the increment T, then other numerical methods should be investigated.

Example 3.3. Make a sketch of the response of the system characterized by the differential equation

$$\dot{x}(t) = (1 - 2t^{-1})x(t) + 10(t - 1)\,, \quad x(1) = 1$$

over the interval (1,1.3) at increments of 0.1.

A basis for this system is $x_1 = t^{-2}e^t$. Thus a Wronskian matrix is $\mathbf{W}(t) = t^{-2}e^t$, and $\mathbf{W}^{-1}(t) = t^2e^{-t}$. As $\phi(t, t_0) = \mathbf{W}(t)\mathbf{W}^{-1}(t_0)$, $\phi(t, t_0) = (t/t_0)^{-2}e^{(t-t_0)}$. Applying Eq. 3.29 with $t_0 = 1$ gives

$$x_{k+1} = \left[\frac{t_0 + (k+1)T}{t_0 + kT}\right]^{-2} e^T\{x_k + 10T[(t_0 + kT) - 1]\}$$

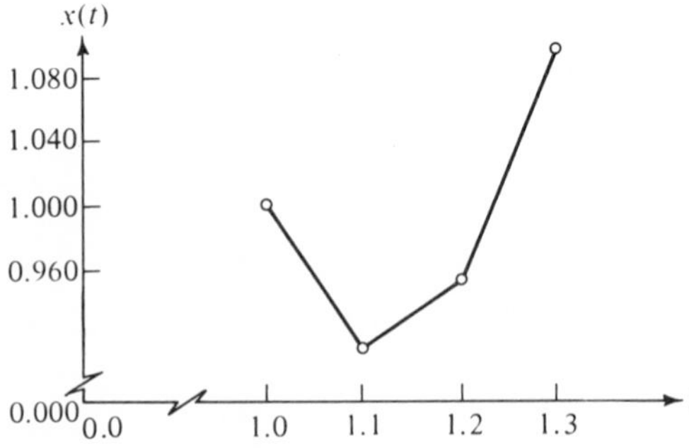

Fig. 3.1. Response of system of Example 3.2.

As $t_0 = 1$ and $T = 0.1$,

$$x_{k+1} = \left(\frac{1.1 + 0.1k}{1 + 0.1k}\right)^{-2} e^{0.1}(x_k + 0.1k)$$

Therefore $x_0 = x(t_0) = x(1) = 1$ as specified;

$$k = 0: \quad x_1 = \left(\frac{1.1}{1}\right)^{-2} e^{0.1}(1) = 0.913$$

$$k = 1: \quad x_2 = \left(\frac{1.2}{1.1}\right)^{-2} e^{0.1}(0.913 + 0.1) = 0.954$$

$$k = 2: \quad x_3 = \left(\frac{1.3}{1.2}\right)^{-2} e^{0.1}(0.954 + 0.21) = 1.088$$

3.2. THE IMPULSIVE-RESPONSE MATRIX

In Sec. 3.1 it is seen how knowledge of the transition matrix $\phi(t, \tau)$ is used to evaluate the state vector $\mathbf{x}(t)$ in response to arbitrary inputs and initial conditions for the system characterized by

$$\begin{aligned} \dot{\mathbf{x}}(t) &= \mathbf{A}(t)\mathbf{x}(t) + \mathbf{f}(t) \\ \mathbf{x}(t_0) &= \mathbf{x}_0 \end{aligned} \tag{3.31}$$

This system is represented in block-diagram form in Fig. 3.2.

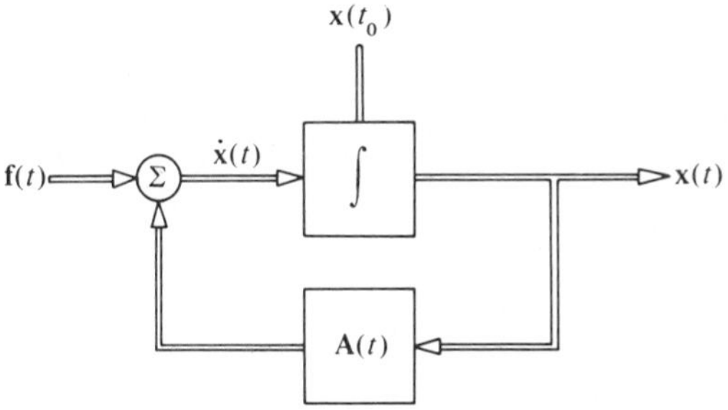

Fig. 3.2. Block diagram of the system characterized by Eqs. 3.31.

In this formulation the outputs are taken to be the state variables $x_i(t)$, $i = 1, \cdots, n$ and there is one input $f_i(t)$ corresponding to each state variable $x_i(t)$.

However, in general, there is no correspondence between the number of inputs, outputs, and states, i.e., a general linear system is characterized by the equations

$$\begin{aligned} \dot{\mathbf{x}}(t) &= \mathbf{A}(t)\mathbf{x}(t) + \mathbf{B}(t)\mathbf{u}(t) \\ \mathbf{y}(t) &= \mathbf{C}(t)\mathbf{x}(t) \\ \mathbf{x}(t_0) &= \mathbf{x}_0 \end{aligned} \tag{3.32}$$

This system is represented in block-diagram form in Fig. 3.3.

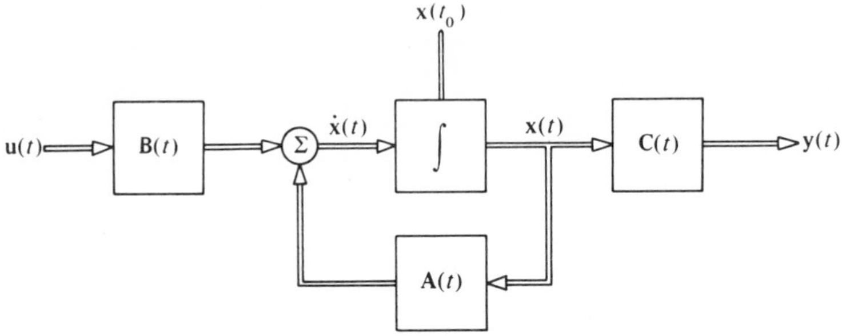

Fig. 3.3. Block diagram of the general linear system characterized by Eqs. 3.32.

In this formulation there are m inputs $u_j(t)$, $j = 1, \cdots, m$, r outputs $y_k(t)$, $k = 1, \cdots, r$ and n states $x_i(t)$, $i = 1, \cdots, n$. Clearly the transition matrix, which is useful in determining the n states from m inputs, is no longer sufficient in determining the r outputs resulting from the m inputs of the nth-order system. For this case the response of the quiescent linear system to applied impulses provides valuable information relating the output of a system to an arbitrary input of a system. Thus, the response, termed the *impulsive response*, is defined and completely characterizes the quiescent linear system between an input-output pair. In the case of a linear system with r outputs and m inputs, an $r \times m$ *impulsive-response matrix* is required for the characterization. Hence, physical significance can be attached to the impulsive-response matrix in that it relates all the inputs of the system to all the outputs of the quiescent system. The close relationship existing between the transition matrix and the impulsive-response matrix is demonstrated.

3.2.1. The Unit Impulse. The mathematical abstraction known as the *unit impulse* (delta function) is defined as the function $\delta(t - \tau)$ such that

$$\delta(t - \tau) = \begin{cases} 0, & t \neq \tau \\ \infty, & t = \tau \end{cases} \tag{3.33}$$

and

$$\int_{-\infty}^{\infty} \delta(t - \tau)\, dt = 1 \tag{3.34}$$

The above definition leads to

$$\int_{-\infty}^{t} \delta(t - \tau)\, dt = \delta^{(-1)}(t - \tau) \tag{3.35}$$

where $\delta^{(-1)}(t - \tau)$ is the unit-step function

$$\delta^{(-1)}(t - \tau) = \begin{cases} 0, & t < \tau \\ 1, & t \geqslant \tau \end{cases} \tag{3.36}$$

Formally, then, $\delta(t)$ is interpretable as the derivative of the unit-step function $u(t)$. As $u(t)$ is a discontinuous function, its derivative can be discussed in a strict sense only in the context of *generalized functions*. The operational properties of the unit-impulse functions, its integrals, and its derivatives are utilized in the sequel without justification; the interested reader can obtain addtional information on this subject from various excellent sources.

The importance of the physically unrealizable impulse function in the study of physical systems stems from the fact that it is, in a sense, easily and effectively approximated. Insofar as the analysis and synthesis of linear time-varying systems is concerned, a meaningful evaluation of an approximation to a unit impulse should be based on a comparison between the responses of a system to an ideal unit impulse and an approximate unit impulse; comparison of the actual wave forms that approximate impulses to the mathematical abstraction defined in Eqs. 3.33 and 3.34 is somewhat meaningless.

A fundamental property of the unit impulse is that

$$\int_{-\infty}^{\infty} f(t)\delta^{(n)}(t - \tau)\, dt = (-1)^n f^{(n)}(\tau) \tag{3.37}$$

Two useful identities involving derivatives of impulses are

$$\frac{d^n\delta(t - \tau)}{dt^n} = (-1)\frac{d^n\delta(t - \tau)}{d\tau^n} \tag{3.38}$$

and

$$f(t)\frac{d^n\delta(t - \tau)}{dt^n} = (-1)^n \frac{d^n[f(\tau)\delta(t - \tau)]}{d\tau^n} \tag{3.39}$$

3.2.2. The Impulsive Response of an *n*th-Order System. The general nth-order linear system, represented in Fig. 3.4, is characterized by Eq. 3.32 where $\mathbf{x}(t)$, $\mathbf{u}(t)$, $\mathbf{y}(t)$ are n-, m-, and r-vectors and $\mathbf{A}(t)$, $\mathbf{B}(t)$, $\mathbf{C}(t)$ are $n \times n$, $n \times m$, and $r \times n$ matrices. In accordance with Eq. 3.5 and the fact that

$$\mathbf{f}(t) = \mathbf{B}(t)\mathbf{u}(t) \tag{3.40}$$

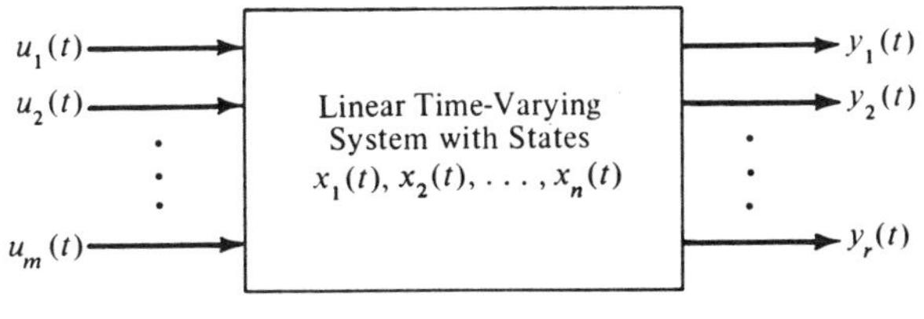

Fig. 3.4. Multi-input multi-output system.

the response to this system is

$$\mathbf{x}(t) = \phi(t, t_0)\mathbf{x}_0 + \int_{t_0}^{t} \phi(t, \tau)\mathbf{B}(\tau)\mathbf{u}(\tau)\, d\tau \tag{3.41}$$

Thus

$$\mathbf{y}(t) = \mathbf{C}(t)\phi(t, t_0)\mathbf{x}_0 + \int_{t_0}^{t} \mathbf{C}(t)\phi(t, \tau)\mathbf{B}(\tau)\mathbf{u}(\tau)\, d\tau \tag{3.42}$$

The output of this system, $\mathbf{y}(t) = \boldsymbol{\omega}_i(t, \tau)$, is said to be the impulsive response of the system when it is the result of a unit impulse $\delta(t - \tau)$ being applied to the ith input of an otherwise unexcited quiescent system. Such an input is denoted by

$$\mathbf{u}(t) = \mathbf{e}_i\delta(t - \tau) \tag{3.43}$$

where $\mathbf{l}_i$ is the ith column of the $m \times m$ identity matrix, i.e.,

$$\mathbf{e}_i = \begin{bmatrix} 0 \\ \vdots \\ 0 \\ 1 \\ 0 \\ \vdots \\ 0 \end{bmatrix} \begin{matrix} \\ \\ \\ \leftarrow i\text{th row} \\ \\ \\ \\ \end{matrix} \tag{3.44}$$

The response to the unit-impulse input of Eq. 3.43 is written

$$\boldsymbol{\omega}_i(t, \tau) = \begin{bmatrix} \omega_{1i}(t, \tau) \\ \omega_{2i}(t, \tau) \\ \vdots \\ \omega_{ri}(t, \tau) \end{bmatrix} \tag{3.45}$$

where $\omega_{ji}(t, \tau)$ is the impulsive response noted at the jth output terminal due to a unit impulse being applied at the ith input terminal.

Substituting from Eq. 3.43 in Eq. 3.42 gives

$$\omega_i(t, \tau) = \int_{t_0}^{t} \mathbf{C}(t)\phi(t, \eta)\mathbf{B}(\eta)\mathbf{e}_i\delta(\eta - \tau)\, d\eta \tag{3.46}$$

which in accordance with Eq. 3.37 reduces to

$$\boldsymbol{\omega}_i(t, \tau) = \mathbf{C}(t)\phi(t, \tau)\mathbf{B}(\tau)\mathbf{e}_i \tag{3.47}$$

Defining the *impulsive-response*[2] matrix by

$$\Omega(t, \tau) \equiv \begin{bmatrix} \omega_{11}(t, \tau) & \omega_{12}(t, \tau) & \cdots & \omega_{1m}(t, \tau) \\ \omega_{21}(t, \tau) & \omega_{22}(t, \tau) & \cdots & \omega_{2m}(t, \tau) \\ \vdots & \vdots & & \vdots \\ \omega_{r1}(t, \tau) & \omega_{r2}(t, \tau) & \cdots & \omega_{rm}(t, \tau) \end{bmatrix} \tag{3.48}$$

[2]The impulsive-response matrix $\Omega(t, \tau)$ is identical to the *weighting pattern*, or the *Green's function*, for the case that $t \geq \tau$.

it is seen that

$$\Omega(t, \tau) = [\boldsymbol{\omega}_1(t, \tau), \boldsymbol{\omega}_2(t, \tau), \cdots, \boldsymbol{\omega}_m(t, \tau)] \tag{3.49}$$

Thus

$$\boldsymbol{\omega}_i(t, \tau) = \Omega(t, \tau)\mathbf{e}_i \tag{3.50}$$

Comparison of Eqs. 3.47 and 3.50 gives the impulsive-response matrix in terms of the transition matrix:

$$\Omega(t, \tau) = \mathbf{C}(t)\phi(t, \tau)\mathbf{B}(\tau) \tag{3.51}$$

Therefore, substitution in Eq. 3.42 gives the output of the system as

$$\mathbf{y}(t) = \mathbf{C}(t)\phi(t, t_0)\mathbf{x}_0 + \int_{t_0}^{t} \Omega(t, \tau)\mathbf{u}(\tau)\, d\tau \tag{3.52}$$

and the output of the quiescent system is

$$\mathbf{y}(t) = \int_{t_0}^{t} \Omega(t, \tau)\mathbf{u}(\tau)\, d\tau \tag{3.53}$$

Equation 3.53 is also referred to as the *superposition* integral (compare with Eq. 3.7 which is also referred to as the superposition integral). Note that the impulsive response at the jth output due to a unit impulse applied at the ith input is

$$\omega_{ji}(t, \tau) = \mathbf{e}_j'\Omega(t, \tau)\mathbf{e}_i \tag{3.54}$$

a sum of n terms—no integration is required.

3.2.3. When is a Signal an Impulse? If one wishes to *identify* a physical system by determining its impulsive response, clearly one must construct a realizable wave form which excites the system in "almost" the same way that an ideal impulse does; the shape that the impulse approximation wave form itself may take is of little interest. The identification problem is complicated by the fact that the actual impulsive response is not known and thus cannot be used for comparison purposes. Further, the actual impulsive response cannot be determined exactly in a finite time from measurements on the system's response. Thus in these situations it is helpful to get a "feel" for what constitutes a good impulse for a particular system.

The idea of approximating an impulse takes on great practical significance in the analysis and synthesis of the class of pulsed-data systems known as *sampled-data systems*. In these systems, due to either the inherent pulse nature of the signals being processed (digital computer output, scanning radar, etc.) or time-sharing considerations, the input signals are of the form of sharp pulses. Analysis and synthesis of these systems is enormously simplified if these signal can be considered to be impulses; the response of a system to a series of n impulses can be found by evaluating a sum of n terms—no integration is required.

Time-Invariant Systems. For the case that the system to be analyzed is time invariant it is relatively simple to establish the degree of validity in assuming that a pulse is an impulse. For example, consider a scalar system whose Laplace transform is $G(s)$. This system is to be excited by the input pulse shown in Fig. 3.5. It is seen that the area of the pulse is unity for any value of a, and in the limit as $a \to 0$, this pulse satisfies the defini-

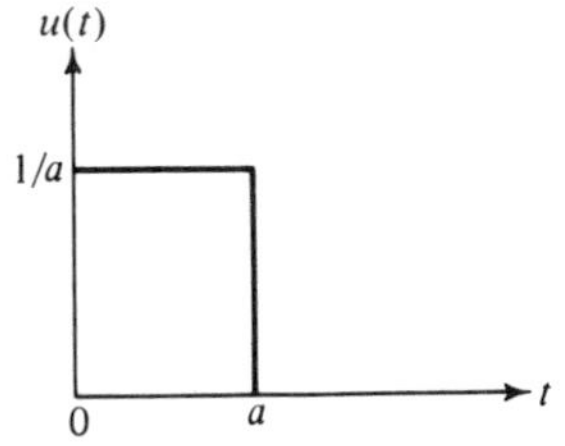

Fig. 3.5. A pulse applied at $t = 0$.

tion of a unit impulse given by Eqs. 3.33 and 3.34. The question to be answered is, "How large can a be so that the system $G(s)$ responds to the pulse $u(t)$ almost as though it would to an ideal unit impulse?" The Laplace transform of the pulse $u(t)$ is

$$U(s) = \frac{1}{sa}(1 - e^{-sa}) = \frac{1}{sa}\left(sa - \frac{s^2a^2}{2!} + \frac{s^3a^3}{3!} - \cdots\right) \tag{3.55}$$

Therefore the Laplace transform of the output response $y(t)$ of this system is

$$\begin{aligned} Y(s) &= G(s)U(s) \\ &= G(s)\left(1 - \frac{sa}{2!} + \frac{s^2a^2}{3!} - \cdots\right) \end{aligned} \tag{3.56}$$

Therefore, taking the inverse Laplace transform gives

$$y(t) = g(t) - \frac{a}{2!}\frac{dg(t)}{dt} + \frac{a^2}{3!}\frac{d^2g(t)}{dt^2} - \cdots \tag{3.57}$$

As $g(t)$ is the response to a unit impulse applied at $t = 0$, it is seen that the unit-pulse response $y(t)$ is a good approximation to the unit-impulse response when either a is small or the derivatives of the unit-impulse is small. Equivalently, a high-pass system requires a narrower pulse than does a low-pass system as an impulse approximation.

Time-Varying Systems. For the case that a pulse is to be applied to a time-varying system, the analysis to establish the merit of approximate impulse-response analysis is more difficult. An approach providing some insight to the problem is as follows.

Consider the scalar linear time-varying system with the impulsive response $\omega(t, \tau)$. In accordance with the superposition integral of Eq. 3.53, the response of the quiescent system to the pulse of Fig. 3.5 is

$$y(t) = \frac{1}{a}\int_0^a \omega(t, \tau)\, d\tau \tag{3.58}$$

Integration by parts gives

$$y(t) = \omega(t, a) - \frac{1}{a}\int_0^a \frac{\partial \omega(t, \tau)}{\partial \tau}\tau\, d\tau \tag{3.59}$$

Continued integration by parts results in the series

$$y(t) = \omega(t, a) - \omega_\tau(t, a)\frac{a}{2!} + \omega_{\tau\tau}(t, a)\frac{a^2}{3!} - \cdots \tag{3.60}$$

where $\omega_\tau(t, a) = \left.\dfrac{\partial \omega(t, \tau)}{\partial \tau}\right|_{\tau=a}$. The expansion of Eq. 3.60 shows that if $\omega(t, a)$ is a good approximation to $\omega(t, 0)$ and if the derivatives of $\omega(t, \tau)$ with respect to τ are small, then the pulse shown in Fig. 3.5 is a good approximation to the unit impulse $\delta(t)$. Note that if the unit pulse is applied at some time other that zero, as shown in Fig. 3.6, the conclusions based on Eq. 3.60 do not apply. For this case

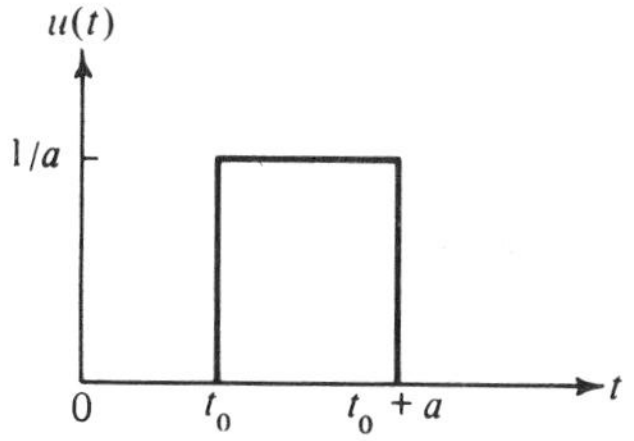

Fig. 3.6. A pulse applied at $t = t_0$.

$$\begin{aligned} y(t) &= \omega(t, t_0 + a) - \omega_\tau(t, t_0 + a)\frac{a}{2!} + \omega_{\tau\tau}(t, t_0 + a)\frac{a^2}{3!} - \cdots \\ &\quad + t_0\left[\frac{\Delta\omega(t, t_0)}{\Delta t_0} - \omega_\tau(t, t_0 + a)\right] \\ &\quad - \frac{t_0^2}{2!}\left[\frac{\Delta\omega_\tau(t, t_0)}{\Delta t_0} - \omega_{\tau\tau}(t, t_0 + a)\right] + \cdots \end{aligned} \tag{3.61}$$

where $\Delta\omega(t, t_0) = \omega(t, t_0 + a) - \omega(t, t_0)$ and $\Delta t_0 = a$. As the square bracket terms vanish for small a, Eq. 3.60 is similar in nature to Eq. 3.61 with the exception that $\omega(t, 0)$ is being considered in the former case and $\omega(t, t_0)$ is being considered in the latter case. Clearly, a pulse of a certain width applied to a time-varying system at a particular time, say t_1, which can be satisfactorily considered to be an impulse, may not be a good impulse approximation if applied at some other time t_2.

3.3. ADJOINT SYSTEMS

Important properties of the adjoint system, as defined by Eq. 2.102, were utilized in Chapter 2 to obtain solutions of nonhomogeneous equations in terms of solutions of the homogeneous adjoint equations. In this section relations between a system and its adjoint are developed that will prove useful in the sequel.

Denoting the transition matrix of the system $\dot{\mathbf{x}}(t) = \mathbf{A}(t)\mathbf{x}(t)$ by $\phi(t, \tau)$ and the transition matrix of the adjoint system $\dot{\mathbf{x}}^*(t) = -\mathbf{A}'(t)\mathbf{x}^*(t)$ by $\phi^*(t, \tau)$, it is determined from Eq. 3.23

$$\frac{\partial \phi(\tau, t)}{\partial t} = -\phi(\tau, t)\mathbf{A}(t) \tag{3.62}$$

and from Eq. 3.22

$$\frac{\partial \phi^*(t, \tau)}{\partial t} = -\mathbf{A}'(t)\phi^*(t, \tau) \tag{3.63}$$

Transposing Eq. 3.62 gives

$$\frac{\partial \phi'(\tau, t)}{\partial t} = -\mathbf{A}'(t)\phi'(\tau, t) \tag{3.64}$$

which, in accordance with Eq. 3.21 results in

$$\frac{\partial [\phi^{-1}(t, \tau)]'}{\partial t} = -\mathbf{A}'(t)[\phi^{-1}(t, \tau)]' \tag{3.65}$$

Comparing Eq. 3.63 and 3.65 relates the transition matrix $\phi^*(t, \tau)$ of the adjoint system to the transition matrix $\phi(t, \tau)$:

$$\phi^*(t, \tau) = [\phi^{-1}(t, \tau)]' \tag{3.66}$$

Further insight to relations between a system and its adjoint is obtained by noting that both the system's Wronskian matrix $\mathbf{\Phi}^*(t) = \mathbf{W}^{*\prime}(t)$ (see Eq. 2.102) play somewhat similar roles in the determination of the transition matrix. Namely, by Eq. 3.4,

$$\phi(t, \tau) = \mathbf{W}(t)\mathbf{W}^{-1}(\tau) = \mathbf{\Phi}^{*-1}(t)\mathbf{\Phi}^*(\tau) \tag{3.67}$$

Theorem 3.1. If the Wronskian $\mathbf{W}(t)$ is a fundamental matrix, then $\mathbf{W}^*(t) = \mathbf{\Phi}^{*\prime}(t)$ is a fundamental matrix for the adjoint system if and only if $\mathbf{\Phi}^*(t)\mathbf{W}(t) = \mathbf{K}$, where $\mathbf{K}$ is a constant nonsingular matrix.

Proof. With $\mathbf{W}(t)$ and $\mathbf{W}^*(t) = \mathbf{\Phi}^{*\prime}(t)$ being fundamental matrices of a system and its adjoint, and thus nonsingular, Eq. 3.67 can be written as

$$\mathbf{\Phi}^*(t)\mathbf{W}(t) = \mathbf{\Phi}^*(\tau)\mathbf{W}(\tau) \tag{3.68}$$

Noting that Eq. 3.67 relates a function of t to a function of τ, with t and

τ being independent variables, gives

$$\mathbf{\Phi}^*(t)\mathbf{W}(t) = \mathbf{W}^{*\prime}(t)\mathbf{W}(t) = \mathbf{K} \tag{3.69}$$

where $\mathbf{K}$ is a nonsingular matrix, thus establishing necessity. Sufficiency is proved by showing that if $\mathbf{W}(t)$ is a fundamental matrix of the system, $\mathbf{W}^{-1\prime}(t)\mathbf{K}'$ is a fundamental matrix of the adjoint system (see Prob. 3.10). Q.E.D.

Thus the Wronskian matrices of a system and its adjoint are algebraically related by

$$\mathbf{W}^*(t) = [\mathbf{W}(t)^{-1}]'\mathbf{K} \tag{3.70}$$

and a basis of a system can be obtained by algebraic manipulations of a basis of the adjoint system.

The definition given for the adjoint relates the *homogeneous* system to the *homogeneous* adjoint system, i.e., the system

$$\dot{\mathbf{x}}(t) = \mathbf{A}(t)\mathbf{x}(t) \tag{3.71}$$

has the associated adjoint system

$$\dot{\mathbf{x}}^*(t) = -\mathbf{A}'(t)\mathbf{x}^*(t) \tag{3.72}$$

Thus this definition as given relates the states of the system to the states of the adjoint system. These relations are provided by Eqs. 3.66 and 3.70. It is desirable to extend the definition of adjoint to include relationships between system inputs and outputs. A formal definition of adjoint is given here which includes the state relationships developed thus far.

Definition 3.1. A linear system N^*, characterized by

$$\begin{aligned} \dot{\mathbf{x}}^*(t) &= \mathbf{A}^*(t)\mathbf{x}^*(t) + \mathbf{B}^*(t)\mathbf{u}^*(t) \\ \mathbf{y}^*(t) &= \mathbf{C}^*(t)\mathbf{x}^*(t) \end{aligned} \tag{3.73}$$

is the *adjoint* of linear system N, characterized by

$$\begin{aligned} \dot{\mathbf{x}}(t) &= \mathbf{A}(t)\mathbf{x}(t) + \mathbf{B}(t)\mathbf{u}(t) \\ \mathbf{v}(t) &= \mathbf{C}(t)\mathbf{x}(t) \end{aligned} \tag{3.74}$$

if and only if

(i) $$\phi^*(t, \tau) = [\phi^{-1}(t, \tau)]' = \phi'(\tau, t) \tag{3.75a}$$

(ii) $$\Omega^*(t, \tau) = -\Omega'(\tau, t) \tag{3.75b}$$

for t and τ on $[a,b]$; if a system satisfies (ii) only it is termed *an input-output adjoint system.*

Property (i) of Definition 3.1, in accordance with Eqs. 3.22 and 3.23, gives

$$\begin{aligned} \frac{\partial \phi^*(t, \tau)}{\partial t} &= \frac{\partial[\phi^{-1}(t, \tau)]'}{\partial t} = \frac{\partial \phi'(\tau, t)}{\partial t} = -[\phi(\tau, t)\mathbf{A}(t)]' \\ &= -\mathbf{A}'(t)\phi'(\tau, t) = -\mathbf{A}'(t)[\phi^{-1}(t, \tau)]' \\ &= -\mathbf{A}'(t)\phi^*(t, \tau) = \mathbf{A}^*(t)\phi^*(t, \tau) \end{aligned} \tag{3.76}$$

Therefore

$$\mathbf{A}^*(t) = -\mathbf{A}'(t) \tag{3.77}$$

as previously defined for the adjoint system.

Property (ii) of Definition 3.1, in accordance with Eq. 3.51, gives

$$\begin{aligned}\Omega^*(t, \tau) &= -\mathbf{B}'(t)\phi'(\tau, t)\mathbf{C}'(\tau)\\ &= -\mathbf{B}'(t)[\phi^{-1}(t, \tau)]'\mathbf{C}'(\tau)\\ &= -\mathbf{B}'(t)\phi^*(t, \tau)\mathbf{C}'(\tau)\\ &= \mathbf{C}^*(t)\phi^*(t, \tau)\mathbf{B}^*(\tau)\end{aligned} \tag{3.78}$$

Therefore

$$\mathbf{B}^*(t) = \pm\mathbf{C}'(t) \tag{3.79}$$

$$\mathbf{C}^*(t) = \mp\mathbf{B}'(t) \tag{3.80}$$

providing relationships for obtaining the nonhomogeneous adjoint system from the nonhomogeneous system. Equations 3.77, 3.79, and 3.80 verify that the adjoint system is

$$\begin{aligned}\dot{\mathbf{x}}^*(t) &= -\mathbf{A}'(t)\mathbf{x}^*(t) \pm \mathbf{C}'(t)\mathbf{u}^*(t)\\ \mathbf{y}^*(t) &= \pm\mathbf{B}'(t)\mathbf{x}^*(t)\end{aligned} \tag{3.81}$$

Note that the roles of $\mathbf{B}(t)$ and $\mathbf{C}(t)$, normally associated with input and output, respectively, are somewhat reversed. The fact that there are negative signs preceding two of the coefficient matrices in Eqs. 3.81 obscures the simple relation that might exist between the system 3.74 and its adjoint 3.81. This motivates the introduction of *dual system*.

3.4. DUAL SYSTEMS

A dual system is defined as follows:

Definition 3.2. A linear system N_D, characterized by

$$\begin{aligned}\dot{\mathbf{x}}_D(t) &= \mathbf{A}_D(t)\mathbf{x}_D(t) + \mathbf{B}_D(t)\mathbf{u}_D(t)\\ \mathbf{y}_D(t) &= \mathbf{C}_D(t)\mathbf{x}_D(t)\end{aligned} \tag{3.82}$$

is the dual of linear system N, characterized by Eq. 3.74, if and only if

(i) $$\phi_D(t, \tau) = [\phi^{-1}(-t, -\tau)]' \tag{8.83a}$$

(ii) $$\Omega_D(t, \tau) = \Omega'(-\tau, -t) \tag{3.83b}$$

for t and τ in $[a, b]$; if a system satisfies (ii) only, it is termed an *input-output dual system*.

Property (i) of Definition 3.2 in accordance with Eqs. 3.22 and 3.23 gives

$$\begin{aligned}\frac{\partial\phi_D(t, \tau)}{\partial t} &= \frac{\partial[\phi^{-1}(-t, -\tau)]'}{\partial t} = [\phi(-\tau, -t)\mathbf{A}(-t)]'\\ &= \mathbf{A}'(-t)\phi'(-\tau, -t) = \mathbf{A}'(-t)[\phi^{-1}(-t, -\tau)]'\\ &= \mathbf{A}'(-t)\phi_D(t, \tau) = \mathbf{A}_D(t)\phi_D(t, \tau)\end{aligned} \tag{3.84}$$

Therefore

$$\mathbf{A}_D(t) = \mathbf{A}'(-t) \tag{3.85}$$

Property (ii) of Definition 3.2, in accordance with Eq. 3.51, gives

$$\begin{aligned}\Omega_D(t, \tau) &= \mathbf{B}'(-t)\phi'(-\tau, -t)\mathbf{C}'(-\tau) \\ &= \mathbf{B}'(-t)[\phi^{-1}(-t, -\tau)]'\mathbf{C}'(-\tau) \\ &= \mathbf{B}'(-t)\phi_D(t, \tau)\mathbf{C}'(-\tau) \\ &= \mathbf{C}_D(t)\phi_D(t, \tau)\mathbf{B}_D(\tau)\end{aligned} \tag{3.86}$$

Therefore

$$\mathbf{B}_D(t) = \mathbf{C}'(-t) \tag{3.87}$$

$$\mathbf{C}_D(t) = \mathbf{B}'(-t) \tag{3.88}$$

Equations 3.85, 3.87, and 3.88 provide relationships from which the dual system can be obtained from the coefficients of the original system:

$$\begin{aligned}\dot{\mathbf{x}}_D(t) &= \mathbf{A}'(-t)\mathbf{x}_D(t) + \mathbf{C}'(-t)\mathbf{u}_D(t) \\ \mathbf{y}_D(t) &= \mathbf{B}'(-t)\mathbf{x}_D(t)\end{aligned} \tag{3.89}$$

Defining $\mathbf{x}_d(t) \equiv \mathbf{x}_D(-t)$, $\mathbf{u}_d(t) \equiv \mathbf{u}_D(-t)$, and $\mathbf{y}_d(t) \equiv \mathbf{y}_D(-t)$ gives

$$\begin{aligned}\mathbf{x}_d(-t) &= \mathbf{A}'(-t)\mathbf{x}_d(-t) + \mathbf{C}'(-t)\mathbf{u}_d(-t) \\ \mathbf{y}_d(-t) &= \mathbf{B}'(-t)\mathbf{x}_d(-t)\end{aligned} \tag{3.90}$$

Running time backward, that is letting $t' = -t$, results in

$$\left.\begin{aligned}\dot{\mathbf{x}}_d(t') &= \mathbf{A}'(t')\mathbf{x}_d(t') + \mathbf{C}'(t')\mathbf{u}_d(t') \\ \mathbf{y}_d(t') &= \mathbf{B}'(t')\mathbf{x}_d(t')\end{aligned}\right\} t' \varepsilon [b, a] \tag{3.91}$$

It is interesting, and often practically useful, to nose that the transition matrix and impulsive-response matrix of system 3.91 are $\phi'(\tau', t')$ and $\Omega'(\tau', t')$. Thus if it is necessary to generate $\phi(t, \tau)$ or $\Omega(t, \tau)$ as a function of τ for some fixed t, simulation of system 3.91 would be in order. It is important to emphasize that all time functions associated with the dual system 3.91 must be reversed in time before they can be related to the original system.

3.5. EQUIVALENT SYSTEMS

If two systems are constructed with identical components interconnected in an identical manner, then the two systems are characterized by identical differential equations and the two systems can be said to be *equivalent* in the strictest sense of the word. However, insofar as the analysis and synthesis of systems are concerned, such a definition of equivalence would not be very useful. For example, in simulation work it is desirable to think of two systems as being equivalent if they are characterized by identical differential equations regardless of their physical dissimilarities; in this sense a hydraulic system could be equivalent to an electronic system.

Carrying this idea one step further leads to a definition in which equivalence is based on whether two systems respond similarly when subjected to the same inputs. According to this definition the two systems need not be either physically similar or satisfy the same differential equations. It is this latter sense of equivalence which is useful in the analysis and synthesis of linear systems and which is considered in detail. Two definitions putting this idea of equivalence on a firm basis are:

Definition 3.3. Two systems are *zero-state equivalent* if both systems have identical outputs when excited from the zero state (quiescent systems) with identical inputs.

Definition 3.4. Two systems are *zero-input equivalent* if initial states (not necessarily equal) exist so that both systems have identical outputs with zero inputs.

As examples of these definitions, consider the two systems characterized by

$$\begin{aligned}\dot{\mathbf{x}}(t) &= \mathbf{A}(t)\mathbf{x}(t) + \mathbf{B}(t)\mathbf{u}(t)\\ \mathbf{y}(t) &= \mathbf{C}(t)\mathbf{x}(t)\end{aligned} \tag{3.92}$$

and

$$\begin{aligned}\dot{\mathbf{z}}(t) &= \mathbf{A}_T(t)\mathbf{z}(t) + \mathbf{B}_T(t)\mathbf{u}(t)\\ \mathbf{w}(t) &= \mathbf{C}_T(t)\mathbf{z}(t)\end{aligned} \tag{3.93}$$

Following Eq. 3.52, these two systems have outputs

$$\mathbf{y}(t) = \mathbf{C}(t)\boldsymbol{\phi}(t, t_0)\mathbf{x}(t_0) + \int_{t_0}^{t} \boldsymbol{\Omega}(t, \tau)\mathbf{u}(\tau)\,d\tau \tag{3.94}$$

and

$$\mathbf{w}(t) = \mathbf{C}_T(t)\boldsymbol{\phi}_T(t, t_0)\mathbf{z}(t_0) + \int_{t_0}^{t} \boldsymbol{\Omega}_T(t, \tau)\mathbf{u}(\tau)\,d\tau \tag{3.95}$$

Thus in accordance with Definition 3.3 the two systems are *zero-state equivalent* if the particular solutions are equal, i.e., if

$$\int_{t_0}^{t} \boldsymbol{\Omega}(t, \tau)\mathbf{u}(\tau)\,d\tau = \int_{t_0}^{t} \boldsymbol{\Omega}_T(t, \tau)\mathbf{u}(\tau)\,d\tau \tag{3.96}$$

or, equivalently, if

$$\boldsymbol{\Omega}(t, \tau) = \boldsymbol{\Omega}_T(t, \tau) \tag{3.97}$$

In accordance with Definition 3.4 the two systems are *zero-input equivalent* if the complementary solutions are equal, i.e., if

$$\mathbf{C}(t)\boldsymbol{\phi}(t, t_0)\mathbf{x}(t_0) = \mathbf{C}_T(t)\boldsymbol{\phi}_T(t, t_0)\mathbf{z}(t_0) \tag{3.98}$$

There is a class of transformations that can be applied to the general linear system characterized by Eq. 3.92 that always results in systems that are always zero-state *and* zero-input equivalent. In particular, the *equiva-*

lence transformation is defined by

$$\mathbf{z}(t) = \mathbf{T}(t)\mathbf{x}(t) \tag{3.99}$$

where $\mathbf{T}(t)$ is an $n \times n$ matrix, nonsingular and continuously differentiable on $[a,b]$. Applying the equivalence transformation to the general system of Eq. 3.92 results in

$$\begin{aligned} \dot{\mathbf{z}}(t) &= \mathbf{A}_T(t)\mathbf{z}(t) + \mathbf{B}_T(t)\mathbf{u}(t) \\ \mathbf{y}(t) &= \mathbf{C}_T(t)\mathbf{z}(t) \end{aligned} \tag{3.100}$$

where

$$\mathbf{A}_T(t) = [\mathbf{T}(t)\mathbf{A}(t) + \dot{\mathbf{T}}(t)]\mathbf{T}^{-1}(t) \tag{3.101a}$$

$$\mathbf{B}_T(t) = \mathbf{T}(t)\mathbf{B}(t) \tag{3.101b}$$

$$\mathbf{C}_T(t) = \mathbf{C}(t)\mathbf{T}^{-1}(t) \tag{3.101c}$$

It can be noted that if $\mathbf{W}(t)$ is a fundamental Wronskian matrix of system 3.92, then $\mathbf{T}(t)\mathbf{W}(t)$ is a fundamental Wronskian matrix of the transformed system 3.100. Therefore, in accordance with Eq. 3.4, the transition matrix of the transformed system is

$$\phi_T(t, \tau) = \mathbf{T}(t)\phi(t, \tau)\mathbf{T}^{-1}(\tau) \tag{3.102}$$

Use of Eqs. 3.51, 3.101, and 3.102 shows that the impulsive-response matrix of the transformed system 3.100 is identical to that of the original system:

$$\begin{aligned} \Omega_T(t, \tau) &= \mathbf{C}_T(t)\phi_T(t, \tau)\mathbf{B}_T(\tau) \\ &= \mathbf{C}(t)\phi(t, \tau)\mathbf{B}(\tau) = \Omega(t, \tau) \end{aligned} \tag{3.103}$$

If the initial state of the transformed system is consistent with the equivalence transformation defined, i.e., if

$$\mathbf{z}(t_0) = \mathbf{T}(t_0)\mathbf{x}(t_0) \tag{3.104}$$

then the output of the transformed system can be expressed in terms of coefficients of the original system:

$$\begin{aligned} \mathbf{y}(t) &= \mathbf{C}_T(t)\phi_T(t, \tau)\mathbf{z}(t_0) + \int_{t_0}^{t} \Omega_T(t, \tau)\mathbf{u}(\tau)\, d\tau \\ &= \mathbf{C}(t)\phi(t, \tau)\mathbf{x}(t_0) + \int_{t_0}^{t} \Omega(t, \tau)\mathbf{u}(\tau)\, d\tau \end{aligned} \tag{3.105}$$

Equation 3.105 establishes the fact that the transformation defined by Eq. 3.99 results in systems that are both *zero-state* and *zero-input* equivalent. Thus the following definition:

Definition 3.5. The system characterized by Eq. 3.92, and denoted by $[\mathbf{A}(t), \mathbf{B}(t), \mathbf{C}(t)]$ is *algebraically equivalent* to the system characterized by Eq. 3.100, and denoted by $[\mathbf{A}_T(t), \mathbf{B}_T(t), \mathbf{C}_T(t)]$, if there is a nonsingular equivalence transformation $\mathbf{T}(t)$ such that Eqs. 3.101 are valid. Such a transformation with $\mathbf{T}(t)$ will be symbolized by

$$[\mathbf{A}(t), \mathbf{B}(t), \mathbf{C}(t)] \xrightarrow{T} [\mathbf{A}_T(t), \mathbf{B}_T(t), \mathbf{C}_T(t)] \tag{3.106}$$

Criteria for establishing the algebraic equivalence of two systems, not requiring knowledge of either the transition matrix or the impulsive-response matrix, is developed in the sequel.

3.6. RELATIONS BETWEEN IMPULSIVE RESPONSES OF INTERCONNECTED SYSTEMS [21]

A control problem for the linear system of Fig. 3.7 is that of determining the input $\mathbf{e}(t)$ that produces a prescribed output $\mathbf{x}(t)$. Analytically, this is essentially the problem involved in solving the superposition integral equation

$$\mathbf{x}(t) = \int_{t_0}^{t} \Omega_p(t, \tau)\mathbf{e}(\tau)\, d\tau \tag{3.107}$$

for $\mathbf{e}(t)$ for specified $\mathbf{x}(t)$ and plant impulsive response $\Omega_p(t, \tau)$. Often, solution of the problem is complicated in that $\mathbf{x}(t)$ is usually related in a prescribed way to an independent function $\mathbf{u}(t)$ which is generally unknown *a priori*.

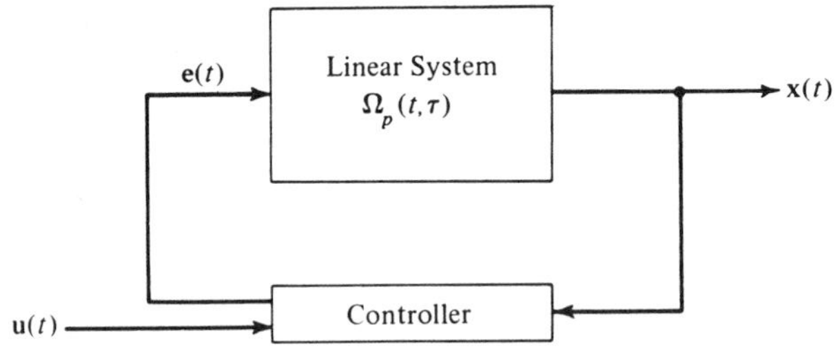

Fig. 3.7. General configuration for the control of a physical system.

In general, this control problem is not soluble. For example, if it is required that $\mathbf{x}(t) = \mathbf{u}(t)$, the necessary $\mathbf{e}(t)$ generally requires that $\mathbf{u}(t)$ be anticipated, incompatible with physical realization of the controller. In such case compromise is required: e.g., to find a function $\mathbf{e}(t)$ such that some specified function of $\mathbf{u}(t)$ and $\mathbf{x}(t)$ say $J(\mathbf{f}, \mathbf{x})$, is minimized within the constraint that the controller be physically realizable. At least one solution to this problem exists. The corresponding synthesis problem is, of course, that of characterizing the controller for a prescribed $\mathbf{u}(t)$, $\mathbf{x}(t)$, and $\mathbf{e}(t)$.

Under restriction that the controller be linear, the control problem can be restated: "Find the impulsive response $\Omega(t, \tau)$ of the overall system with $\mathbf{u}(t)$ the input and $\mathbf{x}(t)$ the output such that some function $J(\mathbf{f}, \mathbf{x})$ is minimized within the constraint that the controller be physically realizable."

The resulting synthesis problem is that of characterizing the controller (its impulsive response) for a prescribed $\Omega_p(t, \tau)$ and $\Omega(t, \tau)$. It is this synthesis problem that is of interest here.

The three basic configurations of Figs. 3.8 are assumed for the controller: parallel, series, and feedback. These configurations are nonrestrictive: knowing how to determine the impulsive response for the controller from the overall impulsive response of any of these configurations enables determining the impulsive response of any single controlling subsystem inserted into an arbitrarily complex system.

3.6.1. Determinaiton of the Overall Impulsive Response: Parallel Systems. The parallel system of Fig. 3.8a has an output $\mathbf{y}(t)$ given by

$$\mathbf{y}(t) = \int_{t_0}^{t} [\Omega_1(t, \tau_1) + \Omega_2(t, \tau_1)]\mathbf{u}(\tau_1)d\tau_1 \tag{3.108}$$

The ith column of the overall impulsive response $\Omega_{12}(t, \tau)$ can be obtained by considering the ith element $u_i(t)$ of the input vector $\mathbf{u}(t)$ to be a unit impulse while all other elements $u_j(t)$, $j \neq i$, are zero. Thus, one can obtain

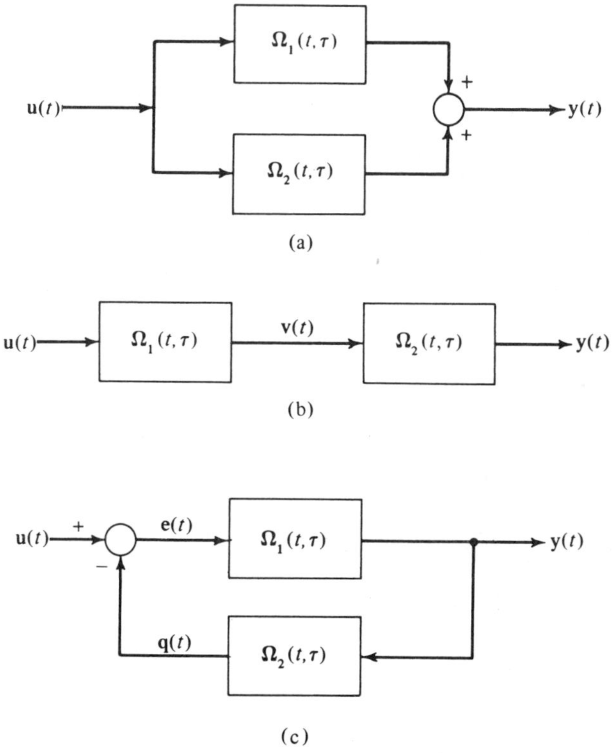

Fig. 3.8. Interconnections of two linear time-varying systems having impulsive responses $\Omega_1(t, \tau)$ and $\Omega_2(t, \tau)$.

the overall impulsive response by considering the input to be $\delta(t-\tau)\mathbf{I}_m$:

$$\Omega_{12}(t, \tau) = \int_{t_0}^{t} [\Omega_1(t, \tau_1) + \Omega_2(t, \tau_1)]\delta(\tau_1 - \tau)\mathbf{I}_m \, d\tau_1 \tag{3.109}$$

Integrating gives the relation for parallel systems,

$$\Omega_{12}(t, \tau) = \Omega_1(t, \tau) + \Omega_2(t, \tau) \tag{3.110}$$

Series Systems. The overall impulsive response $\Omega_{12}(t, \tau)$ of the series system of Fig. 3.8b can be determined by considering an input $\delta(t - \tau)\mathbf{I}_m$. For a proper vector input $\mathbf{u}(t)$, the system output is

$$\mathbf{y}(t) = \int_{t_0}^{t} \Omega_2(t, \tau_1)\mathbf{v}(\tau_1) \, d\tau_1 \tag{3.111}$$

However,

$$\mathbf{v}(t) = \int_{t_0}^{t} \Omega_1(t, \tau_2)\mathbf{u}(\tau_2) \, d\tau_2 \tag{3.112}$$

Therefore substituting from Eq. 3.112 in Eq. 3.111 gives

$$\mathbf{y}(t) = \int_{t_0}^{t} \Omega_2(t, \tau_1) \, d\tau_1 \int_{t_0}^{\tau_1} \Omega_1(\tau_1, \tau_2)\mathbf{u}(\tau_2) \, d\tau_2 \tag{3.113}$$

Thus

$$\Omega_{12}(t, \tau) = \int_{t_0}^{t} \Omega_2(t, \tau_1) \, d\tau_1 \int_{t_0}^{\tau_1} \Omega_1(\tau_1, \tau_2)\delta(\tau_2 - \tau)\mathbf{I}_m \, d\tau_2 \tag{3.114}$$

Integrating gives the relation for series systems,

$$\Omega_{12}(t, \tau) = \int_{\tau}^{t} \Omega_2(t, \tau_1)\Omega_1(\tau_1, \tau) \, d\tau_1 \tag{3.115}$$

Feedback Systems. Analysis similar to the above results in the relation for the feedback system of Fig. 3.8c[1]:

$$\Omega_{12}(t, \tau) = \Omega_1(t, \tau) - \int_{\tau}^{t} \Omega_1(t, \tau_1) \, d\tau_1 \int_{\tau}^{\tau_1} \Omega_2(\tau_1, \tau_2)\Omega_{12}(\tau_2, \tau) \, d\tau_2 \tag{3.116}$$

For the unity feedback, i.e., $\Omega_2(t, \tau) = \mathbf{I}_m$ case, Eq. 3.116, reduces to

$$\Omega_{12}(t, \tau) = \Omega_1(t, \tau) - \int_{\tau}^{t} \Omega_1(t, \tau_1)\Omega_{12}(\tau_1, \tau) \, d\tau_1 \tag{3.117}$$

The relations obtained evidence that the impulsive response of the controller is *easily* determined from knowledge of the overall and system impulsive responses only for parallel compensation. For both the series and feedback connections, the impulsive response of the controller appears in an integrand, thus necessitating solution of an integral equation to determine it.

3.6.2. The Control Problem. Consider first the feedback configuration of Fig. 3.8c. The plant to be controlled is represented by the feed-

[1]See Prob. 3.11.

back component, $\Omega_2(t, \tau)$, and the controller is comprised of the feedforward component, $\Omega_1(t, \tau)$, and the summing component. It is necessary to solve Eq. 3.115 for $\Omega_1(t, \tau)$; i.e., it is necessary to solve an integral equation of the type

$$\Omega_1(t, \tau) = \Omega_a(t, \tau) + \int_\tau^t \Omega_b(t, \tau)\Omega_1(t, \tau_1)\, d\tau_1 \quad (3.118)$$

where $\Omega_a(t, \tau)$ and $\Omega_b(t, \tau)$ are known. Equation 3.118 is a Volterra integra equation of the second kind [22] and, as is well known, its solution can be effected by the method of successive approximations[2].

If in the series configuration either component is considered as the plant, the equation to be solved for the impulsive response characterizing the controller is seen to be of the type

$$\Omega_a(t, \tau) = \int_\tau^t \Omega_b(t, \tau_1)\Omega_1(\tau_1, \tau)\, d\tau_1 \quad (3.119a)$$

or

$$\Omega_a(t, \tau) = \int_\tau^t \Omega_1(t, \tau_1)\Omega_b(\tau_1, \tau)\, d\tau_1 \quad (3.119b)$$

where $\Omega_a(t, \tau)$ and $\Omega_b(t, \tau)$ are known. Equation 3.119 is a Volterra integral equation of the first kind. Under certain conditions[3] it is possible to rewrite a Volterra integral equation of the first kind as a Volterra integral equation of the second kind, solvable by successive approximations.

[2]Assume

$$[\Omega_1(t, \tau)]_1 = \Omega_a(t, \tau) \quad (3.118A)$$

as the first approximation to $\Omega_1(t, \tau)$. The nth approximation $[\Omega_1(t, \tau)]_n$ is found from the iterative equation

$$[\Omega_1(t, \tau)]_n = \Omega_a(t, \tau) + \int_\tau^t \Omega_b(t, \tau)[\Omega_1(t, \tau)]_{n-1}\, d\tau_1 \quad (3.118B)$$

Tricomi [22] shows that

$$\lim_{n\to\infty} [\Omega_1(t, \tau)]_n = \Omega_1(t, \tau) \quad (3.118C)$$

[3]If in a Volterra integral equation [22] of the first kind

$$\int_\tau^t \mathbf{K}(t, \tau_1)\, \Omega(\tau_1, \tau)\, d\tau_1 = \mathbf{f}(t, \tau) \qquad \tau \le t \le h \quad (3.119A)$$

the det $\mathbf{K}(t, t)$, vanishes nowhere in the basic interval $(0, h)$, and if the derivatives

$$\frac{\partial \mathbf{f}(t, \tau)}{\partial t} \equiv \mathbf{f}_t(t)\,, \qquad \frac{\partial \mathbf{K}(t, \tau)}{\partial t} \equiv \mathbf{K}_t(t, \tau)\,, \qquad \frac{\partial \mathbf{K}(t, \tau)}{\partial \tau} \equiv \mathbf{K}_\tau(t, \tau) \quad (3.119B)$$

exist and are continuous, the equation can be reduced to one of the second kind in two ways.

The first and simpler way is to differentiate both sides of Eq. 3.119A with respect to t, yielding

If in the feedback configuration, the feedforward component is considered to be the plant and the feedback component is taken as the controller, then the equation to be solved for the impulsive response characterizing the controller is of the type

$$\Omega_a(t, \tau) = \int_\tau^t \Omega_b(t, \tau_1)\, d\tau_1 \int_\tau^{\tau_1} \Omega_2(\tau_1, \tau_2)\Omega_c(\tau_2, \tau)\, d\tau_2 \qquad (3.120)$$

where $\Omega_a(t, \tau)$, $\Omega_b(t, \tau)$ and $\Omega_c(t, \tau)$ are known. In order to solve Eq. 3.120 for $\Omega_2(t, \tau)$, *two* Volterra equations of the first kind must be solved sequentially: first

$$\Omega_a(t, \tau) = \int_\tau^t \Omega_b(t, \tau_1)\Omega_\gamma(\tau_1, \tau)\, d\tau_1 \qquad (3.121)$$

must be solved for $\Omega_\gamma(t, \tau)$, and then

$$\Omega_\gamma(t, \tau) = \int_\tau^t \Omega_2(t, \tau_2)\Omega_c(\tau_2, \tau)\, d\tau_2 \qquad (3.122)$$

must be solved for $\Omega_2(t, \tau_2)$.

However, considering that Volterra equations of the first kind cannot always be changed to Volterra equations of the second kind, and that Volterra equations of the first kind may not even always have solutions, suggests effort to avoid them. For *scalar* systems, the concept of inverse components makes it possible to do so.

3.6.3. Inverse Components. A pair of components having impul-

---

$$\Omega(t, \tau) + \int_\tau^t \mathbf{K}^{-1}(t, t)\mathbf{K}_t(t, \tau_1)\Omega(\tau_1, \tau)\, d\tau_1 = \mathbf{K}^{-1}(t, t)\, \mathbf{f}_t(t, \tau) \qquad (3.119C)$$

which is a Volterra integral of the second kind and the reduction is complete.

The second way utilizes integration by parts. Setting

$$\int_\tau^t \Omega(t, \tau_1)\, d\tau_1 = \Omega_0(t, \tau) \qquad (3.119D)$$

and integrating Eq. 3.119A by parts gives

$$\mathbf{f}(t, \tau) = [\mathbf{K}(t, \tau_1)\Omega_0(\tau_1, \tau)]_{\tau_1=\tau}^{\tau_1=t} - \int_\tau^t \mathbf{K}_{\tau_1}(t, \tau_1)\Omega_0(\tau_1, \tau)\, d\tau_1 \qquad (3.119E)$$

that is,

$$\Omega_0(t, \tau) - \int_\tau^t \mathbf{K}^{-1}(t, t)\mathbf{K}_{\tau_1}(t, \tau_1)\Omega_0(\tau_1, \tau) d\tau_1 = \mathbf{K}^{-1}(t, t)\mathbf{f}(t, \tau) \qquad (3.119F)$$

Equation 3.119F, a Volterra equation of the second kind, can be solved for $\Omega_0(t, \tau)$ as outlined in footnote 2. The differentiation involved in obtaining $\Omega(t, \tau)$ from $\Omega_0(t, \tau)$ requires that $\mathbf{f}(t, \tau)$ be differentiable.

The most important of the conditions is that concerning the det $\mathbf{K}(t, t)$. If det $\mathbf{K}(t, t)$ vanishes at some point on the basic interval $(0, h)$, Eqs. 3.119C and 3.119F have a character essentially different from that of equations of the second kind.

Clearly, comparable results are obtained for the case that $\mathbf{K}(t, \tau)$ and $\Omega(t, \tau)$ are commuted in Eq. 3.13A.

sive responses $\Omega(t, \tau)$ and $\Omega^{-1}(t, \tau)$ are said to be *inverses* of each other, if and only if

$$\int_\tau^t \Omega(\tau_1, \tau)\Omega^{-1}(t, \tau_1)\, d\tau_1 = \int_\tau^t \Omega^{-1}(\tau_1, \tau)\Omega(t, \tau_1)\, d\tau_1 = \delta(t - \tau) \tag{3.123}$$

Consider the series connection of Fig. 3.8b. The impulsive response $\Omega_1(t, \tau)$, when $\Omega_2(t, \tau)$ and $\Omega_{12}(t, \tau)$ are known, is that of the component characterized by adding the inverse component characterized by $\Omega_2^{-1}(t, \tau)$ to the system of Fig. 3.8b as shown in Fig. 3.9. Thus the overall system is equivalent to a system whose impulsive response is simply $\Omega_1(t, \tau)$. Utilizing Eq. 3.109 for series components gives

$$\Omega_1(t, \tau) = \int_\tau^t \Omega_2^{-1}(t, \tau_1)\Omega_{12}(\tau_1, \tau)\, d\tau_1 \tag{3.124}$$

If $\Omega_1(t, \tau)$ is given and $\Omega_2(t, \tau)$ is to be found, the inverse of the first component should serially precede the system and analysis as above gives

$$\Omega_2(t, \tau) = \int_\tau^t \Omega_{12}(t, \tau_1)\Omega_1^{-1}(\tau_1, \tau)\, d\tau_1 \tag{3.125}$$

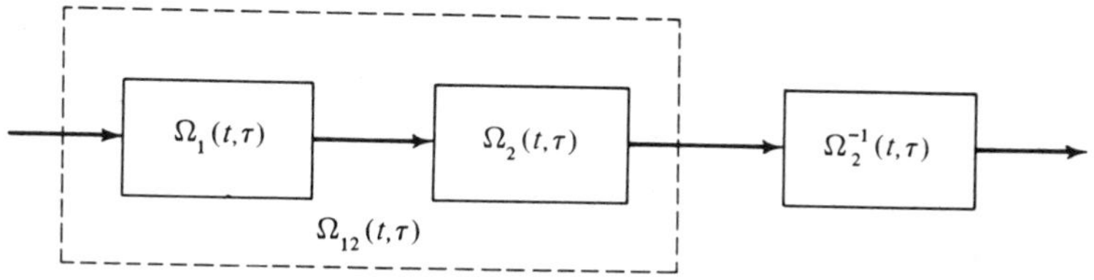

Fig. 3.9. Linear time-varing system having the overall impulsive response $\Omega_1(t, \tau)$.

The impulsive response, $\Omega^{-1}(t, \tau)$, of the inverse of a component is easily found from the knowledge of the differential equation characterizing the component[4]. This analytical manipulation reduces the problem of solving a Volterra equation of the first kind, essentially, to evaluation of an ordinary integral.

[4]Consider a scalar linear system with impulsive response $\Omega(t, \tau)$ and differential operator denoted by L. Serially connecting this system with its inverse and applying to the combination the unit impulses results in the systems of Fig. 3.10. These systems are satisfied by

$$L\Omega(t, \tau) = \delta(t - \tau) \tag{3.125A}$$

$$L^{-1}\delta(t - \tau) = \Omega(t, \tau) \tag{3.125B}$$

and

$$L^{-1}\Omega^{-1}(t, \tau) = \delta(t - \tau) \tag{3.125C}$$

$$L\delta(t - \tau) = \Omega^{-1}(t, \tau) \tag{3.125D}$$

Consider next the feedback connection of Fig. 3.8c and the problem of determining $\Omega_2(t, \tau)$ when $\Omega_1(t, \tau)$ and the overall weight function $\Omega_{12}(t, \tau)$ are known. In this case, again, use of the concept of inverse systems enables the reduction of Volterra equations of the first kind. Equation 3.115 for the feedback system can be rewritten as

$$\Omega_1(t, \tau) - \Omega_{12}(t, \tau) = \int_\tau^t \Omega_1(t, \tau)\, d\tau_1 \int_\tau^{\tau_1} \Omega_2(\tau_1, \tau_2)\Omega_{12}(\tau_2, \tau)\, d\tau_2 \tag{3.126}$$

or simply as

$$\Omega_B(t, \tau) = \int_\tau^t \Omega_1(t, \tau_1)\Omega_A(\tau_1, \tau)\, d\tau_1 \tag{3.127}$$

where

$$\Omega_A(t, \tau) = \int_\tau^t \Omega_2(\tau_1, \tau)\Omega_{12}(t, \tau_1)\, d\tau_1 \tag{3.128}$$

and

$$\Omega_B(t, \tau) = \Omega_1(t, \tau) - \Omega_{12}(t, \tau) \tag{3.129}$$

Equations 3.127 and 3.128 are of the form of Eq. 3.115, pertinent to the overall impulsive response of a series connection. Accordingly, it is to be

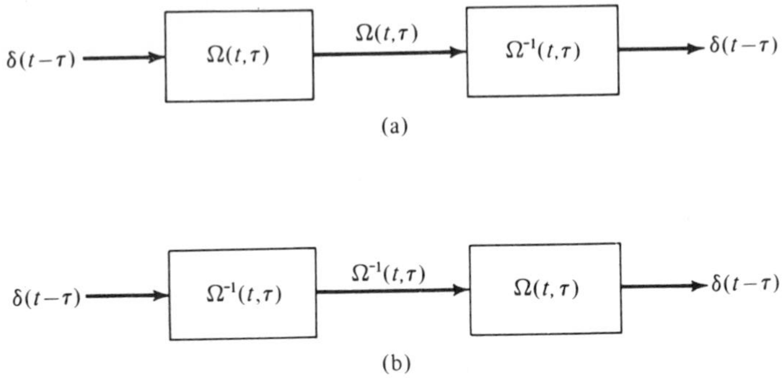

Fig. 3.10. Unity impulsive response obtained by serially connecting inverse systems.

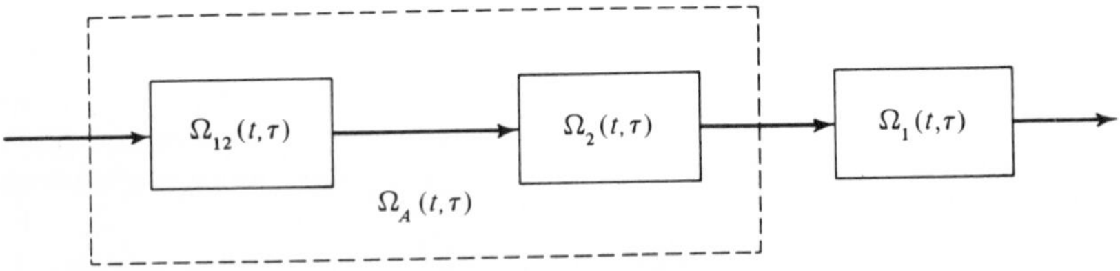

Fig. 3.11. Linear time-varying system having the overall impulsive response $\Omega_B(t, \tau)$ as given in Eq. 3.127.

When the differential equation and thus the L of the system is known, Eq. 3.125D furnishes the impulsive response of the inverse system.

concluded that the impulsive response of the system of Fig. 3.11 is $\Omega_B(t, \tau)$. Using the method of inverse components, and Eq. 3.124 specifically, gives

$$\Omega_A(t, \tau) = \int_{\tau}^{t} \Omega_B(\tau_1, \tau)\Omega_1^{-1}(t, \tau_1)\, d\tau_1 \tag{3.130}$$

and substituting for $\Omega_B(t, \tau)$ from Eq. 3.120 gives

$$\begin{aligned}\Omega_A(t, \tau) &= \int_{\tau}^{t} [\Omega_1(t, \tau) - \Omega_{12}(\tau_1, \tau)]\Omega_1^{-1}(t, \tau_1)\, d\tau_1 \\ &= \delta(t - \tau) - \int_{\tau}^{t} \Omega_{12}(\tau_1, \tau)\Omega_1^{-1}(t, \tau_1)\, d\tau_1\end{aligned} \tag{3.131}$$

Equations 3.128 and 3.131 are identical if

$$\int_{\tau_1}^{t} \Omega_{12}(\tau_1, \tau)[\Omega_2(t, \tau_1) + \Omega_1^{-1}(t, \tau_1)]\, d\tau_1 = \delta(t - \tau) \tag{3.132}$$

which, according to the definition of inverse systems in Eq. 3.123 leads straightforwardly to the desired result:

$$\Omega_2(t, \tau) = \Omega_1^{-1}(t, \tau) - \Omega_{12}^{-1}(t, \tau) \tag{3.133}$$

From this Eq. $\Omega_2(t, \tau)$ can be determined easily if the inverses of $\Omega_1(t, \tau)$ and $\Omega_{12}(t, \tau)$ are known, or if the differential equations of the systems having the impulsive responses $\Omega_1(t, \tau)$ and $\Omega_{12}(t, \tau)$ are known: thus Eq. 3.125D can be used to determine the desired inverses. Unfortunately, neither the differential equation of the overall system nor the inverse of its impulsive response is generally known. It is possible, however, to determine the differential equation of a system whose impulsive response is known by the procedures given in Chapters 5 and 6.

Further manipulation, similar to the foregoing, shows that the inverse of $\Omega_2(t, \tau)$ can be found as the solution of a Volterra equation of the second kind, i.e.,

$$\Omega_2^{-1}(t, \tau) = \Omega_{12}(t, \tau) + \int_{\tau}^{t} \Omega_2^{-1}(t, \tau_1)\, d\tau_1 \int_{\tau}^{\tau_1} \Omega_{12}(\tau_2, \tau)\Omega_1(\tau_1, \tau_2)\, d\tau_2 \tag{3.134}$$

3.7. SAMPLED-DATA LINEAR TIME-VARYING SYSTEMS [23]

Due to the economic attractiveness of time sharing a digital component so that it can be effectively used to perform many tasks simultaneously, there has been an extremely rapid increase in the use of special-purpose digital computrs in the design and compensation of physical systems. As a result the study of discrete-time systems is continually taking on greater significance. In this section methods for the analysis of the *impulse modulated* discrete time, known as *sampled-data* systems is advanced. As shown in Sect. 3.2.3, a system that is *pulse modulated* can, under the proper conditions, be well approximated by a sampled-data system.

A sampled-data linear time-varying system is graphically illustrated in

Fig. 3.12. The sampled input $\mathbf{u}_s(t)$ and the sampled output $\mathbf{y}_s(t)$ are defined as the impulse-modulated functions:

$$\mathbf{u}_s(t) = \sum_{i=0}^{\infty} \mathbf{u}(iT)\delta(t - iT) \tag{3.135a}$$

$$\mathbf{y}_s(t) = \sum_{k=0}^{\infty} \mathbf{y}(kT)\delta(t - kT) \tag{3.135b}$$

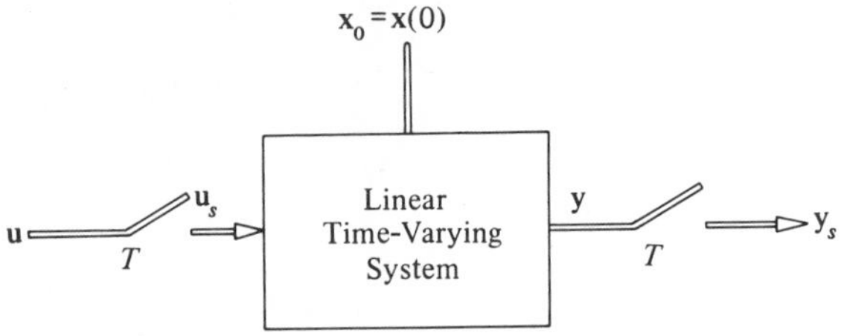

Fig. 3.12. A sampled-data linear time-varying system.

where T denotes the *sampling period.* Assuming that the continuous linear time-varying system is characterized by the state-variable equations

$$\begin{aligned} \dot{\mathbf{x}}(t) &= \mathbf{A}(t)\mathbf{x}(t) + \mathbf{B}(t)\mathbf{u}_s(t) \\ \mathbf{y}(t) &= \mathbf{C}(t)\mathbf{x}(t) \end{aligned} \tag{3.136}$$

the continuous output $\mathbf{y}(t)$ is given by

$$\mathbf{y}(t) = \mathbf{C}(t)\phi(t, 0)\mathbf{x}_0 + \int_0^t \Omega(t, \tau)\mathbf{u}_s(\tau)\, d\tau \tag{3.137}$$

Substituting from Eq. 3.135a in Eq. 3.137 gives

$$\mathbf{y}(t) = \mathbf{C}(t)\phi(t, 0)\mathbf{x}_0 + \int_0^t \Omega(t, \tau) \sum_{i=0}^{\infty} \mathbf{u}(iT)\delta(\tau - iT)\, d\tau \tag{3.138}$$

which, in accordance with Eq. 3.37 results in

$$\mathbf{y}(t) = \mathbf{C}(t)\phi(t, 0)\mathbf{x}_0 + \sum_{i=0}^{\infty} \Omega(t, iT)\mathbf{u}(iT) \tag{3.139}$$

Equation 3.139 reveals the essential computational advantage in working with sampled-data systems: integrals are replaced by sums. Substituting from Eq. 3.139 in Eq. 3.135b gives the sampled output:

$$\begin{aligned} \mathbf{y}_s(t) = &\sum_{k=0}^{\infty} \mathbf{C}(kT)\phi(kT, 0)\mathbf{x}_0\delta(t - kT) \\ &+ \sum_{k=0}^{\infty}\sum_{i=0}^{\infty} \Omega(kT, iT)\mathbf{u}(iT)\delta(t - kT) \end{aligned} \tag{3.140}$$

Invoking causality, i.e., $\Omega(kT, iT) = 0$ for $i > k$, and rearranging results in

$$\mathbf{y}_s(t) = \sum_{k=0}^{\infty} [\mathbf{C}(kT)\phi(kT, 0)\mathbf{x}_0 + \sum_{i=0}^{k} \Omega(kT, iT)\mathbf{u}(iT)]\delta(t - kT) \tag{3.141}$$

Comparing Eq. 3.135b and 3.141 shows that

$$\mathbf{y}(kT) = \mathbf{C}(kT)\phi(kT, 0)\mathbf{x}_0 + \sum_{i=0}^{k} \Omega(kT, iT)\mathbf{u}(iT) \tag{3.142}$$

thus providing a method for determining the sampled output. However, a computationally more convenient form for the sampled-output term $\mathbf{y}(kT)$ would be one that does not involve the summation of k products. A recursive form for $\mathbf{y}(kT)$ having this property can be obtained.

For notational convenience the following definitions are introduced. Let

$$\mathbf{K}_k \equiv \mathbf{C}(kT)\phi(kT, 0) \tag{3.143a}$$

$$\mathbf{D}_i^u \equiv \phi(0, iT)\mathbf{B}(iT)\mathbf{u}(iT) \tag{3.143b}$$

$$\mathbf{S}_k^u \equiv \sum_{i=0}^{k} \mathbf{D}_i^u \tag{3.143c}$$

Equation 3.142 can be written as

$$\mathbf{y}(kT) = \mathbf{C}(kT)\phi(kT, 0)\mathbf{x}_0 + \mathbf{C}(kT)\phi(kT, 0) \sum_{i=0}^{k} \phi(0, iT)\mathbf{B}(iT)\mathbf{u}(iT) \tag{3.144}$$

Therefore, using definitions 3.143 results in

$$\mathbf{y}(kT) = \mathbf{K}_k(\mathbf{x}_0 + \mathbf{S}_k^u) \tag{3.145}$$

But since

$$\mathbf{S}_k^u = \mathbf{S}_{k-1}^u + \mathbf{D}_k^u \tag{3.146}$$

a recursive form is obtained. Thus Eqs. 3.145 and 3.146 provide the recursive equations for determining the sampled output. The following example illustrates the application of these equations.

Example 3.4. Consider the scalar sampled-data system shown in Fig. 3.13. The transition matrix for this system is easily determined from the Laplace transfer function $1/(s + 1)$ to be

$$\phi(t, \tau) = e^{-(t-\tau)}$$

and $B(t) = t$ and $C(t) = t^2$. The input $u(t)$ is specified to be a unit step, i.e., $u(t) = 1$ for all $t \geq 0$ and $u(t) = 0$ for all $t < 0$. In accordance with

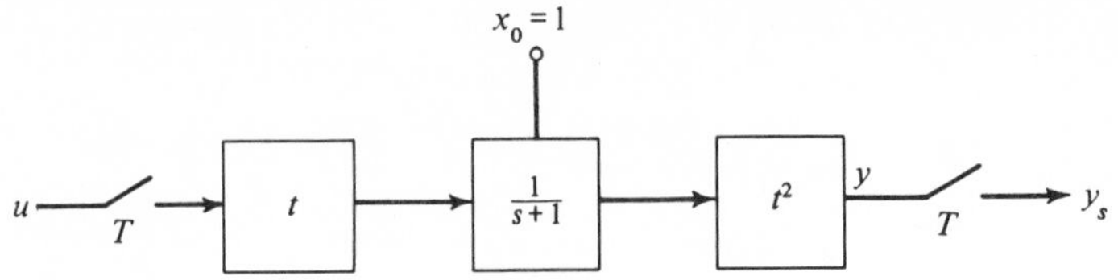

Fig. 3.13. Scalar sampled-data linear time-varying system.

Eqs. 3.143,

$$K_k = k^2T^2e^{-kT}$$
$$D_i^u = e^{iT}iT$$
$$S_k^u = \sum_{i=0}^{k} D_i^u$$

Now sequential application of the recursive Eqs. 3.145 and 3.146 gives

(0) $S_0^u = D_0^u = 0$

$y(0) = K_0(x_0 + S_0^u) = 0$

(1) $S_1^u = S_0^u + D_1^u = Te^T$

$y(T) = K_1(x_0 + \mathbf{S}_1^u) = T^2e^{-T}(1 + Te^T) = T^2e^{-T} + T^3$

(2) $S_2^u = S_1^u + D_2^u = Te^T + 2Te^{2T}$

$$y(2T) = K_2(x_0 + S_2^u) = 4T^2e^{-2T}[1 + (Te^T + 2Te^{2T})]$$
$$= 4T^2e^{-2T} + 4T^3e^{-T} + 8T^3$$

(3) $S_3^u = S_2^u + D_3^u = (Te^T + 2Te^{2T}) + 3Te^{3T}$

$$y(3T) = K_3(x_0 + S_3^u) = 9T^2e^{-3T}[1 + (Te^T + 2Te^{2T} + 3Te^{3T})]$$
$$= 9T^2e^{-3T} + 9T^3e^{-2T} + 18T^3e^{-T} + 27T^3$$

The recursive formulas for a sampled-data servo system shown in Fig. 3.14 are now obtained. It is assumed that the input $\mathbf{u}(t)$ and the output $\mathbf{y}(t)$ are of the same dimension. The sampled output can be written as

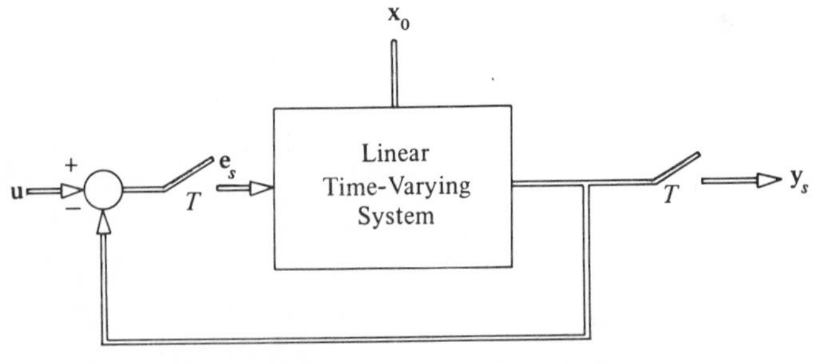

Fig. 3.14. Sampled-data servo system.

$$\mathbf{y}(kT) = \mathbf{C}(kT)\phi(kT, 0)\left[\mathbf{x}_0 + \sum_{i=0}^{k} \phi(0, iT)\mathbf{B}(iT)\mathbf{e}(iT)\right] \tag{3.147}$$

Since

$$\mathbf{e}(iT) = \mathbf{u}(iT) - \mathbf{y}(iT) \tag{3.148}$$

it follows that

$$\mathbf{y}(kT) = \mathbf{C}(kT)\phi(kT, 0)\left[\mathbf{x}_0 + \sum_{i=0}^{k} \phi(0, iT)\mathbf{B}(iT)\mathbf{u}(iT) - \sum_{i=0}^{k} \phi(0, iT)\mathbf{B}(iT)\mathbf{y}(iT)\right] \tag{3.149}$$

or equivalently,

$$\mathbf{y}(kT) = \mathbf{C}(kT)\phi(kT, 0)\left[\mathbf{x}_0 + \sum_{i=0}^{k} \phi(0, iT)\mathbf{B}(iT)\mathbf{u}(iT) - \sum_{i=0}^{k-1} \phi(0, iT)\mathbf{B}(iT)\mathbf{y}(iT)\right] - \Omega(kT, kT)\mathbf{y}(kT) \tag{3.150}$$

Thus

$$\mathbf{y}(kT) = [\mathbf{I}_m + \Omega(kT, kT)]^{-1}\mathbf{C}(kT)\phi(kT, 0) \cdot\left[\mathbf{x}_0 + \sum_{i=0}^{k} \phi(0, iT)\mathbf{B}(iT)\mathbf{u}(iT) - \sum_{i=0}^{k-1} \phi(0, iT)\mathbf{B}(iT)\mathbf{y}(iT)\right] \tag{3.151}$$

This can be written more simply by defining

$$\mathbf{D}_i^y \equiv \phi(0, iT)\mathbf{B}(iT)\mathbf{y}(iT) \tag{3.152a}$$

$$\mathbf{S}_k^y \equiv \sum_{i=0}^{k} \mathbf{D}_i^y \tag{3.152b}$$

and

$$\mathbf{I}_m + \Omega(kT, kT) \equiv \mathbf{U}_k \tag{3.153}$$

Then Eq. 3.151 becomes

$$\mathbf{y}(kT) = \mathbf{U}_k^{-1}\mathbf{K}_k(\mathbf{x}_0 + \mathbf{S}_k^u - \mathbf{S}_{k-1}^y) \tag{3.154}$$

where

$$\mathbf{S}_k^u = \mathbf{S}_{k-1}^u + \mathbf{D}_k^u \tag{3.155a}$$

$$\mathbf{S}_k^y = \mathbf{S}_{k-1}^y + \mathbf{D}_k^y \tag{3.155b}$$

The process is started with

$$\mathbf{y}(0) = \mathbf{U}_0^{-1}\mathbf{K}_0(\mathbf{x}_0 + \mathbf{D}_0^u) \tag{3.156}$$

Example 3.5. Consider the scalar sampled-data system shown in Fig. 3.15. This system has to open-loop system of Example 3.4 as its feedforward portion. Therefore

$$K_k = k^2T^2e^{-kT}$$
$$D_i^u = e^{iT}iT$$
$$S_k^u = \sum_{i=0}^{k} D_i^u$$

and

$$D_i^y = e^{iT}iTy(iT)$$
$$S_k^y = \sum_{i=0}^{k} D_i^y$$
$$U_k = 1 + \Omega(kT, kT) = 1 + k^3T^3$$

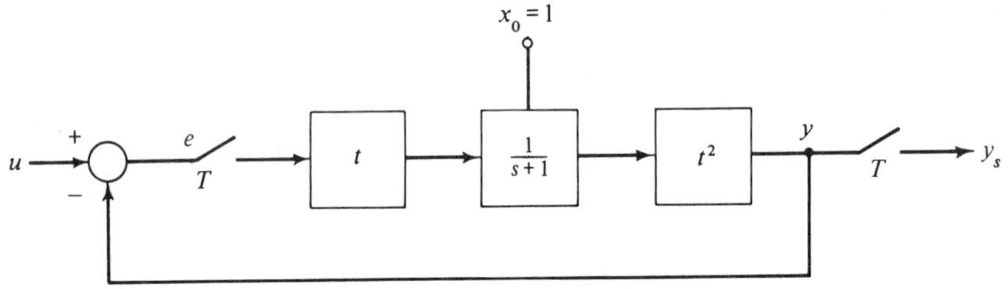

Fig. 3.15. Scalar sampled-data linear time-varying servo system.

Now sequential application of Eqs. 3.154 and 3.155 starting with Eq. 3.156 gives

(0) $y(0) = U_0^{-1}K_0(x_0 + D_0^u) = 0$

(1) $S_1^u = S_0^u + D_1^u = Te^t$

$$S_0^y = D_0^y = 0$$
$$y(T) = U_1^{-1}K_1(x_0 + S_1^u - S_0^y)$$
$$= \frac{T^2e^{-T}}{1 + T^3}(1 + Te^T + 0) = \frac{T^2e^{-T} + T^3}{1 + T^3}$$

(2) $S_2^u = S_1^u + D_2^u = Te^T + 2Te^{2T}$

$$S_1^y = S_0^y + D_1^y = Te^Ty(T)$$
$$y(2T) = U_2^{-1}K_2(x_0 + S_2^u - S_1^y)$$
$$= \frac{4T^2e^{-2T}}{1 + 8T^3}[1 + Te^T + 2Te^{2T} - Te^Ty(T)]$$
$$= \frac{4T^2e^{-2T} + 4T^3e^{-T} + 8T^3}{1 + 8T^3} - \frac{Te^T}{1 + 8T^3}y(T)$$

In working with sampled-data systems it is often desirable to *restore* the sampled signal, i.e., to obtain the continuous signal $y(t)$ from the sampled signal $y_s(t)$. Since information is generally lost in the sampling process, signal restoration can only be achieved in an approximate manner. One simple device which can approximately restore the signal is the *zero-order hold.* A zero-order hold is defined as a system which when forced with a sampled input $u_s(t)$ provides the output

$$h(t) = \sum_{i=0}^{\infty} u(iT)\{\delta^{(-1)}(t - iT) - \delta^{(-1)}[t - (i + 1)T]\} \tag{3.157}$$

where $\delta^{(-1)}(t - \tau)$ is the unit-step function. A recursive analysis technique for systems containing zero-order holds is now advanced.

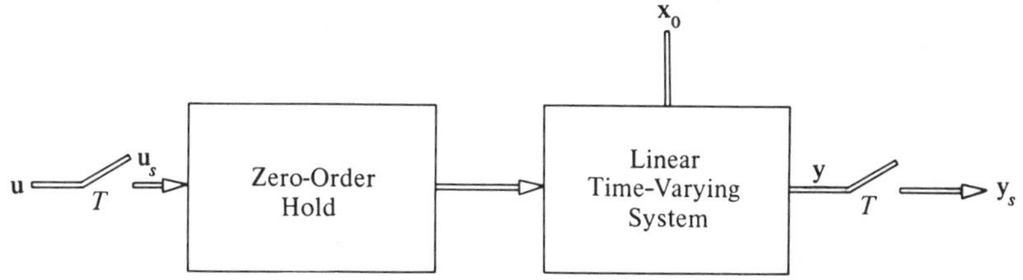

Fig. 3.16. Sampled-data system including zero-order hold.

Consider the sampled-data system which includes a zero-order hold as shown in Fig. 3.16. The output of this system is given by

$$\mathbf{y}(t) = \mathbf{C}(t)\phi(t, 0)\mathbf{x}_0 + \int_0^t \mathbf{C}(t)\phi(t, \tau)\mathbf{B}(\tau)\mathbf{h}(\tau)\, d\tau \tag{3.158}$$

where

$$\mathbf{h}(t) = \sum_{i=0}^{\infty} \mathbf{u}(iT)\{\delta^{(-1)}(t - iT) - \delta^{(-1)}[t - (i + 1)T]\} \tag{3.159}$$

Therefore, substituting from Eq. 3.159 in Eq. 3.158, interchanging the integral and sum, and noting that the unit-step function can be dropped with the proper change in the limits of integration, gives

$$\mathbf{y}(t) = \mathbf{C}(t)\phi(t, 0)\mathbf{x}_0 + C(t)\phi(t, 0) \sum_{i=0}^{\infty} \int_{iT}^{(i+1)T} \phi(0, \tau)\mathbf{B}(\tau)\mathbf{u}(iT)\, d\tau \tag{3.160}$$

Defining

$$\mathbf{\Phi}(iT) \equiv \int_{iT}^{(i+1)T} \phi(0, \tau)\mathbf{B}(\tau) d\tau \tag{3.161}$$

results in

$$\mathbf{y}(t) = \mathbf{C}(t)\phi(t, 0)\left[\mathbf{x}_0 + \sum_{i=0}^{\infty} \mathbf{\Phi}(iT)\mathbf{u}(iT)\right] \tag{3.162}$$

Therefore the sampled signal is provided by

$$\mathbf{y}(kT) = \mathbf{C}(kT)\phi(kT, 0)\left[\mathbf{x}_0 + \sum_{i=0}^{k-1} \mathbf{\Phi}(iT)\mathbf{u}(iT)\right] \tag{3.163}$$

This can be simplified by defining

$$\mathbf{K}_k = \mathbf{C}(kT)\phi(kT, 0) \tag{3.164a}$$

$$\mathbf{H}_i^u = \mathbf{\Phi}(iT)\mathbf{u}(iT) \tag{3.164b}$$

$$\mathbf{Z}_k^u = \sum_{i=0}^{k} \mathbf{H}_i^u \tag{3.164c}$$

Thus Eq. 3.163 becomes

$$\mathbf{y}(kT) = \mathbf{K}_k(\mathbf{x}_0 + \mathbf{Z}_{k-1}^u) \tag{3.165}$$

where

$$\mathbf{Z}_k^u = Z_{k-1}^u + \mathbf{H}_k^u \tag{3.166}$$

provides the recursive formula.

REFERENCES

[1] Bellman, R., *Stability Theory of Lifferential Equations*, McGraw-Hill, New York, 1953.

[2] Borskii, V., "On the Properties of the Impulsive Response Function of Systems with Variable Parameters," *Automation and Remote Control*, vol. 20 (July 1959), pp. 822–830.

[3] Coddington, E., and V. Levinson, *Theory of Ordinary Differential Equations*, McGraw-Hill, New York, 1955.

[4] DeRusso, P., R. Roy, and C. Close, *State Variables for Engineers*, Wiley, New York, 1965.

[5] Kalman, R., "On the General Theory of Control Systems," *Proceedings First International Congress of the International Federation of Automatic Control*, Butterworth, London, 1961, pp. 481–492.

[6] Kalman, R., Y. Ho, and K. Narendra, "Controllability of Linear Dynamical Systems," *Contributions to Differential Equations*, vol. 1, no. 2 (1962), pp. 189–213.

[7] Kalman, R., "Mathematical Description of Linear Dynamical Systems," *J. SIAM Control*, vol. 1, no. 2 (1963), pp. 152–193.

[8] Laning, J., and R. Battin, *Random Processes in Automatic Control Problems*, McGraw-Hill, New York, 1956.

[9] Miller, K., *Linear Differential Equations in the Real Domain*, Norton, N. Y., 1963.

[10] Ragazzini, J., and G. Franklin, *Sampled-Data Control Systems*, McGraw-Hill, New York, 1958.

[11] Schwarz, R., and B. Friedland, *Linear Systems*, McGraw-Hill, New York, 1965.

[12] Silverman, L., *Representation and Realization of Time-Variable Linear Systems*, Technical Report, No. 94, Dept. Electrical Engineering, Columbia University, New York, June 1966.

[13] Silverman, L., "Controllability and Observability in Time-Variable Linear Systems," *J. SIAM Control*, vol. 16, no. 1, 1968.

[14] Solodov, A. V. (trans. by A. Fuller), *Linear Automatic Control Systems with Varying Parameters*, America Elsevier, New York, 1966.

[15] Solodov, A. V., "Statistical Investigation of Nonstationary Processes in Linear Systems by Means of Inverse Simulating Devices," *Automation and Remote Control*, vol. 19 (1958), pp. 305–317.

[16] Tranter, C., *Integral Transformations in Mathematical Physics*, Wiley, New York, 1951.

[17] Weiss, L., and R. Kalman, "Contributions to Linear System Theory," *International Journal of Engineering Science*, vol. 3 (1965), pp. 141–171.

[18] Youla, D., "The Synthesis of Linear Dynamical Systems From Prescribed Weighting Patterns," *J. SIAM Control*, vol. 14, no. 3 (1966), pp. 527–549.

[19] Zadeh, L., and Desoer, C., *Linear System Theory: The State Space* Approach, McGraw-Hill, New York, 1963.

[20] Zemanian, A., *Distribution Theory and Transform Analysis*, McGraw-Hill, New York, 1965.

[21] Mal'chikov, S., "On the Synthesis of Linear Automatic Control Systems with Variable Parameters," *Automation and Remote Control*, vol. 20 (1959), pp. 1543–1549.

[22] Tricomi, F., *Integral Equations*, Interscience, New York, 1957.

[23] D'Angelo, H., and T. Higgins, "A Time Domain Procedure for the Analysis of Time-Variant Sampled Data Systems," *ISA Trans.*, vol. 5, no. 3 (1966), pp. 248–254.

PROBLEMS

3.1 Determine the transition matrix of the system characterized by the homogeneous equation

$$\begin{bmatrix} \dot{x}_1(t) \\ \dot{x}_2(t) \end{bmatrix} = \begin{bmatrix} 0 & 1 \\ -(2 + 6t^{-1} + 2t^{-2}) & -(3 + 4t^{-1}) \end{bmatrix} \begin{bmatrix} x_1(t) \\ x_2(t) \end{bmatrix}$$

given the basis

$$\mathbf{x}_1(t) = \begin{bmatrix} t^{-2}e^{-t} \\ -(2t^{-3} + t^{-2})e^{-t} \end{bmatrix}, \quad \mathbf{x}_2(t) = \begin{bmatrix} t^{-2}e^{-2t} \\ -2(t^{-3} + t^{-2})e^{-2t} \end{bmatrix}$$

3.2 Prove that if the system $\dot{\mathbf{x}}(t) = \mathbf{A}(t)\mathbf{x}(t)$ has the transition matrix $\phi(t, \tau) = \mathbf{K}(t)\mathbf{K}^{-1}(\tau)$, then $\mathbf{K}(t)$ is a fundamental matrix of the system and $[\mathbf{K}^{-1}(t)]'$ is a fundamental matrix of the adjoint system.

3.3 Sketch the response of Prob. 3.1 on the interval [0.1, 1.0] at increments of 0.1. The initial condition is

$$\begin{bmatrix} x_1(0.1) \\ x_2(0.1) \end{bmatrix} = \begin{bmatrix} 1 \\ 0 \end{bmatrix}$$

3.4 Verify Eq. 3.54.

3.5 For the system shown in Fig. P3.4 do the following:

(a) Write the state variable equations taking $x_1(t)$ and $x_2(t)$ as the state variables.

(b) Write the equation relating the state variable $\mathbf{x}(t)$ and the output $\mathbf{y}(t)$ where

$$\mathbf{x}(t) = \begin{bmatrix} x_1(t) \\ x_2(t) \end{bmatrix}, \quad \mathbf{y}(t) = \begin{bmatrix} y_1(t) \\ y_2(t) \\ y_3(t) \\ y_4(t) \\ y_5(t) \\ y_6(t) \end{bmatrix}$$

(c) Determine the state-transition matrix $\phi(t - \tau)$.

(d) Use the state-transition matrix found in part (c) to determine the impulsive-response matrix $\Omega(t, \tau)$.

(e) Verify the validity of part *d* by using some other method to determine $\omega_{53}(t - \tau)$.

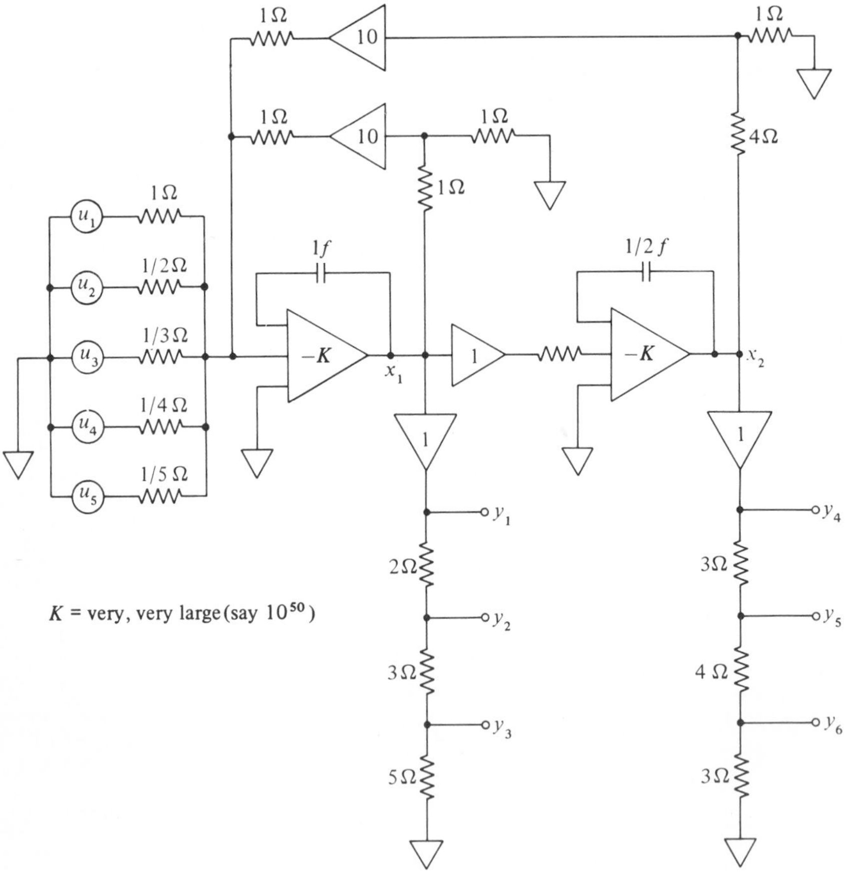

Fig. P3.4. System for Prob. 3.4.

3.6 A quiescent system with the impulsive-response matrix $\Omega(t, \tau)$ is excited by the input

$$\mathbf{u}(t) = \begin{bmatrix} \delta(t) \\ \delta(t - T) \\ \delta(t - 2T) \\ \vdots \\ \delta[t - (n - 1)T] \end{bmatrix}$$

Determine an expression, involving no integrals, for the response of this system.

3.7 Determine an equivalence transformation $\mathbf{T}(t)$ which transforms the system $\dot{\mathbf{x}}(t) = \mathbf{A}(t)\mathbf{x}(t) + \mathbf{B}(t)u(t)$ to the system $\dot{\mathbf{z}}(t) = \mathbf{B}_T(t)\mathbf{u}(t)$.

3.8 Sketch the state-variable diagram for the following system, its adjoint, and its dual.

$$\begin{bmatrix} \dot{x}_1(t) \\ \dot{x}_2(t) \end{bmatrix} = \begin{bmatrix} a_{11}(t) & a_{12}(t) \\ a_{21}(t) & a_{22}(t) \end{bmatrix} \begin{bmatrix} x_1(t) \\ x_2(t) \end{bmatrix} + \begin{bmatrix} b_1(t) \\ b_2(t) \end{bmatrix} u(t)$$

$$\begin{bmatrix} y_1(t) \\ y_2(t) \end{bmatrix} = \begin{bmatrix} c_{11}(t) & c_{12}(t) \\ c_{21}(t) & c_{22}(t) \end{bmatrix} \begin{bmatrix} x_1(t) \\ x_2(t) \end{bmatrix}$$

From comparisons of these three diagrams, determine a general graphical procedure for sketching the state-variable diagrams of the adjoint and dual systems of a general linear system directly from a state-variable diagram of the system *without* writing any of the system equations.

3.9 Verify Eqs. 3.101.

3.10 Show that if $\mathbf{W}(t)$ is a fundamental matrix of a system that $\mathbf{W}^{-1\prime}(t)\mathbf{K}$ is a fundamental matrix of the adjoint system for all constant nonsingular matrices $\mathbf{K}$.

3.11 Show that the impulsive response $\Omega_{12}(t, \tau)$ of the feedback system shown in Fig. 3.8 satisfies Eq. 3.116.

3.12 For the cases that $u(t)$ = unit step and $u(t) = \sin t$, sketch the *zero-state* sampled output $y_s(t)$ against t for each of the following systems ($T = 0.01$, $T = 0.1$, $T = 1$):

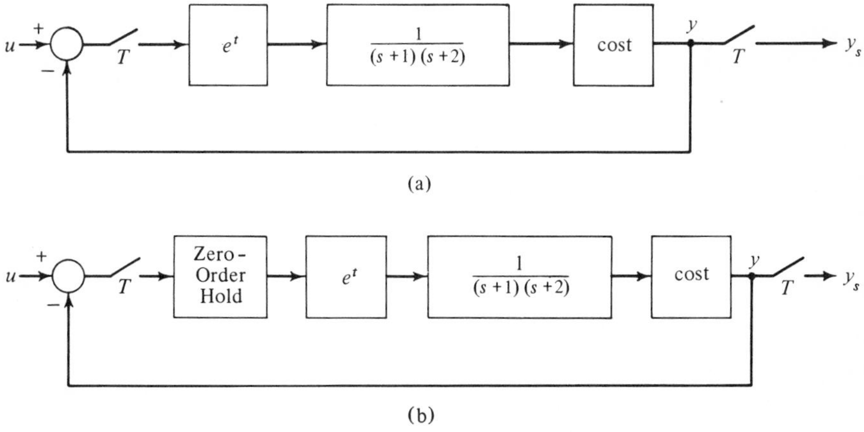

Fig. P3.12. Sampled-data feedback systems for Prob. 3.12.

3.13 Assuming that the impulsive-response matrices of the three systems interconnected as in Fig. P3.13 are known, derive a recursive equation (or set of equations) for determining the output.

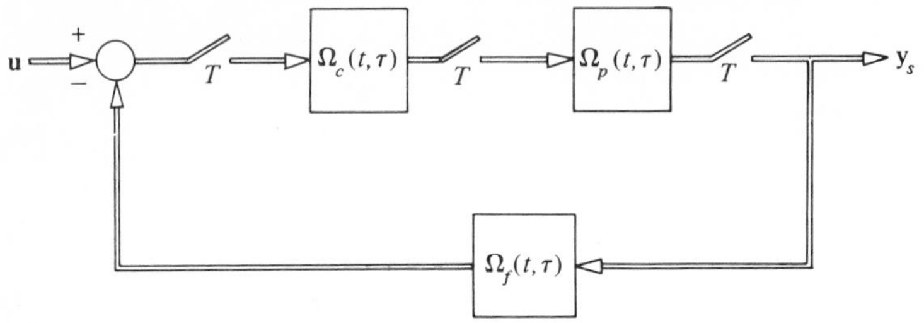

Fig. P3.13. Interconnection of three systems corresponding to Prob. 3.13.

3.14 Derive a set of recursive equations for the sampled-data system shown in Fig. P3.14 which includes the delay d, $0 < d < T$. Note that the recursive equation obtained can be used to examine the response $\mathbf{y}$ at any time $nT + d$ between samples.

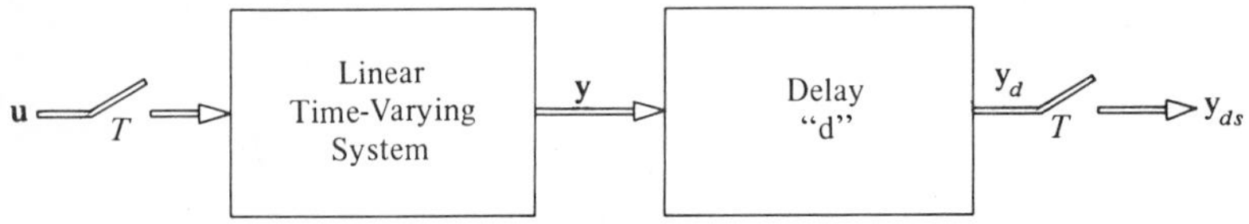

Fig. P3.14. Sampled-data system with delay.

4

Controllability and Observability

In the analysis and synthesis of complex multivariable systems, the concepts of *controllability* and *observability* provide a firm framework within which questions pertaining to the existence of solutions to problems posed can be answered. For example, in the design of a servomechanism it is necessary to determine a plant input $\mathbf{u}(t)$ that slaves the plant output $\mathbf{y}(t)$ to a reference signal $\mathbf{r}(t)$. Certainly, prior knowledge as to the existence of the desired plant input $\mathbf{u}(t)$ is of great value in obtaining insight to the problem and the specified requirements; plant controllability is associated with the existence of an input $\mathbf{u}(t)$ which transforms the output from its initial value $\mathbf{y}(t_0)$ to its final value $\mathbf{y}(t_f)$. If, carrying this example further, it is found that a satisfactory plant input does exist and, as expected, it is a function of the input $\mathbf{r}(t)$ and the plant's state $\mathbf{x}(t)$, then it is also important to know whether or not the state $\mathbf{x}(t)$ can be simply obtained from the plant output $\mathbf{y}(t)$; plant observability is associated with determining the states $\mathbf{x}(t)$ from observations of the system output $\mathbf{y}(t)$. In this chapter, definitions for controllability and observability are given and criteria for their existence in linear systems are developed; the dual relations between controllability and observability are noted.

Of particular importance in this chapter are the system *controllability matrix* and *observability matrix*. These matrices, in addition to their important property of providing controllability and observability information about a system, provide significant structural information and are thus useful in constructing transformations to either change the system to a more desirable form or to reduce it to some canonical form.

4.1. CONTROLLABILITY

The concept of *controllability* was originally introduced [9, 10, 11] to indicate whether or not a *state* transition could be effected by the application of some input. This concept of *state-controllability*[1] was later distinguished from *output-controllability* [12] in which the possibilities of effecting *output* transitions with applied inputs were considered. There are three basic *degrees* of controllability of significance in the analysis and synthesis of linear systems: (1) *complete controllability* implies that a desired state transition can be achieved in a finite time; (2) *total controllability* implies that a desired state transition can be achieved in *any* specified finite interval; (3) *uniform controllability* [16] implies that a desired state transition can be achieved at any time *instantaneously*.

4.1.1. Definitions. In this section, the three degrees of controllability are defined. A distinction is made between state-controllability and output-controllability.

Definition 4.1. A system is said to be *completely state-controllable* if for any t_0 each initial state $\mathbf{x}(t_0)$ can be transferred to any final state $\mathbf{x}_f$ in a finite time $t_f - t_0$ with a bounded input $\mathbf{u}(t)$, $\|\mathbf{u}(t)\| < \infty$. Thus there exists a t_f, $t_0 < t_f < \infty$, such that $\mathbf{x}(t_f) = x_f$.

Definition 4.2. A system is said to be *completely output-controllable* if for any t_0 each initial output $\mathbf{y}(t_0)$ can be transferred to any final output $\mathbf{y}_f$ in a finite time $t_f - t_0$ with a bounded input $\mathbf{u}(t)$, $\|\mathbf{u}(t)\| < \infty$. Thus there exists a t_f, $t_0 < t_f < \infty$, such that $\mathbf{y}(t_f) = \mathbf{y}_f$.

Example 4.1 [12]. As an example of a plant which is not state-controllable but is output-controllable, consider the system shown in Fig. 4.1. The state $\mathbf{x}(t) = [x_1(t), x_2(t)]'$ can only be transferred on a line parallel to $x_1(t) = x_2(t)$ in the state space. Thus regardless of $u(t)$ most states $\mathbf{x}(t_f)$ are inaccessible, and this system is not state-controllable. Obviously, any output $y(t_f)$ can be attained by any input $u(t)$ such that $y(t_f) = \int_{t_0}^{t_f} 2u(t)\,dt$, demonstrating that the system is output controllable.

In the case of multi-input systems it can be useful to distinguish between *strong* and *weak controllability* [12].

Definition 4.3. A system is said to be *strongly controllable* (in

[1]Due to controllability being originally defined with respect to transitions of the state, it is fairly common usage to use the terms *state-controllability* and *controllability* interchangeably.

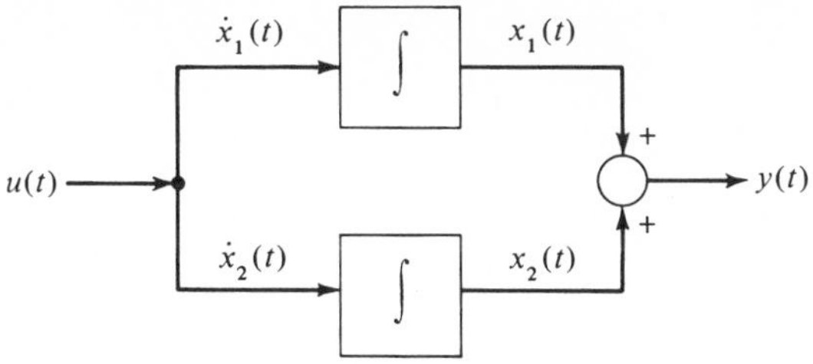

Fig. 4.1. A system which is output-controllable but not state-controllable.

the "state" or "output" sense) if it is controllable by each ontrol varialbe separately while all others are zero; otherwise it is *weakly controllable.*

The definitions of *complete controllability* given allow the input $\mathbf{u}(t)$ to be applied to a system on any finite time interval $[t_0, t_f]$ with t_f unspecified *a priori*. In many practical problems the interval $[t_0, t_f]$ is specified. In these situations a system is practially not controllable unless the desired state, or output, can be attained within the specified time interval. Such problems motivate the definition of *complete controllability on an interval* $[t_0, t_f]$:

Definition 4.4. A system is said to be *completely controllable* (in the "state" or "output" sense, and in the "strong" or "weak" sense) *on the interval* $[t_0, t_f]$, or simply, *controllable on* $[t_0, t_f]$, if each initial state $\mathbf{x}(t_0)$ can be transferred to any final state $\mathbf{x}(t_f)$ using some bounded control $\mathbf{u}(t)$ over the closed interval $[t_0, t_f]$.

In other problems, the specific interval $[t_0, t_f]$ on which control is to be achieved cannot be specified *a priori*. In these situations, the definition of *total controllability* is useful:

Defiinition 4.5. A plant is said to be *totally controllable* (in the "state" or "output" sense, and in the "strong" or "weak" sense) if it is completely controllable on every finite interval $[t_0, t_f]$.

Definition 4.6. A plant is said to be *totally controllable on* $[t_0, t_f]$ if it is completely controllable on every finite subinterval of $[t_0, t_f]$; it is said to be *totally controllable at* t_0 if for a given t_0 it is completely controllable on evergy finite interval $[t_0, t_f]$.

The concept of *uniform controllability*, although perhaps less useful in the control problem where a physically realizable control law $\mathbf{u}(t)$ must be determined to achieve control of a physical plant, is extremely useful in the synthesis of linear systems from either specified differential equations or impulsive-response matrices. The exact definition of uniform controllability involves the criteria developed in the sequel for the determination of complete and total controllability and therefore will be deferred. However, at this point it is sufficient to point out that the state of a uniformly controllable system can be changed at *any* time instantaneously by some input $\mathbf{u}(t)$; such an input obviously cannot be restricted to be bounded.

4.1.2. Controllability Criteria [10]. The development of criteria for controllability of the general system characterized by the equations

$$\begin{aligned}\dot{\mathbf{x}}(t) &= \mathbf{A}(t)\mathbf{x}(t) + \mathbf{B}(t)\mathbf{u}(t)\\ \mathbf{y}(t) &= \mathbf{C}(t)\mathbf{x}(t)\end{aligned} \tag{4.1}$$

is greatly simplified by first developing criteria for controllability of the special system characterized by

$$\begin{aligned}\dot{\mathbf{z}}(t) &= \mathbf{H}(t)\mathbf{u}(t)\\ \mathbf{y}(t) &= \mathbf{G}(t)\mathbf{z}(t)\end{aligned} \tag{4.2}$$

Through the equivalence transformation

$$\mathbf{z}(t) = \mathbf{T}(t)\mathbf{x}(t) \tag{4.3a}$$

where

$$\mathbf{T}(t) = \phi(t_0, t) = \phi^{-1}(t, t_0) \tag{4.3b}$$

and $\phi(t, t_0)$ is the transition matrix, Eqs. 4.1 are, in accordance with Eqs. 3.101 and the established properties of the transition matrix, transformed to Eqs. 4.2 where

$$\mathbf{H}(t) = \phi(t_0, t)\mathbf{B}(t) \tag{4.4}$$

and

$$\mathbf{G}(t) = \mathbf{C}(t)\phi(t, t_0) \tag{4.5}$$

It is emphasized that the criteria developed in this section require that the transition matrix $\phi(t, \tau)$ be known. This requirement is removed in the sequel.

Theorem 4.1. The system

$$\dot{\mathbf{x}}(t) = \mathbf{H}(t)\mathbf{u}(t) \tag{4.6}$$

with $\mathbf{H}(t)$ in $L_2[t_0, t_f]^2$ is completely state controllable on $[t_0, t_f]$ if and only if the $n \times n$ matrix

$$\mathbf{M}_0(t_0, t_f) \equiv \int_{t_0}^{t_f} \mathbf{H}(t)\mathbf{H}'(t)\, dt \tag{4.7}$$

is nonsingular.

Proof. (i) *Sufficiency* is established by assuming an input $\mathbf{u}(t)$ of the form

$$\mathbf{u}(t) = \mathbf{H}'(t)\boldsymbol{\xi} \tag{4.8}$$

where $\boldsymbol{\xi}$ is a constant n-vector. Substituting from Eq. 3.8 in Eq. 4.6 gives

$$\dot{\mathbf{x}}(t) = \mathbf{H}(t)\mathbf{H}'(t)\boldsymbol{\xi} \tag{4.9}$$

Integrating between t_0 and t_f gives

$$\mathbf{x}(t_f) - \mathbf{x}(t_0) = \int_{t_0}^{t_f} \mathbf{H}(t)\mathbf{H}'(t)\, dt\boldsymbol{\xi} \tag{4.10}$$

which, by the definition of $\mathbf{M}_0(t_0, t_f)$, can be written as

$$\mathbf{x}(t_f) - \mathbf{x}(t_0) = \mathbf{M}_0(t_0, t_f)\boldsymbol{\xi} \tag{4.11}$$

Therefore if $\mathbf{M}_0(t_0, t_f)$ is nonsingular,

$$\boldsymbol{\xi} = \mathbf{M}_0^{-1}(t_0, t_f)[\mathbf{x}(t_f) - \mathbf{x}(t_0)] \tag{4.12}$$

exists, and the input $\mathbf{u}(t) = \mathbf{H}'(t)\boldsymbol{\xi}$ transfers the system from state $\mathbf{x}(t_0)$ to state $\mathbf{x}(t_f)$ in the interval $[t_0, t_f]$.

(ii) *Necessity* is established by contradiction. Assume that $\mathbf{M}_0(t_0, t_f)$ is singular *and* the system is controllable. If $\mathbf{M}_0(t_0, t_f)$ is singular, then there exists a constant *nonzero* n-vector $\mathbf{c}$ such that $\mathbf{c}'\mathbf{M}_0(t_0, t_f) = \mathbf{0}$. Thus premultiplying and postmultiplying Eq. 4.7 by $\mathbf{c}'$ and $\mathbf{c}$ results in

$$\int_{t_0}^{t_f} \mathbf{c}'\mathbf{H}(t)\mathbf{H}'(t)\mathbf{c}\, dt = \int_{t_0}^{t_f} \boldsymbol{\lambda}^2(t)\, dt = 0 \tag{4.13}$$

where the n-vector $\boldsymbol{\lambda}(t) = [\lambda_1(t), \lambda_2(t), \cdots, \lambda_n(t)]'$ is defined by

$$\begin{aligned} [\mathbf{c}'\mathbf{H}(t)]^2 &\equiv \boldsymbol{\lambda}^2(t) \equiv \boldsymbol{\lambda}(t)\boldsymbol{\lambda}'(t) \\ &\equiv \lambda_1^2(t) + \lambda_2^2(t) + \cdots + \lambda_n^2(t) \geq 0 \end{aligned} \tag{4.14}$$

Therefore if $\mathbf{M}_0(t_0, t_f)$ is singular there exists a nonzero $\mathbf{c}$ such that

$$\mathbf{c}'\mathbf{H}(t) = \mathbf{0},\ t \in [t_0, t_f] \tag{4.15}$$

However, if the system is controllable, there also exists a $\mathbf{u}(t)$ such that

$$\mathbf{x}(t_f) - \mathbf{x}(t_0) = \int_{t_0}^{t_f} \mathbf{H}(t)\mathbf{u}(t)\, dt \tag{4.16}$$

Select $\mathbf{x}(t_f) = \mathbf{c}$ and $\mathbf{x}(t_0) = \mathbf{0}$, and premultiply Eq. 4.16 by $\mathbf{c}'$. Then

$$\mathbf{c}'\mathbf{c} = \int_{t_0}^{t_f} \mathbf{c}'\mathbf{H}(t)\mathbf{u}(t)\, dt \tag{4.17}$$

But in assuming a singular $\mathbf{M}_0(t_0, t_f)$, Eq. 4.15 results. Therefore

$$\mathbf{c}'\mathbf{c} = \mathbf{c}^2 = 0 \tag{4.18}$$

requiring that $\mathbf{c} = \mathbf{x}(t_f) = \mathbf{0}$ for any $\mathbf{u}(t)$. It can also be noted from Eq. 4.17 that unless $\mathbf{c}'\mathbf{H}(t) \neq \mathbf{0}$ for some finite interval $[t_1, t_2]$ on $[t_0, t_f]$ and not just at a point on $[t_0, t_f]$, that a finite nonzero state $\mathbf{c}$ is obtained only with unbounded $\mathbf{u}(t)$—namely a function of impulses. Thus a nonzero vector $\mathbf{c}$ such that $\mathbf{c}'\mathbf{M}_0(t_0, t_f) = \mathbf{0}$ does not exist when the system is controllable, and $\mathbf{M}_0(t_0, t_f)$ is not singular. Q.E.D.

[2] $L_2[t_0, t_f]$ is the class of functions that are square integrable on the closed interval $[t_0, t_f]$.

Corollary 4.1. The system characterized by Eq. 4.6 is completely state-controllable on the interval $[t_0, t_f]$ if $\mathbf{c}_1'\mathbf{H}(t) = \mathbf{0}$ on $[t_0, t_f]$ only when the constant n-vector $\mathbf{c}_1 = \mathbf{0}$, and if $\mathbf{c}_2'\mathbf{H}(t) \neq 0$ for $\mathbf{c}_2 \neq 0$ on some finite subinterval $[t_1, t_2]$ of $[t_0, t_f]$ (or equivalently, the system is completely state-controllable on $[t_0, t_f]$ if the rows of $\mathbf{H}(t)$ are linearly independent functions of t on some finite subinterval $[t_1, t_2]$ of $[t_0, t_f]$).

Theorem 4.2. The system

$$\dot{\mathbf{x}}(t) = \mathbf{A}(t)\mathbf{x}(t) + \mathbf{B}(t)\mathbf{u}(t) \tag{4.19}$$

with $\phi(t_0, t)\mathbf{B}(t)$ in $L_2[t_0, t_f]$ is completely state-controllable on $[t_0, t_f]$ if and only if the $n \times n$ matrix

$$\mathbf{M}(t_0, t_f) = \int_{t_0}^{t_f} \phi(t_0, t)\mathbf{B}(t)\mathbf{B}'(t)\phi'(t_0, t)\, dt \tag{4.20}$$

is nonsingular.

Proof. The equivalence transform $\mathbf{T}(t) = \phi(t_0, t)$ as shown in Eqs. 4.1 through 4.5 transforms system 4.19 to

$$\dot{\mathbf{z}}(t) = \mathbf{H}(t)\mathbf{u}(t) \tag{4.21}$$

where

$$\mathbf{H}(t) = \phi(t_0, t)\mathbf{B}(t) \tag{4.22}$$

Since $\mathbf{x}(t)$ and $\mathbf{z}(t)$ are related through the nonsingular transformation 4.3, controllability of $\mathbf{z}(t)$ implies controllability of $\mathbf{x}(t)$. Thus it is sufficient to show that the nonsingularity of $\mathbf{M}(t_0, t_f)$ defined in Eq. 4.20 establishes the controllability of the system characterized by Eq. 4.21. By Theorem 4.1 system 4.21 is controllable if and only if $\mathbf{M}_0(t_0, t_f)$ as defined in Eq. 4.7 is nonsingular. Substituting from Eq. 4.22 in Eq. 4.7 results in

$$\mathbf{M}_0(t_0, t_f) = \int_{t_0}^{t_f} \phi(t_0, t)\mathbf{B}(t)\mathbf{B}'(t)\phi'(t_0, t)\, dt \tag{4.23}$$

Thus under the equivalence transformation 4.3 $\mathbf{M}(t_0, t_f) = \mathbf{M}_0(t_0, t_f)$ showing that $\mathbf{z}(t)$ is controllable if and only if $\mathbf{M}(t_0, t_f)$ is nonsingular. Q.E.D.

Corollary 4.2. The system characterized by Eq. 4.19 is completely state-controllable on $[t_0, t_f]$ if the rows of $\phi(t_0, t)\mathbf{B}(t)$ (or, equivalently, the rows of $\mathbf{W}^{-1}(t)\mathbf{B}(t)$, where $\mathbf{W}(t)$ is a fundamental Wronskian matrix) are linearly independent functions of t on some finite subinterval $[t_1, t_2]$ of $[t_0, t_f]$.

Theorem 4.3. The system

$$\begin{aligned} \dot{\mathbf{x}}(t) &= \mathbf{H}(t)\mathbf{u}(t) \\ \mathbf{y}(t) &= \mathbf{G}(t)\mathbf{x}(t) \end{aligned} \tag{4.24}$$

is completely output-controllable on $[t_0, t_f]$ if and only if the $r \times r$ matrix

$$\mathbf{P}_0(t_0, t_f) = \int_{t_0}^{t_f} \mathbf{G}(t_f)\mathbf{H}(t)\mathbf{H}'(t)\mathbf{G}'(t_f)\,dt \tag{4.25}$$

is nonsingular.

Proof. (i) *Sufficiency* is established by assuming an input $\mathbf{u}(t)$ of the form

$$\mathbf{u}(t) = \mathbf{H}'(t)\mathbf{G}'(t_f)\xi_0 \tag{4.26}$$

where ξ_0 is a constant r-vector. Proceeding as in the proof of Theorem 4.1 it is shown that if $\mathbf{P}_0(t_0, t_f)$ is nonsingular, then

$$\xi_0 = \mathbf{P}_0^{-1}(t_0, t_f)[\mathbf{y}(t_f) - \mathbf{y}(t_0)] \tag{4.27}$$

exists and the imput $\mathbf{u}(t) = \mathbf{H}'(t)\mathbf{G}'(t_f)\xi_0$ transfers the system from output $\mathbf{y}(t_0)$ to output $\mathbf{y}(t_f)$ in the interval $[t_0, t_f]$.

(ii) *Necessity* is shown by contradiction as in the proof of Theorem 4.1. If $\mathbf{P}_0(t_0, t_f)$ is singular then a *nonzero* $\mathbf{c}_0$ exists such that $\mathbf{c}_0\mathbf{G}(t_f)\mathbf{H}(t) = \mathbf{0}$; if the system is controllable and $\mathbf{c}_0\mathbf{G}(t_f)\mathbf{H}(t) = 0$, then $\mathbf{c}_0 = 0$. Q.E.D.

Corollary 4.3. The system characterized by Eqs. 4.24 is completely output-controllable on $[t_0, t_f]$ if the rows of $\mathbf{G}(t_f)\mathbf{H}(t)$ (or, equivalently the rows of $\mathbf{H}(t)$ *and* the columns of $\mathbf{G}(t_f)$) are linearly independent functions of t on some finite subinterval $[t_1, t_2]$ of $[t_0, t_f]$.

Theorem 4.4. The system

$$\begin{aligned}\dot{\mathbf{x}}(t) &= \mathbf{A}(t)\mathbf{x}(t) + \mathbf{B}(t)\mathbf{u}(t)\\ \mathbf{y}(t) &= \mathbf{C}(t)\mathbf{x}(t)\end{aligned} \tag{4.28}$$

is completely output-controllable on $[t_0, t_f]$ if and only if the $r \times r$ matrix

$$\mathbf{P}(t_0, t_f) = \int_{t_0}^{t_f} \Omega(t_f, t)\Omega'(t_f, t)\,dt \tag{4.29}$$

is nonsingular.

Proof. Again making the nonsingular transformation $\mathbf{z}(t) = \phi(t_0, t)\mathbf{x}(t)$ it is shown by Eqs. 4.1 through 4.5 that

$$\begin{aligned}\dot{\mathbf{z}}(t) &= \mathbf{H}(t)\mathbf{u}(t)\\ \mathbf{y}(t) &= \mathbf{G}(t)\mathbf{z}(t)\end{aligned} \tag{4.30}$$

where

$$\mathbf{H}(t) = \phi(t_0, t)\mathbf{B}(t) \tag{4.31}$$

and

$$\mathbf{G}(t) = \mathbf{C}(t)\phi(t, t_0) \tag{4.32}$$

which is of the same form as Eqs. 4.24. Thus application of Theorem 4.3

and use of the identity

$$\Omega(t_f, t) = \mathbf{C}(t_f)\phi(t_f, t)\mathbf{B}(t) \tag{4.33}$$

proves Theorem 4.4. Q.E.D.

Corollary 4.4. The system characterized by Eqs. 4.28 is completely output-controllable on $[t_0, t_f]$ if the rows of $\Omega(t_f, t)$ (or, equivalently, the rows of $\mathbf{W}^{-1}(t)\mathbf{B}(t)$ *and* the columns of $\mathbf{C}(t_f)\mathbf{W}(t_f)$ where $\mathbf{W}(t)$ is a fundamental Wronskian matrix) are linearly independent functions of t on some finite subinterval $[t_1, t_2]$ of $[t_0, t_f]$.

4.1.3. Controllability Matrices. Theorems 4.2 and 4.3 give the necessary and sufficient conditions for state- and output-controllability of linear time-varying systems. The major drawback in the application of these theorems is that the transition matrix $\phi(t, t_0)$ of the system must be known. Except for a few special cases the transition matrix is neither known nor easily found. Fortunately algebraic criteria for controllability of most linear time-varying systems can be developed which do not require knowledge of the transition matrix. For the class of systems characterized by equations with $\mathbf{A}(t)$, $\mathbf{B}(t)$ differentiable $n - 2$, $n - 1$ times respectively, sufficient conditions are obtained for complete controllability; necessary and sufficient conditions are obtained for total controllability [2, 6, 18, 19].

Theorem 4.5 [6]. The system

$$\dot{\mathbf{x}}(t) = \mathbf{H}(t)\mathbf{u}(t) \tag{4.34}$$

with $\mathbf{H}(t)$ differentiable $n - 1$ times almost everywhere on the interval $[t_0, t_f]$ is completely state-controllable on $[t_0, t_f]$ if the $n \times nm$ *controllability matrix*

$$\mathbf{Q}_{c0}(t) = \left[\mathbf{H}(t), \frac{d\mathbf{H}(t)}{dt}, \ldots, \frac{d^{n-1}\mathbf{H}(t)}{dt}\right] \tag{4.35}$$

has rank n almost everywhere on some finite subinterval $[t_1, t_2]$ of the interval $[t_0, t_f]$.

Proof. Differentiating $\mathbf{c}_1'\mathbf{H}(t) = \mathbf{0}$ $n - 1$ times results in

$$\mathbf{c}_1'\left[\mathbf{H}(t), \frac{d\mathbf{H}(t)}{dt}, \ldots, \frac{d^{n-1}\mathbf{H}(t)}{dt}\right] = \mathbf{0} \tag{4.36}$$

or simply

$$\mathbf{c}_1'\mathbf{Q}_{c0}(t) = \mathbf{0} \tag{4.37}$$

Clearly, if rank $\mathbf{Q}_{c0}(t) = n$ on $[t_1, t_2]$ then it is necessary that $\mathbf{c}_1 = \mathbf{0}$. Thus $\mathbf{c}_1'\mathbf{H}(t) = \mathbf{0}$ on $[t_1, t_2]$ implies $\mathbf{c}_1 = \mathbf{0}$, and $\mathbf{c}_2\mathbf{H}(t) \neq \mathbf{0}$ implies $\mathbf{c}_2 \neq \mathbf{0}$. Thus, in accordance with Corollary 4.1, the system is completely state-controllable. Q.E.D.

Theorem 4.5 provides a sufficient condition for *complete* state-controllability for the case that the matrix $\mathbf{H}(t)$ is differentiable $n - 1$ times on the interval $[t_0, t_f]$. However, necessary and sufficient conditions can be obtained for the stronger *total* state-controllability.

Theorem 4.6. The system characterized by Eq. 4.34 with $\mathbf{H}(t)$ differentiable $n - 1$ times almost everywhere on the interval $[t_0, t_f]$ is totally state-controllable on $[t_0, t_f]$ if and only if the $n \times nm$ controllability matrix $\mathbf{Q}_{c0}(t)$ has rank n almost everywhere on the interval $[t_0, t_f]$.

Proof. (i) *Sufficiency* is a direct result of Theorem 4.5.

(ii) *Necessity* is established by contradiction. Assume that the system is totally state-controllable on $[t_0, t_f]$ and rank $\mathbf{Q}_{c0}(t) < n$ on some finite subinterval $[t_1, t_2]$ of $[t_0, t_f]$. If rank $\mathbf{Q}_{c0}(t) < n$ on $[t_1, t_2]$, then there exists a nonzero analytic n-vector $\mathbf{b}'(t) = [b_1(t), \cdots, b_n(t)]$ on $[t_1, t_2]$ such that

$$\mathbf{b}'(t)\mathbf{Q}_{c0}(t) = \mathbf{0} \tag{4.38}$$

Expanding Eq. 4.38 gives

$$\begin{aligned} &\mathbf{b}'(t)\mathbf{H}(t) = \mathbf{0} \\ &\mathbf{b}'(t)\frac{d\mathbf{H}(t)}{dt} = \mathbf{0} \\ &\quad\vdots \\ &\mathbf{b}'(t)\frac{d^{n-1}\mathbf{H}(t)}{dt} = \mathbf{0} \end{aligned} \tag{4.39}$$

By differentiating Eqs. 4.39 it can be shown that

$$\begin{aligned} &\mathbf{b}'(t)\mathbf{H}(t) = \mathbf{0} \\ &\frac{d\mathbf{b}'(t)}{dt}\mathbf{H}(t) = \mathbf{0} \\ &\quad\vdots \\ &\frac{d^{n-1}\mathbf{b}'(t)}{dt}\mathbf{H}(t) = \mathbf{0} \end{aligned} \tag{4.40}$$

or

$$\mathbf{W}_n(t)\mathbf{H}(t) = \mathbf{0} \tag{4.41}$$

where

$$\mathbf{W}_n(t) = \begin{bmatrix} \mathbf{b}'(t) \\ \dfrac{d\mathbf{b}'(t)}{dt} \\ \vdots \\ \dfrac{d^{n-1}\mathbf{b}'(t)}{dt^{n-1}} \end{bmatrix} \tag{4.42}$$

As no row of $\mathbf{H}(t)$ is zero (a zero row of $\mathbf{H}(t)$ implies that the corresponding component of the state is not controllable), rank $\mathbf{W}_n(t) < n$ on $[t_1, t_2]$. With no loss of generality, assume that rank $\mathbf{W}_n(t) = (n-1)$ on $[t_1, t_2]$. Thus any row, or column, of $\mathbf{W}_n(t)$ can be expressed as a linear combination of $(n-1)$ linearly independent n-vectors. One can consider $\mathbf{W}_n(t)$ to be the Wronskian matrix of a scalar system with rank $\mathbf{W}_n(t) = (n-1)$ on $[t_1, t_2]$. Therefore the elements of $\mathbf{b}(t)$ can be obtained as a linear combination of $(n-1)$ independent solutions to the following equation:

$$\begin{aligned} b_i(t) &= f_1(t)k_{1i} + f_2(t)k_{2i} + \cdots + f_{n-1}(t)k_{n-1,i} \\ &= \mathbf{f}'(t)\mathbf{k}_i\,, \qquad i = 1, \cdots, n \end{aligned} \tag{4.43}$$

where $\mathbf{f}'(t) = [f_1(t), \cdots, f_{n-1}(t)]$ is an $n-1$ vector representing $(n-1)$ independent solutions on $[t_1, t_2]$ and $\mathbf{k}_i' = [k_{1i}, k_{2i}, \cdots, k_{n-1,i}]$ is a constant $(n-1)$-vector. Equations 4.43 can be written as

$$\mathbf{b}'(t) = \mathbf{f}'(t)[\mathbf{k}_1, \mathbf{k}_2, \cdots, \mathbf{k}_n] \tag{4.44}$$

or as

$$\mathbf{b}'(t) = \mathbf{f}'(t)\mathbf{K} \tag{4.45}$$

where

$$\mathbf{K} = \begin{bmatrix} k_{11} & k_{12} & \cdots & k_{1,n} \\ k_{21} & k_{22} & \cdots & k_{2,n} \\ \vdots & \vdots & & \vdots \\ k_{n-1,1} & k_{n-1,2} & \cdots & k_{n-1,n} \end{bmatrix} \tag{4.46}$$

and as $\mathbf{b}(t)$ and $\mathbf{f}(t)$ are nonzero on $[t_1, t_2]$, $\mathbf{K}$ is also nonzero. Differentiating Eq. 4.45 $n-2$ times gives

$$\begin{bmatrix} \mathbf{b}'(t) \\ \dfrac{d\mathbf{b}'(t)}{dt} \\ \vdots \\ \dfrac{d^{n-2}\mathbf{b}'(t)}{dt^{n-2}} \end{bmatrix} = \begin{bmatrix} f_1(t) & f_2(t) & \cdots & f_{n-1}(t) \\ \dfrac{df_1(t)}{dt} & \dfrac{df_2(t)}{dt} & \cdots & \dfrac{df_{n-1}(t)}{dt} \\ \vdots & \vdots & & \vdots \\ \dfrac{d^{n-2}f_1(t)}{dt^{n-2}} & \dfrac{d^{n-2}f_2(t)}{dt^{n-2}} & \cdots & \dfrac{d^{n-2}f_{n-1}(t)}{dt^{n-2}} \end{bmatrix}\mathbf{K}$$

$$= \mathbf{W}_{n-1}(t)\mathbf{K} \tag{4.47}$$

where $\mathbf{W}_{n-1}(t)$ is the Wronskian matrix of the scalar $(n-1)$-order system with the $(n-1)$ independent solutions $f_1(t), \cdots, f_{n-1}(t)$. Postmultiplying Eq. 4.47 by $\mathbf{H}(t)$, gives

$$\begin{bmatrix} \mathbf{b}'(t)\mathbf{H}(t) \\ \dfrac{d\mathbf{b}'(t)}{dt}\mathbf{H}(t) \\ \vdots \\ \dfrac{d^{n-2}\mathbf{b}'(t)}{dt^{n-2}}\mathbf{H}(t) \end{bmatrix} = \mathbf{W}_{n-1}(t)\mathbf{KH}(t) \tag{4.48}$$

which in accordance with Eqs. 4.40 is

$$\mathbf{0} = \mathbf{W}_{n-1}(t)\mathbf{KH}(t) \tag{4.49}$$

Since $\mathbf{W}_{n-1}(t)$ is the Wronskian matrix of $(n-1)$ independent solutions, $\det \mathbf{W}_{n-1}(t) \neq 0$ for all t in $[t_1, t_2]$ and

$$\mathbf{0} = \mathbf{KH}(t) \tag{4.50}$$

Since $\mathbf{K} \neq 0$, there is a nonzero n-vector $\mathbf{c}$ such that $\mathbf{c}'\mathbf{H}(t) = \mathbf{0}$ on $[t_1, t_2]$. In accordance with Corollary 4.1, this implies that the system is *not* completely state-controllable on $[t_1, t_2]$ and thus is not totally controllable on $[t_0, t_f]$. Therefore the initial assumption is contradicted. Q.E.D.

Theorem 4.7. The system

$$\dot{\mathbf{x}}(t) = \mathbf{A}(t)\mathbf{x}(t) + \mathbf{B}(t)\mathbf{u}(t) \tag{4.51}$$

with $\mathbf{A}(t)$, $\mathbf{B}(t)$ differentiable $n-2$, $n-1$ times almost everywhere on $[t_0, t_f]$ is completely state-controllable on $[t_0, t_f]$ if the $n \times nm$ controllability matrix

$$\mathbf{Q}_c(t) = [\mathbf{B}(t), \Delta_c\mathbf{B}(t), \cdots, \Delta_c^{n-1}\mathbf{B}(t)] \tag{4.52}$$

has rank n almost everywhere on some finite subinterval of the interval $[t_0, t_f]$; the operator Δ_c is defined by

$$\Delta_c = -\mathbf{A}(t) + \frac{d}{dt} \tag{4.53}$$

Proof. As in the proof of Theorem 4.2, the nonsingular transformation $\mathbf{z}(t) = \phi(t_0, t)\mathbf{x}(t)$ is introduced. Thus system 4.51 is transformed to

$$\dot{\mathbf{z}}(t) = \mathbf{H}(t)\mathbf{u}(t) \tag{4.54}$$

where

$$\mathbf{H}(t) = \phi(t_0, t)\mathbf{B}(t) \tag{4.55}$$

Applying Theorem 4.5 to the transformed system 4.54 results in

$$\mathbf{Q}_{c0}(t) = \left[\phi(t_0, t)\mathbf{B}(t), \frac{d}{dt}\{\phi(t_0, t)\mathbf{B}(t)\}, \cdots, \frac{d^{n-1}}{dt^{n-1}}\{\phi(t_0, t)\mathbf{B}(t)\}\right] \tag{4.56}$$

which, in accordance with Eqs. 3.23 and 4.53, can be written as

$$\mathbf{Q}_{c0}(t) = \phi(t_0, t)[\mathbf{B}(t), \Delta_c\mathbf{B}(t), \cdots, \Delta_c^{n-1}\mathbf{B}(t)] \tag{4.57}$$

or simply

$$\mathbf{Q}_{c0}(t) = \phi(t_0, t)\mathbf{Q}_c(t) \tag{4.58}$$

As rank $\phi(t_0, t) = n$, rank $\mathbf{Q}_{c0}(t) = n$ if and only if rank $\mathbf{Q}_c(t) = n$. Q.E.D.

Theorem 4.8. The system characterized by Eq. 4.51 with $\mathbf{A}(t)$, $\mathbf{B}(t)$ differentiable $n - 2$, $n - 1$ times almost everywhere on $[t_0, t_f]$ is totally state-controllable on $[t_0, t_f]$ if and only if the $n \times nm$ controllability matrix $\mathbf{Q}_c(t)$ has rank n almost everywhere on the interval $[t_0, t_f]$.

Proof. The proof is identical to the proof for Theorem 4.7 with the exception that Theorem 4.6 is applied to the transformed system rather than Theorem 4.5. Q.E.D.

Theorem 4.9. The system

$$\begin{aligned} \dot{\mathbf{x}}(t) &= \mathbf{H}(t)\mathbf{u}(t) \\ \mathbf{y}(t) &= \mathbf{G}(t)\mathbf{x}(t) \end{aligned} \tag{4.59}$$

with $\mathbf{H}(t)$ differentiable $n - 1$ times almost everywhere on $[t_0, t_f]$ is completely output-controllable on $[t_0, t_f]$ if the $r \times nm$ *controllability matrix*

$$\begin{aligned} \mathbf{S}_{c0}(t) &= \mathbf{G}(t_f)\left[\mathbf{H}(t), \frac{d\mathbf{H}(t)}{dt}, \cdots, \frac{d^{n-1}\mathbf{H}(t)}{dt^{n-1}}\right] \\ &= \mathbf{G}(t_f)\mathbf{Q}_{c0}(t) \end{aligned} \tag{4.60}$$

has rank r almost everywhere on some finite subinterval $[t_1, t_2]$ of $[t_0, t_f]$.

Proof. Differentiating $\mathbf{c}_1'\mathbf{G}(t_f)\mathbf{H}(t) = \mathbf{0}$ $n - 1$ times and obtaining

$$\mathbf{c}_1'\mathbf{G}(t_f)\mathbf{Q}_{c0}(t) = \mathbf{0} \tag{4.61}$$

or simply

$$\mathbf{c}_1'\mathbf{S}_{c0}(t) = 0 \tag{4.62}$$

Thus if rank $\mathbf{S}_{c0}(t) = r$ on $[t_1, t_2]$ then it is necessary that $\mathbf{c}_1 = \mathbf{0}$. Therefore $\mathbf{c}_1'\mathbf{G}(t_f)\,\mathbf{H}(t) = \mathbf{0}$ on $[t_1, t_2]$ implies that $\mathbf{c}_1 = \mathbf{0}$ and $\mathbf{c}_2\mathbf{G}(t_f)\mathbf{H}(t) \neq \mathbf{0}$ implies $\mathbf{c}_2 \neq \mathbf{0}$. Thus $\mathbf{G}(t_f)\mathbf{H}(t)$ has r linearly independent rows on the subinterval $[t_1, t_2]$ and, in accordance with Corollary 4.3, the system is completely output-controllable. Q.E.D.

Theorem 4.10. The system characterized by Eqs. 4.59 with $\mathbf{H}(t)$ differentiable $n - 1$ times almost everywhere on $[t_0, t_f]$ is totally output-controllable on $[t_0, t_f]$ if and only if $r \times nm$ controllability matrix $\mathbf{S}_{c0}(t)$ has rank r almost everywhere on the interval $[t_0, t_f]$.

Proof. (i) *Sufficiency* is a direct result of Theorem 4.9

(ii) *Necessity*[3] is established by contradiction. Assume that the system is totally output-controllable on $[t_0, t_f]$ and rank $S_{c0}(t) < r$ on some finite subinterval $[t_1, t_2]$ of $[t_0, t_f]$. If rank $\mathbf{S}_{c0}(t) < r$ on $[t_1, t_2]$, then there exists a nonzero r-vector $\mathbf{b}'(t) = [b_1(t), \cdots, b_r(t)]$ on $[t_1, t_2]$ such that

$$\mathbf{b}'(t)\mathbf{S}_{c0}(t) = \mathbf{0} \tag{4.63}$$

Expanding Eq. 4.63 gives

$$\begin{aligned} \mathbf{b}'(t)\mathbf{G}(t_f)\mathbf{H}(t) &= \mathbf{0} \\ \mathbf{b}'(t)\mathbf{G}(t_f)\frac{d\mathbf{H}(t)}{dt} &= \mathbf{0} \\ &\vdots \\ \mathbf{b}'(t)\mathbf{G}(t_f)\frac{d^{n-1}\mathbf{H}(t)}{dt} &= \mathbf{0} \end{aligned} \tag{4.64}$$

By differentiating Eqs. 4.64 it can be shown that

$$\begin{aligned} \mathbf{b}'(t)\mathbf{G}(t_f)\mathbf{H}(t) &= \mathbf{0} \\ \frac{d\mathbf{b}'(t)}{dt}\mathbf{G}(t_f)\mathbf{H}(t) &= \mathbf{0} \\ &\vdots \\ \frac{d^{n-1}\mathbf{b}'(t)}{dt^{n-1}}\mathbf{G}(t_f)\mathbf{H}(t) &= \mathbf{0} \end{aligned} \tag{4.65}$$

or

$$\mathbf{V}(t)\mathbf{G}(t_f)\mathbf{H}(t) = \mathbf{0} \tag{4.66}$$

Where $\mathbf{V}(t)$ is the $n \times r$ matrix,

$$\mathbf{V}(t) = \begin{bmatrix} \mathbf{b}'(t) \\ \dfrac{d\mathbf{b}'(t)}{dt} \\ \vdots \\ \dfrac{d^{n-1}\mathbf{b}'(t)}{dt^{n-1}} \end{bmatrix} \tag{4.67}$$

As no row of $\mathbf{G}(t_f)\mathbf{H}(t)$ is zero (a zero row of $\mathbf{G}(t_f)\mathbf{H}(t)$ implies that the corresponding component of the output is not controllable), rank $\mathbf{V}(t) < r$

[3]The proof of necessity given here follows very closely the proof of necessity given for Theorem 4.6.

on some subinterval of $[t_0, t_f]$. With no loss of generality, assume that rank $\mathbf{V}(t) = (r - 1)$ on $[t_1, t_2]$. Thus the elements of $\mathbf{b}(t)$ can be obtained as a linear combination of $r - 1$ independent solutions of an $(r - 1)$th-order equation on $[t_1, t_2]$:

$$\begin{aligned} b_i(t) &= f_1(t)k_{1i} + f_2(t)k_{2i} + \cdots + f_{r-1}(t)k_{r-1,i} \\ &= \mathbf{f}'(t)\mathbf{k}_i\,, \qquad i = 1, \cdots, r \end{aligned} \tag{4.68}$$

where $\mathbf{f}'(t) = [f_1(t), \cdots, f_{r-1}(t)]$ is an $r - 1$ vector representing $(r - 1)$ independent solutions on $[t_1, t_2]$, and $\mathbf{k}_i' = [k_{1i}, \cdots, k_{r-1,i}]$ is a constant $(r - 1)$ vector. Equations 4.68 can be written as

$$\mathbf{b}'(t) = \mathbf{f}'(t)[\mathbf{k}_1, \mathbf{k}_2, \cdots, \mathbf{k}_r] \tag{4.69}$$

or as

$$\mathbf{b}'(t) = \mathbf{f}'(t)\mathbf{K} \tag{4.70}$$

where the $(r - 1) \times r$ vector $\mathbf{K}$ is given by

$$\mathbf{K} = [\mathbf{k}_1, \mathbf{k}_2, \cdots, \mathbf{k}_r] \tag{4.71}$$

Therefore, since $\mathbf{b}(t)$ and $\mathbf{f}(t)$ are nonzero on $[t_1, t_2]$, $\mathbf{K}$ is also nonzero. Differentiating Eq. 4.70 $r - 2$ times gives

$$\begin{bmatrix} \mathbf{b}'(t) \\ \dfrac{d\mathbf{b}'(t)}{dt} \\ \vdots \\ \dfrac{d^{r-2}\mathbf{b}'(t)}{dt^{r-2}} \end{bmatrix} = \begin{bmatrix} f_1(t) & \cdots & f_{r-1}(t) \\ \dfrac{df_1(t)}{dt} & \cdots & \dfrac{df_{r-1}(t)}{dt} \\ \vdots & & \vdots \\ \dfrac{d^{r-2}f_1(t)}{dt^{r-2}} & \cdots & \dfrac{d^{r-2}f_{r-1}(t)}{dt^{r-2}} \end{bmatrix}\mathbf{K}$$

$$\equiv \mathbf{W}_{r-1}(t)\mathbf{K} \tag{4.72}$$

where $\mathbf{W}_{r-1}(t)$ is the Wronskian matrix of the scalar $(r - 1)$-order system with the $(r - 1)$ independent solutions $f_1(t), \cdots, f_{r-1}(t)$. Postmultiplying Eq. 4.72 by $\mathbf{G}(t_f)\mathbf{H}(t)$ gives

$$\begin{bmatrix} \mathbf{b}'(t)\mathbf{G}(t_f)\mathbf{H}(t) \\ \dfrac{d\mathbf{b}'(t)}{dt}\mathbf{G}(t_f)\mathbf{H}(t) \\ \vdots \\ \dfrac{d^{r-2}\mathbf{b}'(t)}{dt^{r-2}}\mathbf{G}(t_f)\mathbf{H}(t) \end{bmatrix} = \mathbf{W}_{r-1}(t)\mathbf{K}\mathbf{G}(t_f)\mathbf{H}(t) \tag{4.73}$$

which in accordance with Eqs. 4.65 is

$$\mathbf{0} = \mathbf{W}_{r-1}(t)\mathbf{K}\mathbf{G}(t_f)\mathbf{H}(t) \tag{4.74}$$

Since $\mathbf{W}_{r-1}(t)$ is the Wronskian matrix of $(r - 1)$ independent solutions, $\det \mathbf{W}_{r-1}(t) \neq 0$ for all t in $[t_1, t_2]$ and

$$\mathbf{0} = \mathbf{K}\mathbf{G}(t_f)\mathbf{H}(t) \tag{4.75}$$

As $\mathbf{K} \neq 0$, there is a nonzero r-vector $\mathbf{c}_1$ such that $\mathbf{c}_1'\mathbf{G}(t_f)\mathbf{H}(t) = \mathbf{0}$ on $[t_1, t_2]$. This implies that the rows of $\mathbf{G}(t_f)\mathbf{H}(t)$ are linearly dependent on $[t_1, t_2]$ and, in accordance with Corollary 4.3, that the system is not completely output-controllable on $[t_1, t_2]$. Thus the initial assumption is contradicted. Q.E.D.

Theorem 4.11. The system

$$\begin{aligned} \dot{\mathbf{x}}(t) &= \mathbf{A}(t)\mathbf{x}(t) + \mathbf{B}(t)\mathbf{u}(t) \\ \mathbf{y}(t) &= \mathbf{C}(t)\mathbf{x}(t) \end{aligned} \tag{4.76}$$

with $\mathbf{A}(t)$, $\mathbf{B}(t)$ differentiable $n - 2$, $n - 1$ times almost everywhere on $[t_0, t_f]$ is completely output-controllable on $[t_0, t_f]$ is the $r \times nm$ *controllability matrix*

$$\begin{aligned} \mathbf{S}_c(t) &= \mathbf{C}(t_f)[\mathbf{B}(t), \Delta_c\mathbf{B}(t), \cdots, \Delta_c^{n-1}\mathbf{B}(t)] \\ &= \mathbf{C}(t_f)\mathbf{Q}_c(t) \end{aligned} \tag{4.77}$$

has rank r almost everywhere on some finite subinterval $[t_1, t_2]$ of $[t_0, t_f]$; $\Delta_c = -\mathbf{A}(t) + \dfrac{d}{dt}$.

Proof. Making the nonsingular transformation $\mathbf{z}(t) = \phi(t_0, t)\mathbf{x}(t)$, Theorem 4.9 can be applied resulting in

$$\mathbf{S}_{c0}(t) = \mathbf{C}(t_f)\phi(t_f, t)\mathbf{Q}_c(t) \tag{4.78}$$

Thus by Theorem 4.9, system 4.76 is completely output-controllable if

$$\text{rank } \mathbf{S}_{c0}(t) = \text{rank } \mathbf{C}(t_f)\phi(t_f, t)\mathbf{Q}_c(t) = r \tag{4.79}$$

For an nth-order system,

$$\text{rank } \phi(t_f, t) = n \tag{4.80}$$

Comparing Eqs. 4.79 and 4.80 it is seen that

$$\text{rank } \mathbf{S}_{c0}(t) \leq n \tag{4.81}$$

Thus if r, the number of outputs, exceeds n, the order of the system, the system is not output-controllable. For the case that $r \leq n$,

$$\begin{aligned} \text{rank } \mathbf{S}_{c0}(t) &= \text{rank } \mathbf{C}(t_f)\mathbf{Q}_c(t) \\ &= \text{rank } \mathbf{S}_c(t) \end{aligned} \tag{4.82}$$

Thus if $\text{rank } \mathbf{S}_c(t) = r$, the system is completely output-controllable. Q.E.D.

Corollary 4.11. If, for the system characterized by Eqs. 4.76, the number of outputs r exceeds the number of states n, then the system is not completely output-controllable.

Theorem 4.12. The system characterized by Eqs. 4.76 with $\mathbf{A}(t)$ and $\mathbf{B}(t)$ differentiable $n-2$, $n-1$ times almost everywhere on $[t_0, t_f]$ is totally output-controllable on $[t_0, t_f]$ if and only if the $r \times nm$ controllability matrix $\mathbf{S}_c(t)$ has rank r almost everywhere on interval $[t_0, t_f]$.

Proof. The proof is identical to the proof of Theorem 4.11 with the exception that Theorem 4.10 is applied to the transformed system rather than Theorem 4.9. Q.E.D.

For the case that a system is time-invariant complete controllability is determined by

Corollary 4.12. The linear time-invariant system

$$\begin{aligned} \dot{\mathbf{x}}(t) &= \mathbf{A}\mathbf{x}(t) + \mathbf{B}\mathbf{u}(t) \\ \mathbf{y}(t) &= \mathbf{C}\mathbf{x}(t) \end{aligned} \tag{4.83}$$

is totally output-controllable if and only if the $r \times nm$ controllability matrix

$$\mathbf{S}_c = \mathbf{C}[\mathbf{B}, -\mathbf{A}\mathbf{B}, \mathbf{A}^2\mathbf{B}, \cdots, (-\mathbf{A})^{n-1}\mathbf{B} \tag{4.84}$$

has rank r.

The criterion for total state-controllability is obtained from Corollary 4.12 by setting $\mathbf{C} = \mathbf{I}$. Thus $r = n$ and

$$\mathbf{Q}_c = [\mathbf{B}, -\mathbf{A}\mathbf{B}, \mathbf{A}^2\mathbf{B}, \cdots, (-\mathbf{A})^{n-1}\mathbf{B}] \tag{4.85}$$

is required to have rank n for complete state-controllability.

4.1.4. Uniform Controllability. It is apparent from the previous section that controllability is closely related to the rank of the controllability matrix on the interval of interest $[t_0, t_f]$. For the sake of clarifying the following discussion, the specific controllability matrix $\mathbf{Q}_c(t)$ defined by Eq. 4.52 and associated with the state-controllability of system 4.51 will be referred to. Some reflection on Theorems 4.5 and 4.7 and their proofs, reveals that at an instant of time in which the controllability matrix $\mathbf{Q}_c(t)$ has rank n, the input is *coupled* to the state so that each of the state variables is *under control* to the extent that an input can be found to excite each of the state variables in a specified manner. On the other hand, at an instant of time in which the rank of $\mathbf{Q}_c(t)$ is less than n, there is at least one state variable which is not, in some sense, coupled to the input. In the strict sense, this implies that the input does not affect one of the state variables at all. However, in the general sense intended, the implication is that, due to the functional dependence of one state on the others, there exists a nonsingular transformation $\mathbf{T}(t)$ such that one of the *transformed* states is not strictly coupled to the input.

As seen from Corollary 4.7, total controllability exists when the controllability matrix $\mathbf{Q}_c(t)$ has rank n *almost everywhere* on every finite subinterval of the interval of interest $[t_0, t_f]$, i.e., the system is totally state-controllable if each of the state variables are under control amost everywhere on $[t_0, t_f]$. Thus for a totally controllable system there can exist a set of measure zero on $[t_0, t_f]$ for which rank $\mathbf{Q}_c(t) < n$. During these instants in which rank $\mathbf{Q}_c(t) < n$ the state is not controllable, and even if one were permitted to use unbounded inputs to transfer the state, the existing state generally could not be transferred to a desired state in that instant; it is shown in the sequel that this transfer is possible at any instant in which rank $\mathbf{Q}_c(t) = n$ with an impulse made up of impulses and derivatives of impulses.

It follows from the above discussion that a degree of controllability stronger than total controllability would be obtained by requiring the controllability matrix $\mathbf{Q}_c(t)$ to have rank n *everywhere* on $[t_0, t_f]$. Hence, *uniform controllability*:

Definition 4.7. The system characterized by Eq. 4.51 is said to be uniformly state-controllable on $[t_0, t_f]$ if the controllability matrix $\mathbf{Q}_c(t)$ has rank n everywhere on $[t_0, t_f]$. Clearly, if a linear time-invariant system is controllable in either the complete or total sense, then it is also uniformly controllable.

It is now shown how the state of a uniformly state-controllable system can be changed instantaneously with an input made up of impulses and derivatives of impulses. For simplicity, and with no loss of generality, the problem is formulated as that of determining the input $\mathbf{u}(t)$ applied for any instant $t = t_1$ on $[t_0, t_f]$ which changes the state from $\mathbf{x}(t_1) = \mathbf{x}_1^{(-)}$ to $\mathbf{x}(t_1) = \mathbf{x}_1^{(+)}$. The state of a system is determined from Eq. 3.42 by letting $\mathbf{C}(t) = \mathbf{I}_n$:

$$\mathbf{x}(t) = \phi(t, t_1)\mathbf{x}_1^{(-)} + \int_{t_1}^{t} \phi(t, \tau)\mathbf{B}(\tau)\mathbf{u}(\tau)\, d\tau \tag{4.86}$$

It is poposed that the input $\mathbf{u}(t)$, applied for the instant $t = t_1$, be of the form

$$\mathbf{u}(t) = \sum_{i=1}^{n} \mathbf{k}_i \delta^{(i-1)}(t - t_1) \tag{4.87}$$

Substituting from Eq. 4.87 in Eq. 4.86 gives

$$\mathbf{x}(t) = \phi(t, t_1)\mathbf{x}_1^{(-)} + \sum_{i=1}^{n} \frac{d^{i-1}}{d\tau^{i-1}} [\phi(t, \tau)\mathbf{B}(\tau)\mathbf{k}_i] \Big|_{\tau=t_1} \tag{4.88}$$

Using Eqs. 3.23 and 4.53 it can be shown that

$$\frac{d^i}{d\tau^i} \phi[(t, \tau)\mathbf{B}(\tau)] = \phi(t, \tau)\Delta_c^i \mathbf{B}(\tau) \tag{4.89}$$

Substituting from Eq. 4.89 in Eq. 4.88 gives

$$\mathbf{x}(t) = \phi(t, t_1)[\mathbf{x}_1^{(-)} + \sum_{i=1}^{n} (-1)^{i-1}\Delta_c^{i-1}\mathbf{B}(t_1)\mathbf{k}_i] \tag{4.90}$$

At $t = t_1$, and "after" the application of the impulse, the desired state transition from $\mathbf{x}_1^{(-)}$ to $\mathbf{x}_1^{(+)}$should be achieved. Thus, letting $t = t_1$ in Eq. 4.90 gives

$$\mathbf{x}_1^{(+)} = \mathbf{x}_1^{(-)} + \sum_{i=1}^{n} (-1)^{i-1}\Delta_c^{i-1}\mathbf{B}(t_1)\mathbf{k}_i \tag{4.91}$$

Thus the desired instantaneous state transition $\mathbf{x}_1^{(+)} - \mathbf{x}_1^{(-)}$ is achieved if the set of n-vectors $\mathbf{k}_i$, $i = 1, \cdots, n$ can be found such that

$$\mathbf{x}_1^{(+)} - \mathbf{x}_1^{(-)} = \sum_{i=1}^{n} (-1)^{i-1}\Delta_c^{i-1}\mathbf{B}(t_1)\mathbf{k}_i \tag{4.92}$$

Equation 4.92 can be written as

$$\mathbf{x}_1^{(+)} - \mathbf{x}_1^{(-)} = \mathbf{Q}_c(t_1)\mathbf{k} \tag{4.93}$$

where $\mathbf{Q}_c(t_1)$ is the controllability matrix as defined in Eq. 4.52 and $\mathbf{k}$ is the nm-vector defined by

$$\mathbf{k} = \begin{bmatrix} \mathbf{k}_1 \\ -\mathbf{k}_2 \\ \vdots \\ (-1)^{n-1}\mathbf{k}_n \end{bmatrix} \tag{4.94}$$

If the system 4.51 is uniformly controllable on $[t_0, t_f]$ rank $\mathbf{Q}_c(t_1) = n$ for all t_1 on $[t_0, t_f]$. In this case, a solution of Eq. 4.93 for the nm-vector $\mathbf{k}$ can be determined in terms of $\mathbf{x}_1^{(+)} - \mathbf{x}_1^{(-)}$, $\mathbf{Q}_c(t_1)$, and $n(m - 1)$ arbitrarily chosen values of $\mathbf{k}$.

One approach to obtaining the solution of Eq. 4.93 that provides the simplest form for the input $\mathbf{u}(t)$ prescribed in Eq. 4.87, in the sense that $\mathbf{u}(t)$ is in terms of the lowest possible derivatives of the impulses $\delta(t - \tau)$, is as follows:

(i) Form the nonsingular $n \times n$ matrix $\hat{\mathbf{Q}}_c(t_1)$ from the first n linearly independent columns of the controllability matrix $\mathbf{Q}_c(t_1)$.

(ii) Form the n-vector $\hat{\mathbf{k}}$ from the n components of the nm-vector $\mathbf{k}$ corresponding in position to the n columns of $\hat{\mathbf{Q}}_c(t_1)$ in the nm columns of $\mathbf{Q}_c(t_1)$.

(iii) Arbitralily select the other $(n - 1)m$ components of the nm-vector $\mathbf{k}$ to be zero.

(iv) Equation 4.93 can now be written as

$$\mathbf{x}_1^{(+)} - \mathbf{x}_1^{(-)} = \hat{\mathbf{Q}}_c(t_1)\hat{\mathbf{k}} \tag{4.95}$$

and, since $\hat{\mathbf{Q}}_c(t_1)$ is nonsingular, the solution is

$$\hat{\mathbf{k}} = \hat{\mathbf{Q}}_c^{-1}(t_1)[\mathbf{x}_1^{(+)} - \mathbf{x}_1^{(-)}] \tag{4.96}$$

As an application of these results, it is noted that it is occasionally desirable, particularly in simulation work, to change a problem from one of determining the impulsive response of a quiescent system to one of determining the transient response of an unforced system, and vice versa. In such a situation one seeks a forcing function $\mathbf{u}(t)$ which, when applied to the quiescent system, produces the same response as though the system were "relaxing" from a set of initial conditions $\mathbf{x}(t_0) = \mathbf{x}_0$ with no applied forcing function. Certainly, a forcing function which at time $t = t_0$ instantaneously changes the state of the system from $\mathbf{x}(t_0) = 0$ to $\mathbf{x}(t_0) = \mathbf{x}_0$ would produce the desired effect. Thus $\mathbf{u}(t)$, as prescribed in Eq. 4.87, with the appropriate $\mathbf{k}_i$ determined from Eq. 4.96 can be used.

Example 4.2. It is desired to determine the input $\mathbf{u}(t)$ which when applied to the system characterized by

$$\dot{\mathbf{x}}(t) = \mathbf{A}(t)\mathbf{x}(t) + \mathbf{u}(t)\,, \qquad \mathbf{x}(t_0) = 0$$

responds in a manner identical to the homogeneous system

$$\dot{\mathbf{x}}(t) = \mathbf{A}(t)\mathbf{x}(t)\,, \qquad \mathbf{x}(t_0) = \mathbf{x}_0$$

In this case $\mathbf{B}(t) = \mathbf{I}_n$ and the controllability matrix is

$$\mathbf{Q}_c(t) = [\mathbf{I}_n, \Delta_c\mathbf{I}_n, \cdots, \Delta_c^{n-1}\mathbf{I}_n]$$

Since rank $\mathbf{I}_n = n$, select $\hat{\mathbf{Q}}_c(t) = \mathbf{I}_n$. Thus $\hat{\mathbf{k}} = \mathbf{k}_1$ and $\mathbf{k}_2 = \mathbf{k}_3 = \cdots = \mathbf{0}$. Therefore, in accordance with Eq. 4.96 with $\mathbf{x}_1^{(+)} = \mathbf{x}_0$ and $\mathbf{x}_1^{(-)} = 0$,

$$\hat{\mathbf{k}} = \mathbf{k}_1 = \hat{\mathbf{Q}}_c^{-1}(t_0)\mathbf{x}_0 = \mathbf{x}_0$$

and the form of the input, from Eq. 4.87, is

$$\mathbf{u}(t) = \mathbf{x}_0\delta(t - \tau)$$

4.1.5. Illustrative Examples: Some of the ideas on controllability can be clarified by considering the following specific examples.

Example 4.3. Determine whether or not the time-invariant system is state-controllable or output-controllable.

$$\begin{bmatrix}\dot{x}_1\\ \dot{x}_2\end{bmatrix} = \begin{bmatrix}-5/2 & 3/2\\ -1/2 & -1/2\end{bmatrix}\begin{bmatrix}x_1\\ x_2\end{bmatrix} + \begin{bmatrix}3 & 6\\ 1 & 2\end{bmatrix}\begin{bmatrix}u_1\\ u_2\end{bmatrix}$$

$$\begin{bmatrix}y_1\\ y_2\end{bmatrix} = \begin{bmatrix}1 & -1\\ 1 & -2\end{bmatrix}\begin{bmatrix}x_1\\ x_2\end{bmatrix}$$

To establish state-controllability, construct matrix $\mathbf{Q}_c$ as given by Eq. 4.85:

$$\mathbf{Q}_c = [\mathbf{B}, -\mathbf{AB}] = \begin{bmatrix}3 & 6 & 6 & 12\\ 1 & 2 & 2 & 4\end{bmatrix}$$

Since rank $\mathbf{Q}_c = 1 < 2$, the system is neither uniformly, totally, nor completely state-controllable.

To establish output-controllability, construct matrix $\mathbf{S}_c$ as given by Eq. 4.84:

$$\mathbf{S}_c = \mathbf{C}[\mathbf{B}, -\mathbf{AB}] = \begin{bmatrix} 2 & 4 & 4 & 8 \\ 1 & 2 & 2 & 4 \end{bmatrix}$$

As rank $\mathbf{S}_c = 1 < 2$, the system is neither uniformly, totally, nor completely output-controllable. It can be noted that a minimal nth-order system (i.e., a system with n independent states) with n or more outputs is not output-controllable if it is not state-controllable.

Example 4.4. Determine whether or not the system

$$\begin{bmatrix} \dot{x}_1 \\ \dot{x}_2 \end{bmatrix} = \begin{bmatrix} \sin t & \cos t \\ -\cos t & \sin t \end{bmatrix} \begin{bmatrix} x_1 \\ x_2 \end{bmatrix} + \begin{bmatrix} t \\ t^2 \end{bmatrix} u$$

$$y = [|\sin t| \quad |\cos t|]\mathbf{x}$$

is state-controllable or output-controllable.

To determine state-controllability, construct the controllability matrix $\mathbf{Q}_c(t)$ according to Eq. 4.52:

$$\mathbf{Q}_c(t) = [\mathbf{B}(t), \Delta\mathbf{B}(t)] = \begin{bmatrix} t & -t\sin t - t^2\cos t + 1 \\ t^2 & t\cos t - t^2\sin t + 2t \end{bmatrix}$$

Therefore

$$\det \mathbf{Q}_c(t) = (t^2 + t^4)\cos t + t^2$$

Since $\det \mathbf{Q}_c(t) = \mathbf{0}$ on $[0, \infty)$ only for isolated points of t (almost nowhere), *all* finite intervals $[t_0, t_f]$ contain finite subintervals in which $\det \mathbf{Q}_c(t) \neq 0$. Therefore the system is completely state-controllable on every finite interval $[t_0, t_f]$, and is thus totally state-controllable. However it is not uniformly controllable on $[0, \infty)$; it is uniformly controllable on $(0, \pi/2]$.

For output-controllability construct matrix $\mathbf{S}_c(t)$ as given by Eq. 4.77:

$$\begin{aligned} \mathbf{S}_c(t) &= \mathbf{C}(t_f)[\mathbf{B}(t), \Delta\mathbf{B}(t)] \\ &= [|\sin t_f|\,t + |\cos t_f|\,t^2, |\sin t_f|(1 - t\sin t - t^2\cos t) \\ &\quad + |\cos t_f|(2t - t^2\sin t + t\cos t)] \end{aligned}$$

Since rank $\mathbf{S}_c(t) = 1$ almost everywhere, the system is completely output-controllable on every finite interval $[t_0, t_f]$ and is thus totally output-controllable; it is not uniformly output-controllable on $[0, \infty)$ for the case that $\sin t_f = 0$; it is uniformly output-controllable on $(0, \infty)$ otherwise.

Example 4.5. Consider the system

$$\begin{bmatrix} \dot{x}_1(t) \\ \dot{x}_2(t) \end{bmatrix} = -\begin{bmatrix} a & 0 \\ 0 & b \end{bmatrix} \begin{bmatrix} x_1 \\ x_2 \end{bmatrix} + \begin{bmatrix} f_1(t) \\ f_2(t) \end{bmatrix} u(t), \quad a \neq b$$

where

$$f_1(t) = \sin t \sum_{i=0}^{\infty} (-1)^i \delta^{(-1)}(t - i\pi)$$

$$f_2(t) = f_1(t + \pi)$$

where

$$\delta^{(-1)}(t - \tau) \equiv \begin{cases} 1, & t \geq \tau \\ 0, & t < \tau \end{cases} \equiv \text{unit-step function}$$

Theorem 4.7 is applied to determine whether or not this system is completely state-controllable on $[0, 2\pi]$. Construct the controllability matrix $\mathbf{Q}_c(t)$ according to Eq. 4.52:

$$\mathbf{Q}_c(t) = \begin{bmatrix} f_1(t) & af_1(t) + \dot{f}_1(t) \\ f_2(t) & bf_2(t) + \dot{f}_2(t) \end{bmatrix}$$

Since, at any given instant of time, one row of $\mathbf{Q}_c(t)$ is zero, rank $\mathbf{Q}_c(t) = 1$ almost everywhere. Thus one might erroneously conclude that the system is not state-controllable However, the transition matrix of this system is

$$\phi(t, t_0) = \begin{bmatrix} e^{-a(t-t_0)} & 0 \\ 0 & e^{-b(t-t_0)} \end{bmatrix}$$

Therefore

$$\phi(t_0, t)\mathbf{B}(t) = \begin{bmatrix} e^{-a(t_0-t)}f_1(t) \\ e^{-b(t_0-t)}f_2(t) \end{bmatrix}$$

The rows of $\phi(t_0, t)\mathbf{B}(t)$ are linearly independent. Thus in accordance with Corollary 4.2 the system is completely state-controllable on $[0, 2\pi]$.

It appears that application of Theorems 4.2 and 4.7 produce conflicting results. However, if it is recalled that Theorem 4.7 provides only a sufficiency condition, the discrepancy is resolved. Since the system is not completely controllable on the finite subinterval $[0, \pi]$ of $[0, \infty)$ the system, in accordance with Definition 4.6, is not totally controllable. This result is in accordance with Theorem 4.8 which establishes the necessity of rank $\mathbf{Q}_c(t)$ to be n almost everywhere on $[0, \pi]$ for total controllability on $[0, \pi]$.

Example 4.6. Consider the system with a diagonal **A** matrix:

$$\begin{bmatrix} \dot{x}_1(t) \\ \dot{x}_2(t) \end{bmatrix} = -\begin{bmatrix} a & 0 \\ 0 & b \end{bmatrix} \begin{bmatrix} x_1(t) \\ x_2(t) \end{bmatrix} + \begin{bmatrix} e^{-at} \\ e^{-bt} \end{bmatrix} u(t), \qquad a \neq b$$

The controllability matrix $\mathbf{Q}_c(t)$ is formed:

$$\mathbf{Q}_c(t) = \begin{bmatrix} e^{-at} & 0 \\ e^{-bt} & 0 \end{bmatrix}$$

Intuitively one might guess that this system is totally state-controllable since the input affects each mode independently. However $\mathbf{Q}_c(t)$ has rank $1 < 2$ and thus, in accordance with Theorem 4.8, is not state-controllable. Corroboratively, the rows of

$$\phi(t_0, t)\mathbf{B}(t) = \begin{bmatrix} e^{-at_0} \\ e^{-bt_0} \end{bmatrix}$$

are not linearly independent, since

$$\mathbf{c}'\phi(t_0, t)\mathbf{B}(t) = \mathbf{0}$$

for nonzero

$$\mathbf{c} = \begin{bmatrix} e^{-bt_0} \\ e^{-at_0} \end{bmatrix}$$

Thus, from Corollary 4.2 it is seen that the system is not state-controllable.

This example illustrates that intuition can be misleading when one is working with time-varying systems. As is well known, a linear time-invariant system with a diagonal **A** matrix is always controllable if the **B** matrix has no zero rows. This result is not trivially extended to time-varying systems.

4.2. OBSERVABILITY

Closely related to state-controllability, where the capability of the input $\mathbf{u}(t)$ to excite all the states is considered, is *observability*, where the capability of all the states to excite the output is considered. Therefore, whereas state-controllability is determined from the forced system

$$\dot{\mathbf{x}}(t) = \mathbf{A}(t)\mathbf{x}(t) + \mathbf{B}(t)\mathbf{u}(t) \tag{4.97}$$

independent of the output relation, observability can be determined from the unforced system

$$\begin{aligned} \dot{\mathbf{x}}(t) &= \mathbf{A}(t)\mathbf{x}(t) \\ \mathbf{y}(t) &= \mathbf{C}(t)\mathbf{x}(t) \end{aligned} \tag{4.98}$$

The dual nature of state-controllability and observability becomes apparent from the definitions to be given and the criteria to be derived therefrom.

Definition 4.8. The system characterized by

$$\begin{aligned} \dot{\mathbf{x}}(t) &= \mathbf{A}(t)\mathbf{x}(t) + \mathbf{B}(t)\mathbf{u}(t) \\ \mathbf{y}(t) &= \mathbf{C}(t)\mathbf{x}(t) \end{aligned} \tag{4.99}$$

is said to be *completely observable* if there exists some $t_f > t_0$ such that the initial state $\mathbf{x}(t_0) = \mathbf{x}_0$ of the unforced system can be determined from the knowledge of $\mathbf{y}(t)$ on $[t_0, t_f]$.

Definition 4.9. The system characterized by Eqs. 4.99 is said to be *completely observable on the interval* $[t_0, t_f]$ if, for specified t_0 and

t_f, the initial state $\mathbf{x}(t_0) = \mathbf{x}_0$ of the unforced system can be determined from the knowledge of $\mathbf{y}(t)$ on $[t_0, t_f]$.

Definition 4.10. The system characterized by Eqs. 4.99 is said to be *totally observable on the interval* $[t_0, t_f]$ if it is completely observable on every subinterval of $[t_0, t_f]$; it is *totally observable at* t_f if, for a given t_f, it is completely observable on every finite interval $[t_0, t_f]$.

Definition 4.11. The system characterized by Eqs. 4.99 is said to be *totally observable from* t_0 if, for all $t_f > t_0$, it is completely observable on $[t_0, t_f]$.

In view of Definitions 4.8, 4.9, 4.10, and 4.11, an interpretation of the degrees of observability, quite analogous to the situation for state-controllability, is applicable. A system whose initial state $\mathbf{x}(t_0)$ can be determined from knowledge of the output $\mathbf{y}(t)$ on the finite interval $[t_0, t_f]$, where t_f is *any* unspecified time greater than t_0, is said to be completely observable on $[t_0, t_f]$; a system whose initial state $\mathbf{x}(t_1)$ can be determined from knowledge of the output $\mathbf{y}(t)$ on any finite interval $[t_1, t_2]$ for all t_1 and t_2 on $[t_0, t_f]$, $t_1 < t_2$, is said to be totally observable on $[t_0, t_f]$. Thus complete observability implies that the initial state $\mathbf{x}(t_0)$ can be determined from knowledge of the output $\mathbf{y}(t)$ for an unspecified finite time $[t_0, t_f]$ no matter how long, whereas total observability implies that the initial state $\mathbf{x}(t_0)$ can be determined from knowledge of the output $\mathbf{y}(t)$ for any prespecified finite time $[t_0, t_f]$ no matter how small. It follows from the concept of uniform controllability that *uniform observability* should be defined so that the state $\mathbf{x}(t_0)$ can be determined instantaneously from a knowledge of the output $\mathbf{y}(t_0)$ at the instant $t = t_0$.

A condition for observability, which leads to the duality of state-controllability and observability, is now established:

Theorem 4.13. The system characterized by Eqs. 4.99 is completely observable on the interval $[t_0, t_f]$ if and only if the columns $\mathbf{C}(t)\phi(t, t_0)$ are linearly independent on $[t_0, t_f]$.

Proof. (i) *Sufficiency* is established by noting that the state of the unforced system is

$$\mathbf{x}(t) = \phi(t, t_0)\mathbf{x}(t_0) \tag{4.100}$$

and thus the output of the unforced system is

$$\mathbf{y}(t) = \mathbf{C}(t)\phi(t, t_0)\mathbf{x}(t_0) \tag{4.101}$$

Premultiplying Eq. 4.101 by $\phi'(t, t_0)\mathbf{C}'(t)$ and integrating on $[t_0, t_f]$ gives

$$\int_{t_0}^{t_f} \phi'(t, t_0)\mathbf{C}'(t)\mathbf{y}(t)dt = \left[\int_{t_0}^{t_f} \phi'(t, t_0)\mathbf{C}'(t)\mathbf{C}(t)\phi(t, t_0)dt\right]\mathbf{x}(t_0) \tag{4.102}$$

Defining,

$$\mathbf{N}(t_0, t_f) \equiv \int_{t_0}^{t_f} \phi(t, t_0)\mathbf{C}'(t)\mathbf{C}(t)\phi(t, t_0)\, dt \tag{4.103}$$

results in

$$\int_{t_0}^{t_f} \phi'(t, t_0)\mathbf{C}'(t)\mathbf{y}(t)\, dt = \mathbf{N}(t_0, t_f)\mathbf{x}(t_0) \tag{4.104}$$

It can be deduced that $\mathbf{N}(t_0, t_f)$ is nonsingular if and only if the columns of $\mathbf{C}(t)\phi(t, t_0)$ are linearly independent. Thus, in this case, the state $\mathbf{x}(t_0)$ can be determined from knowledge of $\mathbf{y}(t)$ on the interval $[t_0, t_f]$:

$$\mathbf{x}(t_0) = \mathbf{N}^{-1}(t_0, t_f) \int_{t_0}^{t_f} \phi'(t_0, t_f)\mathbf{C}'(t)\mathbf{y}(t)dt \tag{4.105}$$

(ii) *Necessity* is established by noting that if the columns of $\mathbf{C}(t)\phi(t, t_0)$ are not linearly independent, then there exists a nonzero states $\mathbf{x}(t_0)$ such that $\mathbf{y}(t) = 0$ on $[t_0, t_f]$. Thus the states producing this output $\mathbf{y}(t) = 0$ cannot be observed. Q.E.D.

Corollary 4.13. The system characterized by Eqs. 4.99 is completely observable on the interval $[t_0, t_f]$ if and only if the $n \times n$ matrix $\mathbf{N}(t_0, t_f)$ defined by Eq. 4.103 is nonsingular. From Definition 4.10 on total observability, the following theorem is deduced.

Theorem 4.14. The system characterized by Eqs. 4.99 is totally observable on the interval $[t_0, t_f]$ if the columns of $\mathbf{C}(t)\phi(t, t_0)$ are linearly independent on every subinterval of $[t_0, t_f]$.

Corollary 4.14. The system characterized by Eqs. 4.99 is totally observable on $[t_0, t_f]$ if the $n \times n$ matrix $\mathbf{N}(t_1, t_2)$ defined by Eq. 4.103 is nonsingular for every t_1 on $[t_0, t_f]$ and every $t_2 > t_1$ on $[t_0, t_f]$.

Theorem 4.13 (and its associated corollary) pertaining to observability bears a striking resemblance to Theorem 4.2 (and its associated corollary) pertaining to state-controllability. The similarity between these two theorems is used to formalize the dual relation between observability and state-controllability as follows [11]:

Theorem 4.15. The system characterized by Eq. 4.99 is completely observable on $[t_0, t_f]$ if and only if the adjoint system

$$\begin{aligned} \dot{\mathbf{x}}^*(t) &= -\mathbf{A}'(t)\mathbf{x}^*(t) \pm \mathbf{C}'(t)\mathbf{u}^*(t) \\ \mathbf{y}^*(t) &= \mp \mathbf{B}(t)\mathbf{x}^*(t) \end{aligned} \tag{4.106}$$

is completely state-controllable on $[t_0, t_f]$[4].

[4]A theorem linking the observability of a system to the state-controllability of the *dual system* can also be established (see Prob. 20).

Proof. System 4.99 is completely observable, in accordance with Theorem 4.13, if and only if the columns of $\mathbf{C}(t)\phi(t, t_0)$ are linearly independent. The adjoint system is completely state-controllable, in accordance with Corollary 4.2, if and only if the rows of $\phi^*(t_0, t)\mathbf{C}'(t)$ are linearly independent. From Eq. 3.75a it is noted that $\phi^*(t_0, t) = \phi'(t, t_0)$. Thus the adjoint system is completely state-controllable if and only if the rows of $\phi'(t, t_0)\mathbf{C}'(t)$ are linearly independent, or equivalently, if and only if the columns of $\mathbf{C}(t)\phi(t, t_0)$ are linearly independent. Thus the necessary and sufficient conditions for complete observability of a system are identical to the necessary and sufficient conditions for complete state-controllability of the adjoint system. Q.E.D.

Corollary 4.15. The system characterized by Eqs. 4.99 is totally observable on $[t_0, t_f]$ if and only if the adjoint system is totally state-controllable on $[t_0, t_f]$.

Theorem 4.15 is of great significance in that all the criteria used to determine whether or not a system is state-controllable can now be used to determine whether or not a system is observable. Namely, Theorems 4.7 and 4.8 and their associated corollaries can now be applied in determining observability. Therefore Theorem 4.15 establishes the dual relationship between observability and state-controllability. It is important to note that there is no physically meaningful dual to the concept of output-controllability.

For the sake of notational simplicity in the sequel, the *observability matrix* $\mathbf{Q}_0(t)$ is defined as the controllability matrix of the adjoint system 4.106, i.e.,

$$\begin{aligned}\mathbf{Q}_0(t) &\equiv \mathbf{Q}_c^*(t)\\ &= [\mathbf{C}'(t), \Delta_0\mathbf{C}'(t), \cdots, \Delta_0^{n-1}\mathbf{C}'(t)]\end{aligned} \tag{4.107}$$

where

$$\Delta_0 \equiv \mathbf{A}'(t) + \frac{d}{dt} \tag{4.108}$$

Therefore the duals of Theorems 4.7 and 4.8 can be written in terms of the observability matrix $\mathbf{Q}_0(t)$ and provide the algebraic criteria for determining whether or not a system is obsevable:

Theorem 4.16. The system characterized by Eqs. 4.99 with $\mathbf{A}(t)$, $\mathbf{C}(t)$ differentiable $n - 2$, $n - 1$ times almost everywhere on $[t_0, t_f]$ is completely observable on $[t_0, t_f]$ if the $n \times nr$ observability matrix $\mathbf{Q}_0(t)$ has rank n almost everywhere on some finite subinterval of the interval $[t_0, t_f]$.

Theorem 4.17. The system characterized by Eqs. 4.99 with $\mathbf{A}(t)$, $\mathbf{C}(t)$ differentiable $n - 2$, $n - 1$ times on $[t_0, t_f]$ is totally observable on

$[t_0, t_f]$ if and only if the $n \times nr$ observability matrix $\mathbf{Q}_0(t)$ has rank n almost everywhere on the interval $[t_0, t_f]$.

Having defined the observability matrix as the dual of the controllability matrix suggests the definition for *uniform observability*:

Definition 4.12. The system characterized by Eqs. 4.99 is said to be *uniformly observable* on $[t_0, t_f]$ if the observability matrix $\mathbf{Q}_0(t)$ has rank n everywhere on $[t_0, t_f]$.

In Sec. 4.1.4 it is shown that if a system is uniformly state-controllable, then the state of the system can be transferred an arbitrary amount instantaneously. A dual result for uniform observability is also established. Specifically, if a system is uniformly observable its state $\mathbf{x}(t_1)$ at the instant $t = t_1$ can be determined from knowledge of the system output $\mathbf{y}(t_1)$ at that instant. This is demonstrated by noting that for the homogeneous system, the output

$$\mathbf{y}(t) = \mathbf{C}(t)\mathbf{x}(t) \tag{4.109}$$

can be differentiated $n - 1$ times to give

$$\begin{aligned} \mathbf{y}(t) &= \mathbf{C}(t)\mathbf{x}(t) = [\mathbf{C}'(t)]'\mathbf{x}(t) \\ y^{(1)}(t) &= \mathbf{C}(t)\mathbf{A}(t)\mathbf{x}(t) + \mathbf{C}^{(1)}(t)\mathbf{x}(t) = [\Delta_0\mathbf{C}'(t)]'\mathbf{x}(t) \\ &\vdots \\ \mathbf{y}^{(n-1)}(t) &= [\Delta_0^{n-1}\mathbf{C}'(t)]'\mathbf{x}(t) \end{aligned} \tag{4.110}$$

or simply

$$\begin{bmatrix} \mathbf{y}(t) \\ \mathbf{y}^{(1)}(t) \\ \vdots \\ \mathbf{y}^{(n-1)}(t) \end{bmatrix} = \mathbf{Q}_0'(t)\mathbf{x}(t) \tag{4.111}$$

If the system is uniformly observable on $[t_0, t_f]$, then $\mathbf{Q}_0(t)$ has rank n everywhere on $[t_0, t_f]$, and thus the $n \times n$ matrix $\mathbf{Q}_0(t)\mathbf{Q}_0'(t)$ is nonsingular. Therefore, premultiplying Eq. 4.111 by $\mathbf{Q}_0(t)$ enables the state $\mathbf{x}(t_1)$ to be determined from a knowledge of the output $\mathbf{y}(t_1)$:

$$\mathbf{x}(t_1) = [\mathbf{Q}_0(t_1)\mathbf{Q}_0'(t_1)]^{-1} \begin{bmatrix} \mathbf{y}(t_1) \\ \mathbf{y}^{(1)}(t_1) \\ \vdots \\ y^{(n-1)}(t_1) \end{bmatrix} \tag{4.112}$$

REFERENCES

[1] Athans, M., and P. Falb, *Optimal Control*, McGraw-Hill, New York, 1966.

[2] Chang, A., "An Algebraic Characterization of Controllability," *IEEE Trans. on Automatic Control*, vol. AC-10, no. 1 (1965), pp. 112–113.

[3] D'Angelo, H., "Conversion of Initial Conditions in Linear Time-Varying Systems," *IEEE Trans. on Circuit Theory*, vol. CT-14, no. 4 (1967).

[4] DeRusso, P., R. Roy, and C. Close, *State Variables for Engineers*, Wiley New York, 1965.

[5] Gilbert, E. G., "Controllability and Observability in Multivariable Control Systems," *J. SIAM Control*, vol. 2, no. 1 (1963), pp. 128–151.

[6] Haynes, G., "Controllability of Nonlinear Systems," *NASA Report No. NASA-456*, Martin-Marietta Corp., Denver, Colo., for Ames Research Center, April 1966.

[7] Herman, R., "On the Accessibility Problem in Control Theory," in J. P. LaSalle and S. Lefschetz (eds.), *Proceedings International Symposium on Nonlinear Differential Equations and Nonlinear Mechanics*, Academic Press, New York, 1963.

[8] Hermes, H., "Controllability and the Singular Problem," *J. SIAM Control*, vol. 2, no. 2 (1965), pp. 241–260.

[9] Kalman, R., "On the General Theory of Control Systems," *Proceedings First International Congress of the International Federation of Automatic Control*, Butterworth, London, 1961, pp. 481–492.

[10] Kalman, R., Y. C. Ho, and K. Narendra, "Controllability of Linear Dynamical Systems," *Contributions to Differential Equations*, vol. 1, no. 2 (1962), pp. 189–213.

[11] Kalman, R., "Mathematical Description of Linear Dynamical Systems," *J. SIAM Control*, vol. 1, no. 2 (1963), pp. 152–192.

[12] Kreindler, E., and P. Sarachik, "On the Concepts of Controllability and Observability of Linear Systems," *IEEE Trans. on Automatic Control*, vol. AC-9 (1964), pp. 129–136.

[13] Luenberger, D., "Observers for Multivariable Systems," *IEEE Trans. on Automatic Control*, vol. AC-11, no. 2 (1966), pp. 190–197.

[14] Schwarz, R., and B. Friedland, *Linear Systems*, McGraw-Hill, New York, 1965.

[15] Silverman, L., and H. Meadows, "Controllability and Time-Variable Unilateral Network," *IEEE Trans. on Circuit Theory*, vol. CT-12, no. 3 (1965), pp. 308–314.

[16] Silverman, L., and H. Meadows, "Degrees of Controllability in Time-Variable Linear Systems," *Proceedings National Electronics Conference*, November 1965, pp. 689–693.

[17] Silverman, L., *Representation and Realization of Time-Variable Linear* Systems, Technical Report No. 94, Dept. Electrical Engineering, Columbia University, New York, June 1966.

[18] Silverman, L., and H. Meadows, "Controllability and Observability in Time-Variable Linear Systems," *J. SIAM Control*, vol. 5, no. 1 (1967).

[19] Stubberud, A., "A Controllability Criterion for a Class of Linear Systems," *IEEE Trans. on Applications and Industry*, vol. 68 (1964), pp. 411–413.

[20] Solodov, A., "Conversion of Output Initial Conditions in a Linear Sys-

tem with Variable Parameters," *Automation and Remote Control*, vol. 19 (1958), pp. 645–651.

[21] Weiss, L., and R. Kalman, "Contributions to Linear System Theory," *International Journal of Engineering Science*, vol. 3 (1965), pp. 141–171.

[22] Zadeh, L., "Initial Conditions in Linear Varying-Parameter Systems", *J. Appl. Physics*, vol. 22 (1951), pp. 782–786.

[23] Zadeh, L., and C. Desoer, *Linear System Theory: The State Space Approach*, McGraw-Hill, New York, 1963.

PROBLEMS

4.1 Give an example of a third-order system which is not state-controllable, but is output-controllable. Do not give a system (such as the one of Fig. 4.1) in which two states, starting from equal initial conditions, are identical.

4.2 Show that $\mathbf{T}(t) = \phi^{-1}(t, t_0)$ is an equivalence transformation relating the systems characterized by Eq. 4.1 and 4.2 ($\phi(t, t_0)$ is the transition matrix of system 4.1).

4.3 Show that if an $n \times n$ matrix $\mathbf{M}$ is singular, then there is a nonzero n-vector $\mathbf{c}$ such that $\mathbf{c}'\mathbf{M} = 0$.

4.4 Prove Corollary 4.1.

4.5 Prove Corollary 4.2.

4.6 Give a detailed proof of Theorem 4.3.

4.7 Prove Corollary 4.3.

4.8 Give a detailed proof of Theorem 4.4.

4.9 Prove Corollary 4.4.

4.10 Verify that Eqs. 4.40 are a direct consequence of Eqs. 4.39.

4.11 Given that the $n \times m$ matrix $\mathbf{H}(t)$ has no zero rows and $\mathbf{W}_n(t)\mathbf{H}(t) = 0$, where $\mathbf{W}_n(t)$ is an $n \times n$ matrix, show that rank $\mathbf{W}_n(t) < n$.

4.12 Prove Theorem 4.8.

4.13 Prove Corollary 4.11.

4.14 Prove Corollary 4.12.

4.15 Prove Corollary 4.13.

4.16 Prove Theorem 4.14.

4.17 Prove Corollary 4.14.

4.18 Determine the input $\mathbf{u}(t)$ which when applied to the system characterized by

$$\begin{bmatrix} \dot{x}_1(t) \\ \dot{x}_2(t) \end{bmatrix} = \begin{bmatrix} -1 + e^{-t} & e^{-3t} \\ e^{-4t} & -2 + e^{-2t} \end{bmatrix} \begin{bmatrix} x_1(t) \\ x_2(t) \end{bmatrix} + \begin{bmatrix} 1 + t & 1 + t \\ 2 + \sin t & 2 + \sin t \end{bmatrix} \begin{bmatrix} u_1(t) \\ u_2(t) \end{bmatrix}$$

with zero initial conditions, $\mathbf{x}(t_0) = \mathbf{0}$, responds in a manner identical to the corresponding homogeneous system with $\mathbf{x}'(t_0) = [1, 2]$, $t_0 > 0$.

4.19 Show that $\mathbf{N}(t_0, t_f)$, as defined by Eq. 4.103, is nonsingular if and only if the columns of $\mathbf{C}(t)\boldsymbol{\phi}(t, t_0)$ are linearly independent.

4.20 Theorem 4.15 relates the observability of a system to the state-controllability of the *adjoint* system. State and prove a theorem relating the observability of a system to the state-controllability of the *dual* system.

4.21 Show that if the $n \times rn$ matrix $\mathbf{Q}_0(t)$ has rank n everywhere on $[t_0, t_f]$. then the $n \times n$ matrix $\mathbf{Q}_0(t)\mathbf{Q}_0'(t)$ is nonsingular everywhere on $[t_0, t_f]$.

5

Equivalent Transformations and Minimal Realizations

In the analysis, synthesis, and identification of linear systems the idea of *minimal system realizations* leading to canonical structures is of great importance. In this setting, the concepts of controllability and observability play major roles. The existence of equivalence transformations for transforming systems into desired canonical structures is investigated, and several methods for determing such transformations are detailed.

5.1. SYSTEM REALIZATIONS

In this chapter the synthesis problem considered is that of realizing a system from its impulsive-response matrix $\Omega(t, \tau)$. As is known, a linear, causal, lumped, time-varying system can be characterized by the finite-dimension state-variable equations

$$\begin{aligned} \dot{\mathbf{x}}(t) &= \mathbf{A}(t)\mathbf{x}(t) + \mathbf{B}(t)\mathbf{u}(t) \\ \mathbf{y}(t) &= \mathbf{C}(t)\mathbf{x}(t) \end{aligned} \tag{5.1}$$

and has the impulsive-response matrix

$$\Omega(t, \tau) = \mathbf{C}(t)\phi(t, \tau)\mathbf{B}(\tau) \tag{5.2}$$

The system with impulsive response $\Omega(t, \tau)$ is said to be *realized* by the system with finite-dimension coefficient matrices $\mathbf{A}(t)$, $\mathbf{B}(t)$, $\mathbf{C}(t)$. Clearly, using analog-computer techniques, the synthesis of a system with the structure shown in Fig. 3.3 is a simple matter, once the matrices $\mathbf{A}(t)$, $\mathbf{B}(t)$, $\mathbf{C}(t)$ are known. Thus the problem of synthesizing a linear system from its impulsive-response matrix $\Omega(t, \tau)$ is essentially the problem of determining the matrices $\mathbf{A}(t)$, $\mathbf{B}(t)$, $\mathbf{C}(t)$ from the impulsive-response matrix. The problem is complicated by the fact that a realization of a given impulsive response is not unique, i.e., the order of the various systems giving identical impulsive-response matrices need not be the same. Any system realizing $\Omega(t, \tau)$ with a state vector of minimum dimension is said to be a *minimal realization* of $\Omega(t, \tau)$.

Important in this synthesis problem is being able to predict whether or not a given impulsive-response matrix 5.2 can be realized by the finite-dimensional system 5.1 [2].

Theorem 5.1. The impulsive-response matrix $\Omega(t, \tau)$ is realizable by the finite-dimensional system 5.1 if and only if there exists continuous matrices $\mathbf{P}(t)$ and $\mathbf{Q}(\tau)$ such that

$$\Omega(t, \tau) = \mathbf{P}(t)\mathbf{Q}(\tau) \tag{5.3}$$

for all $t \geqslant \tau$.

Proof. (i) *Necessity* is established by substituting from Eq. 3.20, with $t_1 = t_0$, in Eq. 5.2:

$$\Omega(t, \tau) = \mathbf{C}(t)\phi(t, t_0)\phi(t_0, \tau)\mathbf{B}(\tau)\,, \qquad t \geqslant t_0 \geqslant \tau \tag{5.4}$$

Thus

$$\mathbf{P}(t) = \mathbf{C}(t)\phi(t, t_0)\,, \qquad t \geqslant t_0 \tag{5.5}$$

and

$$\mathbf{Q}(\tau) = \phi(t_0, \tau)\mathbf{B}(\tau)\,, \qquad t_0 \geqslant \tau \tag{5.6}$$

(ii) *Sufficiency* is established by constructing the system such that $\mathbf{A}(t) = \mathbf{0}$, $\mathbf{B}(t) = \mathbf{Q}(t)$ and $\mathbf{C}(t) = \mathbf{P}(t)$:

$$\begin{aligned} \dot{\mathbf{x}}(t) &= \mathbf{Q}(t)\mathbf{u}(t) \\ \mathbf{y}(t) &= \mathbf{P}(t)\mathbf{x}(t) \end{aligned} \tag{5.7}$$

Noting that for this system $\phi(t, \tau) = \mathbf{I}_n$, the impulsive response, in accordance with Eq. 5.2, is $\Omega(t, \tau) = \mathbf{P}(t)\mathbf{Q}(\tau)$. Q.E.D.

It can be noted that the impulsive-response matrix of any distributed-parameter system cannot be decomposed in the form of Eq. 5.3 and, as is well known, cannot be characterized by system 5.1.

5.2. A CANONICAL STRUCTURE [2]

From the definitions of controllability and observability it is deduced that portions of a system that are either not completely controllable[1], not

[1]As is the common usage, completely controllable will be understood to be completely state-controllable.

completely observable, or not completely controllable and not completely observable on the interval $[t_0, t_f]$, do not contribute to the impulsive-response matrix on $[t_0, t_f]$: i.e., the input-output transmission of these portions of the system is zero almost everywhere on the interval $[t_0, t_f]$. Thus it follows that a system that is a minimal realization of a given impulsive-response matrix on an interval $[t_0, t_f]$ is both completely controllable and completely observable on $[t_0, t_f]$. in the sequel, it is shown that the converse (i.e., that a system that is both completely controllable and completely observable is a minimal realization) does *not* necessarily follow.

The idea of applying equivalence transformations to separate a system on the basis of controllability and observability of the various portions of the system is introduced here. The discussion of controllability and observability of a *portion* of a system is greatly facilitated by defining controllability and observability of the state components $x_i(t)$, $i = 1, \cdots, n$.

Definition 5.1. A *state component* $x_i(t)$ is completely controllable on $[t_0, t_f]$ if there exists a bounded input function $\mathbf{u}(t)$ that transfers any state component $x_i(t_0)$ to any state component $x_i(t_f)$; otherwise the state component $x_i(t)$ is *uncontrollable*.

Definition 5.2. A *state component* $x_i(t)$ is completely observable on $[t_0, t_f]$ if changes in the state component $x_i(t)$ always produce a change in the output $\mathbf{y}(t)$; otherwise the state component is *unobservable*.

The definitions of *un*controllable and *un*observable *state components* lead to a definition of uncontrollable and unobservable *systems*.

Definition 5.3. A system is *uncontrollable* (*unobservable*) if and only if no state component is controllable (observable).

It is important to note that a distinction is being made between a system that is *not controllable* (at least one state component is uncontrollable) and a system that is *uncontrollable* (all state components are uncontrollable).

A canonical structure for linear systems is introduced by partitioning the state variables into four groups:

$$\mathbf{x}(t) = \begin{bmatrix} \mathbf{x}_1(t) \\ \mathbf{x}_2(t) \\ \mathbf{x}_3(t) \\ \mathbf{x}_4(t) \end{bmatrix} \tag{5.8}$$

where

(i) $\mathbf{x}_1(t)$ are the state components that are controllable but unobservable,

(ii) $\mathbf{x}_2(t)$ are the state components that are controllable and observable,

(iii) $\mathbf{x}_3(t)$ are the state components that ars uncontrollable and unobservable,

(iv) $\mathbf{x}_4(t)$ are the state components that are uncontrollable but observable.

Such a system can be represented by the canonical structure of Fig. 5.1.

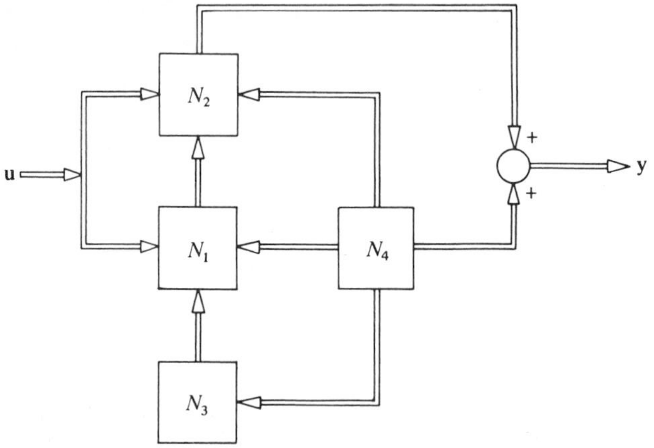

Fig. 5.1. A canonical structure for a linear system corresponding to Eqs. 5.09 and 5.10.

The equations corresponding to the canonical system of Fig. 5.1 are

$$\begin{aligned} N_1:\dot{\mathbf{x}}_1(t) &= \mathbf{A}_{11}(t)\mathbf{x}_1(t) + \mathbf{A}_{12}(t)\mathbf{x}_2(t) + \mathbf{A}_{13}(t)\mathbf{x}_3(t) + \mathbf{A}_{14}(t)\mathbf{x}_4(t) \\ &\quad + \mathbf{B}_1(t)\mathbf{u}(t) \\ N_2:\dot{\mathbf{x}}_2(t) &= \mathbf{A}_{22}(t)\mathbf{x}_2(t) + \mathbf{A}_{24}(t)\mathbf{x}_4(t) + \mathbf{B}_2(t)\mathbf{u}(t) \\ N_3:\dot{\mathbf{x}}_3(t) &= \mathbf{A}_{33}(t)\mathbf{x}_3(t) + \mathbf{A}_{34}(t)\mathbf{x}_4(t) \\ N_4:\dot{\mathbf{x}}_4(t) &= \mathbf{A}_{44}(t)\mathbf{x}_4(t) \end{aligned} \tag{5.9a}$$

$$\mathbf{y}(t) = \mathbf{C}_2(t)\mathbf{x}_2(t) + \mathbf{C}_4(t)\mathbf{x}_4(t) \tag{5.9b}$$

or, in matrix form,

$$\begin{bmatrix} \dot{\mathbf{x}}_1(t) \\ \dot{\mathbf{x}}_2(t) \\ \dot{\mathbf{x}}_3(t) \\ \dot{\mathbf{x}}_4(t) \end{bmatrix} = \begin{bmatrix} \mathbf{A}_{11}(t) & \mathbf{A}_{12}(t) & \mathbf{A}_{13}(t) & \mathbf{A}_{14}(t) \\ \mathbf{0} & \mathbf{A}_{22}(t) & \mathbf{0} & \mathbf{A}_{24}(t) \\ \mathbf{0} & \mathbf{0} & \mathbf{A}_{33}(t) & \mathbf{A}_{43}(t) \\ \mathbf{0} & \mathbf{0} & \mathbf{0} & \mathbf{A}_{44}(t) \end{bmatrix} \begin{bmatrix} \mathbf{x}_1(t) \\ \mathbf{x}_2(t) \\ \mathbf{x}_3(t) \\ \mathbf{x}_4(t) \end{bmatrix} + \begin{bmatrix} \mathbf{B}_1(t) \\ \mathbf{B}_2(t) \\ \mathbf{0} \\ \mathbf{0} \end{bmatrix} \mathbf{u}(t) \tag{5.10a}$$

$$\mathbf{y}(t) = [\mathbf{0}\ \mathbf{C}_2(t)\ \mathbf{0}\ \mathbf{C}_4(t)] \begin{bmatrix} \mathbf{x}_1(t) \\ \mathbf{x}_2(t) \\ \mathbf{x}_3(t) \\ \mathbf{x}_4(t) \end{bmatrix} \tag{5.10b}$$

Example 5.1[2]**.** The state-variable differential equations for the constant-resistance network shown in Fig. 5.2 are

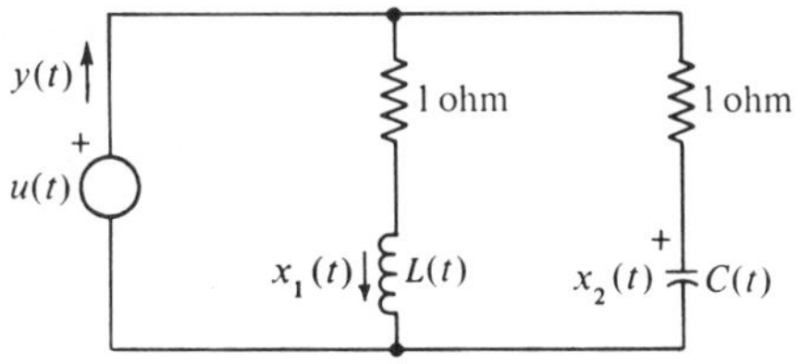

Fig. 5.2. The constant-resistance network.

$$\dot{x}_1(t) = -\frac{1}{L(t)}\left(1 + \frac{dL(t)}{dt}\right)x_1(t) + \frac{1}{L(t)}u(t)$$
$$\dot{x}_2(t) = -\frac{1}{C(t)}\left(1 + \frac{dC(t)}{dt}\right)x_2(t) + \frac{1}{C(t)}u(t)$$
$$y(t) = x_1(t) - x_2(t) + u(t)$$

or, in matrix form,

$$\begin{bmatrix}\dot{x}_1(t)\\ \dot{x}_2(t)\end{bmatrix} = \begin{bmatrix}-\frac{1}{L(t)}\left(1 + \frac{dL(t)}{dt}\right) & 0\\ 0 & -\frac{1}{C(t)}\left(1 + \frac{dC(t)}{dt}\right)\end{bmatrix}\begin{bmatrix}x_1(t)\\ x_2(t)\end{bmatrix} + \begin{bmatrix}\frac{1}{L(t)}\\ \frac{1}{C(t)}\end{bmatrix}u(t)$$
$$y(t) = [1 \quad -1]\begin{bmatrix}x_1(t)\\ x_2(t)\end{bmatrix} + u(t)$$

Take $L(t) = C(t)$ and define a new set of state variables:

$$z_1 = \tfrac{1}{2}(x_1 + x_2)$$
$$z_2 = \tfrac{1}{2}(x_1 - x_2)$$

Therefore

$$\begin{bmatrix}\dot{z}_1(t)\\ \dot{z}_2(t)\end{bmatrix} = \begin{bmatrix}-\frac{1}{L(t)}\left(1 + \frac{dL(t)}{dt}\right) & 0\\ 0 & -\frac{1}{L(t)}\left(1 + \frac{dL(t)}{dt}\right)\end{bmatrix}\begin{bmatrix}z_1(t)\\ z_2(t)\end{bmatrix} + \begin{bmatrix}\frac{1}{L(t)}\\ 0\end{bmatrix}u(t)$$
$$y(t) = [0 \quad 2]\begin{bmatrix}z_1(t)\\ z_2(t)\end{bmatrix} + u(t)$$

Thus it is seen that state component $z_1(t)$ is controllable but unobservable, and state component $z_2(t)$ is uncontrollable but observable. The canonical structure of this system is shown in Fig. 5.3.

[2]This example is from Ref. [2].

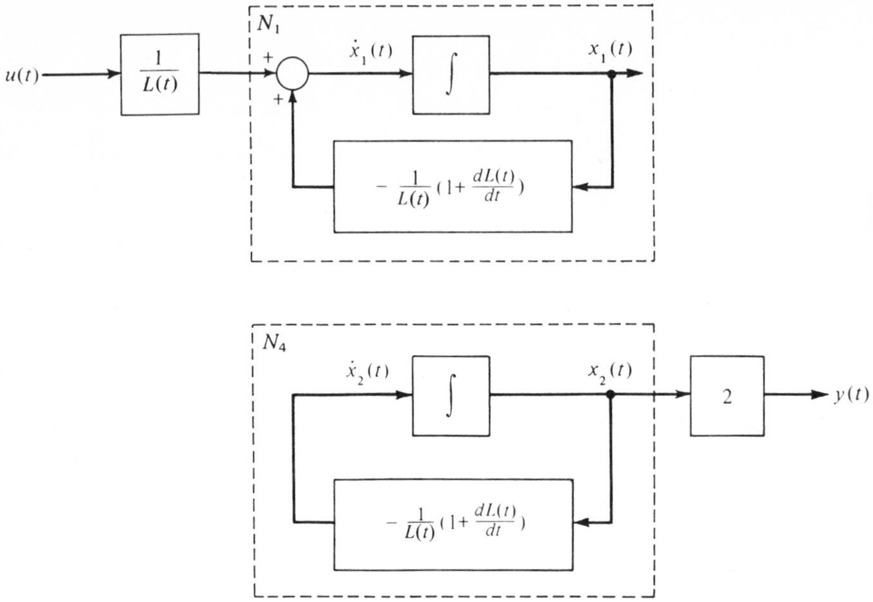

Fig. 5.3. Canonical structure of constant resistance network of Fig. 5.2.

Example 5.2[3]**.** Consider the time-invariant system

$$\dot{\mathbf{x}}(t) = \mathbf{A}\mathbf{x}(t) + \mathbf{B}\mathbf{u}$$

$$\mathbf{y}(t) = \mathbf{C}\mathbf{x}(t)$$

$$\mathbf{A} = \begin{bmatrix} -3 & -3 & 0 & 1 \\ 26 & 36 & -3 & -25 \\ 30 & 39 & -2 & -27 \\ 30 & 43 & -3 & -32 \end{bmatrix}$$

$$\mathbf{B} = \begin{bmatrix} 3 & 3 \\ -2 & -1 \\ 0 & 0 \\ 0 & 1 \end{bmatrix}$$

$$\mathbf{C} = [-5, -8, 1, 5]$$

Introducing the new state variable $\mathbf{z}(t)$ by the nonsingular equivalence transformation $\mathbf{z}(t) = \mathbf{T}\mathbf{x}(t)$, where

$$\mathbf{T} = \begin{bmatrix} 2 & 3 & 0 & -2 \\ 1 & 1 & 0 & -1 \\ -2 & -3 & 0 & 3 \\ -6 & -9 & 1 & 6 \end{bmatrix}$$

[3]This example is from Ref. [2].

and

$$\mathbf{T}^{-1} = \begin{bmatrix} 0 & 3 & 1 & 0 \\ 1 & -2 & 0 & 0 \\ 3 & 0 & 0 & 1 \\ 1 & 0 & 1 & 0 \end{bmatrix}$$

Then

$$\dot{\mathbf{z}}(t) = \mathbf{A}_T\mathbf{z}(t) + \mathbf{B}_T\mathbf{u}(t)$$
$$y(t) = \mathbf{C}_T\mathbf{z}(t)$$

where

$$\mathbf{A}_T = \mathbf{TAT}^{-1} = \begin{bmatrix} 2 & 4 & 1 & -1 \\ 0 & -1 & 0 & 1 \\ 0 & 0 & -3 & -2 \\ 0 & 0 & 0 & 1 \end{bmatrix}$$

$$\mathbf{B}_T = \mathbf{TB} = \begin{bmatrix} 0 & 1 \\ 1 & 1 \\ 0 & 0 \\ 0 & 0 \end{bmatrix}, \qquad \mathbf{C}_T = \mathbf{CT}^{-1} = [0 \quad 1 \quad 0 \quad 1]$$

Thus it is seen that the equivalence transformation $\mathbf{z}(t) = \mathbf{Tx}(t)$ puts the system in the canonical form corresponding to Eqs. 5.10; Fig. 5.4 shows the canonical structure corresponding to Fig. 5.1.

Define still another state variable $\mathbf{w}(t)$ by the nonsingular equivalence transformation $\mathbf{w}(t) = \mathbf{Sx}(t)$, where

$$\mathbf{S} = \begin{bmatrix} 3 & 4 & 0 & -3 \\ 1 & 1 & 0 & -1 \\ -5 & -7.5 & 0.5 & 6 \\ -6 & -9 & 1 & 6 \end{bmatrix}$$

$$\mathbf{S}^{-1} = \begin{bmatrix} 0 & 3 & 1 & -0.5 \\ 1 & -3 & 0 & 0 \\ 3 & -3 & 0 & 1 \\ 1 & -1 & 1 & -0.5 \end{bmatrix}$$

Then

$$\dot{\mathbf{w}}(t) = \mathbf{A}_S\mathbf{w}(t) + \mathbf{B}_S\mathbf{u}(t)$$
$$y(t) = \mathbf{C}_S\mathbf{w}(t)$$

where

$$\mathbf{A}_S = \mathbf{SAS}^{-1} = \begin{bmatrix} 2 & 1 & 1 & -0.5 \\ 0 & -1 & 0 & 1 \\ 0 & 0 & -3 & 0 \\ 0 & 0 & 0 & 1 \end{bmatrix}$$

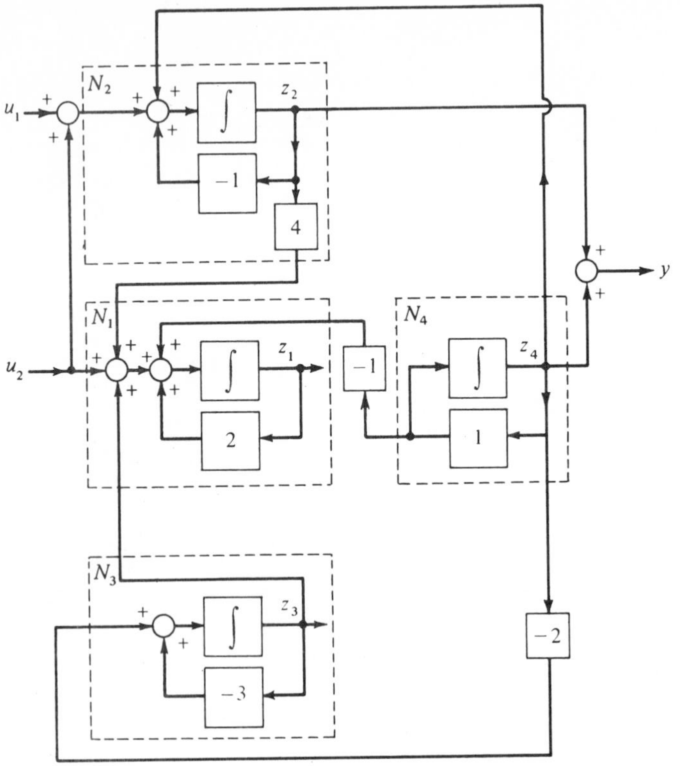

Fig. 5.4. Canonical structure of the system of Example 5.2 corresponding to $\mathbf{z}(t) = \mathbf{T}\mathbf{x}(t)$.

$$\mathbf{B}_S = \mathbf{SB} = \begin{bmatrix} 1 & 2 \\ 1 & 1 \\ 0 & 0 \\ 0 & 0 \end{bmatrix}$$

$$\mathbf{C}_S = \mathbf{CS}^{-1} = [0 \quad 1 \quad 0 \quad 1]$$

Thus it is seen that the transformation $\mathbf{w}(t) = \mathbf{S}\mathbf{x}(t)$ also puts the system in the canonical form of Eq. 5.10b; Fig. 5.5 shows the canonical structure corresponding to Fig. 5.1.

The fact that two distinct equivalence transformations $\mathbf{T}$ and $\mathbf{S}$ have been found to put the system into the canonical form demonstrates that the canonical structure is not unique. It is noted that all the connections between each of the subsystems, as shown in Fig. 5.1 need not be present.

The transfer-function matrix of the system is easily found from either Fig. 5.4 or Fig. 5.5:

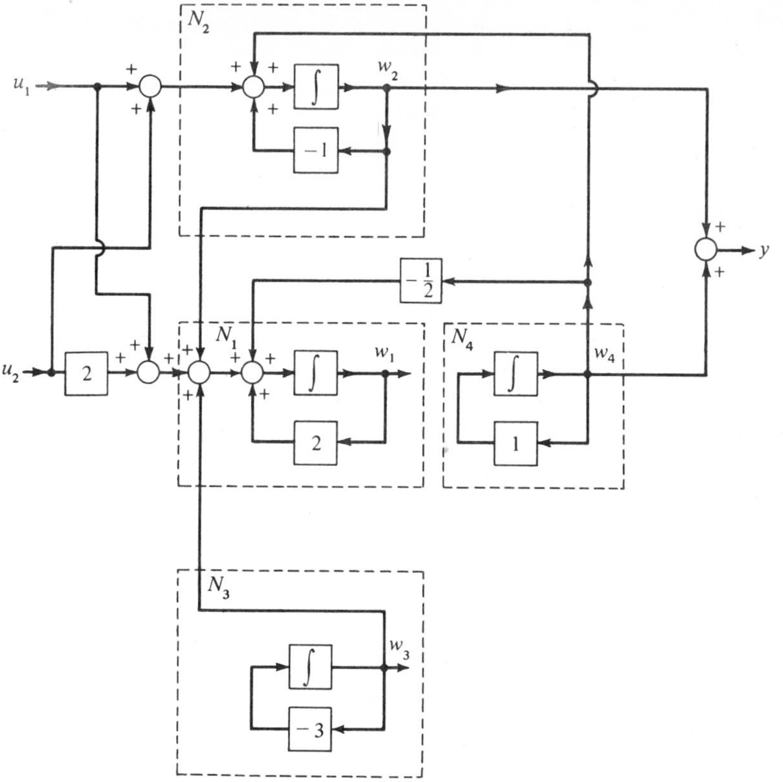

Fig. 5.5. Canonical structure of the system of Example 5.2 corresponding to $\mathbf{w}(t) = S\mathbf{x}(t)$.

$$\mathbf{Z}(s) = \left[\frac{y(s)}{u_1(s)}, \frac{y(s)}{u_2(s)}\right]$$
$$= \left[\frac{1}{s+1}, \frac{1}{s+1}\right]$$

Clearly, only subsystem N_2, the controllable and observable subsystem, affects the input to output transmission. Therefore the transfer-function matrix $Z(s)$ and, more generally, the impulsive-response matrix can be determined from the controllable and observable portion of the system alone.

5.3. REDUCED SYSTEMS [4, 5]

As is seen in the previous section, transforming a system so that it is representable by the canonical structure of Fig. 5.1 can greatly simplify the problems of analysis and synthesis. The uncontrollable subsystems N_3 and N_4 need not be considered in determining the zero-state response of the system states to an arbitrary input $\mathbf{u}(t)$. Similarly, the unobservable subsystems N_1 and N_3 need not be considered in determining the output response of the system due to inputs or initial conditions. In fact, if one is interested only in the input-output relations, i.e., the impulsive-response matrix, of a system, then subsystems N_1, N_3 and N_4 need not be considered; subsystem N_2 alone affects input-output transmission, and thus the impulsive-response matrix. Therefore, effecting an equivalence transformation that gives the *completely* controllable and *completely* observable portion of the system N_2 or equivalently the system characterized by

$$\begin{aligned} \dot{\mathbf{x}}_2(t) &= \mathbf{A}_{22}(t)\mathbf{x}_2(t) + \mathbf{B}_2(t)\mathbf{u}(t) \\ \mathbf{y}(t) &= \mathbf{C}_2(t)\mathbf{x}_2(t) \end{aligned} \tag{5.11}$$

is said to comprise a *global reduction* of the system. Clearly, the system characterized by Eqs. 5.11 of order $n_0 \leq n$ has the same impulsive-response matrix as the original system 5.1 of order n.

5.3.1. Definitions

Definition 5.4. A system is said to be *globally reduced*[4] on an interval $[t_0, t_f]$ if it is both completely state-controllable and completely observable on $[t_0, t_f]$.

It follows from Theorems 4.2 and 4.13, and their associated corollaries, that

Theorem 5.2. A realization of $\Omega(t, \tau)$ is globally reduced on $[t_0, t_f]$ if and only if

$$\begin{aligned} \mathbf{M}(t_0, t_f) &= \int_{t_0}^{t_f} \phi(t_0, t)\mathbf{B}(t)\mathbf{B}'(t)\phi'(t_0, t)\, dt \\ &= \int_{t_0}^{t_f} \mathbf{Q}(t)\mathbf{Q}'(t)\, dt \end{aligned} \tag{5.12}$$

and

$$\begin{aligned} \mathbf{N}(t_0, t_f) &= \int_{t_0}^{t_f} \phi'(t, t_0)\mathbf{C}'(t)\mathbf{C}(t)\phi(t, t_0)\, dt \\ &= \int_{t_0}^{t_f} \mathbf{P}'(t)\mathbf{P}(t)\, dt \end{aligned} \tag{5.13}$$

are nonsingular; $\mathbf{Q}(t)$ and $\mathbf{P}(t)$ are as given in Eqs. 5.5 and 5.6.

[4]It is pointed out that with respect to the system's *weighting pattern* $\Omega_w(t, \tau)$, which is defined for all t and τ but is equal to the impulsive-response matrix $\Omega(t, \tau)$ for $t \geqslant \tau$, a system that is globally reduced is also reduced in the strict sense of being a minimal realization.

Corollary 5.2a. A system is globally reduced on $[t_0, t_f]$ if the columns of $\mathbf{P}(t) = \mathbf{C}(t)\phi(t, t_0)$ and the rows of $\mathbf{Q}(t) = \phi(t_0, t)\mathbf{B}(t)$ are linearly independent on $[t_0, t_f]$, or equivalently, a realization of $\Omega(t, \tau)$ is globally reduced on $[t_0, t_f]$ if and only if for every choice of nonzero vectors **b** and **c**

$$\begin{aligned} \mathbf{P}(t)\mathbf{b} &\neq 0 \\ \mathbf{c}'\mathbf{Q}(t) &\neq \mathbf{0} \end{aligned} \tag{5.14}$$

on some finite subinterval $[t_1, t_2]$ of $[t_0, t_f]$.

Corollary 5.2b. Every realizable $\Omega(t, \tau)$ possesses a globally reduced realization.

To emphasize the possibility that a system that is *globally reduced* might be *reduced* further, *reducibility* is defined and is distinguished from *global reducibility*:

Definition 5.5. A system is said to be *reducible* on an interval $[t_0, t_f]$ if its impulsive-response matrix can be realized on $[t_0, t_f]$ by a system of lower order.

A comparison of Definitions 5.4 and 5.5 show that saying that a system is *reduced* is a stronger statement than saying that a system is *globally reduced*. Practially speaking, a system that is *globally reduced* is often also reduced. However, as an illustration of a system that is globally reduced and yet reducible, consider the following example.

Example 5.3. Global reducibility and reducibility of the following scalar system is investigated on the interval $[t_0, t_f]$.

$$\begin{bmatrix} \dot{x}_1(t) \\ \dot{x}_2(t) \end{bmatrix} = \begin{bmatrix} a & 0 \\ 0 & a \end{bmatrix} \begin{bmatrix} x_1(t) \\ x_2(t) \end{bmatrix} + \begin{bmatrix} b_1(t) \\ b_2(t) \end{bmatrix} u(t)$$

$$y(t) = [1 \;\; c_2(t)] \begin{bmatrix} x_1(t) \\ x_2(t) \end{bmatrix}$$

The time-varying coeffiients are

$$b_1(t) = \begin{cases} 1, & t_0 \leq t < T \\ 0, & T \leq t \leq t_f \end{cases}$$

$$b_2(t) = c_2(t) = \begin{cases} 0, & t_0 \leq t < T \\ 1, & T \leq t \leq t_f \end{cases}$$

and a is a nonzero constant. The transition matrix for this system is readily determined to be

$$\phi(t, t_0) = \begin{bmatrix} e^{a(t-t_0)} & 0 \\ 0 & e^{a(t-t_0)} \end{bmatrix}$$

Thus

$$\phi(t_0, t)\mathbf{B}(t) = \begin{bmatrix} b_1(t)e^{a(t_0-t)} \\ b_2(t)e^{a(t_0-t)} \end{bmatrix} = \mathbf{Q}(t)$$

and

$$\mathbf{C}(t)\phi(t, t_0) = [e^{a(t-t_0)} \quad c_2(t)e^{a(t-t_0)}] = \mathbf{P}(t)$$

Since the rows of $\phi(t_0, t)\mathbf{B}(t)$ and the columns of $\mathbf{C}(t)\phi(t, t_0)$ are linearly independent on $[t_0, t_f]$, it follows that the system is both completely controllable and completely observable on $[t_0, t_f]$ and, in accordance with Corollary 5.4, is globally reduced.

The impulsive response of this system is

$$\begin{aligned} \Omega(t, \tau) &= e^{a(t-\tau)}b_1(\tau) + c_2(t)e^{a(t-\tau)}b_2(\tau) \\ &= e^{a(t-\tau)}, \ t > \tau \end{aligned}$$

Clearly this system is reducible in the sense of Definition 5.5 since it can be realized by the first-order system characterized by

$$\begin{aligned} \dot{x}(t) &= ax(t) + u(t) \\ y(t) &= x(t) \end{aligned}$$

Thus the system described is both globally reduced and reducible.

In view of the preceding example, it is concluded that a globally reduced system is not necessarily a minimal realization of a specified impulsive-response matrix. Whereas *complete* controllability and complete observability are required for a system to be *globally reduced,* it is now shown that a special sequence of the intervals of complete controllability and complete observability are required for a system to be reduced.

5.3.2. Necessary and Sufficient Conditions for Minimal Realizations

Theorem 5.3. An n_0-order system corresponding to the decomposition $\Omega(t, \tau) = \mathbf{P}(t)\mathbf{Q}(\tau)$ is a minimal realization of $\Omega(t, \tau)$ if and only if the n_0 rows of $\mathbf{Q}(\tau)$ are linearly independent on any finite subinterval $[t_1, t_2]$ and the n_0 columns of $\mathbf{P}(t)$ are linearly independent on any finite subinterval $[t_3, t_4]$, where $t_0 \leq t_1 < t_2 \leq t_3 < t_4 \leq t_f$; in this case the integer n_0 is termed the *order* of $\Omega(t, \tau)$ and is the minimum system dimension with which $\Omega(t, \tau)$ can be realized.

Equivalently, a system with impulsive response $\Omega(t, \tau)$ is a minimal realization if and only if there exists a finite subinterval $[t_1, t_2]$ of complete controllability preceding a finite subinterval $[t_3, t_4]$ of complete observability.

Proof. (i) *Sufficiency*: Consider the decomposition

$$\Omega(t, \tau) = \mathbf{P}_0(t)\mathbf{Q}_0(\tau)\delta^{(-1)}(t - \tau) \tag{5.15}$$

such that the n_0 rows of $\mathbf{Q}_0(\tau)$ are linearly independent on $[t_1, t_2]$ and the n_0 columns of $\mathbf{P}_0(t)$ are linearly independent on $[t_3, t_4]$. The $\delta^{(-1)}(t - \tau)$ is the unit-step function defined in Example 4.5; it is included here to emphasize causality which is normally taken for granted and not explicitly stated. Assume the existence of other decompositions of the form $\Omega(t, \tau) = \mathbf{P}(t)\mathbf{Q}(\tau)\delta^{(-1)}(t - \tau)$ where $\mathbf{P}(t)$ and $\mathbf{Q}(\tau)$ have n columns and rows respectively. Thus

$$\mathbf{P}_0(t)\mathbf{Q}_0(\tau)\delta^{(-1)}(t - \tau) = \mathbf{P}(t)\mathbf{Q}(\tau)\delta^{(-1)}(t - \tau) \tag{5.16}$$

Premultiplying both sides of Eq. 5.16 by $\mathbf{P}_0'(t)$ and integrating with respect to t on $[t_3, t_4]$ gives

$$\left[\int_{t_3}^{t_4} \mathbf{P}_0'(t)\mathbf{P}_0(t)\,dt\right]\mathbf{Q}_0(\tau) = \left[\int_{t_3}^{t_4} \mathbf{P}_0'(t)\mathbf{P}(t)dt\right]\mathbf{Q}(\tau), \qquad \tau \le t_3 < t_4 \le t_f \tag{5.17}$$

which, in accordance with Eqs. 5.5 and 4.103 can be written as

$$\left[\int_{t_3}^{t_4} \mathbf{P}_0'(t)\mathbf{P}(t)dt\right]\mathbf{Q}(\tau) = \mathbf{N}(t_3, t_4)\mathbf{Q}_0(\tau),\ \tau \le t_3 \tag{5.18}$$

Since the columns of $\mathbf{P}_0(t)$ are linearly independent on $[t_3, t_4]$, the $n_0 \times n_0$ matrix $\mathbf{N}(t_3, t_4)$ is nonsingular. Thus

$$\mathbf{Q}_0(\tau) = \mathbf{U}(t_3, t_4)\mathbf{Q}(\tau),\ \tau \le t_3 \tag{5.19}$$

where

$$\mathbf{U}(t_3, t_4) = \mathbf{N}^{-1}(t_3, t_4)\int_{t_3}^{t_4} \mathbf{P}_0'(t)\mathbf{P}(t)\,dt\,, \qquad t_0 \le t_3 < t_4 \le t_f \tag{5.20}$$

is an $n_0 \times n$ matrix. Similarly, postmultiplying both sides of Eq. 5.16 by $\mathbf{Q}_0'(\tau)$ and integrating with respect to τ on $[t_1, t_2]$ gives

$$\mathbf{P}_0(t)\int_{t_1}^{t_2} \mathbf{Q}_0(\tau)\mathbf{Q}_0'(\tau)\,d\tau = \mathbf{P}(t)\int_{t_1}^{t_2} \mathbf{Q}(\tau)\mathbf{Q}_0'(\tau)\,d\tau\,, \qquad t_0 \le t_1 < t_2 \le t \tag{5.21}$$

which in accordance with Eqs. 5.6 and 4.20 can be written as

$$\mathbf{P}_0(t)\mathbf{M}(t_1, t_2) = \mathbf{P}(t)\int_{t_1}^{t_2} \mathbf{Q}(\tau)\mathbf{Q}_0'(\tau)\,dt\,, \qquad t_2 \le t \tag{5.22}$$

Since the rows of $\mathbf{Q}_0(\tau)$ are linearly independent on $[t_1, t_2]$, the $n_0 \times n_0$ matrix $\mathbf{M}(t_1, t_2)$ is nonsingular. Thus

$$\mathbf{P}_0(t) = \mathbf{P}(t)\mathbf{V}(t_1, t_2)\,, \qquad t_2 \le t \tag{5.23}$$

where

$$\mathbf{V}(t_1, t_2) = \left[\int_{t_1}^{t_2} \mathbf{Q}(\tau)\mathbf{Q}_0'(\tau)\,d\tau\right]\mathbf{M}^{-1}(t_1, t_2)\,, \qquad t_0 \le t_1 < t_2 \le t_f \tag{5.24}$$

is an $n \times n_0$ matrix. From Eq. 5.19 it is concluded that n_0, the number of linearly independent rows of $\mathbf{Q}_0(\tau)$, cannot exceed rank $\mathbf{U}(t_3, t_4)$ which in turn cannot exceed n, the number of columns of $\mathbf{U}(t_3, t_4)$ and rows of $\mathbf{Q}(\tau)$. Thus

$$n_0 \le \operatorname{rank} \mathbf{U}(t_3, t_4) \le n \tag{5.25a}$$

or simply

$$n_0 \leq n \tag{5.25b}$$

(ii) *Necessity.* For a given realization of the impulsive-response matrix $\Omega(t, \tau)$ only three possibilities exist in which the theorem hypothesis is not satisfied:

(i) The system is not completely controllable on any subinterval. In this case there is at least one state that is never affected by the input and thus it does not affect the impulsive-response matrix. Therefore the system is reducible.

(ii) The system is completely controllable on some subinterval $[t_1, t_2]$ but is not completely observable on any subinterval. In this case there is at least one controlled state that will never affect the output and thus never affect the impulsive-response matrix. Therefore the system is reducible.

(iii) The system is completely controllable on some subinterval $[t_1, t_2]$ and completely observable on the subinterval $[t_3, t_4]$, where the subinterval $[t_3, t_4]$ completely precedes the subinterval $[t_1, t_2]$. In this case prior to, and during, the interval of complete observability there is at least one state that is never affected by the input. Thus the system is reducible on $[t_0, t_4]$. After t_4 the period of complete controllability $[t_1, t_2]$ occurs. However, from t_4 on the system is never completely observable. Therefore, during this period at least one state cannot be observed and thus the system is reducible on $(t_4, t_f]$. Thus the system is reducible on $[t_0, t_4]$ and $(t_4, t]$, and thus on $[t_0, t_f]$[5]. Q.E.D.

Corollary 5.3. An *anticipatory* system (i.e., a system whose impulsive-response matrix $\Omega(t, \tau) \neq \mathbf{0}$ for $t < \tau$) is a minimal realization of $\Omega(t, \tau)$ if it is globally reduced.

5.3.3. Illustrative Examples. The system of Example 5.3 is noted to be completely controllable on all intervals $[t_0, T + \varepsilon]$ such that $\varepsilon > 0$. The system, however, is not observable on any interval $[T + \varepsilon, t_f]$ for any $\varepsilon > 0$. Thus in accordance with Theorem 5.3, the system is reducible. The following illustrative examples further illustrate the implications of Theorem 5.3.

[5]This conclusion is based on the assumption that impulse functions can be used in the A-matrix. This allows a state component $x_i(t)$ to be reset to zero at any time t such that $t_4 \leq t \leq t_1$. Thus any state component can consist of one mode that is observed during $[t_3, t_4]$ and another distinctly different mode that is controlled during $]t_1, t_2]$. Physically, this permits an energy storing device (e.g., an integrator) to be discharged at some time between the intervals $[t_3, t_4]$ and $[t_1, t_2]$ and thus be utilized in generating two distinct modes during these intervals. Example 5.4 illustrates this point.

Example 5.4. Consider the system characterized by the state-variable equations

$$\begin{bmatrix}\dot{x}_1(t)\\ \dot{x}_2(t)\end{bmatrix} = \begin{bmatrix}a & 0\\ 0 & b\end{bmatrix}\begin{bmatrix}x_1(t)\\ x_2(t)\end{bmatrix} + \begin{bmatrix}b_1(t)\\ b_2(t)\end{bmatrix}u(t)$$

$$y(t) = [c_1(t)\ c_2(t)]\begin{bmatrix}x_1(t)\\ x_2(t)\end{bmatrix}$$

where

$$b_1(t) = c_1(t) = \begin{cases}1, & t_0 \le t < T\\ 0, & T \le t \le t_f\end{cases}$$

$$b_2(t) = c_2(t) = \begin{cases}0, & t_0 \le t < T\\ 1, & T \le t \le t_f\end{cases}$$

and a and b are nonzero constants such that $a \neq b$. The transition matrix for this system is readily determined to be

$$\phi(t, \tau) = \begin{bmatrix}e^{a(t-\tau)} & 0\\ 0 & e^{b(t-\tau)}\end{bmatrix}$$

Therefore

$$\mathbf{P}(t) = \mathbf{C}(t)\phi(t, 0) = [c_1(t)e^{at}, c_2(t)e^{bt}]$$

$$\mathbf{Q}(\tau) = \phi(0, \tau)\mathbf{B}(\tau) = \begin{bmatrix}e^{-a\tau}b_1(\tau)\\ e^{-b\tau}b_2(\tau)\end{bmatrix}$$

from which it is seen that this system is not completely controllable on any finite subinterval of $[t_0, t_f]$ preceding a finite subinterval of complete observability. Thus, in accordance with Theorem 5.5, the system is reducible.

The impulsive response of this system is

$$\Omega(t, \tau) = c_1(t)b_1(\tau)e^{a(t-\tau)} + c_2(t)b_2(\tau)e^{b(t-\tau)}$$

Clearly, on the interval $[t_0, T]$ only the mode $e^{a(t-\tau)}$ can be either excited or observed; on the interval $[T, t_f]$ only the mode $e^{b(t-\tau)}$ can be either excited or observed. Thus on the entire interval $[t_0, t_f]$ only *one* mode can be either excited or observed. Thus this impulsive response can be realized

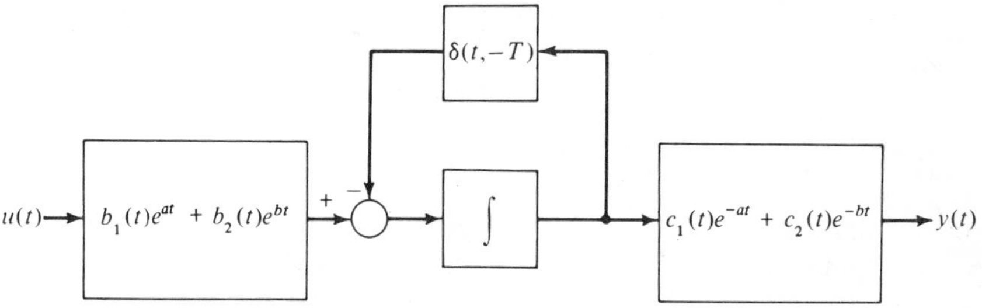

Fig. 5.6. Realization of the impulsive-response $\Omega(t, \tau) = c_1(t)b_1(\tau)e^{a(t-\tau)} + c_2(t)b_2(\tau)e^{b(t-\tau)}$.

by a first-order system. Theoretically this impulsive response can be realized by the first-order system of Fig. 5.6. The state-variable equations for this system are

$$\dot{x}(t) = -\delta(t - T)x(t) + [b_1(t)e^{at} + b_2(t)e^{bt}]u(t)$$
$$y(t) = [c_1(t)e^{-at} + c_2(t)e^{-bt}]x(t)$$

Although this appears to be a perfectly acceptable realization of the given impulsive response, it can be questioned on the basis that it has a discontinuous A-matrix. However, most serious is the fact that the discontinuity is of the form of an impulse function. The physical implications of an impulse function in the A-matrix is that the energy in an energy-storing device (e.g., a capacitor, spring, etc.) must be changed by a finite amount instantaneously. Physically, this can be accomplished only in an approximate fashion. Thus one may argue that the system is not reducible in a physical sense.

It is interesting to look at the *controllability-observability* plane of this system, i.e., the $t - \tau$ plane, as in Fig. 5.7. It is noted that

$$\Omega(t, \tau) = \begin{cases} 0, \text{ in } 1 \\ e^{a(t-\tau)}, \text{ in } 2 \\ 0, \text{ in } 3 \\ e^{b(t-\tau)}, \text{ in } 4 \end{cases}$$

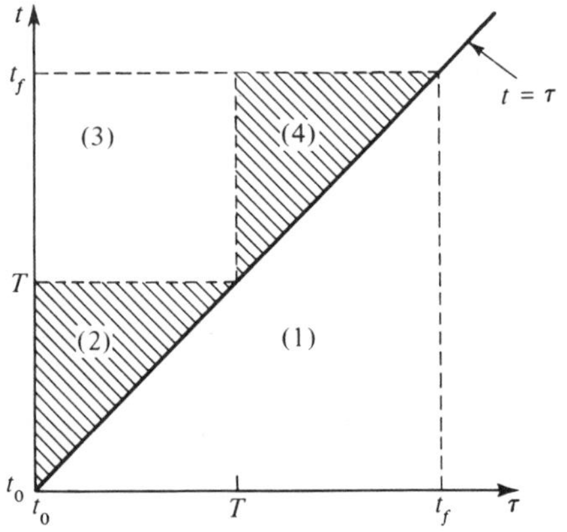

Fig. 5.7. Controllability-observability plane for the system of Example 5.4.

Figure 5.7 pictorially demonstrates that the two modes of the system cannot be either controlled or observed simultaneously. The maximum number of modes that can be controlled at any instant of time on $[t_0, t_f]$ can be determined by noting the maximum total number of *modes* (number of linearly independt columns of $\mathbf{P}(t)$ for the $\Omega(t, \tau)$ defined in that region of the controllability and observability plane) that a vertical line in the controllability-observability plane passes through. Similarly, the maximum total number of *modes* (number of linearly independent rows of $\mathbf{Q}(\tau)$ for the $\Omega(t, \tau)$ defined in that region of the controllability-observability plane) that can be observed at any instant of time can be determine by noting the number of modes that a horizontal line in the controllability-observability plane passes through. Clearly, for this system, any vertical or horizontal line drawn passes through only one mode.

If the maximum total number of modes that any horizontal or vertical line passes through in the $t - \tau$ plane is n_0, then the system can be reduced to at least an n_0-order system if impulses are permitted in the A-matrix.

Example 5.5. Consider the system characterized by the state-variable equations

$$\begin{bmatrix} \dot{x}_1(t) \\ \dot{x}_2(t) \end{bmatrix} = \begin{bmatrix} a & 0 \\ 0 & b \end{bmatrix} \begin{bmatrix} x_1(t) \\ x_2(t) \end{bmatrix} + \begin{bmatrix} b_1(t) \\ b_2(t) \end{bmatrix} u(t)$$

$$y(t) = [1 \ c_2(t)] \begin{bmatrix} x_1(t) \\ x_2(t) \end{bmatrix}$$

where $b_1(t)$, $b_2(t)$, $c_2(t)$ are defined as a Example 5.4. Thus

$$\mathbf{P}(t) = [e^{at}, c_2(t)e^{bt}]$$

$$\mathbf{Q}(\tau) = \begin{bmatrix} e^{-a\tau} b_1(\tau) \\ e^{-b\tau} b_2(\tau) \end{bmatrix}$$

from which it is seen that this system is completely controllable on any interval $[t_0, T + \varepsilon]$, for any $\varepsilon > 0$, and completely observable on any subinterval of $[T, t_f]$. Thus, in accordance with Theorem 5.3, the system is not reducible. The impulsive response for this system is

$$\Omega(t, \tau) = b_1(\tau)e^{a(t-\tau)} + c_2(t)b_2(\tau)e^{b(t-\tau)}$$

Looking at the controllability-observability plane for this system in Fig. 5.8 it is noted that

$$\Omega(t, \tau) = \begin{cases} 0, \text{ in } 1 \\ e^{a(t-\tau)}, \text{ in } 2 \\ e^{b(t-\tau)}, \text{ in } 3 \end{cases}$$

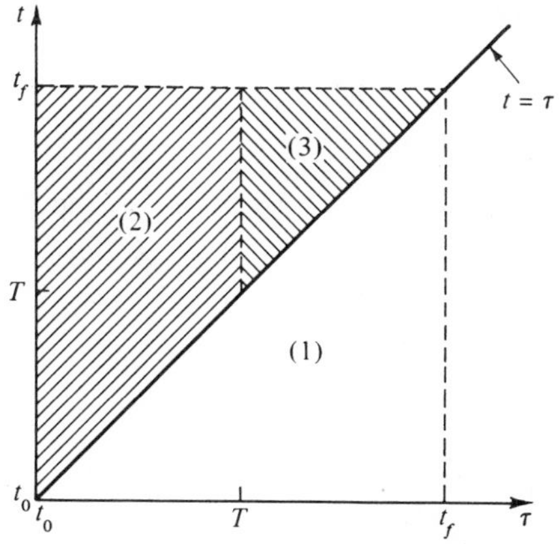

Fig. 5.8. Controllability-observability plane for the system of Example 5.5.

Although only one mode can be controlled at any instant of time on $[t_0, t_f]$, *two* modes can be observed during the period $[T, t_f]$. Thus there is no interval of complete controllability preceding an interval of complete observability. One might expect that the minimal realization of this system would be of higher order than that of the system of Example 5.4. On the other hand, since the controllability-observability plane has no region in it in which the impulsive response is the sum of two modes, one might expect that the minimal realization would be of order less than two. The question then is, "Is there a system of order less than two but greater than one?" If the introduction of *memory* is introduced, then one might answer in the affirmative. For example, a realization of this system is shown in Fig. 5.9, where, with the introduction of memory, only one integrator is used. The state-variable equations for this system are

$$\dot{x}(t) = \delta(t - T)x(t) + [b_1(t)e^{at} + b_2(t)e^{bt}]u(t)$$
$$y(t) = [c_1(t)e^{-at} + c_2(t)e^{-bt}]x(t) + e^{-at}x(T)$$

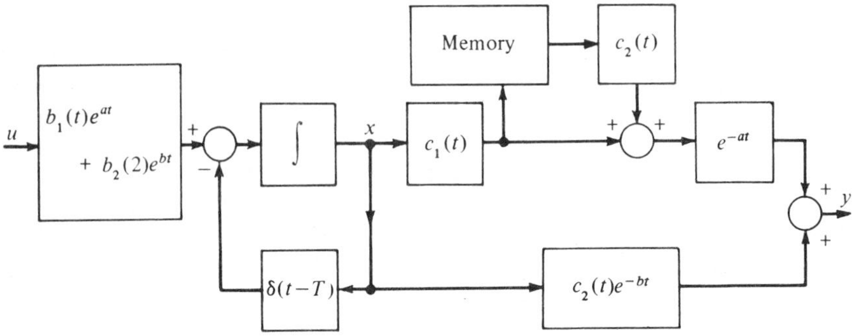

Fig. 5.9. Realization of the impulsive-response $\Omega(t, \tau) = b_1(\tau)e^{a(t-\tau)} + c_2(t)b_2(\tau)e^{(t-\tau)}$.

Clearly the term $e^{-at}x(T)$ on the right-hand side of the output equation is what requires the introduction of memory. The form of the state-variable equations for this system are not of the canonical form

$$\dot{\mathbf{x}}(t) = \mathbf{A}(t)\mathbf{x}(t) + \mathbf{B}(t)\mathbf{u}(t)$$
$$\mathbf{y}(t) = \mathbf{C}(t)\mathbf{x}(t)$$

and, in this sense, this pseudo first-order system cannot be considered a reduction.

Example 5.6. A system somewhat similar to that considered in Example 5.5. is

$$\begin{bmatrix} \dot{x}_1(t) \\ \dot{x}_2(t) \end{bmatrix} = \begin{bmatrix} a & 0 \\ 0 & b \end{bmatrix} \begin{bmatrix} x_1(t) \\ x_2(t) \end{bmatrix} + \begin{bmatrix} b_1(t) \\ 1 \end{bmatrix} u(t)$$
$$y(t) = [c_1(t)c_2(t)] \begin{bmatrix} x_1(t) \\ x_2(t) \end{bmatrix}$$

where $b_1(t)$, $b_2(t)$, $c_2(t)$ are defined as in Example 5.4. Thus

$$\mathbf{P}(t) = [c_1(t)e^{at} \; c_2(t)e^{bt}]$$

$$\mathbf{Q}(\tau) = \begin{bmatrix} e^{-a\tau}b_1(\tau) \\ e^{-b\tau} \end{bmatrix}$$

from which it is noted that the system is completely controllable on any subinterval of $[t_0, T]$ and completely observable on $[T - \varepsilon, t_f]$, for any $\varepsilon > 0$. Thus, in accordance with Theorem 5.3, this system is not reducible.

The impulsive response of this system is

$$\Omega(t, \tau) = c_1(t)b_1(\tau)e^{a(t-\tau)} + c_2(t)e^{b(t-\tau)}$$

Alternatively, looking at the controllability-observability plane for this system in Fig. 5.10 it is noted that

$$\Omega(t, \tau) = \begin{cases} 0, & \text{in } 1 \\ e^{a(t-\tau)}, & \text{in } 2 \\ e^{b(t-\tau)}, & \text{in } 3 \end{cases}$$

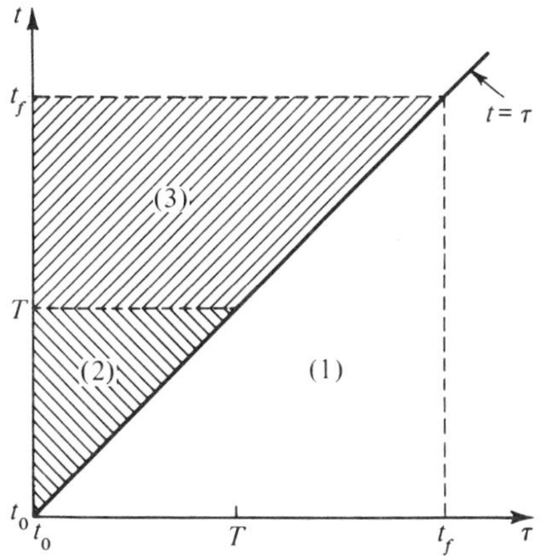

Fig. 5.10. Controllability-observability plane for the system of Example 5.6.

Again, although only one mode can be observed at any instant of time on $[t_0, t_f]$, *two* can be controlled during the period $[t_0, T]$. Clearly this system is completely controllable on $[t_0, T - \varepsilon]$ and completely observable on $[T - \varepsilon, t_f]$, where $0 < \varepsilon < T$, and thus by Theorem 5.3, is not reducible.

5.4. RELATIONS BETWEEN EQUIVALENT SYSTEMS

The two matrices $\mathbf{U}(t_3, t_4)$ and $\mathbf{V}(t_1, t_2)$ defined in Sec. 5.3.2 are closely related to one another and are used to develop relations between equivalent systems. This relation is seen by premultiplying and postmultiplying Eq. 5.16 by $\mathbf{P}_0'(t)$ and $\mathbf{Q}_0'(\tau)$ and then integrating both sides twice on the intervals $[t_3, t_4]$ and $[t_1, t_2]$ with respect to t and τ respectively; due to causality the intervals of integration are chosen so that $t_0 \le t_1 < t_2 \le t_3 < t_4 \le t_f$:

$$\int_{t_3}^{t_4} \mathbf{P}_0'(t)\mathbf{P}_0(t)\, dt \int_{t_1}^{t_2} \mathbf{Q}_0(\tau)\mathbf{Q}_0'(\tau)\, dt$$
$$= \int_{t_3}^{t_4} \mathbf{P}_0'(t)\mathbf{P}(t)\, dt \int_{t_1}^{t_2} \mathbf{Q}(\tau)\mathbf{Q}_0'(\tau)\, dt\,, \qquad t_0 \le t_1 < t_2 \le t_3 < t_4 < t_f \tag{5.26}$$

It follows, from Eqs. 4.20 and 4.103, that

$$\mathbf{N}(t_3, t_4)\mathbf{M}(t_1, t_2) = \int_{t_3}^{t_4} \mathbf{P}_0'(t)\mathbf{P}(t)\, dt \int_{t_1}^{t_2} \mathbf{Q}(\tau)\mathbf{Q}_0'(\tau)\, d\tau\,, \qquad t_0 \le t_1 < t_2 \le t_3 < t_4 \le t_f \tag{5.27}$$

If the system is *completely controllable* on $[t_1, t_2]$ and *completely observable* on $[t_3, t_4]$, then $\mathbf{N}(t_3, t_4)$ and $\mathbf{M}(t_1, t_2)$ are nonsingular and

$$\mathbf{I}_{n_0} = \left[\mathbf{N}^{-1}(t_3, t_4)\int_{t_3}^{t_4} \mathbf{P}_0'(t)\mathbf{P}(t)\, dt\right]\left[\int_{t_1}^{t_2} \mathbf{Q}(\tau)\mathbf{Q}_0'(\tau)\, d\tau M^{-1}(t_1, t_2)\right] \qquad t_0 \le t_1 < t_2 \le t_3 < t_4 \le t_f \tag{5.28}$$

Substituting from Eq. 5.20 and 5.24 in Eq. 5.28 gives

$$\mathbf{I}_{n_0} = \mathbf{U}(t_3, t_4)\, \mathbf{V}(t_1, t_2)\,, \qquad t_0 \le t_1 < t_2 \le t_3 < t_4 \le t_f \tag{5.29}$$

From Eq. 5.29 it is again clear that both $\mathbf{U}(t_3, t_4)$ and $\mathbf{V}(t_1, t_2)$ have rank n_0.

5.4.1. Reduced Systems. For the case that both $\mathbf{P}_0(t)\mathbf{Q}_0(\tau)\delta^{(-1)}(t-\tau)$ and $\mathbf{P}(t)\mathbf{Q}(\tau)\delta^{(-1)}(t-\tau)$ are reduced systems having the impulsive-response matrix $\Omega(t, \tau)$ (i.e., $n = n_0$) $\mathbf{U}(t_3, t_4)$ and $\mathbf{V}(t_1, t_2)$ are nonsingular $n_0 \times n_0$ matrices. Therefore from Eq. 5.29, it follows that

$$\mathbf{U}(t_3, t_4) = \mathbf{V}^{-1}(t_1, t_2) \equiv \mathbf{C} \tag{5.30a}$$

It is noted that in this case $\mathbf{U}(t_3, t_4)$ and $\mathbf{V}(t_1, t_2)$ are independent of t_3, t_4 and t_1, t_2. Therefore

$$\mathbf{U} = \mathbf{V}^{-1} \equiv \mathbf{C} \tag{5.30b}$$

Substituting from Eq. 5.30b in Eq. 5.19 and 5.23 results in

$$\mathbf{Q}(\tau) = \mathbf{C}^{-1}\mathbf{Q}_0(\tau)\,, \quad \tau \le t_3 \tag{5.31a}$$
$$\mathbf{P}(t) = \mathbf{P}_0(t)\mathbf{C}\,, \quad t \ge t_2 \tag{5.31b}$$

Multiplying $\mathbf{P}(t)$ and $\mathbf{Q}(\tau)$ as given in Eq. 5.31 results in

$$\mathbf{P}(t)\mathbf{Q}(\tau) = \mathbf{P}_0(t)\mathbf{C}^{-1}\mathbf{C}\mathbf{Q}_0(\tau) = \Omega(t, \tau) \tag{5.32}$$

from which is concluded

Theorem 5.4. If $\mathbf{P}_0(t)\mathbf{Q}_0(\tau)$ is any reduced decomposition of the impulsive-response matrix $\Omega(t, \tau)$ such that the rows of $\mathbf{Q}_0(\tau)$ are linearly independent on $[t_1, t_2]$ and the columns of $\mathbf{P}_0(t)$ are linearly independent on $[t_3, t_4]$ where $t_0 \leq t_1 < t_2 \leq t_3 < t_4 \leq t_0$, then any other reduced decomposition $\mathbf{P}(t)\mathbf{Q}(\tau)$ satisfies

$$\begin{aligned} \mathbf{P}(t) &= \mathbf{P}_0(t)\mathbf{C}\,, \quad t \geq t_2 \\ \mathbf{Q}(\tau) &= \mathbf{C}^{-1}\mathbf{Q}_0(\tau)\,, \quad \tau \leq t_3 \end{aligned} \tag{5.33}$$

where $\mathbf{C}$ is an arbitrary real, constant $n_0 \times n_0$ nonsingular matrix.

Corollary 5.4. If a system is totally controllable at t_0 and totally observable at t_f, then Eq. 5.33 are valid for all t and τ on (t_0, t_f).

5.4.2. Reducible systems. Theorem 5.4 provides a method for generating reduced decompositions of the impulsive-response matrix $\Omega(t, \tau)$ from a given reduced realization. The situation is more complex for the case that the decomposition $\Omega(t, \tau) = \mathbf{P}(t)\mathbf{Q}(\tau)$ is not reduced. However, the invariance of the product $\mathbf{U}(t_3, t_4)\,\mathbf{V}(t_1, t_2)$ as given in Eq. 5.29 allows similar results to be obtained.

As $\mathbf{U}(t_3, t_4)$ and $\mathbf{V}(t_1, t_2)$ have rank n_0, they can be written as

$$\begin{aligned} \mathbf{U}(t_3, t_4) &= \mathbf{JK} \\ \mathbf{V}(t_1, t_2) &= \mathbf{K}^{-1}\mathbf{J}' \end{aligned} \tag{5.34}$$

where $\mathbf{K}$ is a real, constant, nonsingular $n \times n$ matrix and $\mathbf{J}$ is the $n_0 \times n$ matrix

$$\mathbf{J} = [\mathbf{I}_{n_0}, \mathbf{0}] \tag{5.35}$$

It is noted that the first n_0 rows of $\mathbf{K}$ and the first n_0 columns of $\mathbf{K}^{-1}$ correspond to $\mathbf{U}(t_3, t_4)$ and $\mathbf{V}(t_1, t_2)$ respectively. Clearly $\mathbf{U}(t_3, t_4)\,\mathbf{V}(t_1, t_2) = \mathbf{I}_{n_0}$ as required. Substituting from Eq. 5.34 in Eq. 5.19 and 5.23 gives

$$\begin{aligned} \mathbf{P}_0(t) &= \mathbf{P}(t)\mathbf{K}^{-1}\mathbf{J}'\,, \qquad t \geq t_2 \\ \mathbf{Q}_0(\tau) &= \mathbf{JKQ}(\tau)\,, \qquad \tau \leq t_3 \end{aligned} \tag{5.36}$$

Due to the definition of $\mathbf{J}$ given in Eq. 5.35, Eqs. 5.36 can be written, by partitioning $\mathbf{P}(t)\mathbf{K}^{-1}$ and $\mathbf{KQ}(\tau)$, as

$$\mathbf{P}_0(t) = [\mathbf{P}_0(t),\ \mathbf{P}_a(t)]\mathbf{J}'\,, \qquad t \geq t_2 \tag{5.37a}$$

$$\mathbf{Q}_0(\tau) = \mathbf{J}\begin{bmatrix} \mathbf{Q}_0(\tau) \\ \mathbf{Q}_a(t) \end{bmatrix}, \qquad \tau \leq t_3 \tag{5.37b}$$

where $\mathbf{P}_a(t)$ is an $r \times (n - n_0)$ matrix and $\mathbf{Q}_a(\tau)$ is an $(n - n_0) \times m$ matrix. Thus

$$\mathbf{P}(t)\mathbf{K}^{-1} = [\mathbf{P}_0(t),\ \mathbf{P}_a(t)]\,, \qquad t \geq t_2 \tag{5.38a}$$

$$\mathbf{KQ}(\tau) = \begin{bmatrix} \mathbf{Q}_0(\tau) \\ \mathbf{Q}_a(\tau) \end{bmatrix}, \qquad \tau \leq t_3 \tag{5.38b}$$

and

$$\mathbf{P}(t) = [\mathbf{P}_0(t),\ \mathbf{P}_a(t)]\mathbf{K}\,, \qquad t \geq t_2 \tag{5.39a}$$

$$\mathbf{Q}(\tau) = \mathbf{K}^{-1}\begin{bmatrix}\mathbf{Q}_0(\tau)\\ \mathbf{Q}_a(\tau)\end{bmatrix}, \qquad \tau \le t_3 \tag{5.39b}$$

Multiplication of $\mathbf{P}(t)$ by $\mathbf{Q}(\tau)$ as given in Eqs. 5.39 shows that the choice of $\mathbf{P}_a(\tau)$ and $\mathbf{Q}_a(\tau)$ is not completely arbitrary:

$$\Omega(t, \tau) = \mathbf{P}_0(t)\mathbf{Q}_0(\tau) + \mathbf{P}_a(t)\mathbf{Q}_a(\tau), \qquad t \ge t_2, \quad \tau \le t_3 \tag{5.40}$$

Since $\Omega(t, \tau) = \mathbf{P}_0(t)\mathbf{Q}_0(\tau)$, it is necessary that

$$\mathbf{P}_a(t)\mathbf{Q}_a(\tau) = \mathbf{0}, \qquad t \ge t_2, \quad \tau \le t_3 \tag{5.41}$$

Equations 5.39 and 5.41 provide a method for obtaining decompositions $\Omega(t, \tau) = \mathbf{P}(t)\mathbf{Q}(\tau)$ from a reduced decomposition $\Omega(t, \tau) = \mathbf{P}_0(t)\mathbf{Q}_0(\tau)$. Since each decomposition $\mathbf{P}(t)\mathbf{Q}(\tau)$ corresponds to a realization

$$\begin{aligned}\dot{\mathbf{x}}(t) &= \mathbf{A}(t)\mathbf{x}(t) + \mathbf{B}(t)\mathbf{u}(t)\\ \mathbf{y}(t) &= \mathbf{C}(t)\mathbf{x}(t)\end{aligned} \tag{5.42}$$

denoted by $[\mathbf{A}(t), \mathbf{B}(t), \mathbf{C}(t)]$, a method for developing any such realization from the reduced realization

$$\begin{aligned}\dot{\mathbf{x}}_0(t) &= \mathbf{A}_0(t)\mathbf{x}_0(t) + \mathbf{B}_0(t)\mathbf{u}(t)\\ \mathbf{y}(t) &= \mathbf{C}_0(t)\mathbf{x}_0(t)\end{aligned} \tag{5.43}$$

denoted by $[\mathbf{A}_0(t), \mathbf{B}_0(t), \mathbf{C}_0(t)]$, corresponding to the decomposition $\mathbf{P}(t)\mathbf{Q}(\tau)$, is developed.

Suppose that realizations $[\mathbf{A}(t), \mathbf{B}(t), \mathbf{C}(t)]$ and $[\mathbf{A}_0(t), \mathbf{B}_0(t), \mathbf{C}_0(t)]$ both have the same impulsive-response matrix $\Omega(t, \tau)$. Thus

$$\begin{aligned}\Omega(t, \tau) &= \mathbf{C}_0(t)\phi_0(t, \tau)\mathbf{B}_0(\tau)\\ &= \mathbf{C}(t)\phi(t, \tau)\mathbf{B}(\tau)\end{aligned} \tag{5.44}$$

and

$$\mathbf{A}_0(t) = \left.\frac{\partial\phi_0(t, \tau)}{\partial t}\right|_{\tau=t} \tag{5.45a}$$

$$\mathbf{A}(t) = \left.\frac{\partial\phi(t, \tau)}{\partial t}\right|_{\tau=t} \tag{5.45b}$$

Equation 5.44 can be written as

$$\mathbf{C}_0(t)\phi_0(t, t_0)\phi_0(t_0, \tau)\mathbf{B}_0(\tau) = \mathbf{C}(t)\phi(t, t_0)\phi(t_0, \tau)\mathbf{B}(\tau) \tag{5.46}$$

or simply

$$\mathbf{P}_0(t)\mathbf{Q}_0(\tau) = \mathbf{P}(t)\mathbf{Q}(\tau) \tag{5.47}$$

where

$$\mathbf{P}_0(t) = \mathbf{C}_0(t)\phi_0(t, t_0) \tag{5.48a}$$

$$\mathbf{P}(t) = \mathbf{C}(t)\phi(t, t_0) \tag{5.48b}$$

$$\mathbf{Q}_0(\tau) = \phi_0(t_0, \tau)\mathbf{B}_0(\tau) \tag{5.48c}$$

$$\mathbf{Q}(\tau) = \phi(t_0, \tau)\mathbf{B}(\tau) \tag{5.48d}$$

Substituting from Eqs. 5.48 in Eqs. 5.39 gives

$$\mathbf{C}(t)\phi(t, t_0) = [\mathbf{C}_0(t)\phi_0(t, t_0),\ \mathbf{P}_a(t)]\mathbf{K}, \qquad t \geq t_2 \tag{5.49a}$$

$$\phi(t_0, t)\mathbf{B}(t) = \mathbf{K}^{-1}\begin{bmatrix}\phi_0(t_0, t)\mathbf{B}_0(t)\\ \mathbf{Q}_a(t)\end{bmatrix}, \qquad t \leq t_3 \tag{5.49b}$$

or

$$\mathbf{C}(t) = [\mathbf{C}_0(t)\phi_0(\mathrm{t}, t_0),\ \mathbf{P}_a(t)]\mathbf{K}\,\phi(t_0, t), \qquad t \geq t_2 \tag{5.50a}$$

$$\mathbf{B}(t) = \phi(t, t_0)\mathbf{K}^{-1}\begin{bmatrix}\phi(t_0, t)\mathbf{B}_0(t)\\ \mathbf{Q}_a(t)\end{bmatrix}, \qquad t \leq t_3 \tag{5.50b}$$

Defining the *direct sum* of two matrices by

$$\mathbf{A} \dotplus \mathbf{B} = \begin{bmatrix}\mathbf{A} & \mathbf{0}\\ \mathbf{0} & \mathbf{B}\end{bmatrix} \tag{5.51}$$

and the nonsingular matrix $\mathbf{T}(t)$ by

$$\mathbf{T}(t) \equiv [\phi_0(t, t_0) \dotplus \mathbf{I}_{n-n_0}]\mathbf{K}\,\phi(t_0, t) \tag{5.52}$$

Eqs. 5.50 can be written as

$$\mathbf{C}(t) = [\mathbf{C}_0(t), \mathbf{P}_a(t)]\mathbf{T}(t), \qquad t \geq t_2 \tag{5.53a}$$

$$\mathbf{B}(t) = \mathbf{T}^{-1}(t)\begin{bmatrix}\mathbf{B}_0(t)\\ \mathbf{Q}_a(t)\end{bmatrix}, \qquad t \leq t_3 \tag{5.53b}$$

where

$$\mathbf{T}^{-1}(t) = \phi(t, t_0)\mathbf{K}^{-1}[\phi_0(t_0, t) \dotplus \mathbf{I}_{n-n_0}] \tag{5.54}$$

It is easily verified by direct calculation that

$$\mathbf{T}(t)\phi(t, \tau)\mathbf{T}^{-1}(\tau) = \phi_0(t, \tau) \dotplus \mathbf{I}_{n-n_0} \tag{5.55}$$

Differentiating Eq. 5.55 with respect to t, setting $\tau = t$, and substituting from Eqs. 5.45 results in

$$\dot{\mathbf{T}}(t)\mathbf{T}^{-1}(t) + \mathbf{T}(t)\mathbf{A}(t)\mathbf{T}^{-1}(t) = \mathbf{A}_0(t) \dotplus \mathbf{0}_{n-n_0} \tag{5.56}$$

Thus

$$\mathbf{A}(t) = -\mathbf{T}^{-1}(t)\dot{\mathbf{T}}(t) + \mathbf{T}^{-1}(t)[\mathbf{A}_0(t) \dotplus \mathbf{0}_{n-n_0}]\mathbf{T}(t) \tag{5.57}$$

The above is summarized by

Theorem 5.5. If $\Omega(t, \tau)$ is a realizable impulsive-response matrix of order n_0 and $[\mathbf{A}_0(t), \mathbf{B}_0(t), \mathbf{C}_0(t)]$ is any minimal realization of $\Omega(t, \tau)$ that is completely controllable on $[t_1, t_2]$ and completely observable on $[t_3, t_4]$ where $t_0 \leq t_1 < t_2 \leq t_3 < t_4 \leq t_f$, then the n-dimensional system associated with $[\mathbf{A}(t), \mathbf{B}(t), \mathbf{C}(t)]$ also realizes $\Omega(t, \tau)$ if and only if

$$\mathbf{C}(t) = [\mathbf{C}_0(t), \mathbf{P}_a(t)]\mathbf{T}(t), \qquad t \geq t_2 \tag{5.58a}$$

$$\mathbf{B}(t) = \mathbf{T}^{-1}(t)\begin{bmatrix}\mathbf{B}_0(t)\\ \mathbf{Q}_a(t)\end{bmatrix}, \qquad t \leq t_3 \tag{5.58b}$$

$$\mathbf{A}(t) = -\mathbf{T}^{-1}(t)\dot{\mathbf{T}}(t) + \mathbf{T}^{-1}(t)[\mathbf{A}_0(t) \dotplus \mathbf{0}_{n-n_0}]\mathbf{T}(t) \tag{5.58c}$$

where

(a) $\mathbf{T}(t)$ is an arbitrary real, nonsingular absolutely continuous function of t possessing an absolutely continuous inverse;
(b) $\mathbf{P}_a(t)$ is an arbitrary real $r \times (n - n_0)$ function of t square-integrable on $[t_0, t_f]$;
(c) $\mathbf{Q}_a(t)$ is an arbitrary real $(n - n_0) \times m$ function of t square-integrable on $[t_0, t_f]$;
(d) $\mathbf{P}_a(t)\mathbf{Q}_a(\tau) = \mathbf{0}$.

Proof. Necessity has been established in the development of Eqs. 5.53 and 5.57. Therefore only sufficiency need be established, i.e., it must be shown that the system

$$\begin{aligned} \dot{\mathbf{x}}(t) &= \mathbf{A}(t)\mathbf{x}(t) + \mathbf{B}(t)\mathbf{u}(t) \\ \mathbf{y}(t) &= \mathbf{C}(t)\mathbf{x}(t) \end{aligned} \tag{5.59}$$

with $[\mathbf{A}(t), \mathbf{B}(t), \mathbf{C}(t)]$ as given by Eq. 5.58, has the same impulsive-response matrix $\Omega(t, \tau)$ as the system associated with $[\mathbf{A}_0(t), \mathbf{B}_0(t), \mathbf{C}_0(t)]$ for $t \geq t_2$ and $\tau \leq t_3$.

Denote the impulsive-response matrix of system 5.59 by $\Omega(t, \tau)$:

$$\Omega(t, \tau) = \mathbf{C}(t)\phi(t, t_0)\phi(t_0, \tau)\mathbf{B}(\tau) \tag{5.60}$$

Consider the change of variable in the equation $\dot{\mathbf{x}}(t) = \mathbf{A}(t)\mathbf{x}(t)$ defined by the equivalence transformation

$$\xi(t) = \mathbf{T}(t)\mathbf{x}(t) \tag{5.61}$$

Therefore

$$\begin{aligned} \dot{\xi}(t) &= \dot{\mathbf{T}}(t)\mathbf{x}(t) + \mathbf{T}(t)\dot{\mathbf{x}}(t) \\ &= [\dot{\mathbf{T}}(t)\mathbf{T}^{-1}(t) + \mathbf{T}(t)\mathbf{A}(t)\mathbf{T}^{-1}(t)]\xi(t) \end{aligned} \tag{5.62}$$

and as, according to Eq 5.56,

$$[\dot{\mathbf{T}}(t)\mathbf{T}^{-1}(t) + \mathbf{T}(t)\mathbf{A}(t)\mathbf{T}^{-1}(t)] = \mathbf{A}_0(t) \dotplus \mathbf{0}_{n-n_0} \tag{5.63}$$

Eq. 5.62 can be written

$$\dot{\xi}(t) = [\mathbf{A}_0(t) \dotplus \mathbf{0}_{n-n_0}]\xi(t) \tag{5.64}$$

and the transition matrix for Eq. 5.64 is

$$\phi_\xi(t, t_0) = \begin{bmatrix} \phi_0(t, t_0) & \mathbf{0} \\ \mathbf{0} & \mathbf{I}_{n-n_0} \end{bmatrix} \tag{5.65}$$

Thus

$$\begin{aligned} \xi(t) &= \phi_\xi(t, t_0)\xi(t_0) \\ &= \phi_\xi(t, t_0)\mathbf{T}(t_0)\mathbf{x}(t_0) \end{aligned} \tag{5.66}$$

and

$$\mathbf{x}(t) = \mathbf{T}^{-1}(t)\phi_\xi(t, t_0)\mathbf{T}(t_0)\mathbf{x}(t_0) \tag{5.67}$$

From Eq. 5.67 it is seen that the transition matrix for system 5.59 is

$$\Omega(t, \tau) = \mathbf{T}^{-1}(t)\phi_\xi(t, \tau)\mathbf{T}(\tau) \tag{5.68}$$

Thus the corresponding impulsive-response matrix is

$$\hat{\Omega}(t, \tau) = \mathbf{C}(t)\mathbf{T}^{-1}(t)\boldsymbol{\phi}_{\xi}(t, \tau)\mathbf{T}(\tau)\mathbf{B}(\tau) \tag{5.69}$$

Substituting from Eqs. 5.58 and 5.65 in Eq. 5.69 gives

$$\hat{\Omega}(t, \tau) = \mathbf{C}_0(t)\boldsymbol{\phi}_0(t, \tau)\mathbf{B}_0(\tau) + \mathbf{P}_a(t)\mathbf{Q}_a(\tau)\,, \qquad t \geq t_2\,,\ \tau \leq t_3 \tag{5.70}$$

Since $\mathbf{P}_a(t)\mathbf{Q}_a(\tau) = \mathbf{0}$,

$$\hat{\Omega}(t, \tau) = \mathbf{C}_0(t)\boldsymbol{\phi}_0(t, \tau)\mathbf{B}_0(\tau)\,, \qquad t \geq t_2,\ \tau \leq t_3 \tag{5.71}$$

and it is seen that the systems associated with $[\mathbf{A}(t), \mathbf{B}(t), \mathbf{C}(t)]$ and $[\mathbf{A}_0(t), \mathbf{B}_0(t), \mathbf{C}_0(t)]$ have identical impulsive-response matrices for $t \geq t_2$, $\tau \leq t_3$. Q.E.D.

Corollary 5.5a. If a system is totally controllable at t_0 and totally observable at t_f, then Eq. 5.58 is valid for all t and τ on (t_0, t_f).

Corollary 5.5b. Any minimal realization $[\mathbf{A}(t), \mathbf{B}(t), \mathbf{C}(t)]$ of $\Omega(t, \tau)$ is related to any particular minimal realization $[\mathbf{A}_0(t), \mathbf{B}_0(t), \mathbf{C}_0(t)]$ by the formulas

$$\mathbf{C}(t) = \mathbf{C}_0(t)\mathbf{T}(t)\,, \qquad t \geq t_2 \tag{5.72a}$$

$$\mathbf{B}(t) = \mathbf{T}^{-1}(t)\mathbf{B}_0(t)\,, \qquad t \leq t_3 \tag{5.72b}$$

$$\mathbf{A}(t) = -\mathbf{T}^{-1}(t)\dot{\mathbf{T}}(t) + \mathbf{T}^{-1}(t)\mathbf{A}_0(t)\mathbf{T}(t) \tag{5.72c}$$

where $\mathbf{T}(t)$ is an arbitrary $n_0 \times n_0$ nonsingular absolutely continuous matrix function of t possessing an absolutely continuous inverse and n_0 is the order of $\Omega(t, \tau)$.

5.4.3. Relation with Canonical Systems.

Theorem 5.6. Any n-dimensional system of the type characterized by equations

$$\begin{aligned} \dot{\mathbf{x}}(t) &= \mathbf{A}(t)\mathbf{x}(t) + \mathbf{B}(t)\mathbf{u}(t) \\ \mathbf{y}(t) &= \mathbf{C}(t)\mathbf{x}(t) \end{aligned} \tag{5.73}$$

can be transformed under an admissible change of state variables

$$\boldsymbol{\xi}(t) = \mathbf{T}(t)\mathbf{x}(t) \tag{5.74}$$

into one composed of two subsystems connected in parallel on the input and in series on the output. More specifically,

$$\mathbf{y}(t) = \mathbf{y}_1(t) + \mathbf{y}_2(t) \tag{5.75}$$

where the minimal n_0-order system N_1 is completely controllable on $[t_1, t_2]$ and completely observable on $[t_3, t_4]$, where $t_0 \leq t_1 < t_2 \leq t_3 < t_4 \leq t_f$,

$$\begin{aligned} \dot{\boldsymbol{\xi}}_1(t) &= \mathbf{A}_0(t)\boldsymbol{\xi}_1(t) + \mathbf{B}_0(t)\mathbf{u}(t) \\ \mathbf{y}_1(t) &= \mathbf{C}_0(t)\boldsymbol{\xi}_1(t) \end{aligned} \tag{5.76}$$

and system N_2 is characterized by

$$\begin{aligned}\dot{\boldsymbol{\xi}}_2(t) &= \mathbf{Q}_a(t)\mathbf{u}(t)\\ \mathbf{y}_2(t) &= \mathbf{P}_a(t)\boldsymbol{\xi}_2(t)\end{aligned} \tag{5.77}$$

Here

$$\boldsymbol{\xi}(t) = \begin{bmatrix}\boldsymbol{\xi}_1(t)\\ \boldsymbol{\xi}_2(t)\end{bmatrix} \tag{5.78}$$

and $\mathbf{T}(t)$ is admissible if it is real, nonsingular, and absolutely continuous and possesses an absolutely continuous inverse over any finite interval. This transformation is illustrated in Fig. 5.11.

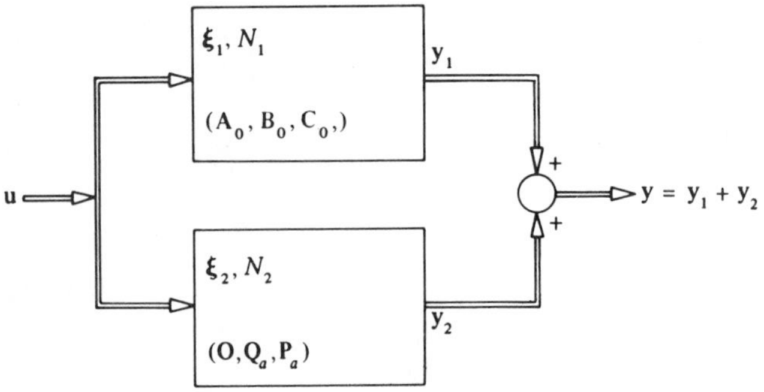

Fig. 5.11. Reduction of a nonminimal system corresponding to Theorem 5.6.

Proof. Adjoining systems N_1 and N_2 as given by Eqs. 5.76 and 5.77 results in

$$\begin{bmatrix}\dot{\boldsymbol{\xi}}_1(t)\\ \dot{\boldsymbol{\xi}}_2(t)\end{bmatrix} = \begin{bmatrix}\mathbf{A}_0(t) & \mathbf{0}\\ \mathbf{0} & \mathbf{0}\end{bmatrix}\begin{bmatrix}\boldsymbol{\xi}_1(t)\\ \boldsymbol{\xi}_2(t)\end{bmatrix} + \begin{bmatrix}\mathbf{B}_0(t)\\ \mathbf{Q}_a(t)\end{bmatrix}\mathbf{u}(t) \tag{5.79a}$$

$$\mathbf{y}(t) = \mathbf{y}_1(t) + \mathbf{y}_2(t) = [\mathbf{C}_0(t)\ \mathbf{P}_a(t)]\begin{bmatrix}\boldsymbol{\xi}_1(t)\\ \boldsymbol{\xi}_2(t)\end{bmatrix} \tag{5.79b}$$

or simply

$$\begin{aligned}\dot{\boldsymbol{\xi}}(t) &= \mathbf{A}_T(t)\boldsymbol{\xi}(t) + \mathbf{B}_T(t)\mathbf{u}(t)\\ \mathbf{y}(t) &= \mathbf{C}_T(t)\boldsymbol{\xi}(t)\end{aligned} \tag{5.80}$$

where

$$\boldsymbol{\xi}(t) = \begin{bmatrix}\boldsymbol{\xi}_1(t)\\ \boldsymbol{\xi}_2(t)\end{bmatrix} \tag{5.81}$$

and

$$\mathbf{A}_T(t) = \begin{bmatrix}\mathbf{A}_0(t) & \mathbf{0}\\ \mathbf{0} & \mathbf{0}\end{bmatrix} \tag{5.82a}$$

$$\mathbf{B}_T(t) = \begin{bmatrix} \mathbf{B}_0(t) \\ \mathbf{Q}_a(t) \end{bmatrix} \tag{5.82b}$$

$$\mathbf{C}_T(t) = [\mathbf{C}_0(t)\ \mathbf{P}_a(t)] \tag{5.82c}$$

Thus an equivalence transformation characterized by $\boldsymbol{\xi}(t) = \mathbf{T}(t)\mathbf{x}(t)$ is sought such that system 5.73 is transformed to system 5.80. By substitution it is readily established that the nonsingular $n \times n$ matrix $\mathbf{T}(t)$ given by Eq. 5.52 provides the desired transformation. Since system N_1 is of minimal order n_0 it is, by Theorem 5.3, completely controllable on $[t_1, t_2]$ and completely observable on $[t_3, t_4]$. Q.E.D.

It can be noted that system N_2 is stable and is also resonant (bounded inputs produce unbounded outputs: see Sec. 8.1). Note that a nonzero duce bounded outputs: see Sec. 8.1), but is not stable. Thus any nonzero initial condition $\xi_2(t_0)$ can produce a lasting perturbation in $\mathbf{y}_2(t)$ and therefore in $\mathbf{y}(t)$. Clearly then, the stability of N_1 does not guarantee the stability of the overall system. Hence the importance of employing minimal realizations in the synthesis of impulsive-response matrices is noted.

Theorem 5.7. Any n-dimensional system of the type characterized by Eq. 5.59 can be transformed under an admissible change of state variables into one composed of four subsystems in parallel on the input and in series on the output. The first N_1 is completely controllable on $[t_1, t_2]$ and completely observable on $[t_3, t_4]$, where $t_0 \le t_1 < t_2 \le t_3 < t_4 \le t_f$. The second N_{2a} is completely uncontrollable on $[t_1, t_2]$ and completely observable on $[t_3, t_4]$. The third N_{2b} is completely controllable on $[t_1, t_2]$ and completely unobservable on $[t_3, t_4]$. The fourth N_{2c} is completely uncontrollable on $[t_1, t_2]$ and completely unobservable on $[t_3, t_4]$. This transformation is illustrated in Fig. 5.12.

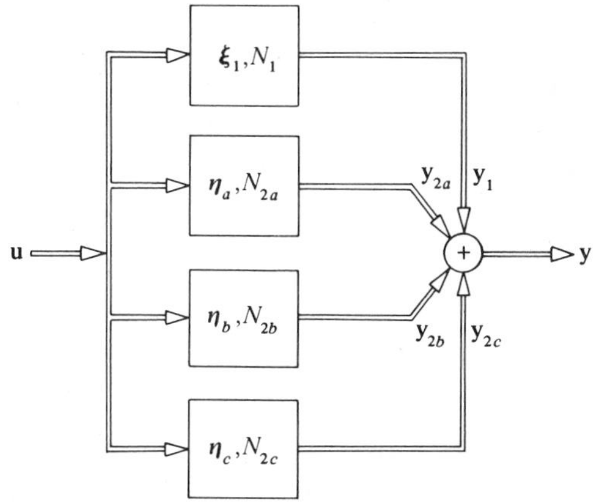

Fig. 5.12. Reduction of a nonminimal system corresponding to Theorem 5.7.

Proof. Theorem 5.6 shows that N_1 is completely controllable on $[t_1, t_2]$ and completely observable on $[t_3, t_4]$. Therefore it suffices to work with N_2.

Assume that $\mathbf{P}_a(t)$ and $\mathbf{Q}_a(\tau)$ have been selected so that the product $\mathbf{P}_a(t)\mathbf{Q}_a(\tau) = \mathbf{0}_{r,m}$. Recall that the dimensions of $\mathbf{P}_a(t)$ and $\mathbf{Q}_a(\tau)$ are $r \times (n - n_0)$ and $(n - n_0) \times m$ where $n \geq n_0$. Denote the number of linearly independent columns of $\mathbf{P}_a(t)$ on $[t_3, t_4]$ by l and the number of linearly independent rows of $\mathbf{Q}_a(\tau)$ on $[t_1, t_2]$ by k_b; ε_1 and ε_2 are any *finite* numbers. Clearly, a constant nonsingular $(n - n_0) \times (n - n_0)$ matrix $\mathbf{D}$ can be found such that

$$\mathbf{P}_a(t)\mathbf{D} = \begin{cases} [\mathbf{P}_{aa}(t) \quad \mathbf{0}_{r,(n-n_0-l)}], & t \in [t_3, t_4] \\ [\mathbf{P}_1(t) \quad \mathbf{P}_2(t)], & t \notin [t_3, t_4] \end{cases} \tag{5.83}$$

where $\mathbf{P}_{aa}(t)$ is an $n \times l$ matrix with linearly independent columns on $[t_3, t_4]$. Let

$$\mathbf{D}^{-1}\mathbf{Q}_a(\tau) = \begin{bmatrix} \mathbf{Q}_{a1}(\tau) \\ \mathbf{Q}_{a2}(\tau) \end{bmatrix}, \quad \tau \in [t_0, t_f] \tag{5.84}$$

where the indicated partitioning is such that $\mathbf{Q}_{a1}(\tau)$ and $\mathbf{Q}_{a2}(\tau)$ are $l \times m$ and $(n - n_0 - l) \times m$ matrices. Multiplication of Eqs. 5.83 and 5.84 gives

$$\mathbf{P}_a(t)\mathbf{Q}_a(\tau) = \mathbf{0}_{r,m} = \begin{cases} \mathbf{P}_{aa}(t)\mathbf{Q}_{a1}(\tau), & t \in [t_3, t_4] \\ \mathbf{P}_1(t)\mathbf{Q}_{a1}(\tau) + \mathbf{P}_2(t)\mathbf{Q}_{a2}(\tau), & t \notin [t_3, t_4] \end{cases} \tag{5.85}$$

However, as the columns of $\mathbf{P}_{aa}(t)$ are linearly independent on $[t_3, t_4]$ $\mathbf{Q}_{a1}(\tau) = \mathbf{0}_{l,m}$ for all τ on $[t_0, t_f]$. Thus

$$\mathbf{D}^{-1}\mathbf{Q}_a(\tau) = \begin{bmatrix} \mathbf{0}_{l,m} \\ \mathbf{Q}_{a2}(\tau) \end{bmatrix}, \quad \tau \in [t_0, t_f] \tag{5.86}$$

and

$$\mathbf{P}_a(t)\mathbf{Q}_a(\tau) = \mathbf{0}_{r,m} = \begin{cases} \mathbf{0}_{r,m}, & t \in [t_3, t_4] \\ \mathbf{P}_2(t)\mathbf{Q}_{a2}(\tau), & \tau \notin [t_3, t_4] \end{cases} \tag{5.87}$$

Similarly, since k_b rows of $\mathbf{Q}_a(\tau)$ are linearly independent on $[t_1, t_2]$ and $\mathbf{D}$ is a nonsingular matrix, $\mathbf{Q}_{a2}(\tau)$ also has k_b linearly independent rows on $[t_1, t_2]$. Therefore a constant nonsingular $(n - n_0 - l) \times (n - n_0 - l)$ matrix $\mathbf{L}$ can be found such that

$$\mathbf{L}^{-1}\mathbf{Q}_{a2}(\tau) = \begin{cases} \begin{bmatrix} \mathbf{Q}_{ab}(\tau) \\ \mathbf{0}_{k_c,m} \end{bmatrix}, & \tau \in [t_1, t_2] \\ \begin{bmatrix} \mathbf{Q}_1(\tau) \\ \mathbf{Q}_2(\tau) \end{bmatrix}, & \tau \notin [t_1, t_2] \end{cases} \tag{5.88}$$

where $\mathbf{Q}_{ab}(\tau)$ is a $k_b \times m$ matrix with linearly independent rows on $[t_1, t_2]$ and

$$k_c = k_b - (n - n_0 - l) \tag{5.89}$$

Define

$$\mathbf{K} \equiv \mathbf{D}(\mathbf{I}_l \dotplus \mathbf{L}) \tag{5.90}$$

Thus $\mathbf{K}$ is a constant $(n - n_0) \times (n - n_0)$ nonsingular matrix, and

$$\mathbf{K}^{-1} = (\mathbf{I}_l \dotplus \mathbf{L}^{-1})\mathbf{D}^{-1} \tag{5.91}$$

Taking the product $\mathbf{P}_a(t)\mathbf{K}$ gives

$$\mathbf{P}_a(t)\mathbf{K} = \begin{cases} [\mathbf{P}_{aa}(t)\,,\ \mathbf{0}_{r,k_b}\,,\ \mathbf{0}_{r,k_c}]\,, & t \in [t_3,\ t_4] \\ [\mathbf{P}_1(t)\mathbf{K}\,,\ \mathbf{P}_2(t)\mathbf{K}]\,, & t \notin [t_3,\ t_4] \end{cases} \tag{5.92}$$

Taking the product $\mathbf{K}^{-1}\mathbf{Q}_a(\tau)$ gives

$$\mathbf{K}^{-1}\mathbf{Q}_a(\tau) = \begin{cases} \begin{bmatrix} \mathbf{0}_{l,m} \\ \mathbf{Q}_{ab}(\tau) \\ \mathbf{0}_{k_c,m} \end{bmatrix}, & \tau \in [t_1,\ t_2] \\ \begin{bmatrix} \mathbf{K}^{-1}\mathbf{Q}_1(\tau) \\ \mathbf{K}^{-1}\mathbf{Q}_2(\tau) \end{bmatrix}, & \tau \notin [t_1,\ t_2] \end{cases} \tag{5.93}$$

Recall from Theorem 5.8 that

$$\begin{aligned} \dot{\boldsymbol{\xi}}_2(t) &= \mathbf{Q}_a(t)\mathbf{u}(t) \\ \mathbf{y}_2(t) &= \mathbf{P}_a(t)\boldsymbol{\xi}_2(t) \end{aligned} \tag{5.94}$$

Rewriting Eq. 5.94 after making the equivalence transformation $\boldsymbol{\eta}(t) = \mathbf{K}^{-1}\boldsymbol{\xi}_2(t)$ gives

$$\begin{aligned} \dot{\boldsymbol{\eta}}(t) &= \mathbf{K}^{-1}\mathbf{Q}_a(t)\mathbf{u}(t) \\ \mathbf{y}_2(t) &= \mathbf{P}_a(t)\mathbf{K}\,\boldsymbol{\eta}(t) \end{aligned} \tag{5.95}$$

Substituting from Eqs. 5.92 and 5.93 in Eqs. 5.95 results in

$$\dot{\boldsymbol{\eta}}(t) = \begin{cases} \begin{bmatrix} \mathbf{0}_{l,m} \\ \mathbf{Q}_{ab}(\tau) \\ \mathbf{0}_{k_c m} \end{bmatrix} \mathbf{u}(t)\,, & t \in [t_1,\ t_2] \\ \begin{bmatrix} \mathbf{K}^{-1}\mathbf{Q}_1(\tau) \\ \mathbf{K}^{-1}\mathbf{Q}_2(\tau) \end{bmatrix} \mathbf{u}(t)\,, & t \notin [t_1,\ t_2] \end{cases} \tag{5.96a}$$

$$\mathbf{y}_2(t) = \begin{cases} [\mathbf{P}_{aa}(t),\ \mathbf{0}_{r,k_b},\ \mathbf{0}_{r,k_c}]\boldsymbol{\eta}(t)\,, & t \in [t_3,\ t_4] \\ [\mathbf{P}_1(t)\mathbf{K},\ \mathbf{P}_2(t)\mathbf{K}]\dot{\boldsymbol{\eta}}(t)\,, & t \notin [t_3,\ t_4] \end{cases} \tag{5.96b}$$

Partitioning Eqs. 5.96 results in the following three systems:

$$N_{2a}: \begin{cases} \dot{\boldsymbol{\eta}}_a(t) = \begin{cases} \mathbf{0}_{l,m}\mathbf{u}(t)\,, & t \in [t_1,\ t_2] \\ \mathbf{B}_a(t)\mathbf{u}(t)\,, & t \notin [t_1,\ t_2] \end{cases} & (5.97a) \\ \mathbf{y}_{2a}(t) = \begin{cases} \mathbf{P}_{aa}(t)\boldsymbol{\eta}_a(t)\,, & t \in [t_3,\ t_4] \\ \mathbf{C}_a(t)\boldsymbol{\eta}_a(t)\,, & t \notin [t_3,\ t_4] \end{cases} & (5.97b) \end{cases}$$

$$N_{2b}: \begin{cases} \dot{\boldsymbol{\eta}}_b(t) = \begin{cases} \mathbf{Q}_{ab}(t)\mathbf{u}(t)\,, & t \in [t_1,\ t_2] \\ \mathbf{B}_b(t)\mathbf{u}(t)\,, & t \notin [t_1,\ t_2] \end{cases} & (5.98a) \\ \mathbf{y}_{2b}(t) = \begin{cases} \mathbf{0}_{r,k_b}\boldsymbol{\eta}_b(t)\,, & t \in [t_3,\ t_4] \\ \mathbf{C}_b(t)\boldsymbol{\eta}_b(t)\,, & t \notin [t_3,\ t_4] \end{cases} & (5.98b) \end{cases}$$

$$N_{2c}: \begin{cases} \dot{\eta}_c(t) = \begin{cases} \mathbf{0}_{k_c,m}\mathbf{u}(t), & t \in [t_1, t_2] \\ \mathbf{B}_c(t)\mathbf{u}(t), & t \notin [t_1, t_2] \end{cases} & (5.99a) \\ \mathbf{y}_{2c}(t) = \begin{cases} \mathbf{0}_{r,k_c}\eta_c(t), & t \in [t_3, t_4] \\ \mathbf{C}_c(t)\eta_c(t), & t \notin [t_3, t_4] \end{cases} & (5.99b) \end{cases}$$

where

$$\eta(t) = \begin{bmatrix} \eta_a(t) \\ \eta_b(t) \\ \eta_c(t) \end{bmatrix} \tag{5.100}$$

$$\mathbf{y}_2(t) = \mathbf{y}_{2a}(t) + \mathbf{y}_{2b}(t) + \mathbf{y}_{2c}(t) \tag{5.101}$$

Equations 5.97 show that subsystem N_{2a} is completely uncontrollable on $[t_1, t_2]$ and completely observable on $[t_3, t_4]$; Eqs. 5.98 show that subsystem N_{2b} is completely controllable on $[t_1, t_2]$ and completely unobservable on $[t_3, t_4]$; Eqs. 5.99 show that subsystem N_{2c} is completely uncontrollable on $[t_1, t_2]$ and completely unobservable on $[t_3, t_4]$. Q.E.D.

5.4.4. Illustrative Examples

Example 5.7. The completely controllable, completely observable, reducible system analyzed in Example 5.3 is again considered. As shown

$$\Omega(t, \tau) = [e^{a(t-T)} \; c_2(t)e^{a(t-T)}] \begin{bmatrix} b_1(\tau)e^{a(T-\tau)} \\ b_2(\tau)e^{a(T-\tau)} \end{bmatrix}$$
$$= \mathbf{P}(t)\mathbf{Q}(\tau)$$

and

$$\Omega(t, \tau) = e^{a(t-T)}e^{a(T-\tau)} = \mathbf{P}_0(t)\mathbf{Q}_0(t)$$

Thus

$$\mathbf{N}(T, t_f) = \int_T^{t_f} \mathbf{P}_0'(t)\mathbf{P}_0(t)dt = \frac{1}{2a}[e^{2a(t_f-T)} - 1]$$

and

$$\mathbf{M}(t_0, T) = \int_{t_0}^{T} \mathbf{Q}_0(\tau)\mathbf{Q}_0'(\tau)d\tau = \frac{1}{2a}[e^{2a(T-t_0)} - 1]$$

Using Eqs. 5.20 and 5.24 it is determined that

$$\mathbf{U}(T, t_f) = [1, \; 1]$$

$$\mathbf{V}(t_0, T) = \begin{bmatrix} 1 \\ 0 \end{bmatrix}$$

verifying that

$$\mathbf{U}(T, t_f)\mathbf{V}(t_0, T) = 1$$

An equivalence transformation relating the two decompositions is now determined. A matrix **K** is determined satisfying Eqs. 5.34:

$$\mathbf{U}(T, t_f) = \mathbf{JK}$$

implies

$$[1 \;\; 1] = [1 \;\; 0]\begin{bmatrix} 1 & 1 \\ k_3 & k_4 \end{bmatrix}$$

and

$$\mathbf{V}(t_0, T) = K^{-1}\mathbf{J}'$$

implies

$$\begin{bmatrix} 1 \\ 0 \end{bmatrix} = \frac{1}{\Delta_k}\begin{bmatrix} 1 & -k_2 \\ 0 & k_1 \end{bmatrix}\begin{bmatrix} 1 \\ 0 \end{bmatrix}$$

where

$$\Delta_k = \det \mathbf{K}$$

It can be verified that these equations are satisfied by

$$k_3 = 0$$

$$k_1 = k_2 = k_4 = 1$$

i.e., by

$$\mathbf{K} = \begin{bmatrix} 1 & 1 \\ 0 & 1 \end{bmatrix}$$

and

$$\mathbf{K}^{-1} = \begin{bmatrix} 1 & -1 \\ 0 & 1 \end{bmatrix}$$

Thus, applying Eq. 5.52 gives a desired equivalence transformation relating the decompositions $\mathbf{P}_0(t)\mathbf{Q}_0(\tau)$ and $\mathbf{P}(t)\mathbf{Q}(\tau)$:

$$\begin{aligned}
\mathbf{T}(t) &= [\phi_0(t, t_0) \dotplus \mathbf{I}_{n-n_0}]\,\mathbf{K}\phi(t_0, t) \\
&= \begin{bmatrix} e^{a(t-t_0)} & 0 \\ 0 & 1 \end{bmatrix}\begin{bmatrix} 1 & 1 \\ 0 & 1 \end{bmatrix}\begin{bmatrix} e^{a(t_0-t)} & 0 \\ 0 & e^{a(t_0-t)} \end{bmatrix} \\
&= \begin{bmatrix} 1 & 1 \\ 0 & e^{a(t_0-t)} \end{bmatrix}
\end{aligned}$$

$$\mathbf{T}^{-1}(t) = \begin{bmatrix} 1 & -e^{-a(t_0-t)} \\ 0 & e^{-a(t_0-t)} \end{bmatrix}$$

$$\dot{\mathbf{T}}(t) = \begin{bmatrix} 0 & 0 \\ 0 & -e^{a(t_0-t)} \end{bmatrix}$$

Therefore

$$\mathbf{A}_T(t) = \mathbf{T}(t)\mathbf{A}(t)\mathbf{T}^{-1}(t) + \dot{\mathbf{T}}(t)\mathbf{T}^{-1}(t) = \begin{bmatrix} a & 0 \\ 0 & 0 \end{bmatrix}$$

$$\mathbf{B}_T(t) = \mathbf{T}(t)\mathbf{B}(t) = \begin{bmatrix} 1 \\ b_2(t)e^{a(t_0-t)} \end{bmatrix}$$

$$\mathbf{C}_T(t) = \mathbf{C}(t)\mathbf{T}^{-1}(t) = [1,\ (c_2(t) - 1)e^{-a(t_0-t)}]$$

Thus

$$\Omega(t, \tau) = \mathbf{C}_T(t)\phi_T(t, \tau)\mathbf{B}_T(\tau) = [1,\ (c_2(t) - 1)e^{-a(t_0-t)}]\begin{bmatrix} e^{a(t-\tau)} & 0 & 1 \\ 0 & 0 & b_2(t)e^{a(t_0-t)} \end{bmatrix} = e^{a(t-\tau)}$$

The transformed system is characterized by

$$\begin{bmatrix} \dot{\xi}_1(t) \\ \dot{\xi}_2(t) \end{bmatrix} = \begin{bmatrix} a & 0 \\ 0 & 0 \end{bmatrix}\begin{bmatrix} \xi_1(t) \\ \xi_2(t) \end{bmatrix} + \begin{bmatrix} 1 \\ b_2(t)e^{a(t_0-t)} \end{bmatrix}\mathbf{u}(t)$$

$$y(t) = [1,\ (c_2(t) - 1)e^{-a(t_0-t)}]\begin{bmatrix} \xi_1(t) \\ \xi_2(t) \end{bmatrix}$$

Example 5.8. Consider the system with the impulsive response

$$\Omega(t, \tau) = f_1(t)g_1(\tau) + f_2(t)g_2(\tau)$$

having the decomposition

$$\Omega(t, \tau) = \left[p(t),\ \frac{1}{2}f_1(t),\ f_2(t),\ \frac{1}{2}f_1(t),\ 0\right]\begin{bmatrix} 0 \\ g_1(\tau) \\ g_2(\tau) \\ g_1(\tau) \\ q(\tau) \end{bmatrix} = \mathbf{P}(t)\mathbf{Q}(\tau)$$

Clearly, if $f_1(t)$ and $f_2(t)$ are linearly independent on $[t_f - \varepsilon_2, t_f]$ and $g_1(\tau)$ and $g_2(\tau)$ are linearly independent on $[t_0, t_0 + \varepsilon_1]$ for any finite ε_1 and ε_2, then a minimal realization is obtained from the decomposition

$$\Omega(t, \tau) = [f_1(t)\ f_2(t)]\begin{bmatrix} g_1(\tau) \\ g_2(\tau) \end{bmatrix} = \mathbf{P}_0(t)\mathbf{Q}_0(\tau)$$

The nonsingular 2×2 matrices $\mathbf{N}(t_f - \varepsilon_2, t_f)$ and $\mathbf{M}(t_0, t_0 + \varepsilon_1)$ are determined from Eq. 4.103 and 4.20:

$$\mathbf{N}(t_f - \varepsilon_2, t_f) = \int_{t_f-\varepsilon_2}^{t_f} \begin{bmatrix} f_1(t) \\ f_2(t) \end{bmatrix}[f_1(t)\ f(t_2)]\,dt = \int_{t_f-\varepsilon_2}^{t_f} \begin{bmatrix} f_1^2(t) & f_1(t)f_2(t) \\ f_1(t)f_2(t) & f_2^2(t) \end{bmatrix} dt \equiv \begin{bmatrix} F_{11} & F_{12} \\ F_{12} & F_{22} \end{bmatrix}$$

$$\mathbf{M}(t_0, t_0 + \varepsilon_1) = \int_{t_0}^{t_0+\varepsilon_1} \begin{bmatrix} g_1(\tau) \\ g_2(\tau) \end{bmatrix} [g_1(\tau)\, g_2(\tau)]\, d\tau$$

$$\equiv \begin{bmatrix} G_{11} & G_{12} \\ G_{12} & G_{22} \end{bmatrix}$$

Therefore

$$\mathbf{N}^{-1}(t_f - \varepsilon_2, t_f) = \frac{1}{\Delta_F} \begin{bmatrix} F_{22} & -F_{12} \\ -F_{12} & F_{11} \end{bmatrix}$$

$$\mathbf{M}^{-1}(t_0, t_0 + \varepsilon_1) = \frac{1}{\Delta_G} \begin{bmatrix} G_{22} & -G_{12} \\ -G_{12} & G_{11} \end{bmatrix}$$

where

$$\Delta_F = F_{11}F_{22} - F_{12}^2$$

$$\Delta_G = G_{11}G_{22} - G_{12}^2$$

Since

$$\Omega(t, \tau) = \mathbf{P}_0(t)\mathbf{Q}_0(\tau) = \mathbf{P}(t)\mathbf{Q}(\tau)$$

the matrices $\mathbf{U}(t_f - \varepsilon_2, t_f)$ and $\mathbf{V}(t_0, t_0 + \varepsilon_1)$ of rank 2 are determined from Eqs. 5.20 and 5.24:

$$\mathbf{U}(t_f - \varepsilon_2, t_f) = \mathbf{N}^{-1}(t_f - \varepsilon_2, t_f) \int_{t_f-\varepsilon_2}^{t_f} \begin{bmatrix} f_1(t) \\ f_2(t) \end{bmatrix} \left[p(t), \frac{1}{2} f_1(t), f_2(t), \frac{1}{2} f_1(t), 0 \right] dt$$

$$= \frac{1}{\Delta_F} \begin{bmatrix} F_{22} & -F_{12} \\ -F_{12} & F_{11} \end{bmatrix} \begin{bmatrix} F_{1p} & \frac{1}{2} F_{11} & F_{12} & \frac{1}{2} F_{11} & 0 \\ F_{2p} & \frac{1}{2} F_{12} & F_{22} & \frac{1}{2} F_{12} & 0 \end{bmatrix}$$

$$= \begin{bmatrix} F_a & \frac{1}{2} & 0 & \frac{1}{2} & 0 \\ F_b & 0 & 1 & 0 & 0 \end{bmatrix}$$

$$\mathbf{V}(t_0, t_0 + \varepsilon_1) = \int_{t_0}^{t_0+\varepsilon_1} \begin{bmatrix} 0 \\ g_1(\tau) \\ g_2(\tau) \\ g_1(\tau) \\ q(\tau) \end{bmatrix} [g_1(\tau)\, g_2(\tau)]\, d\tau\, \mathbf{M}^{-1}(t_0, t_0 + \varepsilon_1)$$

$$= \begin{bmatrix} 0 & 0 \\ 1 & 0 \\ 0 & 1 \\ 1 & 0 \\ G_a & G_b \end{bmatrix}$$

Clearly, the product

$$\mathbf{U}(t_f, - \varepsilon_2, t_f)\, \mathbf{V}(t_0, t_0 + \varepsilon_1) = \mathbf{I}_2$$

Also

$$\mathbf{U}(t_f - \varepsilon_2, t_f)\mathbf{Q}(\tau) = \begin{bmatrix} F_a & \frac{1}{2} & 0 & \frac{1}{2} & 0 \\ F_b & 0 & 1 & 0 & 0 \end{bmatrix} \begin{bmatrix} 0 \\ g_1(\tau) \\ g_2(\tau) \\ g_1(\tau) \\ q(\tau) \end{bmatrix}$$

$$= [f_1(t)\ f_2(t)] = \mathbf{P}_0(t)$$

Consider the two realizations of $\Omega(t, \tau)$ corresponding to the two decompositions $\mathbf{P}_0(t)\mathbf{Q}_0(\tau)$ and $\mathbf{P}(t)\mathbf{Q}(\tau)$ as given by Eq. 5.7:

$$\dot{\xi}_1(t) = \mathbf{Q}_0(t)\mathbf{u}(t) = \mathbf{B}_0(t)\mathbf{u}(t)$$
$$y(t) = \mathbf{P}_0(t)\xi_1(t) = \mathbf{C}_0(t)\xi_1(t)$$

and

$$\dot{\mathbf{x}}(t) = \mathbf{Q}(t)\mathbf{u}(t) = \mathbf{B}(t)\mathbf{u}(t)$$
$$y(t) = \mathbf{P}(t)\mathbf{x}(t) = \mathbf{C}(t)\mathbf{x}(t)$$

In accordance with Theorem 5.6, an equivalence transformation $\xi(t) = \mathbf{T}(t)\mathbf{x}(t)$ can be determined so that the latter system can be transformed to

$$\begin{bmatrix} \dot{\xi}_1(t) \\ \dot{\xi}_2(t) \end{bmatrix} = \begin{bmatrix} \mathbf{Q}_0(t) \\ \mathbf{Q}_a(t) \end{bmatrix} u(t)$$

$$y(t) = y_1(t) + y_2(t) = [\mathbf{P}_0(t)\ \mathbf{P}_a(t)] \begin{bmatrix} \xi_1(t) \\ \xi_2(t) \end{bmatrix}$$

The nonsingular matrix $\mathbf{T}(t)$ defining such a transformation is given by Eq. 5.52. In the evalution of $\mathbf{T}(t)$ from Eq. 5.52 it is noted that for this case $\phi_0(t, t_0) = \mathbf{I}_2$, $\phi(t, t_0) = \mathbf{I}_5$ and $\mathbf{K}$ satisfies Eqs. 5.34. Thus in this case $\mathbf{T}(t) = \mathbf{K}$:

$$\mathbf{T}(t) = \begin{bmatrix} F_a & 1/2 & 0 & 1/2 & 0 \\ F_b & 0 & 1 & 0 & 0 \\ -(F_aG_a + F_bG_b) & -G_a & -G_b & 0 & 1 \\ 0 & 1 & 0 & -1 & 0 \\ 1 & 0 & 0 & 0 & 0 \end{bmatrix}$$

From Eqs. 5.58 it is determined that

$$[\mathbf{C}_0(t)\ \mathbf{P}_a(t)] = \mathbf{C}(t)\mathbf{T}^{-1}(t)$$

$$= \left[p(t), \frac{1}{2}f_1(t), f_2(t), \frac{1}{2}f_1(t), 0\right] \begin{bmatrix} 0 & 0 & 0 & 0 & 1 \\ 1 & 0 & 0 & \frac{1}{2} & -F_a \\ 0 & 1 & 0 & 0 & -F_b \\ 1 & 0 & 0 & -\frac{1}{2} & -F_2 \\ G_a & G_b & 1 & \frac{1}{2}G_a & 0 \end{bmatrix}$$

$$= [f_1(t)\ f_2(t) \ \vdots\ 0\ \ 0\ \ p(t)]$$

$$\begin{bmatrix} \mathbf{B}_0(t) \\ \cdots\cdots \\ \mathbf{Q}_a(t) \end{bmatrix} = \mathbf{T}(t)\mathbf{B}(t)$$

$$= \begin{bmatrix} F_a & 1/2 & 0 & 1/2 & 0 & 0 \\ F_b & 0 & 1 & 0 & 0 & g_1(t) \\ -(F_aG_a + F_bG_b) & -G_a & -G_b & 0 & 1 & g_2(t) \\ 0 & 1 & 0 & -1 & 0 & g_1(t) \\ 1 & 0 & 0 & 0 & 0 & q(t) \end{bmatrix}$$

$$= \begin{bmatrix} g_1(t) \\ g_2(t) \\ \cdots\cdots\cdots\cdots\cdots\cdots \\ -G_ag_1(t) - G_bg_2(t) + g(t) \\ 0 \\ 0 \end{bmatrix}$$

Thus

$$\mathbf{P}_a(t) = [0 \;\; 0 \;\; p(t)]$$

$$\mathbf{Q}_a(t) = \begin{bmatrix} -G_ag_1(t) - G_bg_2(t) + g(t) \\ 0 \\ 0 \end{bmatrix}$$

and $\mathbf{P}_a(t)\mathbf{Q}_a(\tau) = 0$ as required.

In accordance with Theorem 5.7, the subsystem

$$\dot{\xi}_2(t) = \begin{bmatrix} -G_ag_1(t) - G_bg_2(t) + g(t) \\ 0 \\ 0 \end{bmatrix} u(t)$$

$$y_2(t) = [0 \;\; 0 \;\; p(t)]\,\xi_2(t)$$

can be transformed (in this case the identity transformation and a simple partitioning is sufficient) into the three subsystems:

$$N_{2a}: \begin{cases} \dot{\eta}_a(t) = [-G_ag_1(t) - G_bg_2(t) + g(t)]\,u(t) \\ y_{2a}(t) = 0 \end{cases}$$

$$N_{2b}: \begin{cases} \dot{\eta}_b(t) = 0 \\ y_{2b}(t) = 0 \end{cases}$$

$$N_{2c}: \begin{cases} \dot{\eta}_c(t) = 0 \\ y_{2c}(t) = p(t)\eta_c(t) \end{cases}$$

Theorems 5.3 and 5.7, and their associated corollaries accomplish the following:

1. They establish the fact that a minimal realization of the impulsive-response matrix $\Omega(t, \tau)$ on $[t_0, t_f]$ is completely controllable on an interval preceding an interval of complete observability.
2. They give criteria to establish whether or not a given system is reduced.
3. They establish critical relations existing between any realization

of $\Omega(t, \tau)$ and a minimal realization of $\Omega(t, \tau)$, thus providing a method for generating realizations from a minimal realization.

4. They introduce a canonical structure, which any system can be transformed to, separating the reduced subsystem contributing to the impulsive-response matrix from the rest of the system.

They do *not*, however, provide an algorithm for reducing a given arbitrary system to its minimal realization and should not be construed as such. They do not even provide a method for determining what the minimum order n_0 of a system is. These important problems are considered in the next chapter.

REFERENCES

[1] Desoer, C., and P. Variya, "The Minimal Realization of a Nonanticipative Impulse Response Matrix," *J. SIAM Applied Math.*, vol. 15, no. 3 (1967), pp. 754–764.

[2] Kalman, R., "Mathematical Description of Linear Dynamical Systems," *J. SIAM Control*, vol. 1, no. 2 (1963), pp. 152–192.

[3] Silverman, L., *Representation and Realization of Time-Variable Linear Systems*, Technical Report No. 94, Dept. Electrical Engineering, Columbia University, New York, June 1966.

[4] Youla, D. C., "The Synthesis of Linear Dynamical Systems from Prescribed Weighting Patterns," *J. SIAM Applied Math.*, vol. 14, no. 3 (1966), pp. 527–549.

[5] D'Angelo, H., and C. Glass, "Controllability and Reducibility of Nonanalytic Time-Varying Systems," *Proceedings Princeton Conference on Information Sciences and Systems*, March 1968.

PROBLEMS

5.1 Synthesize systems, with nonzero A-matrices having the following impulsive responses:

(i) $\Omega(t, \tau) = e^{-(t-\tau)} + 2e^{-2(t-\tau)}$

(ii) $\Omega(t, \tau) = (t-\tau)e^{-(t-\tau)} + 3\sin[2(t-\tau)]$

(iii) $\Omega(t, \tau) = \sin t \log \tau + (t-\tau)^2 \log t \cos \tau$

(iv) $\Omega(t, \tau) = \begin{bmatrix} e^{-(t-\tau)} & 2e^{-2(t-\tau)} \\ 3\sin[2(t-\tau)] & (t-\tau)e^{-(t-\tau)} \\ \sin t \log \tau & (t-\tau)^2 \log t \cos \tau \end{bmatrix}$

5.2 Determine an equivalence transformation which will put the following system into the canonical form of Eqs. 5.10. Sketch the state-variable diagram of the canonical system.

$$\begin{bmatrix} \dot{x}_1(t) \\ \dot{x}_2(t) \\ \dot{x}_3(t) \end{bmatrix} = \begin{bmatrix} 3 & -1 & 0 \\ 1 & 1 & 0 \\ 1 & -1 & -1 \end{bmatrix} \begin{bmatrix} x_1(t) \\ x_2(t) \\ x_3(t) \end{bmatrix} + \begin{bmatrix} 1 \\ 0 \\ 1 \end{bmatrix} u(t)$$

$$y(t) = [0 \quad -1 \quad 0] \begin{bmatrix} x_1(t) \\ x_2(t) \\ x_3(t) \end{bmatrix}$$

5.3 Prove Corollary 5.3.

5.4 Prove Corollary 5.4.

5.5 Prove Corollary 5.5a.

5.6 Prove Corollary 5.5b.

5.7 Consider the system characterized by the state-variable equations

$$\begin{bmatrix} \dot{x}_1(t) \\ \dot{x}_2(t) \end{bmatrix} = \begin{bmatrix} 3/2 & 1/2 \\ 1/2 & 3/2 \end{bmatrix} \begin{bmatrix} x_1(t) \\ x_2(t) \end{bmatrix} + \begin{bmatrix} 1 \\ -f_1(t) + f_2(t) \end{bmatrix} u(t)$$

$$y(t) = [1/2 + 1/2\, f_1(t)\,, \quad -1/2 + 1/2\, f_2(t)] \begin{bmatrix} x_1(t) \\ x_2(t) \end{bmatrix}$$

where

$$f_1(t) = \delta^{(-1)}(t) - \delta^{(-1)}(t-1)$$
$$f_2(t) = \delta^{(-1)}(t-1) - \delta^{(-1)}(t-2)$$

Discuss controllability, observability, and reducibility of this system on the interval [0, 2]. Sketch the controllability-observability plane for the system.

5.8 In accordance with Theorem 5.5, determine the equivalence transformation $\mathbf{T}(t)$ relating the system of Prob. 5.7 to an equivalent minimal system.

5.9 In accordance with Theorem 5.5, determine the equivalence transformation $\mathbf{T}(t)$ relating the system of Prob. 5.2 to an equivalent minimal system.

6

System Reduction and Synthesis

6.1. INTRODUCTION

In this chapter algorithms are developed for determining equivalence transformations for either reducing a system or putting it into some desirable canonical form. Fundamental to the algorithms developed are the controllability and observability matrices $\mathbf{Q}_c(t)$ and $\mathbf{Q}_0(t)$ defined in Chapter 4. It is convenient for what follows to determine what the effect of an equivalence transformation is on these matrices.

As shown in Sect. 3.5, equivalence transformations of the type

$$\mathbf{z}(t) = \mathbf{T}(t)\mathbf{x}(t) \tag{6.1}$$

where $\mathbf{T}(t)$ is a nonsingular $n \times n$ matrix, can be used to define a new state variable $\mathbf{z}(t)$ which may render a system more tractable for analysis or synthesis. Here the implications of such a transformation on the controllability and observability matrices are considered. The equivalence transformation indicated by Eq. 6.1 applied to the system

$$\begin{aligned} \dot{\mathbf{x}}(t) &= \mathbf{A}(t)\mathbf{x}(t) + \mathbf{B}(t)\mathbf{u}(t) \\ \mathbf{y}(t) &= \mathbf{C}(t)\mathbf{x}(t) \end{aligned} \tag{6.2}$$

results in the transformed system

$$\begin{aligned} \dot{\mathbf{z}}(t) &= \mathbf{A}_T(t)\mathbf{z}(t) + \mathbf{B}_T(t)\mathbf{u}(t) \\ \mathbf{y}(t) &= \mathbf{C}_T(t)\mathbf{z}(t) \end{aligned} \tag{6.3}$$

where

$$\begin{aligned} \mathbf{A}_T(t) &= \mathbf{T}(t)\mathbf{A}(t)\mathbf{T}^{-1}(t) + \dot{\mathbf{T}}(t)\mathbf{T}^{-1}(t) \\ \mathbf{B}_T(t) &= \mathbf{T}(t)\mathbf{B}(t) \\ \mathbf{C}_T(t) &= \mathbf{C}(t)\mathbf{T}^{-1}(t) \end{aligned} \tag{6.4}$$

Thus the controllability and observability matrices of the original system

$$\mathbf{Q}_c(t) = [\mathbf{B}(t), \Delta_c\mathbf{B}(t), \cdots, \Delta_c^{n-1}\mathbf{B}(t)] \tag{6.5}$$

$$\mathbf{Q}_0(t) = [\mathbf{C}'(t), \Delta_0\mathbf{C}'(t), \cdots, \Delta_0^{n-1}\mathbf{C}'(t)] \tag{6.6}$$

are transformed to

$$\mathbf{Q}_{Tc}(t) = [\mathbf{B}_T(t), \Delta_{Tc}\mathbf{B}_T(t), \cdots, \Delta_{Tc}^{n-1}\mathbf{B}_T(t)] \tag{6.7}$$

$$\mathbf{Q}_{T0}(t) = [\mathbf{C}'(t), \Delta_{T0}\mathbf{C}'_T(t), \cdots, \Delta_{T0}^{n-1}\mathbf{C}'_T(t)] \tag{6.8}$$

It is desirable to relate these matrices directly through the transformation matrix $\mathbf{T}(t)$. Since

$$\mathbf{B}_T(t) = \mathbf{T}(t)\mathbf{B}(t) \tag{6.9}$$

and

$$\begin{aligned} \Delta_{Tc} &= -\mathbf{A}_T(t) + \frac{d}{dt} \\ &= -\mathbf{T}(t)\mathbf{A}(t)\mathbf{T}^{-1}(t) - \dot{\mathbf{T}}(t)\mathbf{T}^{-1}(t) + \frac{d}{dt} \end{aligned} \tag{6.10}$$

it follows that

$$\begin{aligned} \Delta_{Tc}\mathbf{B}_T(t) &= -\mathbf{T}(t)\mathbf{A}(t)\mathbf{B}(t) + \mathbf{T}(t)\frac{d\mathbf{B}(t)}{dt} \\ &= \mathbf{T}(t)\Delta_c\mathbf{B}(t) \end{aligned} \tag{6.11}$$

It can be shown that in general

$$\Delta^i{}_{Tc}\mathbf{B}_T(t) = \mathbf{T}(t)\Delta_c^i\mathbf{B}(t) \tag{6.12}$$

Similarly,

$$\Delta^i{}_{T0}\mathbf{C}'_T(t) = (\mathbf{T}^{-1}(t))'\Delta_0^i\mathbf{C}'(t) \tag{6.13}$$

Substituting from Eqs. 6.12 and 6.13 in Eqs. 6.7 and 6.8 respectively, it is seen that

$$\mathbf{Q}_{Tc}(t) = \mathbf{T}(t)\mathbf{Q}_c(t) \tag{6.14}$$

$$\mathbf{Q}_{T0}(t) = (\mathbf{T}^{-1}(t))'\mathbf{Q}_0(t) \tag{6.15}$$

Equations 6.14 and 6.15 verify the fact that a nonsingular transformation of the state variables of the form $\mathbf{z}(t) = \mathbf{T}(t)\mathbf{x}(t)$ does not change either the controllability or observability properties of the system.

6.2. REDUCING A SYSTEM [11]

Although many of the properties of linear systems with regard to reducibility are investigated in detail in Chapter 5, no definitive algorithmic procedure is advanced for reducing a system. In this section an algorithm is developed which can be used to reduce a large class of systems. Since reducibility is so closely related to total controllability and total observability, it is somewhat natural that the reduction procedure involves extracting the totally controllable and totally observable portions of the system in two distinct steps. This process motivates the definitions of *reducibility from the input* and *reducibility from the output.*

Definition 6.1. A system is *reducible* (*from the input*) on the interval $[t_0, t_f]$ to order $k \leq n$, and to no lower order, if there exists an equivalence transformation $\mathbf{z}(t) = \mathbf{T}(t)\mathbf{x}(t)$ such that

$$\begin{bmatrix} \dot{\mathbf{z}}_1(t) \\ \dot{\mathbf{z}}_2(t) \end{bmatrix} = \begin{bmatrix} \mathbf{A}_{11}(t) & \mathbf{A}_{12}(t) \\ \mathbf{0} & \mathbf{A}_{22}(t) \end{bmatrix} \begin{bmatrix} \mathbf{z}_1(t) \\ \mathbf{z}_2(t) \end{bmatrix} + \begin{bmatrix} \mathbf{B}_1(t) \\ \mathbf{0} \end{bmatrix} \mathbf{u}(t) \tag{6.16}$$

$$\mathbf{y}(t) = \mathbf{y}_1(t) + \mathbf{y}_2(t) = [\mathbf{C}_1(t) \quad \mathbf{C}_2(t)]\mathbf{z}(t)$$

and the kth-order subsystem

$$\begin{aligned} \dot{\mathbf{z}}_1(t) &= \mathbf{A}_{11}(t)\mathbf{z}_1(t) + \mathbf{B}_1(t)\mathbf{u}(t) \\ \mathbf{y}_1(t) &= \mathbf{C}_1(t)\mathbf{z}_1(t) \end{aligned} \tag{6.17}$$

is totally controllable on any finite subinterval of $[t_0, t_f]$.

Reduction from the output is defined in a dual manner:

Definition 6.2. A system is *reducible* (*from the output*) on the interval $[t_0, t_f]$ to order $k \leq n$, and to no lower order, if there exists an equivalence transformation $\mathbf{w}(t) = \mathbf{T}(t)\mathbf{x}(t)$ such that

$$\begin{bmatrix} \dot{\mathbf{w}}_1(t) \\ \dot{\mathbf{w}}_2(t) \end{bmatrix} = \begin{bmatrix} \mathbf{A}_{11}(t) & \mathbf{0} \\ \mathbf{A}_{21}(t) & \mathbf{A}_{22}(t) \end{bmatrix} \begin{bmatrix} \mathbf{w}_1(t) \\ \mathbf{w}_2(t) \end{bmatrix} + \begin{bmatrix} \mathbf{B}_1(t) \\ \mathbf{B}_2(t) \end{bmatrix} \mathbf{u}(t) \tag{6.18}$$

$$\mathbf{y}(t) = [\mathbf{C}_1(t) \quad \mathbf{0}]\mathbf{w}(t)$$

and the kth-order subsystem

$$\begin{aligned} \dot{\mathbf{w}}_1(t) &= \mathbf{A}_{11}(t)\mathbf{w}_1(t) + \mathbf{B}_1(t)\mathbf{u}(t) \\ \mathbf{y}(t) &= \mathbf{C}_1(t)\mathbf{w}_1(t) \end{aligned} \tag{6.19}$$

is totally observable on any finite subinterval of $[t_0, t_f]$.

From the dual nature of controllability and observability established in Theorem 4.15, it follows that any results obtained concerning reducibility from the input can be effected in a dual manner to obtain similar results concerning reducibility from the output. Thus in what follows only reducibility from the input is discussed.

Transforming the system

$$\begin{aligned} \dot{\mathbf{x}}(t) &= \mathbf{A}(t)\mathbf{x}(t) + \mathbf{B}(t)\mathbf{u}(t) \\ \mathbf{y}(t) &= \mathbf{C}(t)\mathbf{x}(t) \end{aligned} \tag{6.20}$$

with the nonsingular transformation $\mathbf{z}(t) = \mathbf{T}(t)\mathbf{x}(t)$ results in the transformed system of Eq. 6.16 which is reduced from the input. As the reduced system results in two subsystems, controllable and uncontrollable, the controllability matrix of the reduced system can be written as

$$\mathbf{Q}_{Tc}(t) = \mathbf{T}(t)\mathbf{Q}_c(t) = \begin{bmatrix} \mathbf{Q}_{Tc1}(t) \\ \mathbf{0} \end{bmatrix} \tag{6.21}$$

where $\mathbf{Q}_{Tc1}$ is a $k \times nm$ matrix of rank k.

Theorem 6.1. If a nonsingular transformation $\mathbf{z}(t) = \mathbf{T}(t)\mathbf{x}(t)$ exists such that

$$\mathbf{Q}_{Tc}(t) = \mathbf{T}(t)\mathbf{Q}_c(t) = \begin{bmatrix} \mathbf{Q}_{Tc1}(t) \\ \mathbf{0} \end{bmatrix} \tag{6.22}$$

where $\mathbf{Q}_{Tc1}(t)$ has rank k almost everywhere, then the original system is reducible from the input to a kth-order *totally* controllable subsystem.

Proof. The general form of the transformed system is

$$\begin{bmatrix} \dot{\mathbf{z}}_1(t) \\ \dot{\mathbf{z}}_2(t) \end{bmatrix} = \begin{bmatrix} \mathbf{A}_{11}(t) & \mathbf{A}_{12}(t) \\ \mathbf{A}_{21}(t) & \mathbf{A}_{22}(t) \end{bmatrix} \begin{bmatrix} \mathbf{z}_1(t) \\ \mathbf{z}_2(t) \end{bmatrix} + \begin{bmatrix} \mathbf{B}_1(t) \\ \mathbf{B}_2(t) \end{bmatrix} \mathbf{u}(t) \tag{6.23}$$

The system is reduced from the input if $\mathbf{Q}_{Tc}(t)$ as given in Eq. 6.22 implies that $\mathbf{A}_{21}(t) = \mathbf{0}$ and $\mathbf{B}_2(t) = \mathbf{0}$. By construction of the controllability matrix of the transformed system $\mathbf{Q}_{Tc}(t)$ from Eq. 6.23 it is shown that if $\mathbf{Q}_{Tc}(t)$ has the form of Eq. 6.22, then

$$\mathbf{Q}_{Tc1} = [\mathbf{B}_1(t), \Delta_{Tc1}\mathbf{B}_1(t), \cdots, \Delta_{Tc1}^{n-1}\mathbf{B}_1(t)] \tag{6.24}$$

and

$$\mathbf{B}_2(t) = \mathbf{A}_{21}(t)\mathbf{B}_1(t) = \mathbf{A}_{21}(t)\Delta_{Tc1}\mathbf{B}_1(t) = \cdots = \mathbf{A}_{21}(t)\Delta_{Tc1}^{n-2}\mathbf{B}_1(t) = \mathbf{0} \tag{6.25}$$

where

$$\Delta_{Tc1}(t) = -\mathbf{A}_{11}(t) + \frac{d}{dt} \tag{6.26}$$

Thus

$$\mathbf{B}_2(t) = \mathbf{0} \tag{6.27}$$

and

$$\mathbf{A}_{21}(t)[\mathbf{B}_1(t), \Delta_{Tc1}\mathbf{B}_1(t), \cdots, \Delta_{Tc1}^{n-2}\mathbf{B}_1(t)] = \mathbf{0} \tag{6.28}$$

However, if $k < n$, then $k - 1 \leq n - 2$. Thus

$$\begin{aligned} \operatorname{rank} \mathbf{Q}_{Tc1} &= \operatorname{rank} [\mathbf{B}_1(t), \Delta_{Tc1}\mathbf{B}_1(t), \cdots, \Delta_{Tc1}^{n-1}\mathbf{B}_1(t)] \\ &= \operatorname{rank} [\mathbf{B}_1(t), \Delta_{Tc1}\mathbf{B}_1(t), \cdots, \Delta_{Tc1}^{k-1}\mathbf{B}_1(t)] \\ &= \operatorname{rank} [\mathbf{B}_1(t), \Delta_{Tc1}\mathbf{B}_1(t), \cdots, \Delta_{Tc1}^{n-2}\mathbf{B}_1(t)] \\ &= k \end{aligned} \tag{6.29}$$

almost everywhere. Therefore $\mathbf{A}_{21}(t) = \mathbf{0}$. Q.E.D.

Theorem 6.2. A matrix $\mathbf{T}(t)$ satisfying Theorem 6.1 exists if and only if $\mathbf{Q}_c(t)$ has rank k almost everywhere, and the first km columns of $\mathbf{Q}_c(t)$ can be factored in the form $\mathbf{R}_k(t)\mathbf{Q}_{ck}(t)$ where $\mathbf{R}_k(t)$, an $n \times k$ matrix, has rank k everywhere and $\mathbf{Q}_{ck}(t)$, a $k \times km$ matrix, and the product $\mathbf{R}_k(t)\mathbf{Q}_{ck}(t)$ all have rank k almost everywhere.

Proof. (i) *Sufficiency:* Assume that the first km columns of $\mathbf{Q}_c(t)$ are factorable as $R_k(t)\mathbf{Q}_{ck}(t)$:

$$\mathbf{Q}_c(t) = [\mathbf{R}_k(t)\mathbf{Q}_{ck}(t),\ \mathbf{Q}_c^*(t)] \tag{6.30}$$

where $\mathbf{Q}_c^*(t)$ is the last $(n - k)m$ columns of $\mathbf{Q}_c(t)$. Choose $\mathbf{T}(t)$ so that

$$\mathbf{T}^{-1}(t) = [\mathbf{R}_k(t),\ \mathbf{R}_{n-k}(t)] \tag{6.31}$$

where $R_{n-k}(t)$ is chosen to make $\mathbf{T}^{-1}(t)$ nonsingular. Note that

$$\mathbf{T}(t)\mathbf{T}^{-1}(t) = [\mathbf{T}(t)\mathbf{R}_k(t),\ \mathbf{T}(t)\mathbf{R}_{n-k}(t)]$$
$$= \begin{bmatrix} \mathbf{I}_k & \mathbf{0} \\ \mathbf{0} & \mathbf{I}_{n-k} \end{bmatrix} \tag{6.32}$$

Therefore

$$\mathbf{T}(t)R_k(t) = \begin{bmatrix} \mathbf{I}_k \\ \mathbf{0} \end{bmatrix} \tag{6.33}$$

$$\mathbf{T}(t)\mathbf{R}_{n-k}(t) = \begin{bmatrix} \mathbf{0} \\ \mathbf{I}_{n-k} \end{bmatrix} \tag{6.34}$$

Since, by Eq. 6.14, $\mathbf{Q}_{Tc}(t) = \mathbf{T}(t)\mathbf{Q}_c(t)$, it follows that

$$\mathbf{Q}_{Tc}(t) = \mathbf{T}(t)[\mathbf{R}_k(t)\mathbf{Q}_{ck}(t),\ \mathbf{Q}_c^*(t)]$$
$$= [\mathbf{T}(t)\mathbf{R}_k(t)\mathbf{Q}_{ck}(t),\ \mathbf{T}(t)\mathbf{Q}_c^*(t)]$$
$$= \left[\begin{bmatrix} \mathbf{I}_k \\ \mathbf{0} \end{bmatrix}\mathbf{Q}_{ck}(t),\ \mathbf{T}(t)\mathbf{Q}_c^*(t)\right]$$
$$= \left[\begin{bmatrix} \mathbf{Q}_{ck}(t) \\ \mathbf{0} \end{bmatrix},\ \mathbf{T}(t)\mathbf{Q}_c^*(t)\right] \tag{6.35}$$

But since rank $\mathbf{Q}_{Tc}(t) = k$ and rank $\mathbf{Q}_{ck}(t) = k$, all columns of $\mathbf{T}(t)\mathbf{Q}_c^*(t)$ are linear combinations of columns of $\begin{bmatrix} \mathbf{Q}_{ck}(t) \\ \mathbf{0} \end{bmatrix}$. Therefore as the last $n-k$ rows of $\begin{bmatrix} \mathbf{Q}_{ck}(t) \\ \mathbf{0} \end{bmatrix}$ are zero, the last $n - k$ rows of $\mathbf{T}(t)\mathbf{Q}_c^*(t)$ are also zero, i.e.,

$$\mathbf{Q}_{Tc}(t) = \left[\begin{bmatrix} \mathbf{Q}_{ck}(t) \\ \mathbf{0} \end{bmatrix},\ \begin{bmatrix} \mathbf{Q}_{ck}^*(t) \\ \mathbf{0} \end{bmatrix}\right] \tag{6.36}$$

Therefore

$$\mathbf{Q}_{Tc}(t) = \begin{bmatrix} \mathbf{Q}_{Tc1}(t) \\ \mathbf{0} \end{bmatrix} \tag{6.37}$$

(ii) *Necessity:* Necessity is proved by contradiction. Assume that $\mathbf{Q}_{Tc}(t)$ has the form of Eq. 6.21 and either (i) $\mathbf{Q}_c(t)$ has rank $> k$, or (ii)

$\mathbf{Q}_c(t)$ has rank $< k$, or (iii) $\mathbf{Q}_c(t) \neq [\mathbf{R}_k(t)\ \mathbf{Q}_{ck}(t),\ \mathbf{Q}_c^*(t)]$ for some $\mathbf{R}_k(t)\mathbf{Q}_{ck}(t)$ of rank k (and thus $\mathbf{R}_k(t)$ and $\mathbf{Q}_{ck}(t)$ have rank k).

(i) If rank $\mathbf{Q}_c(t) > k$, a nonsingular transformation $\mathbf{Q}_{Tc}(t) = \mathbf{T}(t)\mathbf{Q}_c(t)$ cannot give the form of Eq. 6.21, i.e., $\mathbf{Q}_{Tc1}(t)$ must have more than k nonzero rows, thus contradicting assumption (i).

(ii) If rank $\mathbf{Q}_c(t) < k$, a nonsingular transformation $\mathbf{Q}_{Tc}(t) = \mathbf{T}(t)\mathbf{Q}_c(t)$ cannot give the form of Eq. 6.21, i.e., $\mathbf{Q}_{Tc1}(t)$ cannot have rank k thus contradicting assumption (ii).

(iii) Partition $\mathbf{Q}_c(t)$ so that $\mathbf{Q}_c(t) = [\mathbf{Q}_{c0}(t)\quad \mathbf{Q}_c^*(t)]$ where $\mathbf{Q}_{c0}(t)$ is the first km columns of $\mathbf{Q}_c(t)$. Therefore

$$\mathbf{Q}_{Tc}(t) = \mathbf{T}(t)\mathbf{Q}_c(t) = [\mathbf{T}(t)\mathbf{Q}_{c0}(t),\ \mathbf{T}(t)\mathbf{Q}_c^*(t)] \tag{6.38}$$

But by hypothesis, and Eq. 6.24

$$\mathbf{Q}_{Tc}(t) = \begin{bmatrix} \mathbf{Q}_{Tc1}(t) \\ \mathbf{0} \end{bmatrix} = \begin{bmatrix} [\mathbf{B}_1(t), \cdots, \Delta_{Tc1}^{k-1}\mathbf{B}_1(t)] & \vdots & [\Delta_{Tc1}^{k}\mathbf{B}_1(t), \cdots, \Delta_{Tc1}^{n-1}\mathbf{B}_1(t)] \\ \cdots & \cdots & \cdots \\ \mathbf{0} & \vdots & \mathbf{0} \end{bmatrix} \equiv \begin{bmatrix} \mathbf{Q}_{Tca}(t) & \mathbf{Q}_{Tcb}(t) \\ \mathbf{0} & \mathbf{0} \end{bmatrix} \tag{6.39}$$

where

$$\mathbf{Q}_{Tca}(t) = [\mathbf{B}_1(t), \cdots, \Delta_{Tc1}^{k}\mathbf{B}_1(t)] \tag{6.40}$$

has rank k. But

$$\mathbf{T}(t)\mathbf{Q}_{c0}(t) = \begin{bmatrix} \mathbf{Q}_{Tca}(t) \\ \mathbf{0} \end{bmatrix} \tag{6.41}$$

implies that $\mathbf{Q}_{c0}(t)$ has rank k thus contradicting assumption (iiii). Q.E.D.

If any k columns of $\mathbf{Q}_c(t)$ have rank k everywhere, they can be used as $\mathbf{R}_k(t)$, thereby avoiding the need to factor any columns of $\mathbf{Q}_c(t)$. It can be shown that because rank $\mathbf{Q}_c(t) = k < n$, that any k columns of $\mathbf{Q}_c(t)$ having rank k everywhere can be factored out as the $\mathbf{R}_k(t)$. This is illustrated in Example 6.1. Note that for time-invariant systems this method of selecting $\mathbf{R}_k(t)$ is always applicable.

Theorem 6.3. A system is reducible to a totally controllable system of order $k \leq n$ if and only if $\mathbf{Q}_c(t)$ has rank k almost everywhere and the first km columns of $\mathbf{Q}_c(t)$ can be factored as in Theorem 6.2.

Theorem 6.3 follows directly from Theorems 6.1 and 6.2. It is essentially an existence theorem, since the choice of $\mathbf{R}_{n-k}(t)$ to complete the $\mathbf{T}(t)$ matrix is not obvious from the theorem statement. Thus, it is now desirable to develop a procedure for determining $\mathbf{T}(t)$ and thus obtain an explicit method for reducing a system from the input. Such a procedure can be obtained for a somewhat smaller class of systems than those satisfying the hypothesis of Theorem 6.3. Important in this procedure is the concept of a *generalized inverse* of a rectangular matrix.

DIGRESSION D6.1

Pseudo and Generalized Inverses [6, 8, 9]

Definition D6.1. A matrix $\mathbf{A}^{\#}$ is a pseudo-inverse of a rectangular (not necessarily square) matrix $\mathbf{A}$ if

$$\mathbf{A}\mathbf{A}^{\#}\mathbf{A} = \mathbf{A} \tag{D6.1}$$

It can be noted that:

(i) If $\mathbf{A}$ has an inverse $\mathbf{A}^{-1}$, then $\mathbf{A}^{\#} = \mathbf{A}^{-1}$.
(ii) $(\mathbf{A}')^{\#} = (\mathbf{A}^{\#})'$.
(iii) The pseudo-inverse is not unique.
(iv) A pseudo-inverse satisfying Eq. D6.1 exists for any rectangular matrix $\mathbf{A}$.

Definition D6.2. A matrix $\mathbf{A}^{\dagger}$ is a *generalized inverse* of a rectangular (not necessarily square) matrix $\mathbf{A}$ if

$$\mathbf{A}\mathbf{A}^{\dagger}\mathbf{A} = \mathbf{A} \tag{D6.2}$$

$$\mathbf{A}^{\dagger}\mathbf{A}\mathbf{A}^{\dagger} = \mathbf{A}^{\dagger} \tag{D6.3}$$

$$(\mathbf{A}\mathbf{A}^{\dagger})' = \mathbf{A}\mathbf{A}^{\dagger} \tag{D6.4}$$

$$(\mathbf{A}^{\dagger}\mathbf{A})' = \mathbf{A}^{\dagger}\mathbf{A} \tag{D6.5}$$

Theorem D6.1. For every rectangular matrix $\mathbf{A}$ there exists one and only one matrix $\mathbf{A}^{\dagger}$ satisfying simultaneously properties D6.2 through D6.5.

Theorem D6.2. Consider the algebraic equation $\mathbf{Ax} = \mathbf{b}$. Let $\mathbf{x}^0 \equiv \mathbf{A}^{\dagger}\mathbf{b}$ and $\mathbf{x}^1 \neq \mathbf{x}^0$. Then either

$$\| \mathbf{A}\mathbf{x}^1 - \mathbf{b} \| > \| \mathbf{A}\mathbf{x}^0 - \mathbf{b} \| \tag{D6.6}$$

or

$$\| \mathbf{A}\mathbf{x}^1 - \mathbf{b} \| = \| \mathbf{A}\mathbf{x}^0 - \mathbf{b} \| \quad \text{and} \quad \| \mathbf{x}^1 \| > \| \mathbf{x}^0 \| \tag{D6.7}$$

where $\| \mathbf{x} \|^2 \equiv \sum_{i=1}^{n} \mathbf{x}_i^2$.

Thus $\mathbf{x}^0 = \mathbf{A}^{\dagger}\mathbf{b}$ provides the solution of $\mathbf{Ax} = \mathbf{b}$ if one exists, and provides the best approximate solution when none exists.

Let $\| \mathbf{A} \|$ denote the norm of a matrix $\mathbf{A}$ defined by

$$\| \mathbf{A} \|^2 \equiv \text{trace } \mathbf{A}'\mathbf{A} = \sum_{i=1}^{n} \sum_{j=1}^{n} a_{ij}^2 \tag{D6.8}$$

Corollary D6.2. Let $\mathbf{A}^\# \neq \mathbf{A}^\dagger$ be a pseudo-inverse of $\mathbf{A}$. Then $\| \mathbf{A}^\# \| > \| \mathbf{A}^\dagger \|$. Thus the generalized inverse is smaller, in the sense of the norm D6.8, than any other pseudo-inverse.

Example D6.1. Consider the algebraic equation $\mathbf{Ax} = \mathbf{b}$:

$$\begin{bmatrix} 1 & 1 & 1 \\ 1 & 1 & 1 \\ 1 & 1 & 1 \end{bmatrix} \begin{bmatrix} \mathbf{x}_1 \\ \mathbf{x}_2 \\ \mathbf{x}_3 \end{bmatrix} = \begin{bmatrix} \mathbf{b}_1 \\ \mathbf{b}_2 \\ \mathbf{b}_3 \end{bmatrix}$$

Two pseudo-inverses of $\mathbf{A}$ are

$$\mathbf{A}_1^\# = \begin{bmatrix} 1/3 & 0 & 0 \\ 0 & 1/3 & 0 \\ 0 & 0 & 1/3 \end{bmatrix}, \quad \mathbf{A}_2^\# = \begin{bmatrix} 1/6 & 1/6 & 0 \\ 1/6 & 1/6 & 0 \\ 0 & 0 & 1/3 \end{bmatrix}$$

and the generalized inverse is

$$\mathbf{A}^\dagger = \begin{bmatrix} 1/9 & 1/9 & 1/9 \\ 1/9 & 1/9 & 1/9 \\ 1/9 & 1/9 & 1/9 \end{bmatrix}$$

In accordance with Corollary D6.2,

$$\| \mathbf{A}_1^\# \|^2 = 1/3 > \| \mathbf{A}_2^\# \|^2 = 2/9 > \| \mathbf{A}^\dagger \|^2 = 1/9$$

Now $\mathbf{x}$ is determined for the case that $\mathbf{b}' = [3, 3, 3]$:

$$\mathbf{x}_1^{0\#} = \mathbf{A}_1^\#\mathbf{b} = [1, 1, 1]', \quad \| \mathbf{A}\mathbf{x}_1^{0\#} - \mathbf{b} \| = 0$$

$$\mathbf{x}_2^{0\#} = \mathbf{A}_2^\#\mathbf{b} = [1, 1, 1]', \quad \| \mathbf{A}\mathbf{x}_2^{0\#} - \mathbf{b} \| = 0$$

$$\mathbf{x}^0 = \mathbf{A}^\dagger\mathbf{b} = [1, 1, 1]', \quad \| \mathbf{A}\mathbf{x}^0 - \mathbf{b} \| = 0$$

Thus in the case where a solution exists, the pseudo-inverses and the generalized inverses give a solution. For the case that $\mathbf{b}' = [1, 2, 3]$, i.e., a solution does not exist:

$$\mathbf{x}_1^{0\#} = \mathbf{A}_1^\#\mathbf{b} = [1/3, 2/3, 3/3]',$$
$$\| \mathbf{A}\mathbf{x}_1^{0\#} - \mathbf{b} \| = 2.0, \quad \| \mathbf{x}_1^{0\#} \| = \sqrt{56/36}$$

$$\mathbf{x}_2^{0\#} = \mathbf{A}_2^\#\mathbf{b} = [1/2, 1/2, 1]',$$
$$\| \mathbf{A}\mathbf{x}_2^{0\#} - \mathbf{b} \| = 2.0, \quad \| \mathbf{x}_2^{0\#} \| = \sqrt{54/36}$$

$$\mathbf{x}^0 = \mathbf{A}^\dagger\mathbf{b} = [2/3, 2/3, 2/3]',$$
$$\| \mathbf{A}\mathbf{x}^0 - \mathbf{b} \| = 2.0, \quad \| \mathbf{x}^0 \| = \sqrt{48/36}$$

Thus in the case where no solution exists, the generalized inverse provides the best approximate solution.

As an important special case, consider the $n \times nm$ matrix $\mathbf{\Psi}$ having rank n. Since Ψ has rank n, the $n \times n$ matrix $(\Psi\Psi')$ also has rank n, and thus $(\Psi\Psi')^{-1}$ exists. The generalized inverse of Ψ is

$$\Psi^{\dagger} = \Psi'(\Psi\Psi')^{-1} \tag{D6.9}$$

That D6.9 provides the generalized inverse is easily verified by showing that properties D6.1 through D6.5 are satisfied:

(i) $\Psi\Psi^{\dagger}\Psi = \Psi\Psi'(\Psi\Psi')^{-1}\Psi = \Psi$
(ii) $\Psi^{\dagger}\Psi\Psi^{\dagger} = \Psi'(\Psi\Psi')^{-1}\Psi\Psi'(\Psi\Psi')^{-1} = \Psi^{\dagger}$
(iii) $(\Psi\Psi^{\dagger})' = (\Psi\Psi'(\Psi\Psi')^{-1})' = \mathbf{I}_n' = \mathbf{I}_n = \Psi\Psi^{\dagger}$
(iv) $(\Psi^{\dagger}\Psi)' = (\Psi'(\Psi\Psi')\Psi)' = \Psi'(\Psi\Psi')^{-1}\Psi = \Psi^{\dagger}\Psi$

Note, with respect to the effect of an equivalence transformation on the controllability matrix $\mathbf{Q}_c(t)$, that the generalized inverse $\mathbf{Q}_c^{\dagger}(t)$, as defined by Eq. D6.9, is useful in solving the Eq. 6.14 $\mathbf{Q}_{Tc}(t) = \mathbf{T}(t)\mathbf{Q}_c(t)$, for $\mathbf{T}(t)$. Clearly

$$\mathbf{T}(t) = \mathbf{Q}_{Tc}(t)\mathbf{Q}_c^{\dagger}(t) \tag{D6.10}$$

Equation D6.10 is particularly useful for obtaining the transformation matrix $\mathbf{T}(t)$ which transforms a given set of equations into some desired canonical form.

Also useful, for the case that $\mathbf{H}$ is an $nm \times m$ matrix of rank m, is the generalized inverse

$$\mathbf{H}^{\dagger} = (\mathbf{H}'\mathbf{H})^{-1}\mathbf{H}' \tag{D6.11}$$

Again, it is easily verified that properties D6.2 through D6.5 are satisfied:

(i) $\mathbf{H}\mathbf{H}^{\dagger}\mathbf{H} = \mathbf{H}(\mathbf{H}'\mathbf{H})^{-1}\mathbf{H}'\mathbf{H} = \mathbf{H}$
(ii) $\mathbf{H}^{\dagger}\mathbf{H}\mathbf{H}^{\dagger} = (\mathbf{H}^{\dagger}\mathbf{H})^{-1}\mathbf{H}'\mathbf{H}(\mathbf{H}'\mathbf{H})^{-1}\mathbf{H}' = \mathbf{H}^{\dagger}$
(iii) $(\mathbf{H}\mathbf{H}^{\dagger})' = (\mathbf{H}(\mathbf{H}'\mathbf{H})^{-1}\mathbf{H}')' = \mathbf{H}(\mathbf{H}'\mathbf{H})^{-1}\mathbf{H}' = \mathbf{H}\mathbf{H}^{\dagger}$
(iv) $(\mathbf{H}^{\dagger}\mathbf{H})' = ((\mathbf{H}'\mathbf{H})^{-1}\mathbf{H}'\mathbf{H}^{-1})' = \mathbf{I}_m' = \mathbf{I}_m = \mathbf{H}^{\dagger}\mathbf{H}$

Note that the generalized inverse $\mathbf{H}^{\dagger}$, as defined in Eq. D6.11, is useful in solving the equation $\mathbf{Hx} = \mathbf{y}$ for $\mathbf{x}$. Clearly $\mathbf{x} = \mathbf{H}^{\dagger}\mathbf{y}$.

A theorem is now given which provides an explicit method of reduction for a practically significant class of systems. In particular, the method is always applicable to systems with analytic coefficient matrices, which, of course, includes all time-invariant systems. Theorem 6.4 provides a simple method of reduction:

Theorem 6.4. If $\mathbf{Q}_c(t)$ has rank $k < n$ everywhere and a submatrix of $\mathbf{Q}_c(t)$, say $\mathbf{Q}_{c1}(t)$ also has rank $k < n$ everywhere, then the system is not controllable and can be reduced by the transformation

$$\mathbf{T}(t) = \begin{bmatrix} \mathbf{I}_k & \mathbf{0} \\ -\mathbf{Q}_{c2}(t)\mathbf{Q}_{c1}^{\dagger}(t) & \mathbf{I}_{n-k} \end{bmatrix} \tag{6.42}$$

to a totally controllable system of order k, where $\mathbf{Q}_{c1}^{\dagger}(t)$ is the generalized inverse of $\mathbf{Q}_{c1}(t)$ and the rows of $\mathbf{Q}_c(t)$ have been reordered so that

$$\mathbf{Q}_c(t) = \begin{bmatrix} \mathbf{Q}_{c1}(t) \\ \mathbf{Q}_{c2}(t) \end{bmatrix} = \begin{bmatrix} \mathbf{Q}_{c1}(t) \\ \mathbf{K}\mathbf{Q}_{c1}(t) \end{bmatrix} \tag{6.43}$$

Proof. The proof is by construction:

$$\begin{aligned}\mathbf{Q}_{Tc}(t) &= \mathbf{T}(t)\mathbf{Q}_c(t) \\ &= \begin{bmatrix} \mathbf{I}_k & 0 \\ -\mathbf{Q}_{c2}(t)\mathbf{Q}_{c1}^{\dagger}(t) & \mathbf{I}_{n-k} \end{bmatrix} \begin{bmatrix} \mathbf{Q}_{c1}(t) \\ \mathbf{Q}_{c2}(t) \end{bmatrix} \\ &= \begin{bmatrix} \mathbf{Q}_{c1}(t) \\ \mathbf{0} \end{bmatrix} \end{aligned} \tag{6.44}$$

Q.E.D.

Example 6.1. Consider the third-order single-input system:

$$\begin{bmatrix} \dot{x}_1 \\ \dot{x}_2 \\ \dot{x}_3 \end{bmatrix} = \begin{bmatrix} t-1 & 0 & -t+2 \\ -t-2 & 1 & t+2 \\ t & 0 & -t+1 \end{bmatrix} \begin{bmatrix} x_1 \\ x_2 \\ x_3 \end{bmatrix} + \begin{bmatrix} 1 \\ 1 \\ 0 \end{bmatrix} u$$

$$\mathbf{y} = \mathbf{x}$$

The controllability matrix for this system is

$$\mathbf{Q}_c(t) = \begin{bmatrix} 1 & 1-t & 0 \\ 1 & 1+t & 2 \\ 0 & -t & -1 \end{bmatrix}$$

The above controllability matrix can be factored as

$$[\mathbf{R}_k(t)\mathbf{Q}_{ck}(t) \vdots \mathbf{Q}_c^*(t)] = \left[\begin{bmatrix} 1 & 1 \\ -1 & 1 \\ 1 & 0 \end{bmatrix} \begin{bmatrix} 0 & -t \\ 1 & 1 \end{bmatrix} \vdots \begin{bmatrix} 0 \\ 2 \\ -1 \end{bmatrix} \right]$$

Thus, in accordance with Theorem 6.2, the transformation $\mathbf{T}_1(t)$ reducing the system from the input is defined by

$$\mathbf{T}_1^{-1}(t) = [\mathbf{R}_k, \mathbf{R}_{n-k}] = \left[\begin{array}{cc:c} 1 & 1 & 0 \\ -1 & 1 & 0 \\ 1 & 0 & 1 \end{array}\right]$$

where $\mathbf{R}_{n-k}$ is arbitrarily chosen to give $\mathbf{T}(t)$ full rank. Using the equivalence transformation defined by $\mathbf{T}_1$ on the original system results in

$$\mathbf{Q}_{T_1c}(t) = \mathbf{T}_1\mathbf{Q}_c(t) = \left[\begin{array}{ccc} 0 & -t & -1 \\ 1 & 1 & 1 \\ \hdashline 0 & 0 & 0 \end{array}\right]$$

$$\mathbf{A}_{T_1}(t) = \mathbf{T}_1\mathbf{A}\mathbf{T}_1^{-1} = \left[\begin{array}{cc:c} 1 & t & -t \\ 0 & -1 & 2 \\ \hdashline 0 & 0 & 1 \end{array}\right]$$

$$\mathbf{B}_{T_1}(t) = \mathbf{T}_1\mathbf{B} = \begin{bmatrix} 0 \\ 1 \\ \cdots \\ 0 \end{bmatrix}$$

$$\mathbf{C}_{T_1} = \mathbf{C}\mathbf{T}_1^{-1} = \begin{bmatrix} 1 & 1 & 0 \\ -1 & 1 & 0 \\ 1 & 0 & 1 \end{bmatrix}$$

Since the first and third columns of $\mathbf{Q}_c$(t) form a submatrix of rank 2, an alternate transformation $\mathbf{T}_2(t)$ can be defined by

$$\mathbf{T}_2^{-1}(t) = \begin{bmatrix} 1 & 0 & \vdots & 0 \\ 1 & 2 & \vdots & 0 \\ 0 & -1 & \vdots & 1 \end{bmatrix}$$

Note that this is an agreement with Theorem 6.2 since the above corresponds to a proper factoring of $\mathbf{Q}_c(t)$:

$$\mathbf{Q}_c(t) = \begin{bmatrix} 1 & 0 \\ 1 & 2 \\ 0 & -1 \end{bmatrix} \begin{bmatrix} 1 & 1-t & 0 \\ 0 & t & 1 \end{bmatrix}$$

Finally application of Theorem 6.4 gives a third transformation in terms of $\mathbf{Q}_{c1}(t)$, $\mathbf{Q}_{c2}(t)$ and $\mathbf{Q}_{c1}^{\dagger}(t)$:

$$\mathbf{Q}_{c1}(t) = \begin{bmatrix} 1 & 1-t & 0 \\ 1 & 1+t & 2 \end{bmatrix}$$

$$\mathbf{Q}_{c2}(t) = [0 \quad -t \quad -1]$$

$$\begin{aligned} \mathbf{Q}_{c1}^{\dagger}(t) &= \mathbf{Q}_{c1}'(t)\,[\mathbf{Q}_{c1}(t)\mathbf{Q}_{c1}'(t)]^{-1} \\ &= \begin{bmatrix} 1 & 1 \\ 1-t & 1+t \\ 0 & 2 \end{bmatrix} \left[\begin{bmatrix} 1 & 1-t & 0 \\ 1 & 1+t & 2 \end{bmatrix} \begin{bmatrix} 1 & 1 \\ 1-t & 1+t \\ 0 & 2 \end{bmatrix} \right]^{-1} \\ &= \begin{bmatrix} 1 & 1 \\ 1-t & 1+t \\ 0 & 2 \end{bmatrix} \begin{bmatrix} t^2 - 2t + 2 & -t^2 + 2 \\ -t^2 + 2 & t^2 + 2t + 6 \end{bmatrix}^{-1} \end{aligned}$$

It is now shown that reducing a system from the input and then reducing the controllable portion of the system from the output (or, first reducing from the output and then reducing the observable portion of the system from the input) results in a transformed system having a canonical structure somewhat different than the canonical structure characterized by Eqs. 6.16. Applying the necessary transformation $\mathbf{T}_1(t)$ to reduce the system from the input results in the transformed system having equations of the form of Eqs. 6.16 (Notation is changed for convenience):

$$\begin{bmatrix}\dot{\boldsymbol{\xi}}_1(t)\\ \dot{\boldsymbol{\xi}}_2(t)\end{bmatrix} = \begin{bmatrix}\mathbf{A}_{aa}(t) & \mathbf{A}_{ab}(t)\\ \mathbf{0} & \mathbf{A}_{bb}(t)\end{bmatrix}\begin{bmatrix}\boldsymbol{\xi}_1(t)\\ \boldsymbol{\xi}_2(t)\end{bmatrix} + \begin{bmatrix}\mathbf{B}_a(t)\\ \mathbf{0}\end{bmatrix}\mathbf{u}(t) \tag{6.45a}$$

$$\mathbf{y}(t) = \mathbf{y}_a(t) + \mathbf{y}_b(t) = [\mathbf{C}_a(t) \quad \mathbf{C}_b(t)]\begin{bmatrix}\boldsymbol{\xi}_1(t)\\ \boldsymbol{\xi}_2(t)\end{bmatrix} \tag{6.45b}$$

Applying a second transformation of the type

$$\mathbf{T}_0(t) = \begin{bmatrix}\mathbf{T}_{01}(t) & \mathbf{0}\\ \mathbf{0} & \mathbf{T}_{02}(t)\end{bmatrix} \tag{6.46}$$

where $\mathbf{T}_{01}(t)$ reduces (from the output) the subsystem characterized by

$$\begin{aligned}\dot{\boldsymbol{\xi}}_1(t) &= \mathbf{A}_{aa}(t)\boldsymbol{\xi}_1(t) + \mathbf{B}_a(t)\mathbf{u}(t)\\ \mathbf{y}_a(t) &= \mathbf{C}_a(t)\boldsymbol{\xi}_1(t)\end{aligned} \tag{6.47}$$

and $\mathbf{T}_{02}(t)$ reduces (from the output) the subsystem characterized by

$$\begin{aligned}\dot{\boldsymbol{\xi}}_2(t) &= \mathbf{A}_{bb}(t)\boldsymbol{\xi}_2(t)\\ \mathbf{y}_b(t) &= \mathbf{C}_b(t)\boldsymbol{\xi}_2(t)\end{aligned} \tag{6.48}$$

results in the transformed system characterized by

$$\begin{bmatrix}\dot{\mathbf{z}}_1(t)\\ \dot{\mathbf{z}}_2(t)\\ \dot{\mathbf{z}}_3(t)\\ \dot{\mathbf{z}}_4(t)\end{bmatrix} = \begin{bmatrix}\mathbf{A}^*_{11}(t) & \mathbf{0} & \mathbf{A}^*_{13}(t) & \mathbf{A}^*_{14}(t)\\ \mathbf{A}^*_{21}(t) & \mathbf{A}^*_{22}(t) & \mathbf{A}^*_{23}(t) & \mathbf{A}^*_{24}(t)\\ \mathbf{0} & \mathbf{0} & \mathbf{A}^*_{33}(t) & \mathbf{0}\\ \mathbf{0} & \mathbf{0} & \mathbf{A}^*_{43}(t) & \mathbf{A}^*_{44}(t)\end{bmatrix}\begin{bmatrix}\mathbf{z}_1(t)\\ \mathbf{z}_2(t)\\ \mathbf{z}_3(t)\\ \mathbf{z}_4(t)\end{bmatrix} + \begin{bmatrix}\mathbf{B}^*_1(t)\\ \mathbf{B}^*_2(t)\\ \mathbf{0}\\ \mathbf{0}\end{bmatrix}\mathbf{u}(t) \tag{6.49a}$$

$$\mathbf{y}(t) = [\mathbf{C}^*_1(t) \quad \mathbf{0} \quad \mathbf{C}^*_3(t) \quad \mathbf{0}]\begin{bmatrix}\mathbf{z}_1(t)\\ \mathbf{z}_2(t)\\ \mathbf{z}_3(t)\\ \mathbf{z}_4(t)\end{bmatrix} \tag{6.49b}$$

For purposes of comparison the state components are renumbered, giving

$$\begin{bmatrix}\dot{\mathbf{x}}_1(t)\\ \dot{\mathbf{x}}_2(t)\\ \dot{\mathbf{x}}_3(t)\\ \dot{\mathbf{x}}_4(t)\end{bmatrix} = \begin{bmatrix}\mathbf{A}_{11}(t) & \mathbf{A}_{12}(t) & \mathbf{A}_{13}(t) & \mathbf{A}_{14}(t)\\ \mathbf{0} & \mathbf{A}_{22}(t) & \mathbf{A}_{23}(t) & \mathbf{A}_{24}(t)\\ \mathbf{0} & \mathbf{0} & \mathbf{A}_{33}(t) & \mathbf{A}_{34}(t)\\ \mathbf{0} & \mathbf{0} & \mathbf{0} & \mathbf{A}_{44}(t)\end{bmatrix} + \begin{bmatrix}\mathbf{B}_1(t)\\ \mathbf{B}_2(t)\\ \mathbf{0}\\ \mathbf{0}\end{bmatrix}\mathbf{u}(t) \tag{6.50a}$$

$$\mathbf{y}(t) = [0 \quad \mathbf{C}_2(t) \quad 0 \quad \mathbf{C}_4(t)]\begin{bmatrix}\mathbf{x}_1(t)\\ \mathbf{x}_2(t)\\ \mathbf{x}_3(t)\\ \mathbf{x}_4(t)\end{bmatrix} \tag{6.50b}$$

This system is represented by the canonical structure of Fig. 6.1.

Comparing the canonical structures of the systems characterized by Eqs. 5.10 and 6.50 it is seen that the primary difference in these structures is that in the latter case subsystem N_3 is not strictly unobservable, since its states are inputs to the observable subsystem N_2 due to the presence of submatrix $\mathbf{A}_{23}(t)$ in the $\mathbf{A}(t)$ matrix.

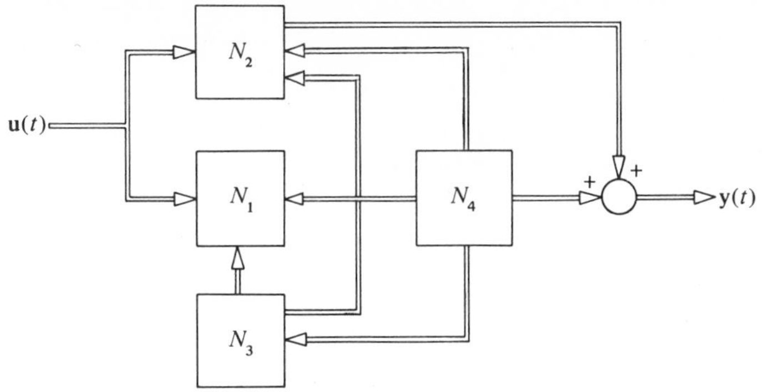

Fig. 6.1. A canonical structure for a linear system corresponding to Eqs. 6.50.

6.3. TRANSFORMATION TO PHASE-VARIABLE CANONICAL FORM [12]

In Sec. 2.2.1 it is seen how any linear scalar system can be put into state-variable form. This particular process resulted in the phase-variable canonical form given in Eq. 2.35. Here the reverse problem of transform- the arbitrary scalar-input state-variable system

$$\dot{\mathbf{x}}(t) = \mathbf{A}(t)\mathbf{x}(t) + \mathbf{b}(t)u(t) \tag{6.51}$$

to the phase-variable canonical form $\dot{\mathbf{z}}(t) = \mathbf{A}_T(t)\mathbf{z}(t) + \mathbf{b}_T u(t)$, i.e., to

$$\dot{\mathbf{z}}(t) = \begin{bmatrix} 0 & 1 & 0 & \cdots & 0 \\ 0 & 0 & 1 & & 0 \\ \vdots & \vdots & \vdots & & \vdots \\ 0 & 0 & 0 & & 1 \\ a_1(t) & a_2(t) & a_3(t) & \cdots & a_n(t) \end{bmatrix} \mathbf{z}(t) + \begin{bmatrix} 0 \\ 0 \\ \vdots \\ 0 \\ 1 \end{bmatrix} u(t) \tag{6.52}$$

is considered. Combining Eqs. 6.4 and D6.10 gives

$$\mathbf{A}_T(t) = \left\{\mathbf{Q}_{Tc}(t)\left[\mathbf{Q}_c^{-1}(t)\mathbf{A}(t) + \frac{d\mathbf{Q}_c^{-1}(t)}{dt}\right]\mathbf{Q}_c(t) + \frac{d\mathbf{Q}_{Tc}(t)}{dt}\right\}\mathbf{Q}_{Tc}^{-1}(t) \tag{6.53}$$

where $\mathbf{Q}_c(t)$ is always a square nonsingular $n \times n$ matrix for a totally controllable system in phase-variable form. Defining

$$\hat{\mathbf{A}}(t) = \left[\mathbf{Q}_c^{-1}(t)\mathbf{A}(t) + \frac{d\mathbf{Q}_c^{-1}(t)}{dt}\right]\mathbf{Q}_c(t) \tag{6.54}$$

gives

$$\mathbf{A}_T(t) = \left[\mathbf{Q}_{Tc}(t)\hat{\mathbf{A}}(t) + \frac{d\mathbf{Q}_{Tc}(t)}{dt}\right]\mathbf{Q}_{Tc}^{-1}(t) \tag{6.55}$$

or

$$-\mathbf{A}_T(t)\mathbf{Q}_{Tc}(t) + \frac{d\mathbf{Q}_{Tc}}{dt} = -\mathbf{Q}_{Tc}(t)\hat{\mathbf{A}}(t) \tag{6.56}$$

Noting that

$$\Delta_{Tc} = -\mathbf{A}_T(t) + \frac{d}{dt} \tag{6.57}$$

gives

$$\Delta_{Tc}\mathbf{Q}_{Tc}(t) = -\mathbf{Q}_{Tc}(t)\hat{\mathbf{A}}(t) \tag{6.58}$$

Define

$$\mathbf{Q}_{T\Delta_c} \equiv \Delta_{Tc}\mathbf{Q}_{Tc}(t) \tag{6.59}$$

Thus

$$\mathbf{Q}_{T\Delta_c} = -\mathbf{Q}_{Tc}(t)\hat{\mathbf{A}}(t) = -\mathbf{T}(t)\mathbf{Q}_c(t)\hat{\mathbf{A}}(t) \tag{6.60}$$

Since $\mathbf{Q}_c^{-1}(t)\mathbf{Q}_c(t) = \mathbf{I}_n$,

$$\frac{d}{dt}[\mathbf{Q}_c^{-1}(t)\mathbf{Q}_c(t)] = \frac{d\mathbf{Q}_c^{-1}(t)}{dt}\mathbf{Q}_c(t) + \mathbf{Q}_c^{-1}(t)\frac{d\mathbf{Q}_c(t)}{dt} = \mathbf{0} \tag{6.61}$$

Therefore

$$\frac{d\mathbf{Q}_c^{-1}(t)}{dt}\mathbf{Q}_c(t) = -\mathbf{Q}_c^{-1}(t)\frac{d\mathbf{Q}_c(t)}{dt} \tag{6.62}$$

Substituting from Eq 6.62 in Eq. 6.54 gives

$$\begin{aligned}\hat{\mathbf{A}}(t) &= -\mathbf{Q}_c^{-1}(t)\left[-\mathbf{A}(t)\mathbf{Q}_c(t) + \frac{d\mathbf{Q}_c(t)}{dt}\right] = -\mathbf{Q}_c^{-1}(\mathrm{t})\Delta_c\mathbf{Q}_c(t)\\ &= -\mathbf{Q}_c^{-1}(t)\mathbf{Q}_{\Delta_c}(t)\end{aligned} \tag{6.63}$$

where

$$\mathbf{Q}_{\Delta_c}(t) \equiv \Delta_c\mathbf{Q}_c(t) \tag{6.64}$$

Substituting from Eq. 6.63 in Eq. 6.60 gives

$$\mathbf{Q}_{T\Delta_c}(t) = \mathbf{T}(t)\mathbf{Q}_{\Delta_c}(t) = -\mathbf{Q}_{Tc}(t)\hat{\mathbf{A}}(t) \tag{6.65}$$

The method of solution stems from Eq. 6.63 and 6.65. Note that since $\mathbf{Q}_c^{-1}(t)\mathbf{Q}_c(t) = \mathbf{I}_n$, it follows that

$$\begin{aligned}-\hat{\mathbf{A}}(t) = \mathbf{Q}_c^{-1}(t)\mathbf{Q}_{\Delta_c}(t) &= \begin{bmatrix} 0 & 0 \cdots 0 & -g_1(t) \\ 1 & 0 \quad 0 & -g_2(t) \\ 0 & 1 \quad 0 & -g_3(t) \\ \vdots & \vdots \quad \vdots & \\ 0 & 0 \quad 1 & -g_n(t) \end{bmatrix}\\ &= [\mathbf{e}_2,\ \mathbf{e}_3,\ \cdots\ \mathbf{e}_n,\ -\mathbf{g}(t)]\end{aligned} \tag{6.66}$$

where $\mathbf{e}_i$ is the ith column of the identity matrix and $\mathbf{g}(t) = [g_1(t), \cdots, g_n(t)]'$. Thus $\hat{\mathbf{A}}(t)$, and therefore $\mathbf{g}(t)$, is determined in a straightforward manner from the original system. Use of Eq. 6.66 in Eq. 6.65 gives

$$\mathbf{Q}_{T\Delta_c}(t) = -\mathbf{Q}_{Tc}\hat{\mathbf{A}}(t) \tag{6.67}$$

or

$$\begin{aligned}
&[\boldsymbol{\Delta}_{Tc}\mathbf{b}_T,\ \boldsymbol{\Delta}_{Tc}^2\mathbf{b}_T,\ \cdots,\ \boldsymbol{\Delta}_{Tc}^n\mathbf{b}_T] \\
&\quad = [\mathbf{b}_T,\ \boldsymbol{\Delta}_{Tc}\mathbf{b}_T,\ \cdots,\ \boldsymbol{\Delta}_T^{n-1}\mathbf{b}_T]\,[\mathbf{e}_2, \cdots, \mathbf{e}_n, -\mathbf{g}(t)] \\
&\quad = [\boldsymbol{\Delta}_{Tc}\mathbf{b}_T,\ \cdots,\ \boldsymbol{\Delta}_{Tc}^{n-1}\mathbf{b}_T,\ -\mathbf{Q}_{Tc}\mathbf{g}(t)]
\end{aligned} \tag{6.68}$$

Thus

$$\boldsymbol{\Delta}_{Tc}^n(t)\mathbf{b}_T = -\mathbf{Q}_{Tc}(t)\mathbf{g}(t) \tag{6.69}$$

It can be shown that Eq. 6.69 can be used to determine the $a_i(t)$, $i = 1, \cdots, n$ defining $\mathbf{A}_T(t)$ and thus the desired scalar canonical structure. This is illustrated with a general third-order example.

Example 6.2. Assume that $\mathbf{g}(t) = [g_1(t), g_2(t), g_3(t)]'$ has been found in accordance with Eq. 6.66 and that it is desired to determine $\mathbf{A}_T(t)$ and the transformation matrix $\mathbf{T}(t)$ which provides it:

$$\mathbf{A}_T(t) = \begin{bmatrix} 0 & 1 & 0 \\ 0 & 0 & 1 \\ a_1(t) & a_2(t) & a_3(t) \end{bmatrix}, \quad \mathbf{b}_T = \begin{bmatrix} 0 \\ 0 \\ 1 \end{bmatrix}$$

Therefore

$$\boldsymbol{\Delta}_{Tc}\mathbf{b}_T = \begin{bmatrix} 0 \\ -1 \\ -a_3(t) \end{bmatrix}, \quad \boldsymbol{\Delta}_{Tc}^2\mathbf{b}_T = \begin{bmatrix} 1 \\ a_3(t) \\ a_2(t) + a_3^2(t) - \dot{a}_3(t) \end{bmatrix}$$

$$\boldsymbol{\Delta}_{Tc}^3\mathbf{b}_T = \begin{bmatrix} -a_3(t) \\ -a_2(t) - a_3^2(t) + 2\dot{a}_3(t) \\ -a_1(t) - 2a_2(t)a_3(t) - a_3^3(t) + 3a_3(t)\dot{a}_3(t) - \dot{a}_2(t)\ddot{a}_3(t) \end{bmatrix}$$

and

$$\mathbf{Q}_{Tc}(t) = \begin{bmatrix} 0 & 0 & 1 \\ 0 & -1 & a_3(t) \\ 1 & -a_3(t) & a_2(t) + a_3^2(t) - \dot{a}_3(t) \end{bmatrix}$$

$$\mathbf{Q}_{Tc}(t)g(t) = \begin{bmatrix} g_3(t) \\ -g_2(t) + a_3(t)g_3(t) \\ g_1(t) - g_2(t)a_3(t) + g_3(t)a_2(t) + g_3(t)a_3^2(t) - g_3(t)\dot{a}_3(t) \end{bmatrix}$$

Thus Eq. 6.69 gives

$$\begin{bmatrix} -a_3 \\ -a_2 - a_3^2 + 2\dot{a}_3 \\ -a_1 - 2a_2a_3 - a_3^3 + 3a_3\dot{a}_3 + \dot{a}_2 - \ddot{a}_3 \end{bmatrix} = -\begin{bmatrix} g_3 \\ -g_2 + a_3g_3 \\ g_1 - g_2a_3 + g_3a_2 + g_2a_3^2 - g_2\dot{a}_3 \end{bmatrix}$$

which can be solved for a_3, a_2, a_1 recursively:

$$a_3 = g_3$$

$$a_2 = -g_2 + a_3g_3 + a_3^2 - 2\dot{a}_3$$

$$a_1 = g_1 - g_2a_3 + g_3a_2 + g_2a_3^2 - g_2\dot{a}_3 - 2a_2a_3 - a_3^3 + 3a_3\dot{a}_3 + \dot{a}_2 - \ddot{a}_3$$

6.4. DIAGONALIZATION OF TIME-INVARIANT SYSTEMS [12]

It is often useful to put time-invariant systems of the form

$$\dot{\mathbf{x}}(t) = \mathbf{A}\mathbf{x}(t) + \mathbf{b}u(t) \tag{6.70}$$

into the diagonal form

$$\dot{\mathbf{z}}(t) = \mathbf{\Lambda}\mathbf{z}(t) + \mathbf{b}_T u(t) \tag{6.71}$$

where, assuming that $\mathbf{A}$ has distinct eigenvalues $\lambda_1, \lambda_2, \cdots, \lambda_n$,

$$\mathbf{\Lambda} \equiv \begin{bmatrix} \lambda_1 & 0 & \cdots & 0 \\ 0 & \lambda_2 & \cdots & 0 \\ \vdots & & \ddots & \vdots \\ 0 & 0 & \cdots & \lambda_n \end{bmatrix} \tag{6.72a}$$

and

$$\mathbf{b}_T = \begin{bmatrix} 1 \\ 1 \\ \vdots \\ 1 \end{bmatrix} \tag{6.72b}$$

In accordance with Eq. D6.10, the required transformation matrix $\mathbf{T}$ is is given by

$$\mathbf{T} = \begin{bmatrix} 1 & -\lambda_1 & \cdots & (-\lambda_1)^{n-1} \\ \vdots & & & \vdots \\ 1 & -\lambda_n & \cdots & (-\lambda_n)^{n-1} \end{bmatrix} = [\mathbf{b}, -\mathbf{A}\mathbf{b}, \cdots, (-\mathbf{A})^{n-1}\mathbf{b}]^{-1} \tag{6.73}$$

Example 6.3. The system

$$\begin{bmatrix} \dot{x}_1 \\ \dot{x}_2 \end{bmatrix} = \begin{bmatrix} -5/2 & 3/2 \\ -1/2 & -1/2 \end{bmatrix} \begin{bmatrix} x_1 \\ x_2 \end{bmatrix} + \begin{bmatrix} 1 \\ 2 \end{bmatrix} u$$

has eigenvalues $\lambda_1 = -1$, $\lambda_2 = -2$. Thus, in accordance with Eq. 6.74, the diagonalizing transformation matrix $\mathbf{T}$ is given by

$$\mathbf{T} = \begin{bmatrix} 1 & 1 \\ 1 & 2 \end{bmatrix} \begin{bmatrix} 1 & -1/2 \\ 2 & 3/2 \end{bmatrix}^{-1} = \frac{1}{5}\begin{bmatrix} -1 & 3 \\ -5 & 5 \end{bmatrix}$$

That $\mathbf{T}$ diagonalizes $\mathbf{A}$ is verified by

$$\mathbf{TAT}^{-1} = \frac{1}{5}\begin{bmatrix} -1 & 3 \\ -5 & 5 \end{bmatrix} \begin{bmatrix} -5/2 & 3/2 \\ -1/2 & -1/3 \end{bmatrix} \begin{bmatrix} 5/2 & -3/2 \\ 5/2 & -1/2 \end{bmatrix} = \begin{bmatrix} -1 & 0 \\ 0 & -2 \end{bmatrix}$$

6.5. EQUIVALENCE OF LINEAR SYSTEMS [14]

For systems in which the controllability and observability matrices $\mathbf{Q}_c(t)$ and $\mathbf{Q}_0(t)$ exist they can be used to establish algebraic equivalence. However, in these developments it is useful to write the controllability and observability matrices using an alternate notation.

$$\mathbf{Q}_c(t) = [\mathbf{R}_0(t), \mathbf{R}_1(t), \cdots, \mathbf{R}_{n-1}(t)] \tag{6.74a}$$

$$\mathbf{Q}_0(t) = [\mathbf{S}_0(t), \mathbf{S}_1(t), \cdots, \mathbf{S}_{n-1}(t)] \tag{6.74b}$$

where

$$\mathbf{R}_{k+1}(t) \equiv -\mathbf{A}(t)\mathbf{R}_k(t) + \dot{\mathbf{R}}_k(t) \tag{6.75a}$$

$$\mathbf{S}_{k+1}(t) \equiv \mathbf{A}'(t)\mathbf{S}_k(t) + \dot{\mathbf{S}}_k(t) \tag{6.75b}$$

and

$$\mathbf{R}_0(t) \equiv \mathbf{B}(t) \tag{6.76a}$$

$$\mathbf{S}_0(t) \equiv \mathbf{C}'(t) \tag{6.76b}$$

The submatrices $\mathbf{R}_k(t)$ and $\mathbf{S}_k(t)$ of the controllability and observability matrices are especially useful in establishing algebraic equivalence. In particular, let

$$\mathbf{Q}_{ij}(t) \equiv \begin{bmatrix} \mathbf{S}_0'(t) \\ \mathbf{S}_1'(t) \\ \vdots \\ \mathbf{S}_{i-1}'(t) \end{bmatrix} [\mathbf{R}_0(t), \mathbf{R}_1(t), \cdots, \mathbf{R}_{j-1}(t)] \tag{6.77}$$

and define the *equivalence matrix* $\Upsilon(t)$ by:

$$\Upsilon(t) \equiv \mathbf{Q}_{n+1,n+1}(t) \tag{6.78}$$

Theorem 6.5. Two minimal order *analytic* systems $[\mathbf{A}(t), \mathbf{B}(t), \mathbf{C}(t)]$ and $[\mathbf{A}_T(t), \mathbf{B}_T(t), \mathbf{C}_T(t)]$ are algebraically equivalent if and only if their equivalence matrices are equal, i.e., $\Upsilon(t) = \Upsilon_T(t)$.

Proof. (i) *Necessity:* From Eq. 6.14 and 6.15 it follows that if $[\mathbf{A}(t), \mathbf{B}(t), \mathbf{C}(t)] \xrightarrow{T} [\mathbf{A}_T(t), \mathbf{B}_T(t), \mathbf{C}_T(t)]$, then

$$\begin{aligned} \mathbf{R}_{Tk}(t) &= \mathbf{T}(t)\mathbf{R}_k(t) \\ \mathbf{S}'_{Tk}(t) &= \mathbf{S}'_k(t)\mathbf{T}^{-1}(t) \end{aligned} \tag{6.79}$$

Therefore, in accordance with Eq. 6.78 and 6.79, $\Upsilon(t) = \Upsilon_T(t)$.

(ii) *Sufficiency* is established by showing that if $\Upsilon(t) = \Upsilon_T(t)$, then there exists a $\mathbf{T}(t)$ such that $[\mathbf{A}(t), \mathbf{B}(t), \mathbf{C}(t)] \xrightarrow{T} [\mathbf{A}_T(t), \mathbf{B}_T(t), \mathbf{C}_T(t)]$. With no loss of generality assume that

$$\mathbf{A}_T(t) = \mathbf{A}(t) = \mathbf{0} \tag{6.80}$$

Clearly, if $\Upsilon(t) = \Upsilon_T(t)$, then

$$\mathbf{Q}'_0(t)\mathbf{Q}_c(t) = \mathbf{Q}'_{T0}(t)\mathbf{Q}_{Tc}(t) \tag{6.81}$$

If $\mathbf{A}(t) = \mathbf{0}$, then $\mathbf{R}_{k+1}(t) = \dot{\mathbf{R}}_k(t)$ and

$$\begin{aligned} \dot{\mathbf{Q}}_c(t) &= \frac{d}{dt}[R_0(t), \mathbf{R}_1(t), \cdots, \mathbf{R}_{n-1}(t)] \\ &= [\mathbf{R}_1(t), \mathbf{R}_2(t), \cdots, \mathbf{R}_n(t)] \end{aligned} \tag{6.82}$$

Thus

$$\mathbf{Q}'_0(t)\dot{\mathbf{Q}}_c(t) = \mathbf{Q}'_{T0}(t)\dot{\mathbf{Q}}_{Tc}(t) \tag{6.83}$$

Denote the order of both systems by n. Since they are minimal-order systems they are controllable and observable, i.e., $\mathbf{Q}_c(t)$, $\mathbf{Q}_0(t)$, $\mathbf{Q}_{Tc}(t)$, $\mathbf{Q}_{T0}(t)$ each has rank n on some finite subinterval of $(-\infty, \infty)$ and due to the assumed analyticity of $\mathbf{A}(t)$, $\mathbf{B}(t)$, $\mathbf{C}(t)$, each has rank n almost everywhere. Premultiplying Eq. 6.81 by $\mathbf{Q}_{T0}(t)$ and rearranging gives

$$\begin{aligned} \mathbf{Q}_{Tc}(t) &= \{[\mathbf{Q}_{T0}(t)\mathbf{Q}'_{T0}(t)]^{-1}\mathbf{Q}_{T0}(t)\mathbf{Q}'_0(t)\}\mathbf{Q}_c(t) \\ &= \mathbf{T}(t)\mathbf{Q}_c(t) \end{aligned} \tag{6.84}$$

where the equivalence transformation $\mathbf{T}(t)$ is noted to be

$$\mathbf{T}(t) = [\mathbf{Q}_{T0}(t)\mathbf{Q}'_{T0}(t)]^{-1}\mathbf{Q}_{T0}(t)\mathbf{Q}'_0(t) \tag{6.85}$$

Similarly, premultiplying Eq. 6.83 by $\mathbf{Q}_{T0}(t)$ and rearranging gives

$$\dot{\mathbf{Q}}_{Tc}(t) = \mathbf{T}(t)\dot{\mathbf{Q}}_c(t) \tag{6.86}$$

Comparison of Eq. 6.84 and 6.86 reveals that $\dot{\mathbf{T}}(t) = \mathbf{0}$ and thus that $\mathbf{T}(t)$ is a constant[1]: $\mathbf{T}(t) = \dot{\mathbf{T}}$. Therefore

$$\mathbf{Q}_{Tc}(t) = \mathbf{T}\mathbf{Q}_c(t) \tag{6.87}$$

and, as can be seen by substitution of Eq. 6.87 in 6.81,

$$\mathbf{Q}_{T0}(t) = (\mathbf{T}^{-1})'\mathbf{Q}_0(t) \tag{6.88}$$

Equations 6.87 and 6.88 imply

[1]It is noted that the fact that $\mathbf{T}(t)$ is a constant matrix is a direct consequence of the nonrestricting simplification obtained by letting $\mathbf{A}_T(t) = \mathbf{A}(t) = \mathbf{0}$.

$$\begin{aligned} \mathbf{B}_T(t) &= \mathbf{T}\mathbf{B}(t) \\ \mathbf{C}_T(t) &= \mathbf{C}(t)\mathbf{T}^{-1} \end{aligned} \tag{6.89}$$

thus establishing the theorem. Q.E.D.

A method for determining the algebraic equivalence of systems of different orders can be obtained with the methods for reducing systems (from the input and the output) established in Theorem 6.1.

Theorem 6.6. An analytic system $[\mathbf{A}(t). \mathbf{B}(t), \mathbf{C}(t)]$ of order n is algebraically equivalent to a system of the form $[\mathbf{A}_T(t), \mathbf{B}_T(t), \mathbf{C}_T(t)]$, also of order n, where

$$\mathbf{A}_T(t) = \begin{bmatrix} \mathbf{A}_{T11}(t) & \mathbf{0} & \mathbf{A}_{T13}(t) \\ \mathbf{A}_{T21}(t) & \mathbf{A}_{T22}(t) & \mathbf{A}_{T23}(t) \\ \mathbf{0} & \mathbf{0} & \mathbf{A}_{T33}(t) \end{bmatrix}$$

$$\mathbf{B}_T(t) = \begin{bmatrix} \mathbf{B}_{T1}(t) \\ \mathbf{B}_{T2}(t) \\ \mathbf{0} \end{bmatrix}, \quad \mathbf{C}_T(t) = [\mathbf{C}_{T1}(t) \quad \mathbf{0} \quad \mathbf{C}_{T3}(t)] \tag{6.90}$$

and subsystem $[\mathbf{A}_{T11}(t), \mathbf{B}_{T1}(t), \mathbf{C}_{T1}(t)]$ is a minimal system of order q (and thus zero-state equivalent to a minimal system of order q) if and only if $\mathbf{Q}_{nn}(t)$ has rank q.

Proof. (i) *Necessity* is established by showing that $\mathbf{Q}_{Tnn}(t)$ corresponding to system $[\mathbf{A}_T(t), \mathbf{B}_T(t), \mathbf{C}_T(t)]$ has rank q. By constructing $\mathbf{Q}_{Tmn}(t) = \mathbf{Q}'_{T0}(t)\mathbf{Q}_{Tc}(t)$ in terms of the controllability and observability matrices of the three subsystems $[\mathbf{A}_{T11}(t), \mathbf{B}_{T1}(t), \mathbf{C}_{T1}(t)]$, $[\mathbf{A}_{T22}(t), \mathbf{B}_{T2}(t), \mathbf{0}]$, $[\mathbf{A}_{T33}(t), \mathbf{0}, \mathbf{C}_{T3}(t)]$ it can be seen that upper left $q \times q$ partition of $\mathbf{Q}_{Tnn}(t)$ is the matrix $\mathbf{Q}'_{10}(t)\mathbf{Q}_{1c}(t)$ of rank q; $\mathbf{Q}_{1c}(t)$ and $\mathbf{Q}_{10}(t)$ are the controllability and observability matrices of system $[\mathbf{A}_{T11}(t), \mathbf{B}_{T1}(t), \mathbf{C}_{T1}(t)]$.

(ii) *Sufficiency* is established by showing that if rank $\mathbf{Q}_{nn}(t) = q$, then a transformation $\mathbf{T}(t)$ exists such that $[\mathbf{A}(t), \mathbf{B}(t), \mathbf{C}(t)] \xrightarrow{T} [\mathbf{A}_T(t), \mathbf{B}_T(t), \mathbf{C}_T(t)]$. Assuming that $q_c \leq n$ is the rank of the controllability matrix $\mathbf{Q}_c(t)$, Theorem 6.1 can be used to reduce $[\mathbf{A}(t), \mathbf{B}(t), \mathbf{C}(t)]$ on the input, i.e., $\mathbf{T}_c(t)$ can be determined such that $[\mathbf{A}(t), \mathbf{B}(t), \mathbf{C}(t)] \xrightarrow{T_c} [\hat{\mathbf{A}}(t), \hat{\mathbf{B}}(t), \hat{\mathbf{C}}(t)]$, where

$$\hat{\mathbf{A}}(t) = \begin{bmatrix} \hat{\mathbf{A}}_{11}(t) & \hat{\mathbf{A}}_{12}(t) \\ \mathbf{0} & \hat{\mathbf{A}}_{22}(t) \end{bmatrix}$$

$$\hat{\mathbf{B}}(t) = \begin{bmatrix} \hat{\mathbf{B}}_1(t) \\ \mathbf{0} \end{bmatrix}, \quad \hat{\mathbf{C}}(t) = [\hat{\mathbf{C}}_1(t) \quad \hat{\mathbf{C}}_2(t)] \tag{6.91}$$

Similarly, assuming that $q_0 \leq q_c$ is the rank of the observability matrix of system $[\hat{\mathbf{A}}_{11}(t), \hat{\mathbf{B}}_1(t), \hat{\mathbf{C}}_1(t)]$, the dual of Theorem 6.1 can be used to reduce this system on the output, i.e., $\mathbf{T}_0^*(t)$ is determined such that $[\hat{\mathbf{A}}_{11}(t), \hat{\mathbf{B}}_1(t), \hat{\mathbf{C}}_1(t)] \xrightarrow{T_0^*} [\tilde{\mathbf{A}}(t), \tilde{\mathbf{B}}(t), \tilde{\mathbf{C}}(t)]$ where

$$\tilde{\mathbf{A}}(t) = \begin{bmatrix} \mathbf{A}_{T11}(t) & \mathbf{0} \\ \mathbf{A}_{T21}(t) & \mathbf{A}_{T22}(t) \end{bmatrix}$$

$$\tilde{\mathbf{B}}(t) = \begin{bmatrix} \mathbf{B}_{T1}(t) \\ \mathbf{B}_{T2}(t) \end{bmatrix}, \ \tilde{\mathbf{C}}(t) = [\mathbf{C}_{T1}(t) \quad \mathbf{0}] \tag{6.92}$$

Therefore system $[\mathbf{A}_{T11}(t), \mathbf{B}_{T1}(t), \mathbf{C}_{T1}(t)]$ is of order q_0, completely controllable and completely observable, and thus a minimal system. Clearly, the equivalence transformation

$$\mathbf{T}_0(t) = \begin{bmatrix} \mathbf{T}_0^*(t) & \mathbf{0} \\ \mathbf{0} & \mathbf{I} \end{bmatrix} \tag{6.93}$$

results in $[\hat{\mathbf{A}}(t), \hat{\mathbf{B}}(t), \hat{\mathbf{C}}(t)] \xrightarrow{T_0} [\mathbf{A}_T(t), \mathbf{B}_T(t), \mathbf{C}_T(t)]$. Thus the equivalence transformation

$$\mathbf{T}(t) = \mathbf{T}_0(t)\mathbf{T}_c(t) \tag{6.94}$$

gives the desired result:

$$[\mathbf{A}(t), \mathbf{B}(t), \mathbf{C}(t)] \xrightarrow{T} [\mathbf{A}_T(t), \mathbf{B}_T(t), \mathbf{C}_T(t)] \tag{6.95}$$

Equations 6.77 and 6.79 show that if two systems are related as in Eq. 6.95, then

$$\mathbf{Q}_{T1j}(t) = \mathbf{Q}_{ij}(t) \tag{6.96}$$

Therefore

$$\mathbf{Q}_{q_0, q_0}(t) = \mathbf{Q}_{Tq_0, q_0}(t) = \mathbf{Q}'_{T10}(t)\mathbf{Q}_{1c}(t) \tag{6.97}$$

and as rank $\mathbf{Q}_{Tq_0, q_0}(t) = q_0$, rank $\mathbf{Q}_{Tnn}(t) = q_0$ and thus rank $\mathbf{Q}_{nn}(t) = q_0$. However, the theorem statement requires that rank $\mathbf{Q}_{nn}(t) = q$. Therefore $q_0 = q$ completing the proof. Q.E.D.

Theorem 6.6 and its proof lead to the equivalence relationship between systems of different order. For example, let $[\mathbf{A}_{T1}(t), \mathbf{B}_{T1}(t), \mathbf{C}_{T1}(t)]$ be a minimal system of order q with equivalence matrix $\Upsilon(t)$. Also let $[\mathbf{A}(t), \mathbf{B}(t), \mathbf{C}(t)]$ be a system of order $n \geq q$ such that

$$[\mathbf{A}(t), \mathbf{B}(t), \mathbf{C}(t)] \xrightarrow{T} [\mathbf{A}_T(t), \mathbf{B}_T(t), \mathbf{C}_T(t)] \tag{6.98}$$

where $[\mathbf{A}_T(t), \mathbf{B}_T(t), \mathbf{C}_T(t)]$ is specified in Eq. 6.90. In accordance with Theorem 6.6

$$\mathbf{Q}_{q+1, q+1} = \Upsilon(t) \tag{6.99}$$

thus providing a strong generalization of Theorem 6.5.

Corollary 6.6. Let $[\mathbf{A}(t), \mathbf{B}(t), \mathbf{C}(t)]$ and $[\mathbf{A}_T(t), \mathbf{B}_T(t), \mathbf{C}_T(t)]$ be analytic systems of order n and n_T respectively. Then the systems are algebraically equivalent if and only if $\mathbf{Q}_{nn}(t)$ and $\mathbf{Q}_{Tnn}(t)$ have the same rank q, and $\Upsilon(t) = \Upsilon_T(t)$ where $\Upsilon(t) \equiv \mathbf{Q}_{q+1, q+1}(t)$ and $\Upsilon_T(t) \equiv \mathbf{Q}_{Tq+1, q+1}(t)$. Therefore it is seen that the equivalence matrix characterizes all realizations of an impulse-response matrix.

A theorem is now given to demonstrate that the relation of Eq. 6.99 can be used to determine a minimal-order system directly from the equivalence matrix of a nonminimal realization. The following definitions simplify the theorem statement. Again, with $\Upsilon(t)$ the equivalence matrix of a class of minimal systems of order q, the following submatrices are isolated.

(a) $\mathbf{Q}(t) = \mathbf{Q}_{qq}(t)$, the matrix formed from the first rq rows and the first mq columns of $\Upsilon(t) = \mathbf{Q}_{q+1,q+1}(t)$

(b) $\mathbf{Q}^*(t)$, the matrix formed from the last rq rows and the first mq columns of $\Upsilon(t) = \mathbf{Q}_{q+1,q+1}(t)$

(c) $\mathbf{F}(t)$ any $q \times q$ submatrix of $\mathbf{Q}(t)$ having rank q for all t

(d) $\mathbf{F}^*(t)$, the submatrix of $\mathbf{Q}^*(t)$ corresponding, in position, to $\mathbf{F}(t)$ in $\mathbf{Q}(t)$

(e) $\mathbf{F}_1(t)$, the columns of the first r rows of $\mathbf{Q}(t)$ corresponding to the columns of $\mathbf{F}(t)$

(f) $\mathbf{F}_2(t)$ the rows of the first m columns of $\mathbf{Q}(t)$ corresponding to the rows of $\mathbf{F}(t)$

It is noted that the matrices $\mathbf{F}(t)$, $\mathbf{F}^*(t)$, $\mathbf{F}_1(t)$, $\mathbf{F}_2(t)$ are submatrices of the equivalence matrix $\Upsilon(t)$ and can be determined without foreknowledge of any minimal realization.

Theorem 6.7. Let $[\mathbf{A}(t), \mathbf{B}(t), \mathbf{C}(t)]$ be an analytic system of order n and let $\Upsilon(t) = \mathbf{Q}_{q+1,q+1}(t)$ be the equivalence matrix of the minimal-order realizations of $[\mathbf{A}(t), \mathbf{B}(t), \mathbf{C}(t)]$. Then for any matrix $\mathbf{F}(t)$ satisfying (c) above, the system $[\mathbf{F}^*(t)\mathbf{F}^{-1}(t), \mathbf{F}_2(t), \mathbf{F}_1(t)\mathbf{F}^{-1}(t)]$ is a minimal realization of $[\mathbf{A}(t), \mathbf{B}(t), \mathbf{C}(t)]$, where $\mathbf{F}^*(t)$, $\mathbf{F}_1(t)$, $\mathbf{F}_2(t)$ are defined by (d), (e), (f), respectively.

The proof of Theorem 6.7 follows directly from the proof of Theorem 6.8 which is given in the next section on synthesis and is therefore not given here. Theorem 6.7 leads to a useful corollary for determining whether or not a system is realizable as a time-invariant system:

Corollary 6.7. Let $[\mathbf{A}(t), \mathbf{B}(t), \mathbf{C}(t)]$ be an analytic system of order n. Then $[\mathbf{A}(t), \mathbf{B}(t), \mathbf{C}(t)]$ is zero-state time-invariant (i.e., has a stationary impulsive-response matrix) if $\mathbf{Q}_{nn}(t)$ has rank $q \leq n$ and $\Upsilon(t) = \mathbf{Q}_{q+1,q+1}(t)$ is a constant matrix.

Proof. Note that if $\Upsilon(t)$ is a constant matrix then $\mathbf{F}(t)$, $\mathbf{F}^*(t)$, $\mathbf{F}_1(t)$, $\mathbf{F}_2(t)$ are constant matrices and the system $[\mathbf{F}^*(t)\mathbf{F}^{-1}(t), \mathbf{F}_2(t), \mathbf{F}_1(t)\mathbf{F}^{-1}(t)]$ is a time-invariant system. Q.E.D.

6.6. SYNTHESIS OF LINEAR SYSTEMS FROM THE IMPULSIVE-RESPONSE MATRIX [14]

In Chapter 5, it is noted that infinitely many realizations of an impulsive-response matrix $\Omega(t, \tau)$, minimal and otherwise, can be obtained from any given minimal realization $[\mathbf{A}(t), \mathbf{B}(t), \mathbf{C}(t)]$. Further, Theorem

5.1 demonstrates that a realization of $\Omega(t, \tau)$ can be obtained if $\Omega(t, \tau)$ can be separated in the form

$$\Omega(t, \tau) = \mathbf{P}(t)\mathbf{Q}(\tau) \tag{6.100}$$

In particular, one can always obtain the realization $[\mathbf{0}, \mathbf{Q}(t), \mathbf{P}(t)]$. Using concepts of reducibility, a minimal realization can be obtained by a transformation of the type $[\mathbf{0}, \mathbf{Q}(t), \mathbf{P}(t)] \xrightarrow{T} [\mathbf{A}(t), \mathbf{B}(t), \mathbf{C}(t)]$. From the minimal realization $[\mathbf{A}(t), \mathbf{B}(t), \mathbf{C}(t)]$ other realizations can be obtained using equivalence transformation as given in Chapter 5.

It is seen, therefore, that a realization of the impulsive-response matrix $\Omega(t, \tau)$ hinges on being able to separate it in the form of Eq. 6.100. Even for relatively simple systems, great difficulty may be experienced in achieving such a separation; it may in fact be completely intractable by inspection methods.

In this section an algorithm is presented for executing the separation. The separation achieved results in a minimal realization $[\mathbf{0}, \mathbf{P}(t), \mathbf{Q}(t)]$. The separation hinges on the results obtained in the last section on algebraically equivalent systems. Again, in what follows, it is assumed that $\mathbf{A}(t)$, $\mathbf{B}(t)$, and $\mathbf{C}(t)$ are analytic functions of time and that $\Omega(t, \tau)$ is analytic in t and τ. Thus, a method of synthesizing the impulsive-response matrix $\Omega(t, \tau)$ is given which does not require that $\Omega(t, \tau)$ be in the separable form $\Omega(t, \tau) = \mathbf{P}(t)\mathbf{Q}(\tau)$.

Let $\Omega(t, \tau)$ be an $r \times m$ matrix function analytic in t and τ, and define

$$\mathbf{Q}_{ij}(t, \tau) \equiv \begin{bmatrix} \Omega_{00}(t, \tau) & \Omega_{01}(t, \tau) & \cdots & \Omega_{0, j-1}(t, \tau) \\ \Omega_{10}(t, \tau) & \Omega_{11}(t, \tau) & \cdots & \Omega_{1, j-1}(t, \tau) \\ \vdots & \vdots & & \vdots \\ \Omega_{i-1,0}(t, \tau) & \Omega_{i-1,1}(t, \tau) & \cdots & \Omega_{i-1, j-1}(t, \tau) \end{bmatrix} \tag{6.101}$$

where

$$\Omega_{ij}(t, \tau) = \frac{\partial^i}{\partial t^i} \frac{\partial^j}{\partial \tau^j} \Omega(t, \tau) \tag{6.102}$$

If $\Omega(t, \tau)$ is realized by the system $[\mathbf{A}(t), \mathbf{B}(t), \mathbf{C}(t)]$, i.e., $\Omega(t, \tau) = \mathbf{C}(t)\phi(t, \tau)\mathbf{B}(\tau)$, it can be verified that

$$\Omega_{ij}(t, \tau) = \mathbf{S}_i'(t)\phi(t, \tau)\mathbf{R}_j(\tau) \tag{6.103}$$

Therefore

$$\Omega_{ij}(t, t) = \mathbf{S}_i'(t)\mathbf{R}_j(t) \tag{6.104}$$

and, in accordance with Eq. 6.77

$$\mathbf{Q}_{ij}(t, t) = \mathbf{Q}_{ij}(t) \tag{6.105}$$

where $\mathbf{Q}_{ij}(t)$ is as defined in Eq. 6.77. Equation 6.105, relating $\mathbf{Q}_{ij}(t, \tau)$ which is formed from the system's impulsive-response matrix $\Omega(t, \tau)$ and

$\mathbf{Q}_{ij}(t)$ which is formed from the system's differential equation characterization, is the basis of the method for synthesizing $\Omega(t, \tau)$.

Theorem 6.8. $\Omega(t, \tau)$ is separable in the form $\Omega(t, \tau) = \mathbf{P}(t)\mathbf{Q}(\tau)$ if and only if there exists a positive integer n such that $\mathbf{Q}_{nn}(t, \tau)$ and $\mathbf{Q}_{n+1,n+1}(t, \tau)$ both have rank n for $t \geq \tau$. Furthermore, n is the order of the minimal realization.

Proof. (i) *Necessity*: If system $[\mathbf{A}(t), \mathbf{B}(t), \mathbf{C}(t)]$ is an nth order minimal realization of $\Omega(t, \tau)$ then, in accordance with Eq. 6.103

$$\mathbf{Q}_{nn}(t, \tau) = \mathbf{Q}_0'(t)\phi(t, \tau)\mathbf{Q}_c(\tau) \tag{6.106}$$

Therefore $\mathbf{Q}_{nn}(t, \tau)$ and thus $\mathbf{Q}_{n+1,n+1}(t, \tau)$ must have rank n.

(ii) *Sufficiency*: Introduce the following definitions:

(a) $\mathbf{Q}_{nn}^*(t, \tau) = \dfrac{\partial \mathbf{Q}_{nn}(t, \tau)}{\partial t}$, the matrix formed by the last rn rows of $\mathbf{Q}_{n+1,n}(t, \tau)$,

(b) $\mathbf{F}(t, \tau)$, any $n \times n$ submatrix of $\mathbf{Q}_{nn}(t, \tau)$ of rank n,

(c) $\mathbf{F}^*(t, \tau)$, the $n \times n$ submatrix of $\mathbf{Q}_{nn}^*(t, \tau)$ corresponding in position to $\mathbf{F}(t, \tau)$ in $\mathbf{Q}_{nn}(t, \tau)$,

(d) $\hat{\mathbf{Q}}_{n+1,n}(t, \tau)$, the $n \times m(n+1)$ matrix formed by the rows of $\mathbf{Q}_{n+1,n}(t, \tau)$ containing $\mathbf{F}(t, \tau)$,

(e) $\hat{\mathbf{Q}}_{n+1,n}^*(t, \tau)$, the $n \times m(n+1)$ matrix formed by the rows of $\mathbf{Q}_{n+1,n}^*(t, \tau)$ containing $\mathbf{F}^*(t, \tau)$,

(f) $\mathbf{A}(t, \tau)$, the $n \times n$ matrix satisfying the equation,

$$\hat{\mathbf{Q}}_{n+1,n}^*(t, \tau) = \mathbf{A}(t, \tau)\hat{\mathbf{Q}}_{n+1,n}(t, \tau) \tag{6.107}$$

Since $\hat{\mathbf{Q}}_{n+1,n}(t, \tau)$ contains $\mathbf{F}(t, \tau)$ as a submatrix, it also has rank n. Thus Eq. 6.107 can be solved for $\mathbf{A}(t, \tau)$:

$$\mathbf{A}(t, \tau) = \hat{\mathbf{Q}}_{n+1,n}^*(t, \tau)\hat{\mathbf{Q}}_{n+1,n}'(t, \tau)[\hat{\mathbf{Q}}_{n+1,n}(t, \tau)\mathbf{Q}_{n+1,n}'(t, \tau)]^{-1} \tag{6.108}$$

Due to the similar positions of $\mathbf{F}(t, \tau)$ and $\mathbf{F}^*(t, \tau)$ in $\hat{\mathbf{Q}}_{n+1,n}(t, \tau)$ and $\hat{\mathbf{Q}}_{n+1,n}^*(t, \tau)$ it follows from Eq. 6.107 and 6.108 that

$$\mathbf{F}^*(t, \tau) = \mathbf{A}(t, \tau)\mathbf{F}(t, \tau) \tag{6.109}$$

and

$$\mathbf{A}(t, \tau) = \mathbf{F}^*(t, \tau)\mathbf{F}^{-1}(t, \tau) \tag{6.110}$$

It is noted that $\dfrac{\partial \mathbf{F}(t, \tau)}{\partial \tau}$ and $\dfrac{\partial \mathbf{F}^*(t, \tau)}{\partial \tau}$ are obtained from $\hat{\mathbf{Q}}_{n+1,n}(t, \tau)$ and $\hat{\mathbf{Q}}_{n+1,n}(t, \tau)$ as the submatrices obtained by shifting m columns to the right from each column corresponding to $\mathbf{F}(t, \tau)$ and $\mathbf{F}^*(t, \tau)$. Therefore, in accordance with Eq. 6.107

$$\frac{\partial \mathbf{F}^*(t, \tau)}{\partial \tau} = \mathbf{A}(t, \tau)\frac{\partial \mathbf{F}(t, \tau)}{\partial \tau} \tag{6.111}$$

Comparison of Eqs. 6.109 and 6.111 shows that $\mathbf{A}(t, \tau)$ is not a function of τ. Thus one can write $\mathbf{A}(t, \tau) = \mathbf{A}(t)$. Taking the derivative of the matrix product $\mathbf{F}^{-1}(t, \lambda)\mathbf{F}(t, \tau)$ with respect to t gives

$$\frac{\partial[\mathbf{F}^{-1}(t, \lambda)\mathbf{F}(t, \tau)]}{\partial t} = \frac{\partial \mathbf{F}^{-1}(t, \tau)}{\partial t} \mathbf{F}(t, \tau) + \mathbf{F}^{-1}(t, \lambda) \frac{\partial \mathbf{F}(t, \tau)}{\partial t} \tag{6.112}$$

By differentiating $[\mathbf{F}(t, \tau)\mathbf{F}^{-1}(t, \tau) = \mathbf{I}]$ with respect to t it is noted that

$$\frac{\partial \mathbf{F}^{-1}(t, \tau)}{\partial t} = -\mathbf{F}^{-1}(t, \tau) \frac{\partial \mathbf{F}(t, \tau)}{\partial t} \mathbf{F}^{-1}(t, \tau) \tag{6.113}$$

Equation 6.109 can be written as

$$\frac{\partial \mathbf{F}(t, \tau)}{\partial t} = \mathbf{A}(t, \tau)\mathbf{F}(t, \tau) \tag{6.114}$$

Substituting from Eq. 6.113 and 6.114 in Eq. 6.112 and rearranging results in

$$\frac{\partial[\mathbf{F}^{-1}(t, \lambda)\mathbf{F}(t, \tau)]}{\partial t} = -\mathbf{F}^{-1}(t, \lambda)[\mathbf{A}(t, \lambda) - \mathbf{A}(t, \tau)]\mathbf{F}(t, \tau) \tag{6.115}$$

Since $\mathbf{A}(t, \tau) = \mathbf{A}(t, \lambda)$

$$\frac{\partial[\mathbf{F}^{-1}(t, \lambda)\mathbf{F}(t, \tau)]}{\partial t} = \mathbf{0} \tag{6.116}$$

and the product $\mathbf{F}^{-1}(t, \lambda)\mathbf{F}(t, \tau)$ is seen not to be a function of t. Therefore

$$\mathbf{F}^{-1}(t, \lambda)\mathbf{F}(t, \tau) = \mathbf{F}^{-1}(\xi, \lambda)\mathbf{F}(\xi, \tau) \tag{6.117}$$

Premultiplying Eq. 6.117 by $\mathbf{F}(t, \lambda)$ gives

$$\mathbf{F}(t, \tau) = \mathbf{F}(t, \lambda)\mathbf{F}^{-1}(\xi, \lambda)\mathbf{F}(\xi, \tau) \tag{6.118}$$

Since $\Omega(t, \tau)$ is a submatrix of $\mathbf{Q}_{nn}(t, \tau)$ and since $\mathbf{Q}_{nn}(t, \tau)$ has rank n, and since $\mathbf{F}(t, \tau)$ is a submatrix of $\mathbf{Q}_{nn}(t, \tau)$ of rank n, it follows that $\mathbf{Q}_{nn}(t, \tau)$, and thus $\Omega(t, \tau)$, can be formed by row and column operations on $\mathbf{F}(t, \tau)$; i.e., matrices $\mathbf{C}_1(t, \tau)$ and $\mathbf{B}_1(t, \tau)$ exist such that

$$\Omega(t, \tau) = \mathbf{C}_1(t, \tau)\mathbf{F}(t, \tau)\mathbf{B}_1(t, \tau) \tag{6.119}$$

In what follows, the procedure for determining $\mathbf{C}_1(t, \tau)$ and $\mathbf{B}_1(t, \tau)$ in terms of submatrices of $\mathbf{Q}_{nn}(t, \tau)$ is detailed. Let $\mathbf{F}_k(t, \tau)$ be the $rn \times n$ matrix formed by the columns of $\mathbf{Q}_{nn}(t, \tau)$ containing $\mathbf{F}(t, \tau)$, and let $\mathbf{F}_R(t, \tau)$ be the $n \times mn$ matrix formed by the rows of $\mathbf{Q}_{nn}(t, \tau)$ containing $\mathbf{F}(t, \tau)$. As $\mathbf{Q}_{nn}(t, \tau)$ and its submatrices $\mathbf{F}_K(t, \tau)$, $\mathbf{F}_R(t, \tau)$ all nave rank n, matrices $\mathbf{R}(t, \tau)$ and $\mathbf{K}(t, \tau)$ exist such that

$$\mathbf{R}(t, \tau)\mathbf{F}_R(t, \tau) = \mathbf{F}_K(t, \tau)\mathbf{K}(t, \tau) = \mathbf{Q}_{nn}(t, \tau) \tag{6.120}$$

It is easily verified that

$$\begin{aligned} \mathbf{R}(t, \tau)\mathbf{F}(t, \tau) &= \mathbf{F}_K(t, \tau) \\ \mathbf{F}(t, \tau)\mathbf{K}(t, \tau) &= \mathbf{F}_R(t, \tau) \end{aligned} \tag{6.121}$$

Comparison of Eq, 6.120 and 6.121 shows that

$$\mathbf{Q}_{nn}(t, \tau) = \mathbf{R}(t, \tau)\mathbf{F}(t, \tau)\mathbf{K}(t, \tau) \tag{6.122}$$

which can be written as

$$\begin{aligned}\mathbf{Q}_{nn}(t, \tau) &= [\mathbf{R}(t, \tau)\mathbf{F}(t, \tau)]\mathbf{F}^{-1}(t, \tau)[\mathbf{F}(t, \tau)\mathbf{K}(t, \tau)] \\ &= \mathbf{F}_K(t, \tau)\mathbf{F}^{-1}(t, \tau)\mathbf{F}_R(t, \tau)\end{aligned} \tag{6.123}$$

Partitioning $\mathbf{R}(t, \tau)$ r rows down, and $\mathbf{K}(t, \tau)$ m columns from the left, results in

$$\begin{aligned}\mathbf{F}_K(t, \tau) &= \begin{bmatrix}\mathbf{R}_1(t, \tau)\\ \mathbf{R}_2(t, \tau)\end{bmatrix}\mathbf{F}(t, \tau) = \begin{bmatrix}\mathbf{F}_1(t, \tau)\\ \mathbf{R}_2(t, \tau)\mathbf{F}(t, \tau)\end{bmatrix}\\ \mathbf{F}_R(t, \tau) &= \mathbf{F}(t, \tau)[\mathbf{K}_1(t, \tau), \mathbf{K}_2(t, \tau)]\\ &= [\mathbf{F}_2(t, \tau), \mathbf{F}(t, \tau)\mathbf{K}_2(t, \tau)]\end{aligned} \tag{6.124}$$

where

$$\begin{aligned}\mathbf{F}_1(t, \tau) &= \mathbf{R}_1(t, \tau)\mathbf{F}(t, \tau)\\ \mathbf{F}_2(t, \tau) &= \mathbf{F}(t, \tau)\mathbf{K}_1(t, \tau)\end{aligned} \tag{6.125}$$

From Eq. 6.124 it is seen that $\mathbf{F}_1(t, \tau)$ is the $r \times n$ matrix formed by the columns of the first r rows of $\mathbf{Q}_{nn}(t, \tau)$ corresponding to the columns of $\mathbf{F}(t, \tau)$, and $\mathbf{F}_2(t, \tau)$ is the $m \times n$ matrix formed by the rows of the first m columns of $\mathbf{Q}_{nn}(t, \tau)$ corresponding to the rows of $F(t, \tau)$. Substituting from Eq. 6.124 in Eq. 6.123 gives

$$\mathbf{Q}_{nn}(t, \tau) = \begin{bmatrix}\mathbf{F}_1(t, \tau)\mathbf{F}^{-1}(t, \tau)\mathbf{F}_2(t, \tau) & \vdots & \mathbf{F}_1(t, \tau)\mathbf{K}_2(t, \tau)\\ \cdots\cdots & \vdots & \cdots\cdots\\ \mathbf{R}_2(t, \tau)\mathbf{F}_2(t, \tau) & \vdots & \mathbf{R}_2(t, \tau)\mathbf{F}(t, \tau)\mathbf{K}_2(t, \tau)\end{bmatrix} \tag{6.126}$$

Since the matrix $\mathbf{F}_1(t, \tau)\mathbf{F}^{-1}(t, \tau)\mathbf{F}_2(t, \tau)$ corresponds to the uppermost $r \times m$ submatrix of $\mathbf{Q}_{nn}(t, \tau)$, Eq. 6.101 shows that

$$\begin{aligned}\Omega(t, \tau) &= \mathbf{F}_1(t, \tau)\mathbf{F}^{-1}(t, \tau)\mathbf{F}_2(t, \tau)\\ &= [\mathbf{F}_1(t, \tau)\mathbf{F}^{-1}(t, \tau)]\mathbf{F}(t, \tau)[\mathbf{F}^{-1}(t, \tau)\mathbf{F}_2(t, \tau)]\\ &= \mathbf{R}_1(t, \tau)\mathbf{F}(t, \tau)\mathbf{K}_1(t, \tau)\\ &= \mathbf{C}_1(t, \tau)\mathbf{F}(t, \tau)\mathbf{B}_1(t, \tau)\end{aligned} \tag{6.127}$$

Therefore

$$\begin{aligned}\mathbf{C}_1(t, \tau) &= \mathbf{R}_1(t, \tau) = \mathbf{F}_1(t, \tau)\mathbf{F}^{-1}(t, \tau)\\ \mathbf{B}_1(t, \tau) &= \mathbf{K}_1(t, \tau) = \mathbf{F}^{-1}(t, \tau)\mathbf{F}_2(t, \tau)\end{aligned} \tag{6.128}$$

Since $\dfrac{\partial \mathbf{F}(t, \tau)}{\partial \tau}$ $\left(\dfrac{\partial \mathbf{F}(t, \tau)}{\partial t}\right)$ is a submatrix obtained by shifting m columns to the right (r columns down) from the elements of $\mathbf{F}(t, \tau)$ in $\mathbf{Q}_{n+1, n+1}(t, \tau)$, and since $\dfrac{\partial \mathbf{F}_1(t, \tau)}{\partial t}$ $\left(\dfrac{\partial \mathbf{F}_2(t, \tau)}{\partial t}\right)$ is obtained by a similar shift from $\mathbf{F}_1(t, \tau)$ ($\mathbf{F}_2(t, \tau)$), it is seen that the same row and column operations shown in Eqs. 6.125, performed on the submatrices $\mathbf{F}(t, \tau)$ of $\mathbf{Q}_{n+1, n+1}(t, \tau)$ to obtain submatrices $\mathbf{F}_1(t, \tau)$ and $\mathbf{F}_2(t, \tau)$, can also be performed on the submatrix $\dfrac{\partial \mathbf{F}(t, \tau)}{\partial \tau}$ and $\dfrac{\partial \mathbf{F}(t, \tau)}{\partial t}$ to obtain matrices $\dfrac{\partial \mathbf{F}_1(t, \tau)}{\partial \tau}$ and $\dfrac{\partial \mathbf{F}_2(t, \tau)}{\partial t}$. Specifically

$$\begin{aligned} \frac{\partial \mathbf{F}_1(t, \tau)}{\partial \tau} &= \mathbf{C}_1(t, \tau) \frac{\partial \mathbf{F}(t, \tau)}{\partial \tau} \\ \frac{\partial \mathbf{F}_2(t, \tau)}{\partial t} &= \frac{\mathbf{F}(t, \tau)}{\partial t} \mathbf{B}_1(t, \tau) \end{aligned} \tag{6.129}$$

Comparing Eqs. 6.125 and 6.129 shows that $\mathbf{C}_1(t, \tau)$ is not a function of τ and $\mathbf{B}_1(t, \tau)$ is not a function of t, i.e.,

$$\begin{aligned} \mathbf{C}_1(t, \tau) &= \mathbf{C}_1(t, \lambda) \\ \mathbf{B}_1(t, \tau) &= \mathbf{B}_1(\xi, \tau) \end{aligned} \tag{6.130}$$

Therefore Eq. 6.127 can be written as

$$\begin{aligned} \Omega(t, \tau) &= \mathbf{C}_1(t, \lambda)\mathbf{F}(t, \tau)\mathbf{B}_1(t, \tau) \\ &= \mathbf{F}_1(t, \lambda)\mathbf{F}^{-1}(t, \lambda)\mathbf{F}(t, \tau)\mathbf{F}^{-1}(\xi, \tau)\mathbf{F}_2(\xi, \tau) \end{aligned} \tag{6.131}$$

Substitution from Eq. 6.118 in Eq. 6.131 gives

$$\Omega(t, \tau) = \mathbf{F}_1(t, \lambda)\mathbf{F}^{-1}(\xi, \lambda)\mathbf{F}(\xi, \tau)\mathbf{F}^{-1}(\xi, \tau)\mathbf{F}_2(\xi, \tau) \tag{6.132}$$

which simplifies to the separable form

$$\Omega(t, \tau) = \mathbf{F}_1(t, \lambda)\mathbf{F}^{-1}(\xi, \lambda)\mathbf{F}_2(\xi, \tau) \tag{6.133}$$

Letting

$$\begin{aligned} \mathbf{A}(t) &= \mathbf{0} \\ \mathbf{B}(t) &= \mathbf{F}^{-1}(\xi, \lambda)\mathbf{F}_2(\xi, \tau) \\ \mathbf{C}(t) &= \mathbf{F}_1(t, \lambda) \end{aligned} \tag{6.134}$$

gives a minimal realization of $\Omega(t, \tau)$. Q.E.D.

Theorem 6.8 is important because it provides a straightforward test for determining whether a given impulsive response is separable in the form $\Omega(t, \tau) = \mathbf{P}(t)\mathbf{Q}(\tau)$ and thus whether it can be realized by a finite-dimensional system of the type $[\mathbf{A}(t), \mathbf{B}(t), \mathbf{C}(t)]$. However, *most important* is the proof of the theorem which gives an algorithm for performing the separation providing a minimal realization of the impulsive-response matrix $\Omega(t, \tau)$. As shown in the previous chapter, other realizations can be obtained from any minimal realization. A block diagram of the realization given by Eq. 6.134 is shown in Fig. 6.2. This system has the disadvantage of having no feedback around the integrators and is therefore undesirable from a practical point of view. A modification is given which results in a physically acceptable realization:

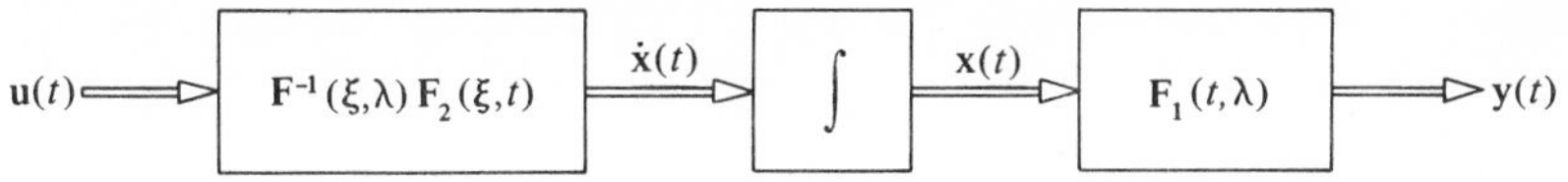

Fig. 6.2. Realization of the impulsive-response matrix $\Omega(t, \tau)$ as given by Eqs. 6.134.

$$\begin{aligned} \mathbf{A}(t) &= \mathbf{F}^*(t, t)\mathbf{F}^{-1}(t, t) = \frac{\partial \mathbf{F}(t, t)}{\partial t} \mathbf{F}^{-1}(t, t) \\ \mathbf{B}(t) &= \mathbf{F}_2(t, t) \\ \mathbf{C}(t) &= \mathbf{F}_1(t, t)\mathbf{F}^{-1}(t, t) \end{aligned} \tag{6.135}$$

The transition matrix for the system corresponding to Eq. 6.134, i.e.,

$$\frac{\partial \mathbf{F}(t, \tau)}{\partial t} = \mathbf{A}(t, \tau)\mathbf{F}(t, \tau) \tag{6.136}$$

with initial condition $\mathbf{F}(t_0, \tau)$ can be determined from the solution given in Eq. 6.118:

$$\mathbf{F}(t, \tau) = [\mathbf{F}(t, \lambda)\mathbf{F}^{-1}(t_0, \lambda)]\mathbf{F}(t_0, \tau) = \phi(t, t_0)\mathbf{F}(t_0, \tau) \tag{6.137}$$

Thus, for this system the transition matrix is

$$\phi(t, t_0) = \mathbf{F}(t, \lambda)\mathbf{F}^{-1}(t_0, \lambda) \tag{6.138}$$

Therefore

$$\begin{aligned} \Omega(t, \tau) &= \mathbf{C}(t)\phi(t, \tau)\mathbf{B}(\tau) \\ &= [\mathbf{F}_1(t, t)\mathbf{F}^{-1}(t, t)]\,[\mathbf{F}(t, \lambda)\mathbf{F}^{-1}(t, \lambda)]\mathbf{F}_2(t, \lambda) \\ &= \mathbf{F}_1(t, \lambda)\mathbf{F}^{-1}(t, \lambda)\mathbf{F}(t, \lambda)\mathbf{F}^{-1}(\xi, \lambda)\mathbf{F}_2(\xi, \tau) \\ &= \mathbf{F}_1(t, \lambda)\mathbf{F}^{-1}(\xi, \lambda)\mathbf{F}_2(\xi, \tau) \end{aligned} \tag{6.139}$$

which corresponds to Eq. 6.133 and verifies that Eqs. 6.135 represent a realization of $\Omega(t, \tau)$. A block diagram of this realization is shown in Fig. 6.3. This realization does provide feedback around the integrators and is thus more desirable for practical simulations.

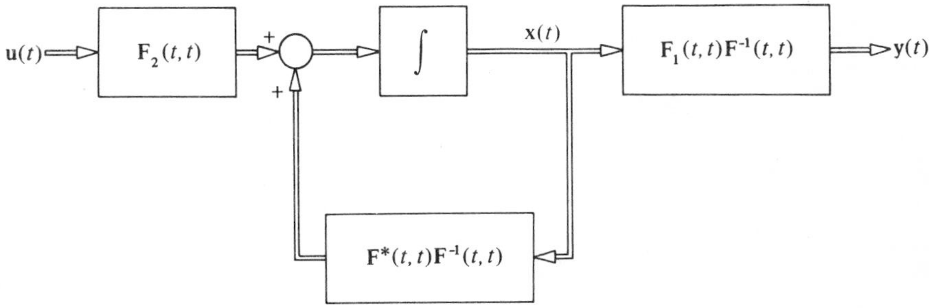

Fig. 6.3. Realization of the impulsive-response matrix $\Omega(t, \tau)$ as given by Eqs. 6.135.

Example 6.4. The method of synthesis given in the proof of Theorem 6.8 is illustrated here. Consider the system having the impulsive-response matrix

$$\Omega(t, \tau) = \begin{bmatrix} t\tau^3 & t^3\tau \\ t^2\tau^2 & \tau \end{bmatrix}$$

The matrix $\mathbf{Q}_{11}(t, \tau) = \Omega(t, \tau)$ and is seen to have rank 2. The matrix $\mathbf{Q}_{22}(t, \tau)$ is formed in accordance with Eq. 6.101

$$\mathbf{Q}_{22}(t, \tau) = \left[\begin{array}{cc|cc} t\tau^3 & t^3\tau & 3t\tau^2 & t^3 \\ t^2\tau^2 & \tau & 2t^2\tau & 1 \\ \hline \tau^3 & 3t^2\tau & 3\tau^2 & 3t^2 \\ 2t\tau^2 & 0 & 4t\tau & 0 \end{array}\right]$$

and is seen to have rank 3. Examination of the matrices $\mathbf{Q}_{33}(t, \tau)$ and $\mathbf{Q}_{44}(t, \tau)$ shows that they also have rank 3. Thus in accordance with Theorem 6.8 the order of the minimal realization is 3. The matrix $\mathbf{Q}_{32}(t, \tau)$ is sufficient to complete the synthesis:

$$\mathbf{Q}_{32}(t, \tau) = \left[\begin{array}{cc|cc} t\tau^3 & t^3\tau & 3t\tau^2 & t^3 \\ t^2\tau^2 & \tau & 2t^2\tau & 1 \\ \hline \tau^3 & 3t^2\tau & 3\tau^2 & 3t^2 \\ 2t\tau^2 & 0 & 4t\tau & 0 \\ \hline 0 & 6t\tau & 0 & 6t \\ 2\tau^2 & 0 & 4\tau & 0 \end{array}\right]$$

$\mathbf{F}(t, \tau)$ is selected as any 3×3 submatrix of $\mathbf{Q}_{22}(t, \tau)$ of rank 3. Therefore

$$\mathbf{F}(t, \tau) = \begin{bmatrix} t\tau^3 & t^3\tau & 3t\tau^2 \\ t^2\tau^2 & \tau & 2t^2\tau \\ \tau^2 & 3t^2\tau & 3\tau^2 \end{bmatrix}$$

$\mathbf{Q}^*_{22}(t, \tau)$ is selected as the last four rows of $\mathbf{Q}_{32}(t, \tau)$:

$$\mathbf{Q}^*_{22}(t, \tau) = \left[\begin{array}{cc|cc} \tau^3 & 3t^2 & 3\tau^2 & 3t^2 \\ 2t\tau^2 & 0 & 4t\tau & 0 \\ \hline 0 & 6t\tau & 0 & 6t \\ 2\tau^2 & 0 & 4\tau & 0 \end{array}\right]$$

$\mathbf{F}^*(t, \tau)$ is selected from $\mathbf{Q}^*_{22}(t, \tau)$ as corresponding in position to $\mathbf{F}(t, \tau)$ in $\mathbf{Q}_{22}(t, \tau)$:

$$\mathbf{F}^*(t, \tau) = \begin{bmatrix} \tau^3 & 3t^2 & 3\tau^2 \\ 2t\tau^2 & 0 & 4t\tau \\ 0 & 6t\tau & 0 \end{bmatrix}$$

$\mathbf{F}_K(t, \tau)$ is the columns of $\mathbf{Q}_{22}(t, \tau)$ containing $\mathbf{F}(t, \tau)$, and $\mathbf{F}_R(t, \tau)$ is the rows of $\mathbf{Q}_{22}(t, \tau)$ containing $\mathbf{F}(t, \tau)$. Therefore

$$\mathbf{F}_K(t, \tau) = \begin{bmatrix} t\tau^3 & t^3\tau & 3t\tau^2 \\ t^2\tau^2 & \tau & 2t^2\tau \\ \tau^3 & 3t^2\tau & 3\tau^2 \\ 2t\tau^2 & 0 & 4t\tau \end{bmatrix}$$

$$\mathbf{F}_R(t, \tau) = \begin{bmatrix} t\tau^3 & t^3\tau & 3t\tau^2 & t^3 \\ t^2\tau^2 & \tau & 2t^2\tau & 1 \\ \tau^3 & 3t^2\tau & 3\tau^2 & 3t^2 \end{bmatrix}$$

$\mathbf{F}_1(t, \tau)$ is the first 2 ($\Omega(t, \tau)$ is a 2×2 matrix) rows of $\mathbf{F}_K(t, \tau)$ and $\mathbf{F}_2(t, \tau)$ is the first 2 ($\Omega(t, \tau)$ is a 2×2 matrix) columns of $\mathbf{F}_R(t, \tau)$:

$$\mathbf{F}_1(t, \tau) = \begin{bmatrix} t\tau^3 & t^3\tau & 3t\tau^2 \\ t^2\tau^2 & \tau & 2t^2\tau \end{bmatrix}$$

$$\mathbf{F}_2(t, \tau) = \begin{bmatrix} t\tau^3 & t^3\tau \\ t^2\tau & \tau \\ \tau^3 & 3t^2\tau \end{bmatrix}$$

A realization is obtained by $[\mathbf{F}^*(t, t)\mathbf{F}^{-1}(t, t), \mathbf{F}_2(t, t), \mathbf{F}_1(t, t)\mathbf{F}^{-1}(t, t)]$ where

$$\mathbf{F}^{-1}(t, t) = \begin{bmatrix} \frac{3}{2}t^{-7} - 3t^{-4} & \frac{3}{2}t^{-4} & t^{-3} - \frac{9}{2}t^{-4} \\ -\frac{1}{2}t^{-4} & 0 & \frac{1}{2}t^{-3} \\ \frac{3}{2}t^{-3} - \frac{1}{2}t^{-6} & -t^{-3} & \frac{1}{2}t^{-5} - \frac{1}{2}t^{-2} \end{bmatrix}$$

REFERENCES

[1] Chidambara, M., "The Transformation to (Phase-Variable) Canonical Form," *IEEE Trans. on Automatic Control*, vol. AC-10 (1965), pp. 492–495.

[2] Chidambara, M., "Comment on the Transformation to (Phase-Variable) Canonical Form," *IEEE Trans. on Automatic Control*, vol. AC-11 (1966), pp. 607–608.

[3] Desoer, C., and P. Varaiya, "The Minimal Realization of a Nonanticipative Impulse Response Matrix," *J. SIAM Applied Mathematics*, vol. 15, no. 3 (1967), pp. 754–764.

[4] Johnson, C., and W. Wonham, "A Note on the Transformation to Canonical (Phase-Variable) Form," *IEEE Trans. on Automatic Control*, vol. AC-9 (1964), pp. 312–313.

[5] Johnson, C., and W. Wonham, "Another Note on the Transformation to Canonical (Phase-Variable) Form," *IEEE Trans. on Automatic Control*, vol. AC-11 (1966), pp. 609–610.

[6] Kalman, R., T. Englar, and R. Bucy, "The Pseudo-Inverse of a Matrix,"

Appendix A of *Fundamental Study of Adaptive Control Systems*, Technical Report No. ASD-TR-61-27, Vol. 1, Wright-Patterson Air Force Base, Ohio, April 1962, pp. 229–234.

[7] Mufti, I., "On the Reduction of a System to Canonical (Phase-Variable) Form," *IEEE Trans. on Automatic Control*, vol. AC-10 (1965), pp. 206–207.

[8] Penrose, R., "A Generalized Inverse for Matrices," *Proc. Cambridge Phil. Soc.*, vol. 51 (1955), pp. 406–413.

[9] Penrose, R., "On Best Approximate Solutions of Linear Matrix Equations," *Proc. Cambridge Phil. Soc.*, vol. 52 (1956), pp. 17–19.

[10] Rane, D., "A Simplified Transformation to (Phase-Variable) Canonical Form," *IEEE Trans. on Automatic Control*, vol. AC-11 (1966), p. 608.

[11] Silverman, L., and H. Meadows, "Degrees of Controllability in Time-Variable Linear Systems," *Proc. National Electronics Conference*, November 1965, pp. 689–693.

[12] Silverman, L., "Transformation of Time-Variable Systems to Canonical (Phase-Variable) Form," *IEEE Trans. on Automatic Control*, vol. AC-11 (1966), pp. 300–303.

[13] Silverman, L., *Representation and Realization of Time-Variable Linear Systems*, Technical Report No. 94, Dept. Electrical Engineering, Columbia University, New York, June 1966.

[14] Silverman, L., and H. Meadows, "Equivalence and Synthesis of Time-Variable Linear Systems," *Proc. Fourth Annual Allerton Conference,* October 1966, pp. 776–784.

[15] Tuel, W., "On the Transformation to (Phase-Variable) Canonical Form," *IEEE Trans. on Automatic Control*, vol. AC-11 (1966), p. 607.

[16] Youla, D., "The Synthesis of Linear Dynamical Systems From Prescribed Weighting Patterns," *J. SIAM Appl. Math.*, vol. 14, no. 3 (1966), pp. 527–549.

[17] Glass, C. and H. D'Angelo, "On Reducing the Order of Linear Time-Varying Systems," *Proceedings, First Asilomar Conference on Circuits and Systems*, Pacific Grove, California, November 1967.

PROBLEMS

6.1 Verify Eqs. 6.12 and 6.13.

6.2 Use Theorem 6.4 to determine the transformation **T** which reduces the system of Prob. 5.2.

6.3 Use Theorem 6.4 to determine the transformation $\mathbf{T}(t)$ which reduces the system characterized by the following equations:

$$\begin{bmatrix} \dot{x}_1(t) \\ \dot{x}_2(t) \\ \dot{x}_3(t) \end{bmatrix} = \begin{bmatrix} e^{-t} + e^{-3t} & e^{-t} - e^{-2t} & e^{-2t} - e^{-3t} \\ e^{-t} - e^{-3t} & e^{-t} + e^{-2t} & -e^{-2t} + e^{-3t} \\ e^{-t} - e^{-3t} & e^{-t} - e^{-2t} & e^{-2t} + e^{-3t} \end{bmatrix} \begin{bmatrix} x_1(t) \\ x_2(t) \\ x_3(t) \end{bmatrix} + \begin{bmatrix} 1 \\ 0 \\ 1 \end{bmatrix} u(t)$$

$$y(t) = [0 \quad -1 \quad 1] \begin{bmatrix} x_1(t) \\ x_2(t) \\ x_3(t) \end{bmatrix}$$

6.4 Repeat Prob. 6.3 for:

$$\begin{bmatrix} \dot{x}_1(t) \\ \dot{x}_2(t) \\ \dot{x}_3(t) \end{bmatrix} = \begin{bmatrix} -t^4/4 & 1 & 0 \\ -t^3/3 & 0 & 1 \\ -t^2/2 & 0 & 0 \end{bmatrix} \begin{bmatrix} x_1(t) \\ x_2(t) \\ x_3(t) \end{bmatrix} + \begin{bmatrix} t^4/4 \\ t^3/3 \\ t^2/2 \end{bmatrix} u(t)$$

$$\begin{bmatrix} y_1(t) \\ y_2(t) \\ y_3(t) \end{bmatrix} = \begin{bmatrix} 1 & 0 & 0 \\ 0 & 1 & 0 \\ 0 & 0 & 1 \end{bmatrix} \begin{bmatrix} x_1(t) \\ x_2(t) \\ x_3(t) \end{bmatrix}$$

6.5 Put the following equations in phase-variable form:

$$\begin{bmatrix} \dot{x}_1(t) \\ \dot{x}_2(t) \\ \dot{x}_3(t) \end{bmatrix} = \begin{bmatrix} 1 & 0 & 0 \\ 0 & 2 & 0 \\ 0 & 0 & 3 \end{bmatrix} \begin{bmatrix} x_1(t) \\ x_2(t) \\ x_3(t) \end{bmatrix} + \begin{bmatrix} 1 \\ 1 \\ 1 \end{bmatrix} u(t)$$

$$y(t) = [1 \quad 1 \quad 1] \begin{bmatrix} x_1(t) \\ x_2(t) \\ x_3(t) \end{bmatrix}$$

6.6 Put the following equations in phase-variable form:

$$\begin{bmatrix} \dot{x}_1(t) \\ \dot{x}_2(t) \\ \dot{x}_3(t) \end{bmatrix} = \begin{bmatrix} 1 & 0 & e^{-t} \\ e^{-2t} & 2 & 0 \\ 0 & e^{-3t} & 3 \end{bmatrix} \begin{bmatrix} x_1(t) \\ x_2(t) \\ x_3(t) \end{bmatrix} + \begin{bmatrix} e^{-t} \\ 1 \\ 1 \end{bmatrix} u(t)$$

$$y(t) = [1 \quad e^{-2t} \quad 1] \begin{bmatrix} x_1(t) \\ x_2(t) \\ x_3(t) \end{bmatrix}$$

6.7 Use the results of Sec. 6.4 to diagonalize the system of Prob. 5.2.

6.8 Justify that there is no loss of generality in the proof of Theorem 6.5 in letting $\mathbf{A}_T(t) = \mathbf{A}(t) = 0$.

6.9 Use the results of Sec. 6.6 to solve Prob. 5.1.

7

Linear Systems with Periodically Varying Parameters

A special class of linear time-varying systems is that comprised of systems with parameters that vary periodically. In particular the *lumped linear parametric systems* are those in which the frequency of all time-varying parameters are *commensurable* (i.e., divisible by some fundamental frequency). These systems are characterized by linear differential equations with periodic coefficient. Because of the periodicity of the coefficients, there are important response properties unique to these systems that simplify their analysis and synthesis; stability studies of these *periodic systems* is considerably more straightforward than of the general time-varying system.

7.1. A FIRST-ORDER PERIODIC SYSTEM

Considerable insight to the response of systems with periodic coefficients and to methods for their analysis can be obtained by a study of a periodic, homogeneous first-order system:

$$\dot{x}(t) = A(t)x(t)\ , \ x(t_0) = x_0 \tag{7.1}$$

where $A(t)$ is continuous and periodic with period T, i.e.,

$$A(t + T) = A(t) \tag{7.2}$$

Using Theorem 2.2, it is seen that the solution to Eq. 7.1 is

$$x(t) = \phi(t, t_0)x_0 \tag{7.3}$$

where $\phi(t, t_0)$ is the one-dimensional transmission matrix given by

$$\phi(t, t_0) = \exp \int_{t_0}^{t} A(\eta)\, d\eta \tag{7.4}$$

For notational simplicity, define

$$\phi_0(t) \equiv \phi(t, t_0)\,|_{t_0=0} = \exp\left[\int_0^t A(\eta)\, d\eta\right] \tag{7.5}$$

Thus, for $t_0 = 0$,

$$x(t) = \phi_0(t)x_0 \tag{7.6}$$

Letting $t = t + T$ it is noted that

$$x(t + T) = \phi_0(t + T)x_0 \tag{7.7}$$

However from Eq. 7.4 it follows that

$$\begin{aligned}\phi_0(t + T) &= \exp \int_0^{t+T} A(\eta)\, d\eta \\ &= \exp \int_0^t A(\eta)\, d\eta \exp \int_t^{t+T} A(\eta) d\eta\end{aligned} \tag{7.8}$$

Since $A(t)$ is periodic with period T, the second integral is a constant independent of t:

$$\exp \int_t^{t+T} A(\eta) d\eta = C \tag{7.9}$$

Thus an important property of the first-order transition matrix is obtained:

$$\phi_0(t + T) = C\phi_0(t) \tag{7.10}$$

Substituting from Eq. 7.10 in Eq. 7.7 gives

$$x(t + T) = C\phi_0(t)x_0 \tag{7.11}$$

which upon substitution from Eq. 7.6 results in

$$x(t + T) = Cx(t) \tag{7.12}$$

This result, typical of periodic systems, shows that the solution in any period $[t, t + T]$ is related through the constant C to the solution in the previous period $[t - T, t]$.

Some insight to the periodicity and stability of solutions is obtained from the relation resulting from using Eq. 7.12 repeatedly,

$$x(t + nT) = C^n x(t) \tag{7.13}$$

Clearly the solution $x(t)$ is periodic with period T only if $C = 1$, i.e., if

$$\int_0^T A(\eta)\, d\eta = 0 \tag{7.14}$$

It is also observed from Eq. 7.13 that the system is asymptotically stable only if $|C| < 1$; in this case

$$\lim_{t\to\infty} x(t) = \lim_{n\to\infty} x(t + nT) = \lim_{n\to\infty} C^n x(t) = 0 \tag{7.15}$$

If $A(t)$ is continuous on the finite period T, then $|C| = 1$ characterizes a stable system (with periodic response). Thus a necessary and sufficient condition for the system characterized by Eq. 7.1 to be stable is that

$$|C| = \left| \exp \int_0^T A(\eta)\, d\eta \right| \leq 1 \tag{7.16}$$

The results of this section comprise what is known as *Floquet theory*, specialized to the first-order system. In the next section it is extended to the general nth-order system with periodic parameters.

7.2. FLOQUET THEORY

As might be inferred from the results of the previous section on first-order periodic systems, Floquet Theory is fundamental to the understanding of the performance and stability of systems with periodic parameters. As such it provides the basis for several approximate procedures for determining the response and stability characteristics of periodic systems.

Consider the nth-order periodic system characterized by

$$\dot{\mathbf{x}}(t) = \mathbf{A}(t)\mathbf{x}(t),\ \mathbf{x}(t_0) = \mathbf{x}_0 \tag{7.17}$$

where $\mathbf{A}(t)$ is continuous and periodic with period T, i.e.,

$$\mathbf{A}(t + T) = \mathbf{A}(t) \tag{7.18}$$

The solution, in terms of the transition matrix, is given by

$$\mathbf{x}(t) = \phi(t, t_0)\mathbf{x}_0 \tag{7.19}$$

It is important, for what follows, to investigate some of the properties of the transition matrix that are unique to periodic systems. For notational simplicity define

$$\phi_0(t) \equiv \phi(t, 0) \tag{7.20}$$

and thus, for $t_0 = 0$,

$$\mathbf{x}(t) = \phi_0(t)\mathbf{x}_0 \tag{7.21}$$

Theorem 7.1. If $\phi_0(t)$ is a fundamental matrix of the system characterized by Eq. 7.17, then so is $\phi_0(t + T)$. Corresponding to every such $\phi_0(t)$ there exists a periodic nonsingular matrix $\mathbf{R}(t)$ with period T and a constant matrix $\mathbf{\Gamma}$ such that

$$\phi_0(t) = \mathbf{R}(t) \exp(\mathbf{\Gamma} t) \tag{7.22}$$

Proof. Since a fundamental matrix satiesfies the system differential equation, i.e., $\dot{\phi}_0(t) = \mathbf{A}(t)\phi_0(t)$, it follows that

$$\begin{aligned} \dot{\phi}_0(t + T) &= \mathbf{A}(t + T)\phi_0(t + T) \\ &= \mathbf{A}(t)\phi_0(t + T) \end{aligned} \tag{7.23}$$

Therefore $\phi_0(t + T)$ also satisfies the system differential equation and is a fundamental matrix.

In accordance with Theorem 2.6, the two fundamental matrices $\phi_0(t)$ and $\phi_0(t + T)$ can be related through a nonsingular constant matrix $\mathbf{C}$:

$$\phi_0(t + T) = \phi_0(t)\mathbf{C} \tag{7.24}$$

Define a constant matrix $\mathbf{\Gamma}$ such that

$$\mathbf{C} \equiv \exp(\mathbf{\Gamma}T) \tag{7.25}$$

Therefore

$$\phi_0(t + T) = \phi_0(t) \exp(\mathbf{\Gamma}T) \tag{7.26}$$

Further, define $\mathbf{R}(t)$ by

$$\mathbf{R}(t) \equiv \phi_0(t) \exp(-\mathbf{\Gamma}t) \tag{7.27}$$

Substituting from Eqs. 7.26 in Eq. 7.27 results in

$$\mathbf{R}(t + T) = \phi_0(t) \exp(\mathbf{\Gamma}T) \exp(-\mathbf{\Gamma}T) \exp(-\mathbf{\Gamma}t) \tag{7.28}$$

$$= \phi_0(t) \exp(-\mathbf{\Gamma}t) \tag{7.29}$$

Comparison of Eqs. 7.27 and 7.29 shows that

$$\mathbf{R}(t + T) = \mathbf{R}(t) \tag{7.30}$$

and thus that $\mathbf{R}(t)$ is periodic. Postmultiplying Eq. 7.27 by $\exp(\mathbf{\Gamma}t)$ gives Eq. 7.22. Q.E.D.

Letting $t = t + T$ in the original differential Eq. 7.17 it is seen that

$$\dot{\mathbf{x}}(t + T) = \mathbf{A}(t)\mathbf{x}(t + T) \tag{7.31}$$

i.e., that if $\mathbf{x}(t)$ is a solution to the differential equation, then so is $\mathbf{x}(t + T)$. From Eq. 7.20 it is noted that

$$\phi_0(0) = \mathbf{I}_n \tag{7.32}$$

Use of this results in Eq. 7.24 results in

$$\phi_0(T) = \mathbf{C} \tag{7.33}$$

which is termed the *discrete transition matrix*. Repeated use of Eqs. 7.24 and 7.33 results in

$$\phi_0(kT) = \mathbf{C}^k \tag{7.34}$$

Substituting from Eq. 7.34 in Eq. 7.21 gives

$$\mathbf{x}(kT) = \phi_0(kT)\mathbf{x}_0$$

$$\mathbf{x}(kT) = \mathbf{C}^k\mathbf{x}_0 \tag{7.35}$$

Equivalently

$$\mathbf{x}(kT) = [\exp(\mathbf{\Gamma}T)]^k\mathbf{x}_0 \tag{7.36}$$

Equation 7.35 can be written as

$$\mathbf{x}[(k + 1)T] = \mathbf{C}\mathbf{C}^k\mathbf{x}_0 = \mathbf{C}\phi_0(kT)\mathbf{x}_0 \tag{7.37}$$

which upon substitution from Eq. 7.34 becomes

$$\mathbf{x}[(k + 1)T] = \mathbf{C}\mathbf{x}(kT) \tag{7.38}$$

Equation 7.38 provides a very important result in the study of periodic systems. It can, however, be misleading. It might, at first glance, appear that this difference equation with *constant coefficients* is a substitute for the original differential equation with *time-varying coefficients*. It is not. Equation 7.38 simply implies that if the solution to the differential equation with periodic coefficients is known on any one period interval $[t, t + T]$, then it can be found everywhere; if the solution is known at any instant of time, it can be determined at other instants of time spaced integral multiples of T away. Clearly, the response is periodic with period T if and only if $\mathbf{C} = \mathbf{I}_n$, or equivalently, $\mathbf{\Gamma} = \mathbf{0}$.

Equations 7.35 and 7.36 reveal that the stability characteristics of periodic systems depend on the discrete transition matrix $\mathbf{C}$, and thus also on the matrix $\mathbf{\Gamma}$ defined from $\mathbf{C}$, in Eq. 7.25. Using Sylvester's theorem[1], Eqs. 7.35 and 7.36 can be written as[2]

$$\mathbf{x}(kT) = \left[\sum_{i=1}^{n} c_i^k \mathbf{Z}_{ci}\right]\mathbf{x}_0 \tag{7.39a}$$

and

$$\mathbf{x}(kT) = \left[\sum_{i=1}^{n} e^{\gamma_i T k} \mathbf{Z}_{\gamma i}\right]\mathbf{x}_0 \tag{7.39b}$$

where $\mathbf{Z}_{ci}$ and $\mathbf{Z}_{\gamma i}$ are constant matrices, the c_i, $i = 1, \cdots, n$ are the eigenvalues of the discrete transition matrix termed the *characteristic roots*, and the γ_i, $i = 1, \cdots, n$ are the eiganvalues of the matrix $\mathbf{\Gamma}$ termed the *characteristic exponents*. Therefore a periodic system characterized by Eq. 7.17 is asymptotically stable with bounded response if and only if

(i) All the characteristic exponents γ_i, $i = 1, \cdots, n$, have negative real parts,

or

(ii) All the characteristic roots, c_i, $i = 1, \cdots, n$ lie within the unit circle.

7.3. APPROXIMATING THE DISCRETE TRANSITION MATRIX [5]

The results obtained in the last section demonstrate the importance of the discrete transition matrix $\mathbf{C}$ in the study of periodic systems. However, since $\mathbf{C} = \phi_0(T)$ there is an implication that the fundamental matrix $\phi_0(t)$ must be known in order to determine $\mathbf{C}$ and, as is well known, fundamental matrices are generally not easily determined. A simple

[1]See footnote 2, Chapter 2.

[2]Equations 7.38 and 7.39 are valid only when the eigenvalues of $\mathbf{C}$ and $\mathbf{\Gamma}$ are distinct. However, the conclusions on stability, based on the properties of the eigenvalues, hold whether or not the eigenvalues are distinct.

procedure for approximating the discrete transition matrix $\mathbf{C} = \phi_0(T)$ which gives excellent results for many practical systems is presented here:

1. Divide the interval of the first period $(0, T)$ into m subintervals (t_{k-1}, t_k), $k = 1, \cdots, m$, i.e.,

$$T = \sum_{k=1}^{m} T_k \tag{7.40}$$

where

$$T_k = t_k - t_{k-1} \tag{7.41}$$

and $t_0 = 0$ and $t_m = T$.

2. In each subinterval T_k, replace $\mathbf{A}(t)$ by its average $\mathbf{A}_k$ over the interval, i.e.,

$$\mathbf{A}_k = \frac{1}{T_k} \int_{t_{k-1}}^{t_k} \mathbf{A}(t)\, dt \tag{7.42}$$

3. The fundamental matrix $\phi_0(t)$ is to be approximated on each subinterval $[t_{k-1}, t_k]$, $k = 1, \cdots, m$, by $\phi_k(t)$, $k = 1, \cdots, m$ where $\phi_k(t)$ satisfies the linear time-invariant differential equation

$$\dot{\phi}_k(t') = \mathbf{A}_k \phi_k(t'),\ k = 1, \cdots, m,\ t' \equiv (t - t_{k-1}) \in [0, T_k] \tag{7.43}$$

where, to preserve the continuity of the approximation to $\phi_0(t)$, the initial condition on one interval is determined from the final value on the preceding interval:

$$\phi_k(t_{k-1}) = \phi_{k-1}(t_{k-1}) \tag{7.44}$$

or in terms of the t' defined specifically for each subinterval

$$\phi_k(0) = \phi_{k-1}(T_{k-1}),\ \phi_1(0) = \phi_0(0) \tag{7.45}$$

where

$$\phi_1(0) = \phi_0(0) = \mathbf{I}_n \tag{7.46}$$

4. The linear time-invariant equation 7.43 has the solution

$$\phi_k(t') = \exp\,[\mathbf{A}_k t']\phi_k(0) \tag{7.47}$$

Thus

$$\begin{aligned} \phi_1(T_1) &= \exp(\mathbf{A}_1 T_1)\phi_1(0) \\ &= \exp(A_1 T_1)\phi_0(0) \\ &= \exp(A_1 T_1) \end{aligned} \tag{7.48a}$$

$$\begin{aligned} \phi_2(T_2) &= \exp(\mathbf{A}_2 T_2)\phi_2(0) \\ &= \exp(\mathbf{A}_2 T_2)\phi_1(T_1) \\ &= \exp(\mathbf{A}_2 T_2)\exp(A_1 T_1) \end{aligned} \tag{7.48b}$$

$$\vdots$$

$$\vdots$$

$$\phi_m(T_m) = \prod_{k-1}^{m} \exp(\mathbf{A}_k T_k) \tag{7.48c}$$

But since $\phi_m(T_m) = \phi_0(T)$, the desired result for approximating the discrete transition matrix is obtained:

$$\mathbf{C} = \exp[\mathbf{\Gamma}T] = \phi_0(T) = \prod_{k=1}^{m} \exp(\mathbf{A}_k T_k) \tag{7.49}$$

It can be noted that if $\mathbf{A}(t)$ is piecewise time-invariant, i.e., $\mathbf{A}(t) = \mathbf{A}_k$ on (t_{k-1}, t_k), then Eq. 7.49 provides an exact determination of the discrete transition matrix.

Example 7.1. Consider the second-order scalar periodic system characterized by

$$\frac{d^2x(t)}{dt^2} + F(t)\frac{dx(t)}{dt} + x(t) = 0$$

where $F(t)$ is periodic with period T and is given on one period by Fig. 7.1.

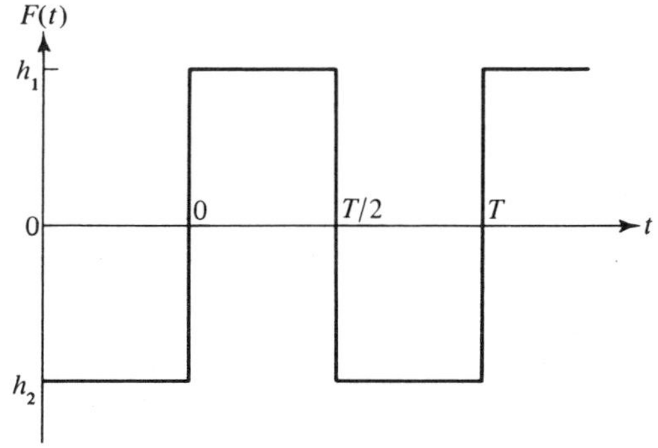

Fig. 7.1. Time-varying coefficient $F(t)$ for Example 7.1.

Defining $x_1(t) \equiv x(t)$ and $x_2(t) \equiv \dot{x}(t)$, the second-oreder equation can be put into state-variable form:

$$\begin{bmatrix} \dot{x}_1(t) \\ \dot{x}_2(t) \end{bmatrix} = \begin{bmatrix} 0 & 1 \\ -1 & -F(t) \end{bmatrix} \begin{bmatrix} x_1(t) \\ x_2(t) \end{bmatrix}$$

The interval $(0, T)$ is divided into the two subintervals, $(0, T/2)$ and $(T/2, T)$, on each of which the system is time-invariant. Thus Eq. 7.49 can be used to determine the transition matrix $\mathbf{C}$. Note that

$$T_1 = T_2 = T/2$$

$$\mathbf{A}_1 = \begin{bmatrix} 0 & 1 \\ -1 & -h_1 \end{bmatrix}, \quad \mathbf{A}_2 = \begin{bmatrix} 0 & 1 \\ -1 & -h_2 \end{bmatrix}$$

Thus

$$\begin{aligned}\mathbf{C} &= \exp(\mathbf{A}_1T_1)\exp(\mathbf{A}_2T_2)\\ &= \exp\left[(\mathbf{A}_1 + \mathbf{A}_2)\frac{T}{2}\right]\\ &= \exp\left\{\begin{bmatrix} 0 & 1 \\ -1 & -\frac{1}{2}(h_1 + h_2)\end{bmatrix} T\right\}\\ &= \exp(\mathbf{\Gamma}T)\end{aligned}$$

and thus

$$\mathbf{\Gamma} = \begin{bmatrix} 0 & 1 \\ -1 & -\frac{1}{2}(h_1 + h_2)\end{bmatrix}$$

The eigenvalues of $\mathbf{\Gamma}$ are easily determined by solving for γ in

$$\det(\mathbf{\Gamma} - \gamma\mathbf{I}_2) = 0$$

and results in

$$\gamma_1, \gamma_2 = -\frac{h_1 + h_2}{4} \pm \sqrt{\frac{(h_1 + h_2)^2}{16} - 1}$$

Since the system is asymptotically stable if the real parts of the eigenvalues of $\mathbf{\Gamma}$ are negative, it follows that the condition for asymptotic stability is that

$$(h_1 + h_2) > 0$$

7.4. RESPONSE OF PERIODIC SYSTEMS TO FORCING FUNCTIONS

7.4.1. First-Order Periodic Systems. Insight to the nature of the response of a periodic system to an applied forcing function is obtained here by a detailed investigation of the general first-order periodic system

$$\dot{x}(t) = A(t)x(t) + f(t), \; x(t_0) = x_0 \tag{7.50}$$

where $A(t)$ is continuous and periodic with period T and $f(t)$ is continuous on $[0, \infty)$. Due to its continuity, $A(t)$ can be expressed by its Fourier series

$$A(t) = \sum_{k=0}^{\infty} (\Gamma_k \cos k\omega t + \Delta_k \sin k\omega t) \tag{7.51}$$

where

$$\omega = \frac{2\pi}{T} \tag{7.52}$$

Define the function $G(t)$ by the indefinite integral

$$G(t) = \int A(\eta)\, d\eta \tag{7.53}$$

Therefore substituting from Eq. 7.52 in Eq. 7.53 gives

$$G(t) = \mathbf{\Gamma}_0 t + \sum_{k=1}^{\infty} \frac{1}{k\omega}(\Gamma_k \sin k\omega t - \Delta_k \cos k\omega t) \tag{7.54}$$

Therefore, in accordance with Theorem 2.2, the solution to Eq. 7.50 is

$$x(t) = \exp\,[G(t) - G(0)]x_0 + \int_0^t \exp\,[G(t) - G(\tau)]f(\tau)\, d\tau \tag{7.55}$$

The first term on the right-hand side of Eq. 7.55 is the solution to the homogeneous equation (or the complementary solution) which is studied in Secs. 7.2 and 7.3. It is helpful to relate some of the previous results to the Fourier-series coefficients. The homogeneous solution is

$$x_c(t) = \exp\,[G(t) - G(0)]x_0 \tag{7.56}$$

where it is observed from Eq. 7.54 that

$$G(0) = -\sum_{k=1}^{\infty} \frac{\Delta_k}{k\omega} \tag{7.57}$$

Therefore

$$\begin{aligned} x_c(t) &= \exp\left[G(t) + \sum_{k=1}^{\infty} \frac{\Delta_k}{k\omega}\right]x_0 \\ &= K \exp\,[G(t)] \end{aligned} \tag{7.58}$$

where

$$K = \exp\left[+\sum_{k=1}^{\infty} \frac{\Delta_k}{k\omega}\right]x_0 \tag{7.59}$$

Substituting from Eq. 7.54 in Eq. 7.58 gives

$$x_c(t) = KR(t) \exp\,(\Gamma_0 t) \tag{7.60}$$

where

$$R(t) = \exp\left[\sum_{k=1}^{\infty} \frac{1}{k\omega}(\Gamma_k \sin k\omega t - \Delta_k \cos k\omega t)\right] \tag{7.61}$$

and it is seen that $R(t)$ is periodic with period T. Therefore Eq. 7.60 demonstrates the homogeneous solution is periodic if and only if $\Gamma_0 = 0$; the solution is asymptotically stable if and only if the real part of Γ_0 is negative. Clearly Γ_0 is the characteristic exponent for the first-order system.

The second term on the right-hand side of Eq. 7.55 is the solution due to the forcing function $f(t)$ (or the particular solution). In terms of the

Fourier-series expansion of $A(t)$ and the definition of Eq. 7.61, the particular solution can be written as

$$x_p(t) = R(t) \exp(\Gamma_0 t) \int_0^t \exp(-\Gamma_0 \tau) R^{-1}(\tau) f(\tau)\, d\tau \tag{7.62}$$

Note that since $R(t)$ is periodic, has continuous derivatives, and is never zero, that $R^{-1}(t)$ also is periodic, has continuous derivatives and is never zero. Therefore $R^{-1}(t)$ can also be replaced by its Fourier series:

$$R^{-1}(t) = \sum_{k=-\infty}^{\infty} B_k e^{ik\omega t}, \quad i = \sqrt{-1} \tag{7.63}$$

Substituting from Eq. 7.63 in Eq. 7.62 gives

$$x_p(t) = R(t) \exp(\Gamma_0 t) \sum_{k=-\infty}^{\infty} B_k \int_0^t \exp(-\Gamma_0 \tau) f(\tau) e^{ik\omega\tau}\, d\tau \tag{7.64}$$

Clearly, if anything is to be said about the nature of the particular solution of periodic systems something must be known about the specific forcing function $f(t)$.

Consider the important case that the forcing function is an exponential:

$$f(t) = \exp(\alpha t) \tag{7.65}$$

Then, the particular solution is[3]

$$\begin{aligned} x_p(t) &= R(t) \exp(\Gamma_0 t) \sum_{k=-\infty}^{\infty} B_k \int_0^t \exp(-\Gamma_0 \tau) \exp(\alpha\tau) e^{ik\omega\tau}\, d\tau \\ &= R(t) \exp(\Gamma_0 t) \sum_{k=-\infty}^{\infty} \frac{B_k(\exp[(-\Gamma_0 + \alpha + ik\omega)t] - 1)}{(-\Gamma_0 + \alpha + ik\omega)} \end{aligned} \tag{7.66}$$

Defining the periodic function $\beta(t)$ by

$$\beta(t) \equiv R(t) \sum_{k=-\infty}^{\infty} \frac{B_k e^{ik\omega t}}{(-\Gamma_0 + \alpha + ik\omega)} \tag{7.67}$$

and the constant h by

$$h \equiv -\sum_{k=-\infty}^{\infty} \frac{B_k}{(-\Gamma_0 + \alpha + ik\omega)} \tag{7.68}$$

results in

$$x_p(t) = \exp(\alpha t)\beta(t) + R(t) \exp(\Gamma_0 t) h \tag{7.69}$$

[3]Term by term integration of the infinite series is justified because the series is uniformly convergent. If for some k, $(-\Gamma_0 + \alpha + ik\omega) = 0$, then the corresponding term in $F(t)$ should be $B_k t$. With this exception, $F(t)$ is periodic.

Some of the properties of the particular solution of a periodic system forced by an exponential can be deduced from Eq. 7.69.

If $\Gamma_0 < 0$, then the term $R(t) \exp(\Gamma_0 t)h$ of the particular solution is a transient which goes to zero as $t \to \infty$; if $\Gamma_0 = 0$, then this term is periodic with period T; if $\Gamma_0 > 0$, then this term increases without bound as $t \to \infty$ and the system, as determined previously, is unstable. It is interesting to note that for the case that $\Gamma_0 > 0$ *both* the complementary and the particular solution increase without bound as $t \to \infty$. It can thus be concluded that the steady-state response $x_{ss}(t)$ of stable (first-order) periodic systems to an exponential forcing function $f(t) = \exp(\alpha t)$ has the form $\exp(\alpha t)\beta(t)$, where $\beta(t)$ has period T. In particular, a constant input $f(t)$ is the case that $\alpha = 0$ and the steady-state solution of a stable system is

$$x_{ss}(t) = \beta(t)\,, \; \alpha = 0 \tag{7.70}$$

For the case that $f(t)$ is a sinusoid of frequency ω_1, i.e., $\alpha = i\omega_1$, the steady-state solution is

$$x_{ss}(t) = \exp(i\omega_1 t)\beta(t), \; \alpha = i\omega \tag{7.71}$$

and since $\beta(t)$ is periodic it can be replaced by its Fourier series

$$\beta(t) = \sum_{k=-\infty}^{\infty} \beta_i e^{ik\omega t} \tag{7.72}$$

and thus

$$x_{ss}(t) = \sum_{k=-\infty}^{\infty} \beta_k \exp[i(\omega_1 + k\omega)t], \; \alpha = i\omega \tag{7.73}$$

Therefore it is seen that the steady-state response of a (first-order) stable periodic system to a sinusoid has an infinite frequency spectrum consisting *only* of the frequencies $\omega_1 \pm n\omega$, $n = 0, 1, 2, \cdots,$; neither the frequency of the input sinusoid nor the frequency of the varying parameters (nor integral multiples of either) appear in the steady-state response. It follows then, that unless ω_1 and ω are commensurable it cannot be concluded that the steady-state response of a periodic system is periodic.

It is now shown that the nature of the steady-state response of higher-order periodic systems is much the same as that of the first-order system.

7.4.2. Higher-Order Periodic Systems. Consider the nth-order periodic system characterized by

$$\dot{\mathbf{x}}(t) = \mathbf{A}(t)\mathbf{x}(t) + \mathbf{f}(t), \; \mathbf{x}(0) = \mathbf{x}_0$$

where $\mathbf{A}(t)$ is continuous and periodic with period T and $f(t)$ is continuous on $[0, \infty)$. The solution, in terms of the transition matrix $\phi(t, \tau) = \phi_0(t)\phi_0^{-1}(\tau)$, is

$$\begin{aligned}\mathbf{x}(t) &= \phi(t, 0)\mathbf{x}_0 + \int_0^t \phi(t, \tau)\mathbf{f}(\tau)\,d\tau \\ &= \phi_0(t)\mathbf{x}_0 + \phi_0(t)\int_0^t \phi_0^{-1}(\tau)\mathbf{f}(\tau)\,d\tau\end{aligned} \tag{7.74}$$

Substituting from Eq. 7.22 in Eq. 7.74 gives

$$\mathbf{x}(t) = \mathbf{R}(t)\exp(\mathbf{\Gamma}t)\mathbf{x}_0 + \mathbf{R}(t)\exp(\mathbf{\Gamma}t)\int_0^t \exp(-\Gamma\tau)\mathbf{R}^{-1}(\tau)f(\tau)\,d\tau \tag{7.75}$$

It can be noted that since $\mathbf{R}(t)$ is periodic, has continuous derivatives, and is nonsingular, that $\mathbf{R}^{-1}(t)$ also is periodic, has continuous derivatives, and is nonsingular.

The first term on the right-hand side of Eq. 7.75 is the solution to the homogeneous equation with initial condition $\mathbf{x}(0) = \mathbf{x}_0$:

$$\mathbf{x}_c(t) = \mathbf{R}(t)\exp(\mathbf{\Gamma}t)\mathbf{x}_0 \tag{7.76}$$

Equation 7.76 verifies that the unforced solution is periodic if and only if $\mathbf{\Gamma} = \mathbf{0}$, and that the unforced system is asymptotically stable if and only if all the eigenvalues of $\mathbf{\Gamma}$, i.e., the characteristic exponents γ_i, $i = 1, \cdots, n$, have negative real parts.

The second term on the right-hand side of Eq. 7.75 is the forced part of the solution (particular solution):

$$\mathbf{x}_p(t) = \mathbf{R}(t)\exp(\mathbf{\Gamma}t)\int_0^t \exp(-\mathbf{\Gamma}\tau)\mathbf{R}^{-1}(\tau)f(\tau)\,d\tau \tag{7.77}$$

Since $\mathbf{R}^{-1}(t)$ is continuous, it can be replaced by its Fourier series:

$$\mathbf{R}^{-1}(t) = \sum_{k=-\infty}^{\infty} \mathbf{B}_k e^{ik\omega t} \tag{7.78}$$

Thus Eq. 7.77 can be written as

$$\mathbf{x}_p(t) = \mathbf{R}(t)\exp(\mathbf{\Gamma}t)\int_0^t \exp(-\mathbf{\Gamma}\tau)\sum_{k=-\infty}^{\infty} \mathbf{B}_k e^{ik\omega\tau}\mathbf{f}(\tau)\,d\tau \tag{7.79}$$

Consider now the important case of an exponential input:

$$\mathbf{f}(t) = \mathbf{d}\exp(\alpha t) \tag{7.80}$$

Using Sylvester's theorem[4], $\exp(\mathbf{\Gamma}t)$ and $\exp(-\mathbf{\Gamma}t)$ can be expressed by

$$\exp(\mathbf{\Gamma}t) = \sum_{j=1}^{n} e^{\gamma_j t}\mathbf{Z}_{\gamma_j} \tag{7.81a}$$

$$\exp(-\mathbf{\Gamma}t) = \sum_{j=1}^{n} e^{-\gamma_j t}\mathbf{Z}_{\gamma_j} \tag{7.81b}$$

[4]See footnote 3, Chapter 2.

Substituting from Eqs. 7.80 and 7.81b in Eq. 7.79 results in

$$\begin{aligned}\mathbf{x}_p(t) &= \mathbf{R}(t)\exp(\boldsymbol{\Gamma}t)\sum_{j=1}^{n}\sum_{k=-\infty}^{\infty}\mathbf{Z}_{\gamma j}\mathbf{B}_k\mathbf{d}\int_0^t \exp[(-\gamma_j+\alpha+ik\omega)\tau]\,d\tau \\ &= \mathbf{R}(t)\exp(\boldsymbol{\Gamma}t)\sum_{j=1}^{n}\sum_{k=-\infty}^{\infty}\mathbf{Z}_{\gamma j}\mathbf{B}_k\mathbf{d}\frac{\exp[(-\gamma_j+\alpha+ik\omega)t]-1}{(-\gamma_j+\alpha+ik\omega)} \\ &= \mathbf{R}(t)\exp(\boldsymbol{\Gamma}t)\sum_{j=1}^{n}e^{-\gamma_j t}\mathbf{Z}_{\gamma j}\sum_{k=-\infty}^{\infty}\mathbf{B}_k\mathbf{d}\frac{\exp[(\alpha+ik\omega)t]}{(-\gamma_j+\alpha+ik\omega)} \\ &\quad - \mathbf{R}(t)\exp(\boldsymbol{\Gamma}t)\sum_{j=1}^{n}\sum_{k=-\infty}^{\infty}\frac{\mathbf{Z}_{\gamma j}\mathbf{B}_k\mathbf{d}}{(-\gamma_j+\alpha+ik\omega)}\end{aligned} \tag{7.82}$$

Substituting from Eq. 7.81a in Eq. 7.82 and noting from Eqs. 2.79L that $\mathbf{Z}_{\gamma s}\mathbf{Z}_{\gamma j} = \mathbf{0}$ when $s \neq j$ and $\mathbf{Z}_{\gamma j}^2 = \mathbf{Z}_{\gamma j}$ results in

$$\mathbf{x}_p(t) = \exp(\alpha t)\beta(t) + \mathbf{R}(t)\exp(\boldsymbol{\Gamma}t)\mathbf{h} \tag{7.83}$$

where

$$\beta(t) = \mathbf{R}(t)\sum_{j=1}^{n}\sum_{k=-\infty}^{\infty}\mathbf{Z}_{\gamma j}\mathbf{B}_k\mathbf{d}\frac{e^{ik\omega t}}{(-\gamma_j+\alpha+ik\omega)} \tag{7.84}$$

and

$$\mathbf{h} = -\sum_{j=1}^{n}\sum_{k=-\infty}^{\infty}\frac{\mathbf{Z}_{\gamma j}\mathbf{B}_k\mathbf{d}}{(-\gamma_j+\alpha+ik\omega)}$$

Thus it is seen that the form of the particular solution of the higher-order periodic system perturbated by an exponential forcing function is the same as that of the first-order periodic system. Thus the conclusions drawn for the first-order system can be extended to the general nth-order system. Specifically, for the case that $\mathbf{f}(t) = \mathbf{d}e^{\alpha t}$ the following conclusions can be drawn:

1. The particular solution has the form

$$\mathbf{x}_p(t) = \exp(\alpha t)\boldsymbol{\beta}(t) + \mathbf{R}(t)\exp(\boldsymbol{\Gamma}t)h \tag{7.86}$$

   where $\boldsymbol{\beta}(t)$ and $\mathbf{R}(t)$ are periodic with period T, $\mathbf{h}$ is a constant vector, and $\boldsymbol{\Gamma}$ is as defined in Eq. 7.25.
2. If all the real parts of the eigenvalues of $\boldsymbol{\Gamma}$ (i.e., all the real parts of the characteristic exponents γ_j, $j = 1, \cdots, n$) are negative, then the term $\mathbf{R}(t)\exp(\boldsymbol{\Gamma}t)\mathbf{h}$ is a transient which goes to zero as $t \to \infty$.
3. If all the real parts of the characteristic exponents γ_j, $j = 1, \cdots, n$, are zero, then the term $\mathbf{R}(t)\exp(\boldsymbol{\Gamma}t)\mathbf{h}$ is periodic with period T.
4. If the real parts of any of the characteristic exponents γ_j, $j = 1, \cdots, n$ are positive, then the term $\mathbf{R}(t)\exp(\boldsymbol{\Gamma}t)\mathbf{h}$ increases without bound as $t \to \infty$.

5. The steady-state response of a stable periodic system has the form

$$\mathbf{x}_{ss}(t) = \exp(\alpha t)\boldsymbol{\beta}(t) \tag{7.87}$$

where $\boldsymbol{\beta}(t)$ is periodic with period T:

(a) For a constant input, i.e., $\alpha = 0$ this reduces to the periodic solution

$$\mathbf{x}_{ss}(t) = \boldsymbol{\beta}(t),\ \alpha = 0 \tag{7.88}$$

(b) For a sinusoidal input with frequency ω_1, i.e., $\alpha = i\omega_1$, this reduces to

$$\mathbf{x}_{ss}(t) = \sum_{j=-\infty}^{\infty} \boldsymbol{\beta}_j \exp\left[i(\omega_1 + j\omega)t\right],\ \alpha = i\omega \tag{7.89}$$

where the coefficient matrices $\boldsymbol{\beta}_i$ are determined from the Fourier series of $\mathbf{F}(t)$;

$$\boldsymbol{\beta}(t) = \sum_{j=-\infty}^{\infty} \boldsymbol{\beta}_j e^{ij\omega t} \tag{7.90}$$

Therefore neither the frequency of the parameters ω nor the frequency of the input ω_1 appear in the steady-state solution, and unless ω and ω_1 are commensurable, the steady-state solution is not periodic.

It is interesting to compare the steady-state response of linear time-invariant systems and linear time-varying systems with periodic coefficients to sinusoidal inputs. A linear time-invariant system when forced with the sinusoidal input

$$\mathbf{f}(t) = \mathbf{a} \sin \omega_1 t + \mathbf{b} \sin \omega_2 t \tag{7.91}$$

has a steady-state response of the form

$$\mathbf{x}_{ss}(t) = \mathbf{c} \sin(\omega_1 t + \phi_1) + \mathbf{d} \sin(\omega_2 t + \phi_2) \tag{7.92}$$

A linear time-varying system with parameters varying with a fundamental frequency of ω when forced with the same input has a steady-state response of the form

$$\mathbf{x}_{ss}(t) = \sum_{j=-\infty}^{\infty} \mathbf{c}_n \sin\left[(\omega_1 + j\omega)t + \phi_{1j}\right] + \sum_{j=-\infty}^{\infty} \mathbf{d}_n \sin\left[(\omega_2 + j\omega)t + \phi_{2j}\right] \tag{7.93}$$

Clearly frequencies of integral multiples of ω_1, ω_2 or ω do not appear in the steady-state response. Cross products of frequencies of integral multiplies of ω_1 and ω_2 also do not appear as might be expected in the steady-state response of a nonlinear system to the same input.

7.5. SECOND-ORDER SYSTEMS WITH PERIODICALLY VARYING PARAMETERS

Second-order linear time-variant differential equations have been investigated in great detail for the simple reason that the exact general solutions of first-order equations can be effected, in principle, by quadrature, and that the general solution of third- and higher-order equations is extremely complex. Unlike first-order linear differential equations, there is no relatively simple general method of exact solution for second-order linear differential equations; there is a large body of literature on the exact solution of a small limited group of second-order equations (the Besel, Airy, Legendre, Laguerre, confluent hypergeometric, hypergeometric, Mathieu, Weber, etc., equations). However, of considerable interest relative to the design of automatic control systems are several approximation methods which, considered collectively, enable determining approximate solutions to a fairly large group of second-order linear differential equations. These methods can be used to obtain the responses of systems characterized by higher-order equations when they can be satisfactorily approximated by second-order equation. In this section primary concern is with second-order syetems with *periodically varying parameters.* However, before studying these special systems it is useful to obtain some general information on a canonical structure of a second-order linear differential equation.

7.5.1. General Second-Order Systems. A canonic form for the general second-order differential equation is

$$\frac{d^2x(t)}{dt^2} + a(t)\frac{dx(t)}{dt} + b(t)x(t) = f(t) \tag{7.94}$$

Introducing the change of variable

$$x(t) = y(t)\exp\left[-\frac{1}{2}\int a(t)\,dt\right] \tag{7.95}$$

in Eq. 7.94 yields the simpler canonic form

$$\frac{d^2y(t)}{dt^2} + Q(t)y(t) = H(t) \tag{7.96}$$

where

$$Q(t) = b(t) - \frac{1}{4}a^2(t) - \frac{1}{2}\dot{a}(t) \tag{7.97}$$

and

$$H(t) = f(t)\exp\left[\frac{1}{2}\int a(t)\,dt\right] \tag{7.98}$$

Both Eqs. 7.94 and 7.96 are of interest in that methods of effecting approximate solutions are usually based on one of these two canonic forms.

The properties of the Wronskians are now investigated. Assume that a basis of the scalar second-order system of Eq. 7.94 is given as $x_1(t)$ and $x_2(t)$. Then, in accordance with Eq. 2.96, the Wronskian matrix for this system is

$$\mathbf{W}(t) = \begin{bmatrix} x_1(t) & x_2(t) \\ \dot{x}_1(t) & \dot{x}_2(t) \end{bmatrix} \tag{7.99}$$

and the Wronskian, denoted by $w(t)$, is

$$w(t) \equiv \det \mathbf{W}(t) = x_1(t)\dot{x}_2(t) - \dot{x}_1(t)x_2(t) \tag{7.100}$$

The derivative of the Wronskian is

$$\dot{w}(\mathbf{t}) = x_1(t)\ddot{x}_2(t) - \ddot{x}_1(t)x_2(t) \tag{7.101}$$

The basis functions are solutions to the original homogeneous differential equation 7.94:

$$\ddot{x}_1(t) + a(t)\dot{x}_1(t) + b(t)x_1(t) = 0 \tag{7.102a}$$

$$\ddot{x}_2(t) + a(t)\dot{x}_2(t) + b(t)x_2(t) = 0 \tag{7.102b}$$

Multiplying each of Eqs. 7.102 by $-x_2(t)$ and $x_1(t)$ respectively gives

$$-\ddot{x}_1(t)x_2(t) - a(t)\dot{x}_1(t)x_2(t) - b(t)x_1(t)x_2(t) = 0 \tag{7.103a}$$

$$x_1(t)\ddot{x}_2(t) + a(t)x_1(t)\dot{x}_2(t) + b(t)x_1(t)x_2(t) = 0 \tag{7.103b}$$

Adding Eqs. 7.103 gives

$$[x_1(t)\ddot{x}_2(t) - \ddot{x}_1(t)x_2(t)] + a(t)[x_1(t)\dot{x}_2(t) - \dot{x}_1(t)x_2(t)] = 0 \tag{7.104}$$

Substituting from Eqs. 7.100 and 7.101 in Eq. 7.104 results in a first-order linear differential equation for the Wronskian $w(t)$:

$$\dot{w}(t) + a(t)w(t) = 0 \tag{7.105}$$

Using Eq. 2.19 the solution to Eq. 7.105 is obtained:

$$w(t) = \exp\left[-\int_{t_0}^{t} a(\eta)\, d\eta\right] w(t_0) \tag{7.107}$$

Clearly if in the original differential equation 7.94 the coefficient of the first derivative term $\dfrac{dx(t)}{dt}$ is zero (i.e., $a(t) = 0$), then the Wronskian is constant. Thus the Wronskian of the second-order canonic form represented by Eq. 7.96 is always constant.

7.5.2. Hill's Equation. A canonic form of homogeneous second-order linear differential equations with periodic coefficients is that termed Hill's equation:

$$\frac{d^2x(t)}{dt^2} + [a - 2qp(t)]x(t) = 0 \tag{7.108}$$

where $p(t)$ denotes a periodic function. Starting with Floquet's work in 1883, many of the properties of the solutions of Hill's equations concerning stability have been determined and are well known. Actual determination of the solutions of a particular equation is, however, often difficult or intractable.

Mathieu originally (1868) studied the particular Hill equation,

$$\frac{d^2x(t)}{dt^2} + [a - 2q \cos 2t]x(t) = 0 \qquad (7.109)$$

now termed Mathieu's equation, in solving the boundary-value problem associated with the vibrating membrane with elliptical perimeter. In boundary-value problems, the corresponding solutions of interest for Hill's equation are periodic functions: thus the periodic solutions of the Mathieu equation are the well-known, well-tabulated Mathieu functions. However, for most electric networks and automatic control systems characterized by a Hill equation, initial-value problems are of interest, and these generally give rise to aperiodic solutions which have not been as well studied as the periodic solutions. Several techniques for approximating the aperiodic solutions of a Hill equation, and in particular the Mathieu equation, are now outlined.

7.5.3. Approximate Matrix Solution of Equations of the Mathieu-Hill Type. The method given here furnishes approximate solutions to the Hill equation in the first full period of $p(t)$, $(0, T)$, by approximating $p(t)$ by a series of suitably delayed step functions and solving the resulting linear time-invariant differential equations in a piecewise manner. The solution is then extended beyond the first period using an interesting variation of Floquet theory based on the fact, established in Sec. 7.5.1, that the Wronskian of the Hill equation is a constant [7].

Let $x_1(t)$ and $x_2(t)$ be a complete basis of Hill's equation 7.108 in the first fundamental interval $(0, T)$, which is the first full period of $p(t)$. The solution of Hill's equation, and its first derivative, can be written in terms of the basis functions as

$$x(t) = A_1x_1(t) + A_2x_2(t) \qquad (7.110a)$$

$$\dot{x}(t) = A_1\dot{x}_1(t) + A_2\dot{x}_2(t) \qquad (7.110b)$$

or, in matrix form, as

$$\begin{bmatrix} x(t) \\ \dot{x}(t) \end{bmatrix} = \begin{bmatrix} x_1(t) & x_2(t) \\ \dot{x}_1(t) & \dot{x}_2(t) \end{bmatrix} \begin{bmatrix} A_1 \\ A_2 \end{bmatrix} \qquad (7.111)$$

The determinant of the square matrix in Eq. 7.111 is recognized as the Wronskian of Hill's equation 7.108 and, as shown in Sec. 7.5.1, is constant on the interval $(0, T)$. This constant Wronskian is denoted by w_0. Note that the Wronskian w_0 can be determined from knowledge of a $x_1(t)$, $x_2(t)$, $\dot{x}_1(t)$, $\dot{x}_2(t)$ at any instant of time, say $t = 0$. Thus, the matrix solution of Eq. 7.111 for A_1 and A_2 is

$$\begin{bmatrix} A_1 \\ A_2 \end{bmatrix} = \frac{1}{w_0} \begin{bmatrix} \dot{x}_2(0) & -x_2(0) \\ -\dot{x}_1(0) & x_1(0) \end{bmatrix} \begin{bmatrix} x(0) \\ x(0) \end{bmatrix} \tag{7.112}$$

Substituting from Eq. 7.112 in Eq. 7.111 gives the solution to Hill's equation in the interval (0, T) as

$$\begin{bmatrix} x(t) \\ \dot{x}(t) \end{bmatrix} = \frac{1}{w_0} \begin{bmatrix} x_1(t) & x_2(t) \\ \dot{x}_1(t) & \dot{x}_2(t) \end{bmatrix} \begin{bmatrix} \dot{x}_2(0) & -x_2(0) \\ -\dot{x}_1(0) & x_1(0) \end{bmatrix} \begin{bmatrix} x(0) \\ \dot{x}(0) \end{bmatrix} \tag{7.113}$$

The solution is now extended beyond the fundamental period (0, T). Introducing a change of independent variable in Hill's equation through

$$\tau = t - nT\,, \quad 0 \le \tau \le T\,, \quad n = 0, 1, 2, \cdots \tag{7.114}$$

gives

$$\frac{d^2x(\tau)}{d\tau^2} + [a - 2qp(\tau)]x(\tau) = 0 \tag{7.115}$$

which, due to the periodicity of $p(t)$ with period T, shows that Hill's equation is invariant under the change of independent variable given by Eq. 7.114. Accordingly, it follows that the basis functions $x_1(t)$ and $x_2(t)$ given for the interval (0, T) are also basis functions in the general interval $[nT, (n + 1)T]$, $n = 0, 1, 2, \ldots$ The solution to Eq. 7.115 in this general interval, as written by a simple modification of the solution given by Eq. 7.113 for the first interval (0, T), is

$$\begin{bmatrix} x(\tau) \\ \dot{x}(\tau) \end{bmatrix} = \frac{1}{w_0} \begin{bmatrix} x_1(\tau) & x_2(\tau) \\ \dot{x}_1(\tau) & \dot{x}_2(\tau) \end{bmatrix} \begin{bmatrix} \dot{x}_2(nT) & -x_2(nT) \\ -\dot{x}_1(nT) & x_1(nT) \end{bmatrix} \begin{bmatrix} x(nT) \\ \dot{x}(nT) \end{bmatrix} \tag{7.116}$$

Equation 7.116 is a recursive equation furnishing the solution to Hill's equation for all t. The initial values, $x(nT)$ and $\dot{x}(nT)$, for the interval $[nT, (n + 1)T]$ are found by computing the final values of the preceding interval $[(n - 1)T, nT]$. Using the property that w_0 is a constant, it is easily shown that the values $x(nT)$ and $\dot{x}(nT)$ can be found directly from the equation

$$\begin{bmatrix} x(nT) \\ \dot{x}(nT) \end{bmatrix} = \begin{bmatrix} A & B \\ C & D \end{bmatrix}^n \begin{bmatrix} x(0) \\ \dot{x}(0) \end{bmatrix} = C^n \begin{bmatrix} x(0) \\ \dot{x}(t) \end{bmatrix} \tag{7.117}$$

where

$$\mathbf{C} = \begin{bmatrix} A & B \\ C & D \end{bmatrix} = \frac{1}{w_0} \begin{bmatrix} x_1(T) & x_2(T) \\ \dot{x}_1(T) & \dot{x}_2(T) \end{bmatrix} \begin{bmatrix} \dot{x}_2(0) & -x_2(0) \\ -\dot{x}_1(0) & x_1(0) \end{bmatrix} \tag{7.118}$$

thus making it possible to use Eq. 7.115 to determine the solution of Hill's equation, for any t, in a *nonrecursive* manner. A comparison of Eq. 7.117 and 7.35 identifies matrix $\mathbf{C}$ as the discrete transition matrix. It can be noted that

$$\det \mathbf{C} = AD - BC = 1 \tag{7.119}$$

The nth power of the matrix $\mathbf{C}$ required in Eq. 7.117 is readily computed using Sylvester's theorem[5]. A useful table, prepared by Pipes [7], for evaluating the integral powers of the 2×2 matrix $\mathbf{C}$ is given in Table 7.1.

In the special case that $p(t)$ is a square wave, Hill's equation is the special form termed the Meissner equation. In this case, the method provides the exact solution of the Meissner equation. The Meissner equation can be used as a crude approximation to the Mathieu equation. For example, a square wave approximation to the cosine function is given in Fig. 7.2. In the fundamental period Meissner's equation corresponds to the two linear time-invariant equations

$$\frac{d^2x(t)}{dt^2} + [a + 2q\beta]x(t) = 0\,, \quad 0 \leq t \leq \frac{T}{4}\,, \quad \frac{3T}{4} \leq t \leq T \qquad (7.120a)$$

$$\frac{d^2x(t)}{dt^2} + [a + 2q\beta]x(t) = 0\,, \quad \frac{T}{4} \leq t \leq \frac{3T}{4} \qquad (7.120b)$$

Table 7.1: Fundamental relations for obtaining integral powers of the 2×2 discrete transition matrix $\mathbf{C}$.

(1) The matrix $\mathbf{C} = \begin{bmatrix} A & B \\ C & D \end{bmatrix}$

(2) $\det \mathbf{C} = AD - BC = 1$

(3) Characteristic equation of $\mathbf{C}$: $c^2 - c(A + D) + 1 = 0$

(4) Eigenvalues of $\mathbf{C}$: $c_1, c_2 = \frac{1}{2}(A + D) \pm \frac{1}{2}\sqrt{(A + D)^2 - 4}$

(5) Integral powers of $\mathbf{C}$:

(a) Distinct eigenvalues

(i) $(A + D) \neq \pm 2$, $\cosh(a) = \frac{1}{2}(A + D)$:

$$\mathbf{C}^n = \frac{1}{S_1}\begin{bmatrix} S_{n+1} - DS_n & BS_n \\ CS_n & S_n{}^+{}_1 - AS_n \end{bmatrix}$$

where $S_n = \sinh(an)$

(ii) $A = D \neq \pm 1$, $\cosh(a) = A$:

$$C^n = \begin{bmatrix} C_n & Z_0 S_n \\ \frac{1}{Z_0} S_n & C_n \end{bmatrix}$$

where $S_n = \sinh(an)$, $C_n = \cos(an)$, $Z_0 = \sqrt{C/B}$

(b) Equal eigenvalues:

(i) $(A + D) = +2$, $c_1 = C_2 = 1$

$$\mathbf{C}_n = \begin{bmatrix} n(A - 1) + 1 & nB \\ nC & n(D - 1) + 1 \end{bmatrix}$$

(ii) $(A + D) = -2$, $c_1 = c_2 = -1$:

$$\mathbf{C}^n = nE_{n-1}\begin{bmatrix} (A + 1) & B \\ C & (D + 1) \end{bmatrix} + E_{n+1}\mathbf{I}_n$$

where $E_n = \exp(-in)$

[5]See footnote 3, Chapter 2.

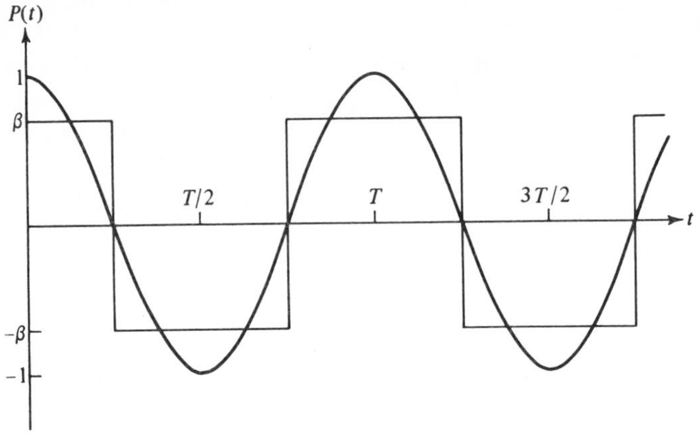

Fig. 7.2. Piecewise approximation to cosine function used in approximate solution of Mathieu equation.

The basis functions for Eqs. 7.120 are

$$\left.\begin{array}{l}\cos(\sqrt{a-2q\beta t})\\ \sin(\sqrt{a-2q\beta t})\end{array}\right\} \quad 0 \le t \le \frac{T}{4};\ \frac{3T}{4} \le t \le T \tag{7.121a}$$

$$\left.\begin{array}{l}\cos(\sqrt{a+2q\beta t})\\ \sin(\sqrt{a+2q\beta t})\end{array}\right\} \quad \frac{T}{4} \le t \le \frac{3T}{4} \tag{7.121b}$$

The solution on the interval $(0, T)$ is easily found from the basis functions by matching the final values of one subinterval with the initial conditions of the next subinterval. With this solution on $(0, T)$, the discrete transition matrix **C** of Eq. 7.117 can be evaluated, enabling the solution to be found in any other interval from Eq. 7.116.

If a better approximation to the Mathieu equation is to be found by this technique, it is necessary that $\cos 2t$ be approximated with a greater number of step functions in the interval $(0, T)$. Clearly, this method can be used to approximate a solution to any Hill equation.

Example 7.2. Consider the Meissner equation

$$\frac{d^2x(t)}{dt^2} + F(t)x(t) = 0$$

where $F(t)$ is as given in Fig. 7.1. Thus the Meissner equation can be replaced by the two equations

$$\frac{d^2x(t)}{dt^2} + h_1x(t) = 0, \qquad t \in \left(0, \frac{T}{2}\right)$$

$$\frac{d^2x(t)}{dt^2} + h_2x(t) = 0, \qquad t \in \left(\frac{T}{2}, T\right)$$

Define ω_1 and ω_2 by

$$\omega_1 \equiv \sqrt{h_1}$$
$$\omega_2 \equiv \sqrt{h_2}$$

Therefore on the interval $\left(0, \frac{T}{2}\right)$ a basis is

$$x_{11}(t) = \cos \omega_1 t$$
$$x_{12}(t) = \frac{1}{\omega_1} \sin \omega_1 t$$

and the Wronskian on this interval is

$$w_{10} = \det \begin{bmatrix} \cos \omega_1 t & \frac{1}{\omega_1} \sin \omega_1 t \\ -\omega_1 \sin \omega_1 t & \cos \omega_1 t \end{bmatrix} = 1$$

The solution on $\left(0, \frac{T}{2}\right)$, in terms of the initial conditions $x_1(0)$ and $\dot{x}_1(0)$, is found to be

$$\begin{bmatrix} x(t) \\ \dot{x}(t) \end{bmatrix} = \begin{bmatrix} \cos \omega_1 t & \frac{1}{\omega_1} \sin \omega_1 t \\ -\omega_1 \sin \omega_1 t & \cos \omega_1 t \end{bmatrix} \begin{bmatrix} x(0) \\ \dot{x}(0) \end{bmatrix}, \qquad t \in \left(0, \frac{T}{2}\right)$$

Defining

$$\theta_1 \equiv \omega_1 \frac{T}{2}$$
$$\theta_2 \equiv \omega_2 \frac{T}{2}$$

the solution at $\frac{T}{2}$ is determined by

$$\begin{bmatrix} x\left(\frac{T}{2}\right) \\ \dot{x}\left(\frac{T}{2}\right) \end{bmatrix} = \begin{bmatrix} \cos \theta_1 & \frac{1}{\omega_1} \sin \theta_1 \\ -\omega_1 \sin \theta_1 & \cos \theta_1 \end{bmatrix} \begin{bmatrix} x(0) \\ \dot{x}(0) \end{bmatrix}$$

A similar analysis on the ihterval $\left(\frac{T}{2}, T\right)$ results in

$$\begin{bmatrix} x(t) \\ \dot{x}(t) \end{bmatrix} = \begin{bmatrix} \cos \omega_2 \left(t - \frac{T}{2}\right) & \frac{1}{\omega_2} \sin \omega_2 \left(t - \frac{T}{2}\right) \\ -\omega_2 \sin \omega_2 \left(t - \frac{T}{2}\right) & \cos \omega_2 \left(t - \frac{T}{2}\right) \end{bmatrix} \begin{bmatrix} k_1 \\ k_2 \end{bmatrix}, \qquad t \in \left(\frac{T}{2}, T\right)$$

where

$$\begin{bmatrix} k_1 \\ \\ k_2 \end{bmatrix} = \begin{bmatrix} x\left(\frac{T}{2}\right) \\ \dot{x}\left(\frac{T}{2}\right) \end{bmatrix}$$

Therefore

$$\begin{bmatrix} x(t) \\ \\ x(t) \end{bmatrix} = \begin{bmatrix} \cos \omega_2\left(t - \frac{T}{2}\right) & \frac{1}{\omega_2} \sin \omega_2 \left(t - \frac{T}{2}\right) \\ -\omega_2 \sin \omega_2 \left(t - \frac{T}{2}\right) & \cos \omega_2 \left(t - \frac{T}{2}\right) \end{bmatrix}$$

$$\cdot \begin{bmatrix} \cos \theta_1 & \frac{1}{\omega_1} \sin \theta_1 \\ -\omega_1 \sin \theta_1 & \cos \theta_1 \end{bmatrix} \begin{bmatrix} x(0) \\ \dot{x}(0) \end{bmatrix}$$

and at the end of one full period

$$\begin{bmatrix} x(T) \\ \dot{x}(T) \end{bmatrix} = \begin{bmatrix} \cos \theta_2 & \frac{1}{\omega_2} \sin \theta_2 \\ -\omega_2 \sin \theta_2 & \cos \theta_2 \end{bmatrix} \begin{bmatrix} \cos \theta_1 & \frac{1}{\omega_1} \sin \theta_1 \\ -\omega_1 \sin \theta_1 & \cos \theta_1 \end{bmatrix} \begin{bmatrix} x(0) \\ \dot{x}(0) \end{bmatrix}$$

$$= \mathbf{C} \begin{bmatrix} x(0) \\ \\ \dot{x}(0) \end{bmatrix}$$

where the discrete transition matrix **C** is given by

$$\mathbf{C} = \begin{bmatrix} A & B \\ C & D \end{bmatrix}$$

$$= \begin{bmatrix} \cos \theta_2 \cos \theta_1 - \frac{\omega_1}{\omega_2} \sin \theta_1 \sin \theta_2 & \frac{1}{\omega_1} \cos \theta_2 \sin \theta_1 + \frac{1}{\omega_2} \sin \theta_2 \cos \theta_1 \\ -\omega_2 \sin \theta_2 \cos \theta_1 - \omega_1 \cos \theta_2 \sin \theta_1 & -\frac{\omega_2}{\omega_1} \sin \theta_2 \sin \theta_1 + \cos \theta_2 \cos \theta_1 \end{bmatrix}$$

Now Eqs. 7.116 and 7.117 can be used to determine the solution anywhere. To illustrate the evaluation of $\mathbf{M}^n$ assume the specific values

$$T = \Pi, \quad h_1 = 4, \quad h_2 = 1$$

Thus

$$\omega_1 = 2, \qquad \omega_2 = 1$$

and

$$\theta_1 = \pi, \qquad \theta_2 = \frac{\pi}{2}$$

Therefore

$$\mathbf{C} = \begin{bmatrix} 0 & -1 \\ 1 & 0 \end{bmatrix}$$

Using Table 7.1 the characteristic equation of **C** is determined to be

$$c^2 + 1 = 0$$

The eigenvalues of **C** are determined to be

$$c_1, c_2 = \pm \sqrt{-1}$$

and are thus distinct. Therefore

$$\mathbf{C}^n = \frac{1}{S_1}\begin{bmatrix} S_{n+1} - DS_n & BS_n \\ CS_n & S_{n-1} - AS_n \end{bmatrix}$$

where

$$A + D = 0 \neq 2$$

$$\cosh a = \frac{A + D}{2} = 0$$

Therefore $a = \frac{i\pi}{2}$ where n is any integer:

$$S_n = \sinh(an) = \sinh\frac{jn\pi}{2} = j \sin\frac{n\pi}{2}$$

$$= \begin{cases} 0, & n \text{ even} \\ +i, & \frac{n-1}{2} \text{ even} \\ -i, & \frac{n-1}{2} \text{ odd} \end{cases}$$

Therefore

$$\mathbf{C} = \begin{bmatrix} 0 & -1 \\ 1 & 0 \end{bmatrix}, \qquad \mathbf{C}_2 = \begin{bmatrix} -1 & 0 \\ 0 & -1 \end{bmatrix}$$

$$\mathbf{C}^{322} = \begin{bmatrix} -1 & 0 \\ 0 & -1 \end{bmatrix}$$

The stability of the solution is easily determined by checking to see whether or not the eigenvalues of the discrete transition matrix lie within the unit circle. Since the eigenvalues are

$$c_1, c_2 = \pm i$$

the eigenvalues lie on the unit circle showing that the system is stable, but not asymptotically stable. This, of course, could have been deduced from the repetitive nature of the discrete transition matrix C when raised to integral powers.

7.5.4. An Iterative Approximation to the Mathieu Equation. An iterative method useful for approximating solutions to second-order equations is particularly convenient for solving the Mathieu equation. Of specific value are the general equations which Smith derives for the first and second approximations to the solution. These equations can be used simply by substituting the parameters of the Mathieu equation into them, and generally provide better accuracy than a comparable effort using the piecewise time-invariant approximations of the previous section. However, increasing accuracy with this method by using higher-order approximations becomes quickly intractable. Although the method is advanced as a means of approximating solutions to the Mathieu equation, the approach can also be used for solving the general Hill equation, as well as for equations of the canonic form of Eq. 7.96 which are not periodic. In these latter cases, it is necessary to evaluate rather complex integrals.

This technique is based on the fact that basis functions, valid for $t > 0$, of a homogeneous differential equation can be obtained from the nonhomogeneous equation, with impulse functions (and derivatives of impluse functions) at $t = 0$ as forcing functions. Thus the Mathieu equation can be written in the form (compare with the canonic form of Eq. 7.109)

$$\frac{d^2x(t)}{dt^2} + (m^2 - 2q \cos 2at)x(t) = 0 \tag{7.122}$$

With a unit-impulse forcing function, it is

$$\frac{d^2x(t)}{dt^2} + (m^2 - 2q \cos 2at)x(t) = \delta(t) \tag{7.123}$$

which can be rearranged as

$$\frac{d^2x(t)}{dt^2} + m^2x(t) = \delta(t) + x(t)2q \cos 2at \tag{7.124}$$

Since the forcing function $\delta(t) = 0$, for $t > 0$, a solution of Eq. 7.124 for $t > 0$, provides one of the two basis functions, i.e., a solution to the homogeneous equation associated with Eq. 7.124. Equation 7.124 can be regarded as a linear differential equation with constant coefficients with a forcing function $\delta(t) + x(t)\, 2q \cos 2at$. Since the basis functions for the homogeneouse equation associated with Eq. 7.124 are $\sin mt$ and $\cos mt$, the impulsive response of a system characterized by Eq. 7.124 is

$$\Omega(t, \tau) = (1/m) \sin m(t - \tau) \tag{7.125}$$

The solution of Eq. 7.124, with zero initial conditions is therefore

$$\begin{aligned} x(t) &= \int_0^t \frac{1}{m} \sin m(t - \tau)[\delta(\tau) + x(\tau)2q \cos 2a\tau]\, d\tau \\ &= \frac{1}{m} \sin m(t) + \frac{2q}{m} \int_0^t x(\tau) \cos 2a\tau \sin m(t - \tau)\, d\tau \end{aligned} \tag{7.126}$$

which can be written in the iterative form as

$$x_n(t) = \frac{1}{m} \sin m(t) + \frac{2q}{m} \int_0^t x_{n-1}(\tau) \cos 2a\tau \sin m(t - \tau)\, d\tau \tag{7.127}$$

Taking the zeroth approximation as

$$x_0(t) = \frac{1}{m} \sin mt \tag{7.128}$$

the first and second approximations are found from Eq. 7.127:

$$x_1(t) = \frac{1}{m} \sin mt - \frac{q}{2m}\left[\frac{\sin (m + 2a)t}{2a(m + a)} - \frac{\sin mt}{m^2 - a^2} - \frac{\sin (m - 2a)t}{2a(m - a)}\right] \tag{7.129}$$

and

$$\begin{aligned} x_2(t) = x_1(t) + \frac{q^2}{16m}\Bigg\{ & \frac{1}{2a(m + a)}\left[\frac{\sin (m + 4a)t}{4a(m + 2a)} - \frac{\sin mt}{4a(m + 2a)} + \frac{t \cos mt}{m}\right] + \frac{1}{2a(m - a)}\left[\frac{\sin (m + 2a)t}{4a(m - 2a)} - \frac{\sin mt}{4a(m - 2a)} - \frac{t \cos mt}{m}\right] \\ & - \frac{1}{(m^2 - a^2)}\left[\frac{\sin (m + 2a)t}{2a(m + a)} - \frac{\sin (m - 2a)t}{2a(m - a)} - \frac{\sin mt}{m^2 - a^2}\right]\Bigg\} \end{aligned} \tag{7.130}$$

These approximations give one of the two basis functions of the Mathieu equation. The second basis function is found from the solution of

$$\frac{d^2x(t)}{dt^2} + [m^2 - 2q \cos 2at]x(t) = \dot{\delta}(t) \tag{7.131}$$

where $\dot{\delta}(t)$, is the first derivative of the unit impulse, often termed the unit doublet. Rewriting Eq. 7.131

$$\frac{d^2x(t)}{dt^2} + m^2x(t) = \dot{\delta}(t) + 2q \cos 2at \tag{7.132}$$

puts it into the general form of Eq. 7.124 whose solution is given by Eq. 7.126. Therefore the solution of Eq. 7.132 is

$$\begin{aligned} x(t) &= \int_0^t \left[\frac{1}{m} \sin m(t - \tau)\right][\dot{\delta}(\tau) + x(\tau)2q \cos 2a\tau]\, d\tau \\ &= \cos mt + \frac{2q}{m}\int_0^t x(\tau) \cos 2a\tau \sin m(t - \tau)\, d\tau \end{aligned} \tag{7.133}$$

which can be rewritten in the iterative form

$$x_n(t) = \cos mt + \frac{2q}{m}\int_0^t x_{n-1}(\tau) \cos 2a\tau \sin m(t - \tau)\, d\tau \tag{7.134}$$

Taking the zeroth approximation as

$$x_0(t) = \cos mt \tag{7.135}$$

the first approximation found by substituting for $x_0(t)$ from Eq. 7.135 in Eq. 7.134:

$$x_1(t) = \cos mt - \frac{q}{2}\left[\frac{\cos(m+2a)t}{2a(m+a)} + \frac{\cos mt}{m^2 - a^2} - \frac{\cos(m-2a)t}{2a(m-a)}\right] \tag{7.136}$$

Thus a complete set of basis functions for the Mathieu equation and their approximations are determined.

REFERENCES

[1] Bellman, R., *Stability Theory of Differential Equations*, McGraw-Hill, New York, 1963.

[2] Cesari, L., *Asymptotic Behavior and Stability and Stability Problems in Ordinary Differential Equations*, 2nd ed., Springer-Verlag, Berlin, 1963.

[3] Floquet, M., "Sur les equations differentielles linéaires a coefficients périodiques," *Annales Scientifiques de l'Ecole Normale Superieure*, series 2, vol. 12 (1883), pp. 47–89.

[4] Kaplan, W., *Operational Methods for Linear Systems*, Addison-Wesley, Reading, Mass., 1962.

[5] Lee, I., "On the Theory of Linear Dynamic Systems with Periodic Parameters," *Information and Control*, vol. 6 (1963), pp. 265–275.

[6] McLachlan, N., *Theory and Application of Mathieu Functions*, Oxford, New York, 1947.

[7] Pipes, L., "Matrix Solutions of Equations of the Mathieu-Hill Type," *J. Appl. Physics*, vol. 24 (1953), pp. 902–910.

[8] Smith, O. J., "A Method of Solving Mathieu's Equation," *AIEE Trans.*, vol. 74, part 1 (1955), pp. 520–525.

[9] Whittaker, E. and Watson, G., *Modern Analysis*, 4th ed., *Cambridge U. P.*, New York, 1935.

PROBLEMS

7.1 Show that $\phi_0(kT) = \mathbf{C}^k$.

7.2 From Eqs. 7.38 and 7.39 it is concluded that the periodic system is asymptotically stable if the *n distinct* characteristic roots $c_i = 1, \ldots, n$ lie within the unit circle of the complex plane. Show that the same conclusion is valid when the characteristic roots are not distinct.

7.3 Using the discrete transition matrix, determine whether or not the following systems have

(a) periodic solutions (if so, what is the period)
(b) stable solutions

(i) $\dot{x} = (\sin t)x$
(ii) $\dot{x} = (\sin^2 t)x$
(iii) $\dot{x} = -(\sin^2 t)x$
(iv) $\dot{x} = \left(\frac{1}{2}\sin^2 t\right)x$
(v) $\dot{x} = -\left(\frac{1}{2}\sin^2 t\right)x$

(vi) $\dot{x} = (1 + \sin^2 t)x$
(vii) $\dot{x} = -(1 + \sin^2 t)x$

7.4 Investigate the stability of the system characterized by

$$\frac{d^2y}{dt^2} + F(t)\frac{dx}{dt} + x = 0$$

where $F(t)$ is periodic and is as shown in Fig. P7.4.

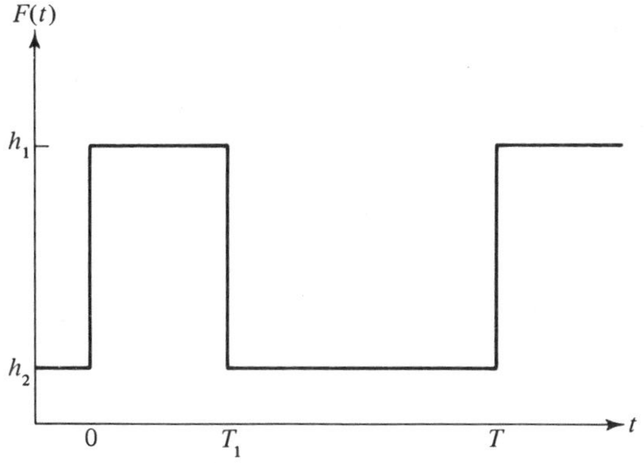

Fig. P7.4.

7.5 Show that the system characterized by

$$\frac{d^2x}{dt^2} + G(t)\frac{dx}{dt} + x = 0$$

is unstable for any periodic $G(t)$ such that

$$\int_0^T G(t)dt < 0$$

7.6 Prove that $\mathbf{R}(t)$ defined in Eq. 7.27, is periodic, has continuous derivatives, and is nonsingular.

7.7 Prove that the variable transformation defined by Eq. 7.95 puts Eq. 7.94 into the canonical form of Eq. 7.96.

7.8 Put the second-order differential equation

$$\frac{d^2x}{dt^2} + (t + e^{-2t})\frac{dx}{dt} + e^{-t}x = \sin t$$

into the canonical form of Eq. 7.96.

7.9 Put the second-order differential equation

$$\frac{d^2x}{dt^2} + (1 + \cos t)\frac{dx}{dt} + \sin tx = 0$$

into the canonical form of Eq. 7.108.

7.10 Use the approximation scheme of Sec. 7.5.3 to determine the solution of the second-order linear differential equation of Prob. 7.9. ($x(0) = 1$, $\dot{x}(0) = 0$), and using Table 7.1 determine the stability characteristics of the equation. Give an explicit solution on the interval $[200\,\pi, 202\,\pi]$.

7.11 Derive Eq. 7.117 from Eq. 7.116.

7.12 Show that the determinant of the discrete transition matrix **C**, defined in Eq. 7.118 is unity.

7.13 Use the results of Secs. 7.5.3 and 7.5.4 to obtain two approximations to the solution of the following differential equation

$$\frac{d^2t}{dt^2} + (1 - 2\cos 2t)\,x = 0$$

$$x(0) = 1\,, \qquad \dot{x}(0) = 0$$

Compare the solutions thus obtained and evaluate the results.

8

Stability of Linear Time-Varying Systems

8.1. INTRODUCTION: COMPARISON WITH LINEAR TIME-INVARIANT SYSTEMS

An understanding of the special problems associated with determining whether or not a linear time-varying system is stable is best achieved by reviewing some of the stability concepts of linear time-invariant systems, paying special attention to possible ambiguities in definitions. In particular the concepts of *stability* and *resonance* are often confused.

Definition 8.1. A linear system is said to be *stable* if all outputs $\mathbf{y}(t)$ to an arbitrary input $\mathbf{u}(t)$ approach each other as time increases regardless of initial conditions. Thus for the system characterized by

$$\begin{aligned} \dot{\mathbf{x}}(t) &= \mathbf{A}(t)\mathbf{x}(t) + \mathbf{B}(t)\mathbf{u}(t), \ \mathbf{x}(t_0) = \mathbf{x}_0 \\ \mathbf{y}(t) &= \mathbf{C}(t)\mathbf{x}(t) \end{aligned} \tag{8.1}$$

the following limit process holds for all $\mathbf{x}_0$:

$$\lim_{t \to \infty} \left[\mathbf{y}(t) - \int_{t_0}^{t} \Omega(t, \tau)\mathbf{u}(\tau)\, d\tau \right] = 0 \tag{8.2}$$

Equivalently, a linear system is said to be stable if the output response of the unforced system to arbitrary initial conditions $\mathbf{x}_0$ approach zero as $t \to \infty$.

Definition 8.2. A linear system is said to be *resonant* if for some input $\mathbf{u}(t)$ which is bounded[1] ($\|\mathbf{u}(t)\| \leq$ constant) for $t \geq 0$, the output $\mathbf{y}(t)$ is not bounded for $t \geq 0$. A system that is *not* resonant is often referred to as *stable b.i.b.o.* (bounded-input, bounded-output).

Thus the implication for a stable system is that system response to any initial conditions approach zero as time increases, i.e., a system is stable if

$$\lim_{t\to\infty} [\mathbf{C}(t)\phi(t, t_0)\mathbf{x}_0] = \mathbf{0} \tag{8.3}$$

On the other hand, the implication for a system that is *nonresonant* is that if $\|\mathbf{u}(t)\| = K_u$, then

$$\left\| \int_{t_0}^{t} \Omega(t, \tau)\mathbf{u}(\tau)\, d\tau \right\| = K_y \tag{8.4}$$

where K_u and K_y are finite constants. In general *stability* and *nonresonance* are not equivalent, i.e., a system can be stable and nonresonant. However, much confusion stems from the great exposure that most workers have to linear time-invariant systems for which stability and nonresonance are generally equivalent.

Theorem 8.1. For the completely controllable linear time-invariant system

$$\dot{\mathbf{x}}(t) = \mathbf{A}\mathbf{x}(t) + \mathbf{B}\mathbf{u}(t)\,, \quad \mathbf{x}(t_0) = \mathbf{x}_0$$
$$\mathbf{y}(t) = \mathbf{C}\mathbf{x}(t)$$

with the impulsive-response matrix $\Omega(t, \tau)$, the following statements are equivalent:

(a) The system is stable.
(b) The system is nonresonant.
(c) $\int_{t_0}^{\infty} \|\Omega(t)\|\, dt = K < \infty$

Proof. If the linear time-invariant system is stable then each element of the impulsive-response matrix $\Omega(t)$ is of the form

[1]In what follows $\|\mathbf{x}(t)\|$ denotes the norm of the vector $\mathbf{x}(t)$, and $\|\mathbf{A}(t)\|$ denotes the norm of the matrix $\mathbf{A}(t)$. In particular, and unless specified otherwise,

$$\|\mathbf{x}(t)\| \equiv \sum_{i=1}^{n} |x_i(t)| \tag{8.2A}$$

and

$$\|\mathbf{A}(t)\| \equiv \sum_{i=1}^{n} \sum_{j=1}^{n} |a_{ij}(t)| \tag{8.2B}$$

$$\omega_{ij}(t) = \sum_{r=1}^{m} c_r t^{k_r} e^{s_r t} \tag{8.6}$$

where $R_e[s_r] < 0$ and k_r is a finite nonnegative integer for all r. Clearly

$$\int_{t_0}^{\infty} |\omega_{ij}(t)|\, dt = K_{ij} < \infty \tag{8.7}$$

Thus it follows from the definition of a norm, i.e., Eq. 8.2B, that Eq. 8.5 is valid. The zero-state response of the system to a forcing function is

$$\mathbf{y}_p(t) = \int_{t_0}^{t} \Omega(t - \tau)\mathbf{u}(\tau)\, d\tau \tag{8.8}$$

or equivalently

$$\mathbf{y}_p(t) = \int_{t_0}^{t} \Omega(\tau)\mathbf{u}(t - \tau)\, d\tau \tag{8.9}$$

Thus

$$||\mathbf{y}_p(t)|| \leq \int_{t_0}^{t} ||\Omega(\tau)||\ ||\mathbf{u}(t - \tau)||\, d\tau$$

If $\mathbf{u}(t)$ is bounded, i.e., $||\mathbf{u}(t)|| = K_u < \infty$, then

$$||\mathbf{y}_p(t)|| \leq K_u \int_{t_0}^{t} ||\Omega(\tau)||\, d\tau \leq K_u K \tag{8.11}$$

Therefore, a bounded input always produces a bounded output and the system is nonresonant. A similar argument is used to deduce that a nonresonant system implies a stable system. In this case, however, complete controllability is necessary to ensure a one-to-one relationship between the input-output modes and the states of the system. It should be noted that if one requires a stronger stability in which the state vector $x(t)$ as well as the output vector $y(t)$ approaches zero as $t \to \infty$ for all initial conditions, then complete observability is also required. Q.E.D.

In linear time-varying systems, stability and nonresonance are not necessarily equivalent statements. The following example illustrates this point.

Example 8.1. Consider the first-order system characterized by the equation

$$\dot{\mathbf{x}}(t) = -\frac{1}{t + 2}x(t) + f(t)$$

The solution for this unforced system ($f(t) = 0$) with initial condition $x(0) = x_0$ is

$$x_c(t) = \frac{2}{t + 2}x_0$$

Clearly all solutions of the homogeneous system are bounded and $\lim_{t\to\infty} [x_c(t)] = 0$, thus establishing that the system is stable. The forced solution is

$$x(t) = \frac{2}{t+2}x_0 + \int_0^t \frac{\tau + 2}{t+2} f(\tau)\,d\tau$$

Therefore for the case that the forcing function $f(t)$ is a unit-step function, i.e., $f(t) = 1$ for $t \geq 0$,

$$x(t) = \frac{2}{t+2}x_0 + \frac{1}{2}(t+2) - \frac{2}{t+2}$$

and

$$\lim_{t \to \infty} [x(t)] = \infty$$

It is seen that this system has an unbounded output $x(t)$ for a bounded input $f(t)$ and is therefore a resonant system that is also stable.

This example establishes that stability alone is not equivalent to nonresonance. In the next section it is shown that the additional requirement that transients die out exponentially is sufficient to establish nonresonance—this, of course, is satisfied for stable linear time-invariant systems.

8.2. RESONANT SYSTEMS [16]

A criterion for nonresonance is given in terms of the impulsive-response matrix.

Theorem 8.2. A scalar linear system is nonresonant (stable b.i.b.o.) in the sense of Definition 8.2 if and only if

$$\int_{t_0}^{t} |\Omega(t, \tau)|\,d\tau = K < \infty \tag{8.12}$$

Proof. (i) *Sufficiency* is established by assuming the bounded input $u(t)$ such that $|u(t)| = K_u$. Therefore

$$|y_p(t)| \leq K_u \int_{t_0}^{t} |\Omega(t, \tau)|\,d\tau \leq K_u K \tag{8.13}$$

(ii) *Necessity* is established by contradiction. Assume that the system is nonresonant and

$$\int_{t_0}^{t_1} |\Omega(t_1, \tau)|\,d\tau = \infty \tag{8.14}$$

Since

$$y_p(t_1) = \int_{t_0}^{t_1} \Omega(t_1, \tau)u(\tau)\,d\tau \tag{8.15}$$

selecting the bounded input

$$u(t) = \text{sign}\,\Omega(t_1, t)$$

results in the output (8.16)

$$y_p(t_1) = \int_{t_0}^{t_1} \Omega(t_1, \tau) | \, d\tau \tag{8.17}$$

which, in accordance with Eq. 8.14, is unbounded. Thus the original assumption of nonresonance is contradicted. Q.E.D.

Corollary 8.2. A linear system is nonresonant (stable b.i.b.o.) in the sense of Definition 8.2 if and only if

$$\int_{t_0}^{t} ||\Omega(t, \tau)|| \, d\tau = K < \infty \tag{8.18}$$

Proof. In accordance with Theorem 8.2, each component of the impulsive-response matrix $\omega_{ij}(t, \tau)$ satisfies the inequality

$$\int_{t_0}^{t} |\omega_{ij}(t, \tau)| \, d\tau = K_{ij} < \infty \tag{8.19}$$

Therefore, in accordance with the definition of a norm given by Eq. 8.2B, it follows that

$$\int_{t_0}^{t} ||\Omega(t, \tau)|| \, d\tau = K \leq \sum_{i=1}^{n} \sum_{j=1}^{n} K_{ij} < \infty \tag{8.20}$$

thus establishing sufficiency. Necessity can be established by contradiction as in Theorem 8.2 from the fact that if $\int_{t_0}^{t_1} ||\Omega(t_1, \tau)|| \, d\tau = \infty$ then, for some i and j, $\int_{t_0}^{t_1} |\omega_{ij}(t_1, \tau)| \, d\tau = \infty$ and the scalar argument follows. Q.E.D.

Valuable insight into the asymptotic behavior of linear time-varying systems is obtained by relating stability (Definition 8.1) to resonance (Definition 8.2). Example 8.1 clearly points out the fact that a stable system need not be nonresonant. One might then ask if there are any other characteristics that a stable system might display which would guarantee that it is not resonant. The following two theorems comprise answers to such a question.

Theorem 8.3. If the coefficient matrix $\mathbf{A}(t)$ is continuous for all $t \in [0, \infty)$ and constants $a > 0$, $b > 0$ exist such that for every solution of the homogeneous differential equation

$$\dot{\mathbf{x}}(t) = \mathbf{A}(t)\mathbf{x}(t) \tag{8.21}$$

one has

$$||\mathbf{x}(t)|| \leq b \, ||\mathbf{x}(t_0)|| \, e^{-a(t-t_0)}, \qquad 0 \leq t_0 < t < \infty \tag{8.22}$$

then for each $f(t)$ bounded and continuous on $[0, \infty)$, every solution of the nonhomogeneous equation

$$\dot{\mathbf{x}}(t) = \mathbf{A}(t)\mathbf{x}(t) + \mathbf{f}(t), \ \mathbf{x}(t_0) = \mathbf{0} \tag{8.23}$$

is also bounded for $t \in [0, \infty)$. (Or, equivalently, if the homogeneous system has exponentially bounded responses, then the system is nonresonant.)

Proof. Since $\mathbf{x}(t) = \phi(t, t_0)\mathbf{x}(t_0)$ is the solution of the homogeneous equation 8.21, by hypothesis of Eq. 8.22

$$||\phi(t, t_0)\mathbf{x}(t_0)|| \leq b\,||\mathbf{x}(t_0)||\,e^{-a(t-t_0)} \tag{8.24}$$

The solution to the nonhomogeneous Eq. 8.23 is

$$\mathbf{x}(t) = \phi(t, t_0)\mathbf{x}(t_0) + \int_{t_0}^{t} \phi(t, \tau)\mathbf{f}(\tau)\,d\tau \tag{8.25}$$

Therefore, in accordance with Eq. 8.24

$$||\mathbf{x}(t)|| \leq b||\mathbf{x}(t_0)||\,e^{-a(t-t_0)} + \int_{t_0}^{t} b||\mathbf{f}(\tau)||\,e^{-a(t-\tau)}\,d\tau \tag{8.26}$$

Assuming a bounded input, i.e., $||\mathbf{f}(t)|| < K_f < \infty$, gives

$$\begin{aligned} ||\mathbf{x}(t)|| &\leq b||\mathbf{x}(t_0)||\,e^{-a(t-t_0)} + bK_f e^{-at}\int_{t_0}^{t} e^{a\tau}d\tau \\ &= b||\mathbf{x}(t_0)||\,e^{-a(t-t_0)} + \frac{bK_f}{a}[1 - e^{-a(t-t_0)}] \end{aligned} \tag{8.27}$$

Therefore if $\mathbf{x}(t_0) = \mathbf{0}$ and the input $\mathbf{f}(t)$ is bounded, then

$$||\mathbf{x}(t)|| \leq \frac{bK_f}{a}[1 - e^{-a(t-t_0)}] \tag{8.28}$$

and the particular solution is also bounded. Clearly the complementary solution is also bounded for every finite $\mathbf{x}(t_0)$. Thus all solutions to the nonhomogeneous equation 8.23 are bounded. Q.E.D.

Theorem 8.3 is illustrated by Example 8.1 where it is noted that the solution to the homogeneous system, $x_c(t) = \dfrac{2}{t+2}x_0$, though bounded on $[0, \infty)$ and approaching zero as $t \to \infty$, is not exponentially bounded. Therefore in accordance with Theorem 8.3 the system may be resonant. As shown, the system is resonant in that it gives an unbounded response $x(t)$ with a bounded input $\mathbf{f}(t) = 1$.

Theorem 8.4. If the coefficient matrix $\mathbf{A}(t)$ is continuous and $||\mathbf{A}(t)|| < K_A < \infty$ for $t \in [0, \infty)$, and for each $\mathbf{f}(t)$ bounded and continuous on $[0, \infty)$, every solution of $\mathbf{x}(t)$ of the nonhomogeneous equation 8.23 is also bounded, then there exists constants $a > 0$ and $b > 0$ such that inequality 8.22 is valid for every solution $\mathbf{x}(t)$ of the homogeneous equation 8.21. (Or, equivalently, if the system is nonresonant, the homogeneous system has exponentially bounded responses.)

Proof. The proof of this theorem hinges on a rather intuitive, but difficult to prove, result which is given here without proof[2]. If the response of the nonhomogeneous system 8.23

[2]See Kaplan, Ref. [16], pp. 505–510.

$$\mathbf{x}(t) = \phi(t, t_0)\mathbf{x}(t_0) + \int_{t_0}^{t} \phi(t, \tau)\mathbf{f}(\tau)\, d\tau \tag{8.29}$$

is bounded for all bounded inputs $\mathbf{f}(t)$ and initial conditions $\mathbf{x}(t_0)$, then the transition matrix $\phi(t, t_0)$ is also bounded, i.e,

$$||\phi(t, t_0)|| < K_\phi < \infty \tag{8.30}$$

Note that, in accordance with inequality 8.30,

$$\begin{aligned} ||(t - t_0)\phi(t, t_0)|| &= \left|\left|\int_{t_0}^{t} \phi(t, t_0)\, d\tau\right|\right| \\ &= \left|\left|\int_{t_0}^{t} \phi(t, \tau)\phi(\tau, t_0)\, d\tau\right|\right| \\ &\leq \int_{t_0}^{t} ||\phi(t, \tau)||\, ||\phi(\tau, t_0)||\, d\tau \\ &< K_\phi \int_{t_0}^{t} ||\phi(t, \tau)||\, d\tau \\ &< K_\phi K_\Phi < \infty, \qquad 0 \leq t_0 \leq t < \infty \end{aligned} \tag{8.31}$$

Since the magnitude of a scalar can be factored out of a properly defined norm, inequality 8.31 can be written as

$$||\phi(t, t_0)|| < \frac{K_\phi K_\Phi}{t - t_0} \tag{8.32}$$

Defining

$$T \equiv 2K_\phi K_\Phi \tag{8.33}$$

results in

$$||\phi(t_0 + T, t_0)|| < \frac{1}{2} \tag{8.34}$$

and in general

$$||\phi(t_0 + kT, t_0)|| < n2^{-k}, \qquad k = 0, 1, 2, \cdots \tag{8.35}$$

where the factor n is inserted on the right-hand side of inequality 8.35 to take care of the case that $k = 0$ where $||\phi(t_0, t_0)|| = ||\mathbf{I}_n|| = n$. Constant K_e and t_k are defined by

$$K_e \equiv \frac{\log 2}{T} \tag{8.36}$$

and

$$t_k \equiv t_0 + kT \tag{8.37}$$

Thus inequality 8.35 can be written as

$$||\phi(t_k, t_0)|| \leq n\, e^{-K_e(t_k - t_0)} \tag{8.38}$$

If a variable τ is defined such that $0 \leq \tau < T$, then

$$\begin{aligned}||\phi(t_k + \tau, t_0)|| &= ||\phi(t_k + \tau, t_k)\phi(t_k, t_0)|| \\ &< ||\phi(t_k + \tau, t_k)||\, n\, e^{-K_e(t_k - t_0)} \\ &< nK_\phi\, e^{-K_e(t_k - t_0)} \\ &= nK_\phi\, e^{K_e\tau}\, e^{-K_e(t_k + \tau - t_0)} \\ &< K_n\, e^{-K_e(t_k + \tau - t_0)}\end{aligned} \tag{8.39}$$

where

$$K_n = n\, K_\phi\, e^{K_e T} > nK_\phi\, e^{K_e \tau} \tag{8.40}$$

Since every $t \in [0, \infty)$ can be represented by $t = t_k + \tau$, inequality 8.39 can be written as

$$||\phi(t, t_0)|| < b\, e^{-a(t - t_0)} \tag{8.41}$$

where $b = K_n < \infty$ and $a = K_e < \infty$. Therefore taking the norm of the solution of the homogeneous equation results in

$$\begin{aligned}||\mathbf{x}(t)|| &\leq ||\phi(t, t_0)||\ ||\mathbf{x}(t_0)|| \\ &< b||\mathbf{x}(t_0)||\, e^{-a(t - t_0)}\end{aligned} \tag{8.42}$$

Q.E.D.

In this section the fact that stability and nonresonance (stability b.i.b.o.) may not be equivalent for linear time-varying systems, as is the case for linear time-invariant systems, is pointed out; theorems relating stability and nonresonance are established. In the next section the concept of *relative stability* is introduced.

8.3. RELATIVE STABILITY [2, 5]

The concept of relative stability is an important one in that it allows one to predict, under certain conditions, the properties of one *homogeneous* system by comparing it to another known *homogeneous* system. Specifically,

Definition 8.3. The solutions of the homogeneous system

$$\dot{\mathbf{x}}(t) = \mathbf{A}(t)\mathbf{x}(t) \tag{8.43}$$

are *stable with respect to property P* (or simply *P-stable*) and perturbations $\Delta(t)$ of type T, if the solutions of the homogeneous system

$$\dot{\mathbf{z}}(t) = [\mathbf{A}(t) + \Delta(t)]\mathbf{z}(t) \tag{8.44}$$

also possess property P. If this is not true, then the solutions are said to be *unstable with respect to property P* (or simply P-unstable) under perturbations of type T.

Example 8.2. It is desired to determine whether or not the system

$$\dot{x}(t) = -ax(t)\,, \qquad a > 0$$

is P-stable under T-perturbations where P and T are defined by

$$P: \quad \lim_{t \to \infty} x(t) = a \text{ finite quantity}$$

$$T: \quad \Delta(t) \to 0 \text{ as } t \to 0$$

The solution of the perturbated system

$$\dot{z}(t) = [-a + \Delta(t)]z(t)\,, \quad a > 0$$

is

$$z(t) = \exp\left\{\int_{t_0}^{t} [-a + \Delta(\eta)]\, d\eta\right\} z(t_0)$$
$$= z(t_0)e^{-a(t-t_0)} \exp\left[\int_{t_0}^{t} \Delta(\eta)\, d\eta\right]$$

Therefore it can be seen that the perturbated system satisfies property P only if $e^{-a(t-t_0)}$ is decreasing at a faster rate than $\exp\left[\int_{t_0}^{t} \Delta(\eta)\, d\eta\right]$ is increasing, i.e., if

$$\lim_{t \to \infty}\left[-a(t - t_0) + \int_{t_0}^{t} \Delta(\eta)\, d\eta\right] = K < \infty$$

For example, consider $\Delta(t) = t$ which satisfies condition T. Clearly

$$\int_{t_0}^{t} \Delta(\eta)\, d\eta = \frac{1}{2}(t^2 - t_0^2)$$

and

$$\lim_{t \to \infty}\left[-a(t - t_0) + \frac{1}{2}(t^2 - t_0^2)\right] = \infty$$

Thus property P is not satisfied and the system is P-unstable under perturbations of type T.

Now consider perturbations of the type T':

$$T': \quad \Delta(t) \to 0 \text{ as } t \to \infty$$

For example, consider $\Delta(t) = \dfrac{1}{t}$ which satisfies condition T'. Clearly

$$\int_{t_0}^{t} \Delta(\eta)\, d\eta = \ln t - \ln t_0$$

and

$$\lim_{t \to \infty} [-a(t - t_0) + \ln t - \ln t_0] = -\infty$$

Thus property P is satisfied and the system may be P-stable under perturbations of type T'. However, it is interesting to note that for the case that $t_0 = 0$, the solution $z(t)$ of the perturbated system is not bounded for finite t. Thus if property P' is defined by

$$P': \quad x(t) \text{ bounded on } [0, \infty)$$

then the system is P'-unstable under perturbations of type T'.

8.3.1. Almost-Constant Coefficient Matrices. The coefficient matrix $\mathbf{A}(t)$ is said to be *almost constant* if

$$\lim_{t\to\infty} \mathbf{A}(t) = \mathbf{A}_\infty$$

where $\mathbf{A}_\infty$ is a constant matrix. There is a strong intuitive tendency to declare that a system with an almost-constant coefficient matrix $\mathbf{A}(t)$ has bounded solutions if all the eigenvalues of $\mathbf{A}_\infty$ have negative real parts. As seen in Example 8.2, this is not necessarily the case. However, before determining what condition on an almost-constant coefficient matrix do guarantee boundedness of solutions, a fundamental lemma is established which is useful in the development of several relative-stability theorems.

Fundamental Lemma. If $u(t) \geq 0$, $v(t) \geq 0$, c_1 is a positive constant and

$$u(t) \leq c_1 + \int_{t_0}^{t} u(\tau)v(\tau)\, d\tau \tag{8.46}$$

then

$$u(t) \leq c_1 \exp\left[\int_{t_0}^{t} v(\tau)\, d\tau\right] \tag{8.47}$$

Proof. Dividing both sides of inequality 8.46 by the right-hand side and multiplying by $v(t)$ result in

$$\frac{u(t)v(t)}{c_1 + \displaystyle\int_{t_0}^{t} u(\tau)v(\tau)\, d\tau} \leq v(t) \tag{8.48}$$

Integrating both sides of inequality 8.48 between t_0 and t gives

$$\ln\left[c_1 + \int_{t_0}^{t} u(\tau)v(\tau)\, d\tau\right] - \ln c_1 \leq \int_{t_0}^{t} v(\tau)\, d\tau \tag{8.49}$$

Using inequality 8.46 again results in

$$\ln u(t) - \ln c_1 \leq \int_{t_0}^{t} v(\tau)\, d\tau \tag{8.50}$$

Exponentiating results in inequality 8.47. Q.E.D.

In the sequel this important lemma is referred to as the Fundamental Lemma without further explanation.

An important result on the boundedness of responses of systems with almost-constant coefficient matrices is the following.

Theorem 8.5. If all the solutions of

$$\dot{\mathbf{x}}(t) = \mathbf{A}\mathbf{x}(t) \tag{8.51}$$

where $\mathbf{A}$ is a constant matrix, are bounded on $[0, \infty)$, then the same is true of all the solutions of

$$\dot{\mathbf{z}}(t) = [\mathbf{A} + \Delta(t)]\mathbf{z}(t) \tag{8.52}$$

provided that

$$\int_{t_0}^{\infty} || \Delta(\tau) || \, d\tau < \infty \tag{8.53}$$

where the norm is defined as in Eq. 8.2A and 8.2B[3].

Proof. Equation 8.52 can be written as

$$\dot{\mathbf{z}}(t) = \mathbf{A}\mathbf{z}(t) + \Delta(t)\mathbf{z}(t) \tag{8.54}$$

Identifying $\Delta(t)\mathbf{z}(t)$ as a forcing function leads to the integral equation

$$\mathbf{z}(t) = \exp [\mathbf{A}(t - t_0)]\mathbf{x}(t_0) + \int_{t_0}^{t} \exp [\mathbf{A}(t - \tau)]\Delta(\tau)\mathbf{z}(\tau) \, d\tau \tag{8.55}$$

Therefore

$$\begin{aligned} || \mathbf{z}(t) || \leq & \; || \exp [\mathbf{A}(t - t_0)]\mathbf{x}(t_0) || \\ & + \int_{t_0}^{t} || \exp [\mathbf{A}(t - \tau)] || \; || \Delta(\tau) || \; || \mathbf{z}(\tau) || \, d\tau \end{aligned} \tag{8.56}$$

Since all solutions of Eq. 8.51 are bounded, there exists a constant c_1 such that

$$|| \exp [\mathbf{A}(t - t_0)]\mathbf{x}(t_0) || < c_1 \tag{8.57a}$$

$$|| \exp [\mathbf{A}(t - t_0)] || < c_1 \tag{8.57b}$$

Use of inequalities 8.57 in inequality 8.56 results in

$$|| \mathbf{z}(t) || < c_1 + c_1 \int_{t_0}^{t} || \Delta(\tau) || \; || \mathbf{z}(\tau) || \, d\tau \tag{8.58}$$

Application of the Fundamental Lemma to inequality 8.58 gives

$$|| \mathbf{z}(t) || < c_1 \exp \int_{t_0}^{t} || \Delta(\tau) || \, d\tau \tag{8.59}$$

[3]A better, more general theorem than Theorem 8.5 is given here without proof (see Bellman [2] pp. 37ff for proof):

Theorem 8.5A. If for the homogeneous system

$$\dot{\mathbf{x}}(t) = [\mathbf{A} + \Delta_1(t) + \Delta_2(t)] \, \mathbf{x}(t) \tag{8.53A}$$

(i) $\mathbf{A}$ is constant matrix whose eigenvalues all have nonpositive real parts with those having zero real parts being simple,

(ii) $\Delta_1(t) \to \mathbf{0}$ as $t \to \infty$ and

$$\int_{t_0}^{\infty} || \dot{\Delta}_1(t) || \, dt < \infty \tag{8.53B}$$

(iii) $$\int_{t_0}^{\infty} || \Delta_2(t) || \, dt < \infty \tag{8.54C}$$

(iv) The eigenvalues of $[\mathbf{A} + \Delta_1(t)]$ have nonpositive real parts for $t \geq t_0$, then under these conditions, all solutions of the homogeneous system 8.53A are bounded.

Therefore if $\int_{t_0}^{t} \| \Delta(\tau) \| \, d\tau$ is bounded so is $\| \mathbf{z}(t) \|$, and thus all the solutions of Eq. 8.52 are bounded. Q.E.D.

Example 8.3. Consider a second-order system characterized by the equation

$$\ddot{y}(t) + [a + \delta(t)]y(t) = 0$$

or in state-variable form

$$\begin{bmatrix} \dot{x}_1(t) \\ \dot{x}_2(t) \end{bmatrix} = \begin{bmatrix} 0 & 1 \\ -a - \delta(t) & 0 \end{bmatrix} \begin{bmatrix} x_1(t) \\ x_2(t) \end{bmatrix}$$

As is well known, all solutions of this system are bounded when $a > 0$ and $\delta(t) = 0$. However, in accordance with Theorem 8.5, if $a > 0$ and $\delta(t)$ is any function such that

$$\int_{t_0}^{\infty} | \delta(t) | \, dt < \infty$$

Then the solutions are also bounded. For example $\delta(t) = \dfrac{1}{1 + t^2}$ or $\delta(t) = e^{-t} \sin t$ also provide bounded solutions.

A statement on the symptotic relative stability of systems with almost-constant coefficient matrices is provided by the following theorem:

Theorem 8.6. If all the solutions of Eq. 8.51 approach zero as $t \to \infty$, then the same holds for all solutions of Eq. 8.52 provided that $\| \mathbf{\Delta}(t) \| \leq c_1$ for $t \geq t_0$ and c_1 is a constant which depends on $\mathbf{A}$.

Proof. Since $\mathbf{A}$ is a stability matrix (i.e., $\exp [\mathbf{A}t] \to 0$ as $t \to \infty$ implying that all eigenvalues of $\mathbf{A}$ have negative real parts), it follows that there exists a positive constant a such that

$$\| \exp [\mathbf{A}(t - t_0)]\mathbf{x}(t_0) \| \leq c_2 \, e^{-a(t-t_0)} \tag{8.60}$$

As in the proof of Theorem 8.5, integral Eq. 8.55 is valid. Use of inequality 8.60 in enequality 8.55 results in

$$\| \mathbf{z}(t) \| \leq c_2 \, e^{-a(t-t_0)} + c_2 \int_{t_0}^{t} e^{-a(t-\tau)} \, \| \mathbf{\Delta}(\tau) \| \, \| \mathbf{z}(\tau) \| \, d\tau \tag{8.61}$$

Multiplying by e^{at} and noting that by hypothesis $\| \mathbf{\Delta}(t) \| \leq c_1$ gives

$$\| \mathbf{z}(t) \| \, e^{at} \leq c_2 e^{at_0} + c_1 c_2 \int_{t_0}^{t} e^{a\tau} \| \mathbf{z}(\tau) \| \, d\tau \tag{8.62}$$

Applying the Fundamental Lemma results in

$$\| \mathbf{z}(t) \| e^{at} \leq c_2 e^{at_0} \exp \left[\int_{t_0}^{t} c_1 c_2 d\tau \right] \tag{8.63}$$

Thus integrating and rearranging gives

$$||\mathbf{z}(t)|| \leq c_2 e^{-(a-c_1c_2)(t-t_0)} \tag{8.64}$$

Therefore $||\mathbf{z}(t)|| \to 0$ if $c_1c_2 < a$. Since, as seen in Eq. 8.60, c_2 and a depend on $\mathbf{A}$, the necessary c_1 satisfying the inequality $c_1c_2 < a$ also depends on $\mathbf{A}$. Q.E.D.

Thus it is seen that the stability properties of systems with almost-constant coefficients can be determined in many cases by a comparison with systems with constant coefficients. Since the stability of constant-coefficient systems is easily determined by checking to see that all the real parts of the eigenvalues of the A matrix have negative real parts, these results have great practical value. Since Floquet theory provides some insight to the stability of periodic systems, results on the relative stability of *almost-periodic* systems would similarly prove useful.

8.3.2. Almost-Periodic Coefficient Matrices. The coefficient matrix $\mathbf{A}(t)$ is said to be *almost periodic* if

$$\lim_{t \to \infty} \mathbf{A}(t) = \mathbf{A}_T(t) \tag{8.65}$$

where $\mathbf{A}_T(t)$ is periodic with period T, i.e.,

$$\mathbf{A}_T(t + T) = \mathbf{A}_T(t) \tag{8.66}$$

Theorem 8.7. If all the solutions of

$$\dot{\mathbf{x}}(t) = \mathbf{A}_T(t)\mathbf{x}(t) \tag{8.67}$$

are bounded, then all the solutions of

$$\dot{\mathbf{z}}(t) = [\mathbf{A}_T(t) + \Delta(t)]\mathbf{z}(t) \tag{8.68}$$

are also bounded, provided that

(i) $\mathbf{A}_T(t)$ is periodic, i.e., $\mathbf{A}_T(t + T) = \mathbf{A}(t)$,

(ii) $$\int_{t_0}^{\infty} ||\Delta(t)||\, dt < \infty \tag{8.69}$$

In addition, if all the solutions of the periodic system 8.67 approach zero as $t \to \infty$ then the same holds for the almost-periodic system 8.68, under the same hypothesis.

Proof. The solution to Eq. 8.67 can be written, in accordance with Theorem 7.1, as

$$\begin{aligned} \mathbf{x}(t) &= \phi(t, t_0)\mathbf{x}(t_0) \\ &= \mathbf{R}(t) \exp [\mathbf{\Gamma}(t - t_0)]\mathbf{R}^{-1}(t_0)\mathbf{x}(t_0) \\ &= \mathbf{R}(t) \exp (\mathbf{\Gamma}(t)\mathbf{K}\mathbf{x}(t_0) \end{aligned} \tag{8.70}$$

By hypothesis $\mathbf{x}(t)$ is bounded. Therefore $||\mathbf{R}(t)||$ is bounded and $||\exp(\mathbf{\Gamma}t)||$ is bounded. If $\mathbf{x}(t) \to \mathbf{0}$ as $t \to \infty$ then $||\exp(\mathbf{\Gamma}t)|| \to \mathbf{0}$ as $t \to \infty$ and does so exponentially; i.e.,

$$||\exp(\mathbf{\Gamma}t)|| \leq c_1 e^{-at}, \quad a > 0 \tag{8.71}$$

Taking $[\Delta(t)\mathbf{z}(t)]$ as a forcing function, the solution to Eq. 8.68 can be written as

$$\mathbf{z}(t) = \phi(t, t_0)\mathbf{z}(t_0) + \int_{t_0}^{t} \phi(t, \tau)\Delta(\tau)\mathbf{z}(\tau)\, d\tau$$
$$= \mathbf{x}(t) + \int_{t_0}^{t} \mathbf{R}(t) \exp[\mathbf{\Gamma}(t - \tau)]\, R^{-1}(\tau)\Delta(\tau)\mathbf{z}(\tau)\, d\tau \qquad (8.72)$$

Therefore

$$\|\mathbf{z}(t)\| \leq \|\mathbf{x}(t)\| + \int_{t_0}^{t} \|\mathbf{R}(t) \exp[\mathbf{\Gamma}(t - \tau)]\mathbf{R}^{-1}(\tau)\|\, \|\Delta(\tau)\|\, \|\mathbf{z}(\tau)\|\, d\tau \qquad (8.73)$$

Since the solution to Eq. 8.67 is bounded, and since $\mathbf{R}(t)$ is continuous and periodic with finite period T, there exists a constant c_2 such that

$$\|\mathbf{x}(t)\| = \|\mathbf{R}(t) \exp[\mathbf{\Gamma}(t - t_0)]\mathbf{R}^{-1}(t_0)\mathbf{x}(t_0)\| < c_2 \qquad (8.74a)$$
$$\|\mathbf{R}(t) \exp[\mathbf{\Gamma}(t - \tau)]\mathbf{R}^{-1}(\tau)\| < c_2 \qquad (8.74b)$$

Use of inequalities 8.74 in inequality 8.73 results in

$$\|\mathbf{z}(t)\| \leq c_2 + c_2 \int_{t_0}^{t} \|\Delta(\tau)\|\, \|\mathbf{z}(\tau)\|\, d\tau \qquad (8.75)$$

Application of the Fundamental Lemma gives

$$\|\mathbf{z}(t)\| \leq c_2 \exp\left[\int_{t_0}^{t} \|\Delta(\tau)\|\, d\tau\right] \qquad (8.76)$$

Therefore the solution $\mathbf{z}(t)$ is bounded if Eq. 8.69 holds.

For the case that $\mathbf{x}(t) \to \mathbf{0}$ as $t \to \infty$, inequalities 8.74 can be rewritten *for large t* as

$$\|\mathbf{x}(t)\| = \|\mathbf{R}(t) \exp[\mathbf{\Gamma}(t - t_0)]\mathbf{R}^{-1}(t_0)\mathbf{x}(t_0)\| < c_1 e^{-at} \qquad (8.77a)$$
$$\|\mathbf{R}(t) \exp[(t - \tau)]R^{-1}(\tau)\| < c_1 e^{-at} \qquad (8.77b)$$

where $a > 0$. Therefore inequality 8.73 can now be replaced by

$$\|\mathbf{z}(t)\| < \left[c_1 + c_1 \int_{t_0}^{t} \|\Delta(\tau)\|\, \|\mathbf{z}(\tau)\|\, d\tau\right] e^{-at}, \quad a > 0, \quad t \to \infty \qquad (8.78)$$

Application of the Fundamental Lemma gives

$$\|\mathbf{z}(t)\| < c_1 \exp\left[\int_{t_0}^{t} \|\Delta(\tau)\|\, d\tau\right] e^{-at}, \quad a > 0, \quad t \to \infty \qquad (8.79)$$

Therefore if $\int_{t_0}^{\infty} \|\Delta(\tau)\|\, d\tau$ is bounded, then $\|\mathbf{z}(t)\| \to 0$ as $t \to \infty$. Q.E.D.

Example 8.4. Consider the almost-periodic system characterized by

$$\frac{d^2x(t)}{dt^2} + [F(t) + \delta(t)]x(t) = 0$$

where $F(t)$ is the periodic function described in Fig. 7.1 and

$$\delta(t) = e^{-t}(t + \sin t)$$

Writing the equations for this system in state-variable form gives

$$\dot{\mathbf{z}}(t) = [A_T(t) + \Delta(t)]\mathbf{z}(t)$$

where

$$\mathbf{A}_T(t) = \begin{bmatrix} 0 & 1 \\ -1 & -F(t) \end{bmatrix}$$

and

$$\Delta(t) = \begin{bmatrix} 0 & 0 \\ 0 & -e^{-t}(t + \sin t) \end{bmatrix}$$

Clearly

$$\int_{t_0}^{\infty} \|\Delta(t)\|\, dt = \int_{t_0}^{\infty} |e^{-t}(t + \sin t)|\, dt < \infty$$

As seen in Example 7.1 the periodic system $\dot{\mathbf{x}}(t) = \mathbf{A}_T(t)\mathbf{x}(t)$ is stable if $(h_1 + h_2) > 0$. Therefore, in accordance with Theorem 8.7, the almost-periodic system is also stable if $(h_1 + h_2) > 0$.

8.3.3. Equations with general variable coefficients. It is shown in Example 8.2 the boundness of solutions of

$$\dot{\mathbf{x}}(t) = \mathbf{A}(t)\mathbf{x}(t) \tag{8.80}$$

together with the condition that $\|\Delta(t)\| \to \mathbf{0}$ as $t \to \infty$ is not sufficient to ensure the boundness of all solutions of

$$\dot{\mathbf{z}}(t) = [\mathbf{A}(t) + \Delta(t)]\mathbf{z}(t) \tag{8.81}$$

However, based on the theorems established for almost-constant and almost-periodic systems, it might be very tempting to assume that such a conclusion on relative stability is valid provided that the condition

$$\|\Delta(t)\| \to \mathbf{0} \quad \text{as} \quad t \to \infty \tag{8.82}$$

is amended to

$$\int_{t_0}^{\infty} \|\Delta(t)\|\, dt < \infty \tag{8.83}$$

Unfortunately, this conclusion is erroneous, and is shown to be so by the following negative theorem proved by demonstrating a counterexample.

Theorem 8.8. There is an equation of the type 8.80 with the property that all solutions approach zero as $t \to \infty$, and a matrix $\Delta(t)$ for which inequality 8.83 is valid, such that all solutions of Eq. 8.81 are not bounded

Proof. The system

$$\begin{bmatrix} \dot{x}_1(t) \\ \dot{x}_2(t) \end{bmatrix} = \begin{bmatrix} -a & 0 \\ 0 & \sin \log t + \cos \log t - 2a \end{bmatrix} \begin{bmatrix} x_1(t) \\ x_2(t) \end{bmatrix}$$

has the general solution

$$\begin{bmatrix} x_1(t) \\ x_2(t) \end{bmatrix} = \begin{bmatrix} e^{-at} & 0 \\ 0 & \exp\,[t \sin \log t - 2at] \end{bmatrix} \begin{bmatrix} x_1(0) \\ x_2(0) \end{bmatrix}$$

Therefore the perturbed system

$$\begin{bmatrix} \dot{\mathbf{z}}_1(t) \\ \dot{\mathbf{z}}_2(t) \end{bmatrix} \left\{ \begin{bmatrix} -a & 0 \\ 0 & \sin \log t + \cos \log t - 2a \end{bmatrix} + \begin{bmatrix} 0 & 0 \\ e^{-at} & 0 \end{bmatrix} \right\} \begin{bmatrix} z_1(t) \\ z_2(t) \end{bmatrix}$$

has the general solution

$$\begin{bmatrix} z_1(t) \\ z_2(t) \end{bmatrix} = \begin{bmatrix} e^{-at} & 0 \\ e^{(t \sin \log t - 2at)} \int_0^t e^{-\tau \sin \log \tau}\, d\tau & e^{t \sin \log t - 2at} \end{bmatrix} \begin{bmatrix} z_1(0) \\ z_2(0) \end{bmatrix}$$

It is now necessary to examine this solution for boundedness. Special attention is focused on the portion of $z_2(t)$ excited by initial condition $z_1(0)$. In particular

$$z_2(t)\big|_{z_2(0)=0} \equiv z_{21}(t) = e^{(t \sin \log t - 2at)} \int_0^t e^{-\tau \sin \log \tau}\, d\tau \; z_1(0)$$

It can be noted that since $e^{-\tau \sin \log \tau}$ is always positive,

$$\int_0^t e^{-\tau \sin \log \tau}\, d\tau > \int_{te^{-\pi}}^{te^{-2\pi/3}} e^{-\tau \sin \log \tau}\, d\tau$$

Further that, if there is a constant V such that

$$V \leq e^{-\tau \sin \log \tau}$$

Then

$$\int_{te^{-\pi}}^{te^{-2\pi/3}} e^{-\tau \sin \log \tau}\, d\tau > V(te^{-2\pi/3} - te^{-\pi})$$

Thus

$$z_{21}(t) > e^{(t \sin \log t - 2at)} V(te^{-2\pi/3} - te^{-\pi}) z_1(0)$$

A value for V bounded by $e^{-\tau \sin \log \tau}$ on the interval $[te^{-\pi}, te^{-2\pi/3}]$ is now determined which reveals the nature of $z_{21}(t)$. Introduce the change of variable represented by

$$t \equiv e^{(2n+\frac{1}{2})\pi}$$

Therefore, the endpoints of the interval of interest are

(i) $\tau = te^{-\pi} = e^{(2n-\frac{1}{2})\pi}$ where

$$e^{-\tau \sin \log \tau} = e^{-\tau \sin [(2n-\frac{1}{2})\pi]} = e^{\tau}$$
$$= e^{te^{-\pi}}$$

(ii) $\tau = te^{-2\pi/3} = e^{(2n-\frac{1}{6})\pi}$ where

$$e^{-\tau \sin \log \tau} = e^{-\tau \sin [(2n-\frac{1}{6})\pi]} = e^{\tau/2}$$

$$= \exp\left[\frac{te^{-2\pi/3}}{2}\right]$$

As τ varies from $te^{-\pi}$ to $te^{-2\pi/3}$ on the interval of interest, $\sin \log \tau$ varies from -1 to $-\frac{1}{2}$ without changing sign. Therefore on this interval

$$\max [e^{-\tau \sin \log \tau}] = e^{te^{-\pi}}$$

$$\min [e^{-\tau \sin \log \tau}] = \exp\left[\frac{te^{-2\pi/3}}{2}\right] > \exp\left[\frac{te^{-\pi}}{2}\right]$$

Thus, select V bounded by $e^{-\tau \sin \log \tau}$ on $[te^{-\pi}, te^{-2\pi/3}]$ as

$$V \equiv e^{te^{-\pi/2}}$$

Therefore

$$z_{21}(t) > \exp\left[t \sin \log t - 2at + \frac{te^{-\pi}}{2}\right] t(e^{-2\pi/3} - e^{-\pi})$$

from which it follows that $z_{21}(t)$, and therefore $z_2(t)$, is not bounded whenever

$$a > \frac{1}{2} + \frac{e^{-\pi}}{4}$$

However, the solution of the unperturbated system is bounded whenever

$$a > \frac{1}{2}$$

Therefore, for any a such that

$$\frac{1}{2} < a < \frac{1}{2} + \frac{e^{-\pi}}{4}$$

the unperturbated system is bounded while the perturbated system is unbounded. Q.E.D.

Although Theorem 8.8 negates what might have been a useful result, a statement on the relative stability of systems with general variable coefficients can be made. However, first a preliminary result, fundamental to the proof, is established.

Lemma. The transition matrix $\phi(t, t_0)$ is not singular on the interval $[t_0, t_f]$. In particular,

$$\det \phi(t, t_0) = \exp\left\{\int_{t_0}^{t} \operatorname{tr}[A(\tau)]\, d\tau\right\} \tag{8.84}$$

where the *trace* of $\mathbf{A}(t)$ is defined by

$$\operatorname{tr}[\mathbf{A}(t)] = \sum_{i=1}^{n} a_{ii}(t) \tag{8.85}$$

Proof of Lemma. The proof depends on the following definitions and results:

$$\text{(i)} \quad \boldsymbol{\phi}(t, t_0) \equiv \begin{bmatrix} \boldsymbol{\phi}_1(t) \\ \boldsymbol{\phi}_2(t) \\ \vdots \\ \boldsymbol{\phi}_n(t) \end{bmatrix} \tag{8.86}$$

where $\boldsymbol{\phi}_i(t)$ is a row n-vector.

$$\text{(ii)} \quad \frac{d}{dt}[\det \boldsymbol{\phi}(t, 0)] = \sum_{i=1}^{n} \det \boldsymbol{\phi}_{(i)}(t, 0) \tag{8.87}$$

where

$$\text{(iii)} \quad \boldsymbol{\phi}_{(i)}(t, 0) \equiv \begin{bmatrix} \boldsymbol{\phi}_1(t) \\ \vdots \\ \dfrac{d\boldsymbol{\phi}_i(t)}{dt} \\ \vdots \\ \boldsymbol{\phi}_n(t) \end{bmatrix} \tag{8.88}$$

$$\text{(iv)} \quad \mathbf{A}(t) \equiv \begin{bmatrix} \mathbf{a}_1(t) \\ \mathbf{a}_2(t) \\ \vdots \\ \mathbf{a}_n(t) \end{bmatrix} \tag{8.89}$$

where $\mathbf{a}_i(t)$ is a row n-vector.

Therefore

$$\mathbf{a}_i(t)\boldsymbol{\phi}(t, t_0) = \frac{d\boldsymbol{\phi}_i(t)}{dt} \tag{8.90}$$

Substituting from Eq. 8.90 in Eq. 8.88 gives

$$\boldsymbol{\phi}_{(i)}(t, t_0) = \begin{bmatrix} \boldsymbol{\phi}_1(t) \\ \vdots \\ \mathbf{a}_i(t)\boldsymbol{\phi}(t, t_0) \\ \vdots \\ \boldsymbol{\phi}_n(t) \end{bmatrix} \tag{8.91}$$

However, inspection of the product $\mathbf{a}_i(t)\boldsymbol{\phi}(t, t_0)$ reveals that

$$\mathbf{a}_i(t)\boldsymbol{\phi}(t, t_0) = \sum_{j=1}^{n} a_{ij}(t)\boldsymbol{\phi}_j(t) \tag{8.92}$$

Therefore

$$\boldsymbol{\phi}_{(i)}(t, t_0) = \begin{bmatrix} \boldsymbol{\phi}_1(t) \\ \vdots \\ \sum_{j=1}^{n} \mathbf{a}_{ij}(t)\boldsymbol{\phi}_j(t) \\ \vdots \\ \boldsymbol{\phi}_n(t) \end{bmatrix} \tag{8.93}$$

and

$$\det \boldsymbol{\phi}_{(i)}(t, t_0) = \sum_{j=1}^{n} a_{ij}(t) \det \begin{bmatrix} \boldsymbol{\phi}_1(t) \\ \vdots \\ \boldsymbol{\phi}_{i-1}(t) \\ \boldsymbol{\phi}_j(t) \\ \boldsymbol{\phi}_{i+1}(t) \\ \vdots \\ \boldsymbol{\phi}_n(t) \end{bmatrix} \tag{8.94}$$

or

$$\det \boldsymbol{\phi}_{(i)}(t, t_0) = a_{ii}(t) \det \boldsymbol{\phi}(t, t_0) \tag{8.95}$$

Summing gives

$$\sum_{i=1}^{n} \det \boldsymbol{\phi}_{(i)}(t, t_0) = \sum_{i=1}^{n} a_{ii}(t) \det \boldsymbol{\phi}(t, t_0) \tag{8.96}$$

or, which in accordance with Eq. 8.87, can be written as

$$\frac{d}{dt}[det\, \boldsymbol{\phi}(t, t_0)] = \mathrm{tr}[\mathbf{A}(t)] \det \boldsymbol{\phi}(t, t_0) \tag{8.97}$$

This first-order equation has the solution

$$\begin{aligned} \det \boldsymbol{\phi}(t, t_0) &= \exp\left\{\int_{t_0}^{t} \mathrm{tr}[\mathbf{A}(\tau)]\, d\tau\right\} \det \boldsymbol{\phi}(t_0, t_0) \\ &= \exp\left\{\int_{t_0}^{t} \mathrm{tr}[\mathbf{A}(\tau)]\, d\tau\right\} \end{aligned} \tag{8.98}$$

Q.E.D.

Theorem 8.9. If all the solutions of Eq. 8.80 are bounded, then all the solutions of Eq. 8.81 are also bounded, provided that[4]

(i) $$\int_{t_0}^{\infty} \|\boldsymbol{\Delta}(t)\|\, dt < \infty \tag{8.99}$$

(ii) $$\lim_{t\to\infty} \int_{t_0}^{t} \mathrm{tr}[\mathbf{A}(t)]\, dt > -\infty \tag{8.100}$$

Proof. The solution of Eq. 8.81 can be written as

$$\mathbf{z}(t) = \mathbf{x}(t) + \int_{t_0}^{t} \boldsymbol{\phi}(t, t_0)\boldsymbol{\phi}(t_0, \tau)\boldsymbol{\Delta}(\tau)\mathbf{z}(\tau)\, d\tau \tag{8.102}$$

Therefore

$$\|\mathbf{z}(t)\| \le \|\mathbf{x}(t)\| + \int_{t_0}^{t} \|\boldsymbol{\phi}(t, t_0)\|\, \|\boldsymbol{\phi}(t_0, \tau)\|\, \|\boldsymbol{\Delta}(\tau)\|\, \|\mathbf{z}(\tau)\|\, d\tau \tag{8.103}$$

[4]If all the solution of Eq. 8.80 are *exponentially* bouuded then all the solution of Eq. 8.81 are also bounded, provided that inequality 8.99 is statisfied [5].

Since $\|\phi(t, t_0)\|$ is bounded (see Eq. 8.30), and since by the lemma

$$\det \phi(t, t_0) = \exp\left\{\int_0^t \operatorname{tr}[\mathbf{A}(\tau)]\, d\tau\right\} \tag{8.104}$$

it follows that $\|\phi(t_0, \tau)\| = \|\phi^{-1}(\tau, t_0)\|$ is bounded if Eq. 8.100 is satisfied. Therefore there exists a constant c_1 such that

$$\|\mathbf{z}(t)\| \leq c_1 + c_1 \int_{t_0}^{t} \|\boldsymbol{\Delta}(\tau)\|\, \|\mathbf{x}(\tau)\|\, d\tau \tag{8.105}$$

Application of the Fundamental Lemma results in

$$\|\mathbf{z}(t)\| \leq c_1 \exp \int_{t_0}^{t} \|\boldsymbol{\Delta}(\tau)\|\, d\tau \tag{8.106}$$

from which it is seen that $\mathbf{z}(t)$ is bounded if $\int_{t_0}^{t} \|\boldsymbol{\Delta}(\tau)\|\, d\tau$ is bounded Q.E.D.

8.4. SHORT-TIME STABILITY

In a practical sense, the concept of *short-time stability* is perhaps more useful than the classical concept of stability (and resonance) thus far discussed. Short-time stability deals with determining whether a system response lies within *specified* bounds over *specified* intervals of time when the initial conditions (or inputs) are within specified bounds. Clearly, such a concept can be of greater practical use since in many systems, the approximate operational time interval of interest is often known in advance and, due to physical limitations, inputs and outputs greater than some finite value are essentially "unbounded."

8.4.1. Short-time Stability (Undriven Systems) [12].

Analogous to Definition 8.1 of classical stability is the definition of short-time stability:

Definition 8.4. The linear system characterized by the homogeneous equation

$$\dot{\mathbf{x}}(t) = \mathbf{A}(t)\mathbf{x}(t) \tag{8.107}$$

is said to be short-time stable with respect to ε, C, T if

$$\mathbf{x}'(t_0)\mathbf{x}(t_0) \leq \varepsilon \tag{8.108}$$

implies that[5]

$$\mathbf{x}'(t)\mathbf{x}(t) \leq C \tag{8.109}$$

on the interval $[t_0, t_0 + T]$.

Figure 8.1a illustrates the response of a system that is classically

[5]It should be noted that this definition of short-time stability, unlike the Definition 8.1 of classical stability, considers the response of the system to be the state $\mathbf{x}(t)$ and not the output $\mathbf{y}(t) = \mathbf{C}(t)\mathbf{x}(t)$. Clearly, a bound on the state

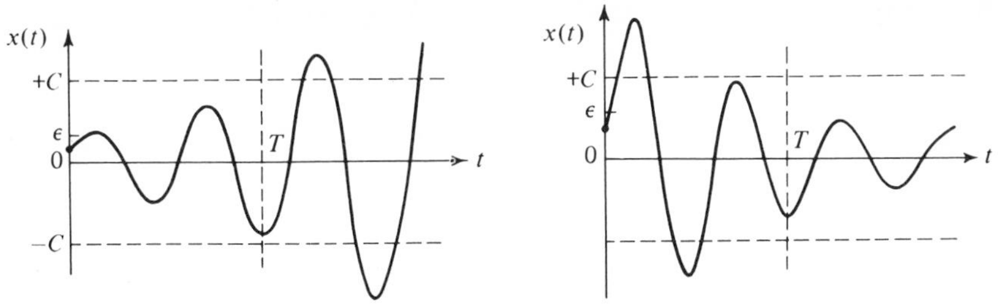

(a) Short-time stable, classically unstable (b) Short-time unstable, classically stable

Fig. 8.1. Short-time and classical stability.

unstable but short-time stable. Figure 8.1b illustrates the response of a system that is classically stable but short-time unstable. Note that a system can be short-time stable for one choice of ε, C, T and unstable for another choice.

Three theorems are established which give sufficient conditions for short-time stability.

Theorem 8.10a. A sufficient condition for a solution of the system 8.107 to be short-time stable with respect to ε, C, T is that

$$\int_{t_0}^{t} \lambda_M(\tau)d\tau \leq \frac{1}{2} \ln \frac{C}{\varepsilon}, \quad t_0 \leq t \leq t_0 + T \tag{8.110}$$

where $\lambda_M(t)$ is the maximum eigenvalue of the symmetric matrix $\mathbf{U}(t)$ defined by

$$\mathbf{U}(t) \equiv \frac{1}{2} [\mathbf{A}(t) + \mathbf{A}'(t)] \tag{8.111}$$

at each instant t.

Proof. The proof of the theorem hinges on a well-known inequality [33] from the theory of quadratic forms.

$$\mathbf{x}'(t)\mathbf{U}(t)\mathbf{x}(t) \leq \lambda_M(t)\mathbf{x}'(t)\mathbf{x}(t) \tag{8.112}$$

$\mathbf{x}(t)$ as given in Eq. 8.109 can be used to provide a bound on the output $\mathbf{y}(t)$. For example, since $\mathbf{y}(t) = \mathbf{C}(t)\mathbf{x}(t)$,

$$\mathbf{y}'(t)\mathbf{y}(t) = \mathbf{x}'(t)\mathbf{C}'(t)\mathbf{C}(t)\mathbf{x}(t)$$

where $\mathbf{C}'(t)\mathbf{C}(t)$ is a symmetric matrix. Use of a well-known inequality from the theory of quadratic forms (see Eq. 8.112) gives

$$\mathbf{y}'(t)\mathbf{y}(t) \leq \lambda_{\max}(t)\mathbf{x}'(t)\mathbf{x}(t)$$

where $\lambda_{\max}(t)$ is the maximum eigenvalue of $\mathbf{C}'(t)\mathbf{C}(t)$ and thus, in accordance with inequality 8.109,

$$\mathbf{y}'(\mathrm{t})y(t) \leq \lambda_{\max}(t)\mathbf{C}$$

where $\mathbf{U}(t)$ is a symmetric matrix with all its eigenvalues, $\lambda_i(t)$, $i = 1, \cdots$ $\cdots, n$, real

Taking the derivative of the scalar $\mathbf{x}'(t)\mathbf{x}(t)$ results in

$$\frac{d}{dt}[\mathbf{x}'(t)\mathbf{x}(t)] = \dot{\mathbf{x}}'(t)\mathbf{x}(t) + \mathbf{x}'(t)\dot{\mathbf{x}}(t) \tag{8.113}$$

However, since $\dot{\mathbf{x}}(t) = \mathbf{A}(t)\mathbf{x}(t)$, Eq. 8.113 can be written as

$$\begin{aligned}\frac{d}{dt}[\mathbf{x}'(t)\mathbf{x}(t)] &= \mathbf{x}'(t)\mathbf{A}'(t)\mathbf{x}(t) + \mathbf{x}'(t)\mathbf{A}(t)\mathbf{x}(t)\\ &= \mathbf{x}'(t)[\mathbf{A}'(t) + \mathbf{A}(t)]\mathbf{x}(t)\\ &= 2\mathbf{x}'(t)\mathbf{U}(t)\mathbf{x}(t)\end{aligned} \tag{8.114}$$

Thus, use of inequality 8.112 gives

$$\frac{d}{dt}[\mathbf{x}'(t)\mathbf{x}(t)] \leq 2\lambda_M(t)\mathbf{x}'(t)\mathbf{x}(t) \tag{8.115}$$

Dividing both sides of inequality 8.115 by the positive scalar function $\mathbf{x}'(t)\mathbf{x}(t)$, integrating between t_0 and t, and rearranging results in

$$\mathbf{x}'(t)\mathbf{x}(t) \leq \mathbf{x}'(t_0)\mathbf{x}(t_0) \exp\left[2\int_{t_0}^{t} \lambda_M(\tau)\, d\tau\right] \tag{8.116}$$

Since Definition 8.3 specifies $\mathbf{x}'(t_0)\mathbf{x}(t_0) \leq \varepsilon$,

$$\mathbf{x}'(t)\mathbf{x}(t) \leq \varepsilon \exp\left[2\int_{t_0}^{t} \lambda_M(\tau)\, d\tau\right] \tag{8.117}$$

Therefore, if

$$\exp\left[2\int_{t_0}^{t} \lambda_M(\tau)\, d\tau\right] \leq \frac{C}{\varepsilon} \tag{8.118}$$

Then $\mathbf{x}'(t)\mathbf{x}(t) \leq C$.

Noting that inequality 8.118 is derived from inequality 8.110 by exponentiation proves the theorem. Q.E.D.

Closely related to Theorem 8.10a, which gives a sufficient condition for short-time *stability*, is the following theorem giving a sufficient condition for short-time *instability*:

Theorem 8.10b. A sufficient condition for a solution of the system 8.107 to be short-time *unstable* is that

$$\int_{t_0}^{t} \lambda_m(\tau) d\tau > \frac{1}{2}\ln\frac{C}{\varepsilon}, \quad t_0 \leq t \leq t_0 + T \tag{8.119}$$

where $\lambda_m(\tau)$ is the minimum eigenvalue of the symmetric matrix $\mathbf{U}(t)$ defined by Eq. 8.111.

The proof of Theorem 8.10b is similar in nature to the proof of Theorem 8.10b (inequality 8.112 is reversed if the minimum eigenvalue $\lambda_m(t)$ is used in place of the maximum eigenvalue $\lambda_M(t)$ [33]) and is not given here.

Application of Theorems 8.10 to establish short-time stability or instability of a system requires that the time-varying eigenvalues of the matrix $\mathbf{U}(t)$ be determined. Thus, for systems of order higher than 2, one might expect to encounter some computational difficulty in applying this theorem. In addition, if the largest eigenvalue $\lambda_M(t)$ is negative, then short-time stability can be established only when C is less than ε, i.e., the bound on the output is smaller than the bound on the input.

A theorem somewhat easier to apply, although generally providing coarser bounds is:

Theorem 8.11. A sufficient condition for a solution of the system 8.107 to be short-time stable with respect to ε, C, T is that all the principle minors of the matrix

$$\mathbf{M}(t) = \left[-\mathbf{U}(t) + \frac{1}{2T}\ln\frac{C}{\varepsilon}\mathbf{I}_n\right] \tag{8.120}$$

be nonnegative on the interval $[t_0, t_0 + T]$.

Proof. Equation 8.114 developed in the proof of Theorem 8.10 is repeated here for convenience:

$$\frac{d}{dt}[\mathbf{x}'(t)\mathbf{x}(t)] = 2\mathbf{x}'(t)\mathbf{U}(t)\mathbf{x}(t) \tag{8.121}$$

Assume a positive constant μ exists such that

$$\mathbf{x}'(t)\mathbf{U}(t)\mathbf{x}(t) \leq \mu\mathbf{x}'(t)\mathbf{x}(t) \tag{8.122}$$

Therefore

$$\frac{d}{dt}\left[\mathbf{x}'(t)\mathbf{x}(t)\right] \leq 2\,\mu\mathbf{x}'(t)\mathbf{x}(t) \tag{8.123}$$

Dividing by $\mathbf{x}'(t)\mathbf{x}(t)$, integrating between t_0 and t, and rearranging gives

$$\mathbf{x}'(t)\mathbf{x}(t) \leq \mathbf{x}'(t_0)\mathbf{x}(t_0)\exp\,[2\mu(t - t_0)] \tag{8.124}$$

Since it is specified that $\mathbf{x}'(t_0)\mathbf{x}(t_0) \leq \varepsilon$,

$$\mathbf{x}'(t)\mathbf{x}(t) \leq \varepsilon\exp\,[2\mu(t - t_0)] \tag{8.125}$$

Therefore, if

$$[\exp\,[2\mu(t - t_0)]] = \frac{C}{\varepsilon} \tag{8.126}$$

then

$$\mathbf{x}'(t)\mathbf{x}(t) \leq C \tag{8.127}$$

Therefore, a proper choice of μ guaranteeing inequality 8.127 is

$$\mu = \frac{1}{2(t - t_0)}\ln\frac{C}{\varepsilon},\quad t \in [t_0, t_0 + T] \tag{8.128}$$

However, since μ is to be a constant, one can conservatively set $(t - t_0)$ of the denominator of Eq. 8.128 to T; i.e.,

$$\mu = \frac{1}{2T} \ln \frac{C}{\varepsilon} \tag{8.129}$$

Substituting from Eq. 8.129 in Eq. 8.122 gives

$$\mathbf{x}'(t)\mathbf{U}(t)\mathbf{x}(t) \leq \frac{1}{2T} \ln \frac{C}{\varepsilon} \mathbf{x}'(t)\mathbf{x}(t) \tag{8.130}$$

which can be written as

$$\mathbf{x}'(t) \left[-\mathbf{U}(t) + \frac{1}{2T} \ln \frac{C}{\varepsilon} \mathbf{I}_n \right] \mathbf{x}(t) \geq 0 \tag{8.131}$$

or

$$\mathbf{x}'(t)\mathbf{M}(t)\mathbf{x}(t) \geq 0 \tag{8.132}$$

Since, inequality 8.132 is true if $\mathbf{M}(t)$ is positive semidefinite the theorem is proved. Q.E.D.

The next theorem is often too restrictive on the elements of $\mathbf{A}(t)$; however, it can be applied by testing $\mathbf{A}(t)$ directly and is computationally the simplest.

Theorem 8.12. A sufficient condition for a solution of the system 8.107 to be short-time stable with respect to ε, C, T is that

$$\int_{t_0}^{t_0+T} ||\mathbf{U}(\tau)|| \, d\tau \leq \frac{1}{2} \ln \frac{C}{\varepsilon} \tag{8.133}$$

Proof. The proof follows from the fact that the norm of a matrix always exceeds the maximum eigenvalue. Thus

$$\lambda_M(t) \leq ||\mathbf{U}(t)|| \tag{8.134}$$

Use of inequality 8.134 in inequality 8.117 gives

$$\mathbf{x}'(t)\mathbf{x}(t) \leq \varepsilon \exp \left[2 \int_{t_0}^{t} ||\mathbf{U}(\tau)|| \, d\tau \right] \tag{8.135}$$

Since $t \in [t_0, t_0 + T]$,

$$\int_{t_0}^{t} ||\mathbf{U}(\tau)|| \, d\tau \leq \int_{t_0}^{t_0+T} ||\mathbf{U}(\tau)|| \, d\tau \tag{8.136}$$

and

$$\mathbf{x}'(t)\mathbf{x}(t) \leq \varepsilon \exp \left[2 \int_{t_0}^{t_0+T} ||\mathbf{U}(\tau)|| \, d\tau \right] \tag{8.137}$$

Therefore, if

$$\exp \left[2 \int_{t_0}^{t_0+T} ||\mathbf{U}(\tau)|| \, d\tau \right] \leq \frac{C}{\varepsilon} \tag{8.138}$$

then

$$\mathbf{x}'(t)\mathbf{x}(t) \leq C \tag{8.139}$$

and since inequalities 8.138 and 8.133 are identical, the theorem is proved. Q.E.D.

Some reffection on inequality 8.134 which is fundamentaly to the proof of Theorem 8.12, reveals that it is an extremely coarse inequality in that $||\mathbf{U}(t)||$ is often many times larger than $\lambda_M(t)$. Thus one can similarly expect that the theorem itself may often provide no information about the short-time stability of the system. Some numerical examples will illustrate the application of the three short-time stability theorems given and provide some insight to their relative merits.

Example 8.5. The short-time stability of the linear time-invariant circuit shown in Fig. 8.2 is investigated. The state-variable equation for this system is

$$\frac{d}{dt}\begin{bmatrix} i_1 \\ i_2 \end{bmatrix} = \begin{bmatrix} 2 & -1 \\ -1 & 2 \end{bmatrix}\begin{bmatrix} i_1 \\ i_2 \end{bmatrix}, \qquad \begin{bmatrix} i_1(0) \\ i_2(0) \end{bmatrix} = \begin{bmatrix} i_{10} \\ i_{20} \end{bmatrix}$$

Therefore

$$\mathbf{U} = \frac{1}{2}(\mathbf{A} + \mathbf{A}') = \mathbf{A} = \begin{bmatrix} 2 & -1 \\ -1 & 2 \end{bmatrix}$$

The eigenvalues of $\mathbf{U}$ are

$$\lambda_M = 3, \qquad \lambda_m = 1$$

Consider the case that

$$\ln \frac{C}{\varepsilon} = 2$$

Thus application of Theorem 8.10a shows that the system is short-time *stable* if

$$\int_0^T 3d\tau \leq 1$$

or

$$T \leq \frac{1}{3}$$

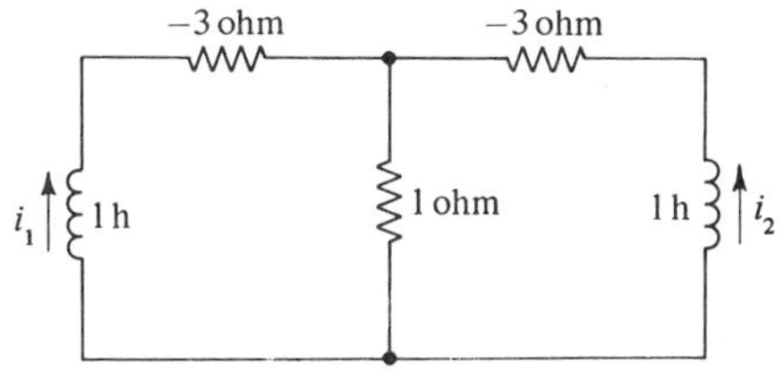

Fig. 8.2. Circuit for Example 8.4.

Application of Theorem 8.10b shows that the system is short-time *unstable* if

$$\int_0^T d\tau > 1$$

or

$$T > 1$$

Therefore, for ε and C such that $\ln(C/\varepsilon) = 2$, this system goes from short-time stability to short-time instability somewhere on the interval $(\frac{1}{3}, 1)$.

Example 8.6. The Mathieu equation

$$\ddot{x}(t) + (1 - \alpha \cos 2t)x(t) = 0$$

is programmed on an analog computer. The operation time is 2π seconds. For purposes of obtaining a good phase-plane plot, the ratio C/ε is chosen such that $\ln(C/\varepsilon) = 2$. It is required that the restrictions on the parameter α be determined such that the choice af C/ε can be realized.

The Mathieu equation is put into the state-variable form

$$\begin{bmatrix} \dot{x}_1(t) \\ \dot{x}_2(t) \end{bmatrix} = \begin{bmatrix} 0 & 1 \\ -(1 - \alpha \cos 2t) & 0 \end{bmatrix} \begin{bmatrix} x_1(t) \\ x_2(t) \end{bmatrix}$$

Thus

$$\mathbf{A}(t) = \begin{bmatrix} 0 & 1 \\ -(1 - \alpha \cos 2t) & 0 \end{bmatrix}$$

$$\mathbf{U}(t) = \begin{bmatrix} 0 & \frac{\alpha}{2} \cos 2t \\ \frac{\alpha}{2} \cos 2t & 0 \end{bmatrix}$$

and the eigenvalues of $\mathbf{U}(t)$ are

$$\lambda_{1,2} = \pm \frac{1}{2} \alpha \cos 2t$$

Therefore

$$\lambda_M = \frac{1}{2} |\alpha|\ |\cos 2t|, \qquad \lambda_m = -\frac{1}{2} |\alpha|\ |\cos 2t|$$

(i) Applying Theorem 8.10a results in

$$\int_0^t \frac{1}{2} |\alpha|\ |\cos 2\tau|\, d\tau \leq 1, \qquad 0 \leq t \leq 2\pi$$

Since

$$\int_0^t |\cos 2\tau|\, d\tau \leq \int_0^{2\pi} |\cos 2\tau|\, d\tau = 4$$

it follows that

$$\frac{1}{2}\,|\alpha|(4) \leq 1$$

is a conservative inequality for selecting α, and

$$|\alpha| \leq \frac{1}{2}$$

(ii) Applying Theorem (8.11) requires that matrix $\mathbf{M}(t)$ be determined

$$\mathbf{M}(t) = \begin{bmatrix} \dfrac{1}{2T}\ln\dfrac{C}{\varepsilon} & -\dfrac{1}{2}\,\alpha\cos 2t \\ -\dfrac{1}{2}\,\alpha\cos 2t & \dfrac{1}{2T}\ln\dfrac{C}{\varepsilon} \end{bmatrix}$$

and that $\mathbf{M}(t)$ be positive semidefinite, i.e., all principle minors must be nonnegative. Therefore

$$\frac{1}{2T}\ln\frac{C}{\varepsilon} \geq 0\,, \qquad 0 \leq t \leq T$$

But the above is always true since ε, C, and T are always positive. Also

$$\left(\frac{1}{2T}\ln\frac{C}{\varepsilon}\right)^2 - \left(\frac{1}{2}\alpha\cos 2T\right)^2 \geq 0\,, \qquad 0 \leq t \leq T$$

or

$$\left|\frac{1}{2T}\ln\frac{C}{\varepsilon}\right| \geq \frac{1}{2}|\alpha|\;|\cos 2t|$$

Therefore

$$|\alpha| \leq \frac{1}{T}\ln\frac{C}{\varepsilon}$$

is a conservative inequality for selecting α, and

$$|\alpha| \leq \frac{1}{\pi}$$

(iii) Applying Theorem 8.12 results in

$$\int_0^{2\pi} \|\mathbf{U}(\tau)\|\,d\tau = \int_0^{2\pi} |\alpha|\;|\cos 2\tau|\;d\tau \leq 1$$

Therefore

$$|\alpha|(4) \leq 1$$

or

$$|\alpha| \leq \frac{1}{4}$$

It is noted that although Theorem 8.10a is the most difficult to apply, it is, in this case, the least restrictive on the parameter α for a given ratio C/ε. On the other hand, Theorem 8.12, although the easiest to apply, is the most restrictive.

Example 8.7. It is desired to determine the restrictions that be placed on the time-varying gain $K(t)$ of the servomechanism shown in Fig. 8.3 to assure short-time stability with respect to ε, C, T. Letting $x_1 = y$ and $x_2 = \dot{y}$ the state-variable equation for this system is

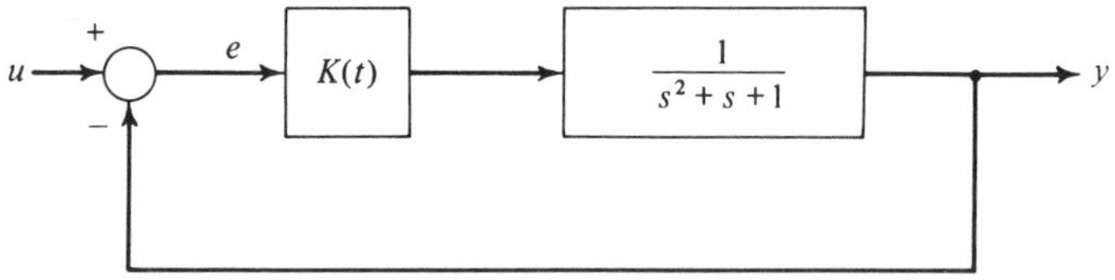

Fig. 8.3. Servomechanism of Example 8.6.

$$\begin{bmatrix} \dot{x}_1 \\ \dot{x}_2 \end{bmatrix} = \begin{bmatrix} 0 & 1 \\ -[1 + K(t)] & -1 \end{bmatrix} \begin{bmatrix} x_1 \\ x_2 \end{bmatrix}$$

Therefore

$$\mathbf{U}(t) = \begin{bmatrix} 0 & -\frac{1}{2}K(t) \\ -\frac{1}{2}K(t) & -1 \end{bmatrix}$$

The eigenvalues of $\mathbf{U}(t)$ are

$$\lambda_M(t) = -\frac{1}{2} + \frac{1}{2}\sqrt{1 + K^2(t)}$$

$$\lambda_m(t) = -\frac{1}{2} - \frac{1}{2}\sqrt{1 + K^2(t)}$$

Also

$$\mathbf{M}(t) = \begin{bmatrix} \frac{1}{2T}\ln\frac{C}{\varepsilon} & \frac{1}{2}K(t) \\ \frac{1}{2}K(t) & \frac{1}{2}\ln\frac{C}{\varepsilon} + 1 \end{bmatrix}$$

(i) Application of Theorem 8.10a results in

$$\int_0^t \left(-\frac{1}{2} + \frac{1}{2}\sqrt{1 + K^2(\tau)} \right) d\tau \leq \frac{1}{2}\ln\frac{C}{\varepsilon}, \quad 0 \leq t \leq T$$

Thus for a given $K(t)$, short-time stability with respect to ε, C, T may be determined.

(ii) Application of Theorem 8.11 results in

$$\left(\frac{1}{2T}\ln\frac{C}{\varepsilon}\right)^2 + \frac{1}{2T}\ln\frac{C}{\varepsilon} - \frac{1}{4}K^2(t) \geq 0$$

implying that

$$|K(t)| \leq 2\sqrt{\left(\frac{1}{2T}\ln\frac{C}{\varepsilon}\right)^2 + \frac{1}{2T}\ln\frac{C}{\varepsilon}}$$

Thus for design purposes, a bound on the gain $K(t)$ is provided.

Example 8.8. For design purposes it is necessary to determine restrictions on $p(t)$ and $q(t)$ in order that the system characterized by

$$\begin{bmatrix} \dot{x}_1 \\ \dot{x}_2 \\ \dot{x}_3 \end{bmatrix} = \begin{bmatrix} p(t) & 1 & 1 \\ -1 & 2 & q(t) \\ 1 & q(t) & 2 \end{bmatrix} \begin{bmatrix} x_1 \\ x_2 \\ x_3 \end{bmatrix}$$

be short-time stable given that $T = 1$ and $\frac{1}{2}\ln(C/\varepsilon) = 3$. For this system

$$\mathbf{U}(t) = \begin{bmatrix} p(t) & 0 & 1 \\ 0 & 2 & q(t) \\ 1 & q(t) & 2 \end{bmatrix}$$

and

$$\mathbf{M}(t) = \begin{bmatrix} 3 - p(t) & 0 & -1 \\ 0 & 1 & -q(t) \\ -1 & -q(t) & 1 \end{bmatrix}$$

(i) Application of Theorem 8.11 shows that the system is short-time stable if the following two inequalities are satisfied:

$$1 - q^2(t) \geq 0$$
$$[3 - p(t)][1 - q^2(t)] - 1 \geqslant 0$$

(ii) Application of Theorem 8.12 shows that the system is short-time stable if the following inequality is satisfied:

$$\int_0^1 [\,|p(\tau)| + 2|q(\tau)| + 6]\,d\tau \leq 3$$

8.4.2. Short-Time Nonresonance (Driven Systems). Analogous to Definition 8.2 of classical resonance, is the concept of short-time resonance. The definition of short-time *non*resonance (stable b.i.b.o. with respect to specified bounds) is given:

Definition 8.5. The linear system characterized by the nonhomogeneous equation

$$\dot{\mathbf{x}}(t) = \mathbf{A}(t)\mathbf{x}(t) + \mathbf{f}(t) \tag{8.140a}$$

$$\mathbf{y}(t) = \mathbf{C}(t)\mathbf{x}(t) \tag{8.140b}$$

with input $\mathbf{f}(t)$ such that $\mathbf{f}(t) = \mathbf{0}$ for $t < t_0$ is said to be short-time *nonresonant* with respect to ε, C, T if

$$\|\mathbf{f}(t)\| \leq \varepsilon \tag{8.141}$$

implies

$$\|y(t)\| \leq C \tag{8.142}$$

on the interval $[t_0, t_0 + T]$.

A theorem giving necessary and sufficient conditions for short-time nonresonance of scalar linear systems is the following:

Theorem 8.13. A necessary and sufficient condition for a *scalar* linear system characterized by Eqs. 8.140, with impulsive response $\Omega(t, \tau)$, to be short-time nonresonant with respect to ε, C, T is that

$$\int_{t_0}^{t_0+t} |\Omega(t, \tau)|\, d\tau \leq \frac{C}{\varepsilon}, \qquad t_0 \leq t \leq t_0 + T \tag{8.143}$$

Proof. (i) *Sufficiency* is established by noting that the zero-state output of the system is given by

$$y(t) = \int_{t_0}^{t_0+t} \Omega(t, \tau) f(\tau) d\tau, \qquad t_0 \leq t \leq t_0 + T \tag{8.144}$$

Therefore

$$|y(t)| \leq \int_{t_0}^{t_0+t} |\Omega(t, \tau)|\, |f(\tau)|\, d\tau, \qquad t_0 \leq t \leq t_0 + T \tag{8.145}$$

Since it is specified that $|f(t)| \leq \varepsilon$ on $[t_0, t_0 + T]$,

$$|y(t)| \leq \varepsilon \int_{t_0}^{t_0+t} |\Omega(t, \tau)|\, d\tau, \qquad t_0 \leq t \leq t_0 + T \tag{8.146}$$

Clearly, if

$$\int_{t_0}^{t_0+t} |\Omega(t, \tau)|\, d\tau \leq \frac{C}{\varepsilon} \quad \text{on} \quad [t_0, t_0 + T]$$

then $|y(t)| \leq C$.

(ii) *Necessity* is established by showing that whenever $\int_0^t |\Omega(t, \tau|\, d\tau > (C/\varepsilon)$ that an input $f(t)$, bounded by ε, can be found that causes $|y(t)| > C$ for at least one instant t on $[t_0, t_0 + T]$.

Assume that the condition specified by inequality 8.143 is not satisfied at $t = t_0 + t_1$, i.e.,

$$\int_{t_0}^{t_0+t_1} |\Omega(t_1, \tau)|\, d\tau > \frac{C}{\varepsilon}, \qquad t_0 \leq t_1 \leq t_0 + T \tag{8.147}$$

Choose an input $f(t)$ such that

$$f(\tau) = \begin{cases} +\ \varepsilon, & \Omega(t_1, \tau) > 0 \\ -\ \varepsilon, & \Omega(t_1, \tau) \leq 0 \end{cases} \tag{8.148}$$

Therefore

$$\begin{aligned} y(t_1) &= \int_{t_0}^{t_0+t_1} \Omega(t_1, \tau) f(\tau)\, d\tau \\ &= \varepsilon \int_{t_0}^{t_0+t_1} |\Omega(t_1, \tau)|\, d\tau \end{aligned} \tag{8.149}$$

Substituting from inequality 8.147 in Eq. 8.149 shows that $y(t) > C$. Thus inequality 8.143 is necessary. Q.E.D.

Corollary 8.13. A necessary and sufficient condition for the (multivariable) linear system characterized by Eqs. 8.140, with impulsive-response matrix $\Omega(t, \tau)$, to be short-time nonresonant with respect to ε, C, T is that

$$\int_{t_0}^{t_0+t} ||\Omega(t, \tau)||\, d\tau \leq \frac{C}{\varepsilon}, \qquad t_0 \leq t \leq t_0 + T \tag{8.150}$$

Example 8.9. The system characterized by

$$\dot{y}(t) = -\frac{1}{1+t} y(t) + f(t)$$

has the impulsive response

$$\Omega(t, \tau) = \frac{1+\tau}{1+t}$$

Since

$$\int_0^t |\Omega(t, \tau)|\, d\tau = \int_0^t \left| \frac{1+\tau}{1+t} \right| d\tau = \frac{1}{2}\left(t + 1 - \frac{1}{t+1}\right)$$

it follows from Theorem 8.2 that the system is classically resonant.

However, for short-time nonresonance it is required that inequality 8.143 be satisfied. Since

$$\int_0^t |\Omega(t, \tau)|\, d\tau = \frac{1}{2}\left(t + 1 - \frac{1}{t+1}\right)$$

is monotonically increasing,

$$\max_{[0, T]} \int_0^t |\Omega(t, \tau)|\, d\tau = \frac{1}{2}\left(T + 1 - \frac{1}{T+1}\right)$$

Thus the system is short-time nonresonant if

$$\frac{1}{2}\left[T + 1 - \frac{1}{T+1}\right] \leq \frac{C}{\varepsilon}$$

or, equivalently, if

$$T \leq \frac{C}{\varepsilon} - 1 \pm \sqrt{\left(\frac{C}{\varepsilon}\right)^2 + 1}$$

Example 8.10. Restrictions on $K(t)$ are to be determined which assure that the driven scalar system having the impulsive response $\Omega(t, \tau) = K(t)e^{t-\tau}$ is short-time nonresonant with respect to $\varepsilon = 1$, $C = 10$, $T = 1$. Application of Theorem 8.13 results in

$$|K(t)| \leq \frac{10}{e^t - 1}, \qquad 0 \leq t \leq 1$$

Example 8.11. The time-invariant system having the impulsive response $\Omega(t) = 2te^{-\frac{1}{2}t}$ is to be tested for short-time nonresonance with respect to $\varepsilon = 1$, $C = 5$, $T = \infty$. It is noted that although $T = \infty$ that short-time stability is invoked because the input and output bounds are specified. Since $\Omega(t, \tau) = \Omega(t - \tau)$ for time-invariant systems, letting $\xi = t - \tau$ gives the necessary and sufficient conditions for short-time nonresonance as

$$\int_0^t |\Omega(\xi)|\, d\xi \leq \frac{C}{\varepsilon}, \qquad 0 \leq t \leq T$$

Thus in this example, the system is short-time nonresonant if

$$\int_0^\infty |2\xi e^{-\frac{1}{2}\xi}|\, d\xi \leq 5$$

Since

$$\int_0^\infty |2\xi e^{-\frac{1}{2}\xi}|\, d\xi = 8$$

the inequality is not true and the system is short-time resonant.

8.4.3. Short-Time Boundedness (General). Application of Theorem 8.13 (or Corollary 8.13) to establish short-time nonresonance requires that the impulsive response of the system be known. In general, however, the impulsive response of the system is not known, nor can it easily be determined. Clearly, it is desirable to obtain a sufficient condition for short-time nonresonance directly in terms of the coefficient matrix $\mathbf{A}(t)$ and the forcing function $\mathbf{f}(t)$. In this section such sufficient conditions for short-time nonresonance are established. The results obtained here are sufficiently general so that they can be applied to both driven systems and undriven systems as well as to systems excited by both inputs and initial conditions. However, in order to accurately speak of the boundedness of the output to the combined effects of the inputs and the initial conditions, the concept of *short-time boundedness* (compared to short-time *stability* and short-time *nonresonance*) is introduced:

Definition 8.6. The system characterized by the differential equation

$$\dot{x}(t) = \mathbf{A}(t)\mathbf{x}(t) + \mathbf{f}(t),\ \mathbf{x}(t_0) = x_0 \tag{8.151}$$

is said to be short-time bounded with respect to ε_0, ε_f, C, T, $\|\cdot\|$ if

$$\|\mathbf{x}(t_0)\| \leq \varepsilon_0 \tag{8.152}$$

and

$$\|\mathbf{f}(t)\| \leq \varepsilon_f \tag{8.153}$$

implies that

$$\|\mathbf{x}(t)\| \leq C \tag{8.154}$$

on the interval $[t_0, t_0 + T]$.

The main results of this section take the form of two theorems which can be proved in a straightforward manner once the following two lemmas are established:

Lemma 1a. If

$$\mathbf{q}(t, \tau) = \phi(t, \tau)\mathbf{g}(\tau) \tag{8.155}$$

then

$$\|\mathbf{q}(t, \tau)\| \leq \|\mathbf{g}(\tau)\| \exp \int_\tau^t \lambda_M(\xi)\, d\xi \tag{8.156}$$

where $\lambda_M(t)$ is the maximum eigenvalue of $\mathbf{U}(t) = \frac{1}{2}[\mathbf{A}(t) + \mathbf{A}'(t)]$, and $\|\cdot\|$ denotes the Euclidian norm.

Proof. Taking the derivative of Eq. 8.155 with respect to t and noting that $\dfrac{\partial\phi(t, \tau)}{\partial t} = \mathbf{A}(t)\phi(t, \tau)$ it follows that

$$\frac{d\mathbf{q}(t, \tau)}{\partial t} = \mathbf{A}(t)\mathbf{q}(t, \tau) \tag{8.157}$$

Thus

$$\begin{aligned}\frac{\partial}{\partial t}[\mathbf{q}'(t, \tau)\mathbf{q}(t, \tau)] &= \mathbf{q}'(t, \tau)[\mathbf{A}'(t) + \mathbf{A}(t)]\mathbf{q}(t, \tau)\\ &= 2\mathbf{q}'(t, \tau)\mathbf{U}(t)\mathbf{q}(t, \tau)\end{aligned} \tag{8.158}$$

Use of inequality 8.112 results in

$$\frac{\partial}{\partial t}[\mathbf{q}'(t,\tau)\mathbf{q}(t,\tau)] \le 2\lambda_M(t)\mathbf{q}'(t,\tau)\mathbf{q}(t,\tau) \tag{8.159}$$

Integrating between the limits τ and t, noting that

$$\mathbf{q}'(\tau,\tau)\mathbf{q}(\tau,\tau) = \mathbf{g}'(\tau)\mathbf{g}(\tau) \tag{8.160}$$

and exponentiating gives

$$\mathbf{q}'(t,\tau)\mathbf{q}(t,\tau) \le \mathbf{g}'(\tau)\mathbf{g}(\tau)\exp\int_\tau^t 2\lambda_M(\xi)\,d\xi \tag{8.161}$$

In accordance with the definition of the Euclidian norm,

$$\|\mathbf{q}'(t,\tau)\| \equiv [\mathbf{q}'(t,\tau)\mathbf{q}(t,\tau)]^{1/2} \tag{8.162}$$

Use of Eq. 8.162 in Eq. 8.161 proves the lemma. Q.E.D.

Lemma 1b. If

$$\mathbf{q}(t,\tau) = \phi(t,\tau)\mathbf{g}(\tau) \tag{8.163}$$

then

$$\|\mathbf{q}(t,\tau)\| \le \|\mathbf{g}(\tau)\|\exp\int_\tau^t \|\mathbf{A}(\xi)\|\,d\xi \tag{8.164}$$

where $\|\cdot\|$ is any proper norm.

Proof. The proof follows the proof of Lemma 1a with the inequality

$$\frac{\partial\|\mathbf{q}(t,\tau)\|}{\partial t} \le \left\|\frac{\partial\mathbf{q}(t,\tau)}{\partial t}\right\| \tag{8.165}$$

which follows from

$$\frac{\partial\|\phi(t,\tau)\|}{\partial t} \le \left\|\frac{\partial\phi(t,\tau)}{\partial t}\right\| \tag{8.166}$$

Q.E.D.

Lemma 2. If

$$\mathbf{q}(t,\tau) = \phi(t,\tau)\mathbf{g}(\tau) \tag{8.167}$$

and

$$P(t) = \max_i \sum_{j=1}^{n}[\delta_{ij}u_{ij}(t) + (1-\delta_{ij})|u_{ij}(t)|] \tag{8.168}$$

where $P(t)$ is integrable, $u_{ij}(t)$, $i, j = 1, \cdots, n$ are the elements of $\mathbf{U}(t)$, and δ_{ij} is the Kronecker delta, then

$$\|\mathbf{q}(t,\tau)\| \le \mathbf{g}(\tau)\exp\int_\tau^t P(\xi)\,d\xi \tag{8.169}$$

Proof. The proof begins with Eq. 8.158:

$$\frac{\partial}{\partial t}[\mathbf{q}'(t, \tau)\mathbf{q}(t, \tau)] = 2\mathbf{q}'(t, \tau)\mathbf{U}(t)\mathbf{q}(t, \tau) \tag{8.170}$$

By rewriting and using obvious inequalities it follows that

$$\begin{aligned}
\frac{\partial}{\partial t}[\mathbf{q}'(t, \tau)\mathbf{q}(t, \tau)] &= 2\sum_{i=1}^{n} u_{ii}(t)q_i^2(t, \tau) \\
&\quad + 2\sum_{i=1}^{n}\sum_{\substack{j=1 \\ j\neq i}}^{n} u_{ij}(t)q_i(t, \tau)q_j(t, \tau) \\
&\leq 2\sum_{i=1}^{n} q_i^2(t, \tau)\sum_{j=1}^{n}\delta_{ij}u_{ij}(t) \\
&\quad + 2\sum_{i=1}^{n}\sum_{j=1}^{n}(1 - \delta_{ij})\,|u_{ij}(t)|\,q_i(t, \tau)q_j(t, \tau)\operatorname{sgn} u_{ij}(t) \\
&\leq 2\sum_{i=1}^{n} q_i^2(t, \tau)\sum_{j=1}^{n}\delta_{ij}u_{ij}(t) \\
&\quad + \sum_{i=1}^{n}\sum_{j=1}^{n}(1 - \delta_{ij})\,|u_{ij}(t)|\,[q_i^2(t, \tau) + q_j^2(t, \tau)] \\
&= 2\sum_{i=1}^{n} q_i^2(t, \tau)\sum_{j=1}^{n}\delta_{ij}u_{ij}(t, \tau) \\
&\quad + \sum_{i=1}^{n} q_i^2(t, \tau)\sum_{j=1}^{n}(1 - \delta_{ij})\,|u_{ij}(t)| \\
&\quad + \sum_{j=1}^{n} q_j^2(t, \tau)\sum_{i=1}^{n}(1 - \delta_{ij})\,|u_{ij}(t)| \\
&= 2\sum_{i=1}^{n} q_i^2(t, \tau)\sum_{j=1}^{n}\delta_{ij}u_{ij}(t) \\
&\quad + 2\sum_{i=1}^{n} q_i^2(t, \tau)\sum_{j=1}^{n}(1 - \delta_{ij})\,|u_{ij}(t)|
\end{aligned}$$

Since $u_{ij}(t) = u_{ij}(t)$,

$$\begin{aligned}
&= 2\sum_{i=1}^{n} q_i^2(t, \tau)\sum_{j=1}^{n}[\delta_{ij}u_{ij}(t) + (1 - \delta_{ij})\,|u_{ij}(t)|\,] \\
&\leq 2\max_i \sum_{j=1}^{n}[\delta_{ij}u_{ij}(t) + (1 - \delta_{ij})\,|u_{ij}(t)|\,]\sum_{i=1}^{n} q_i^2(t, \tau)
\end{aligned} \tag{8.171}$$

Using the definition of $P(t)$ as given in Eq. 8.168 results in

$$\frac{\partial}{\partial t}[\mathbf{q}'(t, \tau)\mathbf{q}(t,\tau)] \leq 2P(t)\mathbf{q}'(t, \tau)\mathbf{q}(t, \tau) \tag{8.172}$$

The remainder of the proof of Lemma 2 proceeds as in Lemma 1. Q.E.D.
The two theorems giving sufficient conditions for short-time boundedness are now given.

Theorem 8.14a. A sufficient condition for the linear system characterized by Eq. 8.151 to be short-time bounded with respect to ε_0, $\varepsilon_f(t)$, $c(t)$, T is:

$$\varepsilon_0 \exp \int_{t_0}^{t} \lambda_M(\xi)\, d\xi + \int_{t_0}^{t} \varepsilon_f(\tau) \exp \int_{\tau}^{t} \lambda_M(\xi)\, d\xi d\tau \leq c(t) \tag{8.173}$$

on the interval $[t_0, t_0 + T]$, where $\lambda_M(t)$ is the maximum eigenvalue of $\mathbf{U}(t) = \frac{1}{2}[\mathbf{A}(t) + \mathbf{A}'(t)]$.

Proof. The solution of Eq. 8.151 is

$$\mathbf{x}(t) = \phi(t, t_0)\mathbf{x}(t_0) + \int_{t_0}^{t} \phi(t, \tau)\mathbf{f}(\tau)\, d\tau \tag{8.174}$$

Defining

$$\mathbf{q}_x(t, t_0) = \phi(t, t_0)\mathbf{x}(t_0) \tag{8.175}$$

$$\mathbf{q}_f(t, \tau) = \phi(t, \tau)\mathbf{f}(\tau) \tag{8.176}$$

gives

$$\mathbf{x}(t) = \mathbf{q}_x(t, t_0) + \int_{t_0}^{t} \mathbf{q}_f(t, \tau)\, d\tau \tag{8.177}$$

Thus

$$\| \mathbf{x}(t) \| \leq \| \mathbf{q}_x(t, t_0) \| + \int_{t_0}^{t} \| \mathbf{q}_f(t, \tau) \|\, d\tau \tag{8.178}$$

Application of Lemma 1 results in

$$\| \mathbf{x}(t) \| \leq \| \mathbf{x}(t_0) \| \exp \int_{t_0}^{t} \lambda_M(\xi)\, d\xi + \int_{t_0}^{t} \| \mathbf{f}(\tau) \| \exp \int_{\tau}^{t} \lambda_M(\xi)\, d\xi d\tau \tag{8.179}$$

Since

$$\| \mathbf{x}(t_0) \| \leq \varepsilon_0 \tag{8.180}$$

and

$$\| \mathbf{f}(t) \| \leq \varepsilon_f(t) \tag{8.181}$$

it follows that

$$\|\mathbf{x}(t)\| \leq \varepsilon_0 \exp \int_{t_0}^{t} \lambda_M(\xi)\, d\xi + \int_{t_0}^{t} \varepsilon_f(\tau) \exp \int_{\tau}^{t} \lambda_M(\xi)\, d\xi d\tau \tag{8.182}$$

If the right-hand side of inequality 8.182 is less than $c(t)$, then $\|\mathbf{x}(t)\| \leq c(t)$ and the system is short-time bounded. Thus a sufficient condition for short-time boundedness is that Eq. 8.173 be satisfied on the interval $[t_0, t_0 + T]$. Q.E.D.

Theorem 8.14b. A sufficient condition for the linear system characterized by Eq. 8.151 to be short-time bounded with respect to ε_0, $\varepsilon_f(t)$, $c(t)$, T is:

$$\varepsilon_0 \exp \int_{t_0}^{t} \|\mathbf{A}(\xi)\|\, d\xi + \int_{t_0}^{t} \varepsilon_f(\tau) \exp \int_{\tau}^{t} \|\mathbf{A}(\xi)\|\, d\xi d\tau \leq c(t) \tag{8.183}$$

on the interval $[t_0, t_0 + T]$, where $\|\cdot\|$ is any proper norm.

Proof. The proof follows the proof of Theorem 8.14a using Lemma 1b instead of Lemma 1a. Q.E.D.

Since all kernels of the integral inequality 8.183 are positive, the upper limit of any, or all, integrations can be changed from t to $t_0 + T$ without changing the inequality:

Corollary 8.14b. A sufficient condition for the linear system characterized by Eq. 8.151 to be short-time bounded with respect to ε_0, $\varepsilon_f(t)$, $c(t)$, T is:

$$\varepsilon_0 \exp \int_{t_0}^{t_0+T} \|\mathbf{A}(\xi)\|\, d\xi + \int_{t_0}^{t_0+T} \|\varepsilon_f(\tau) \exp \int_{\tau}^{t_0+T} \|\mathbf{A}(\xi)\|\, d\xi d\tau \leq c(t) \tag{8.184}$$

Theorem 8.15. A sufficient condition for the linear system characterized by Eq. 8.151 to be short-time bounded with respect to ε_0, $\varepsilon_f(t)$, $c(t)$, T is:

$$\varepsilon_0 \exp \int_{\tau}^{t} P(\xi) d\xi + \int_{t_0}^{t} \varepsilon_f(\tau) \exp \int_{\tau}^{t} P(\xi)\, d\xi d\tau \leq c(t) \tag{8.185}$$

on $[t_0, t_0 + T]$ where $P(t)$ is as defined in Eq. 8.168.

Proof. The proof of Theorem 8.15 follows the proof of Theorem 8.14 very closely, with the exception that Lemma 2 is used in place of Lemma 1. Q.E.D.

Example 8.12. Consider the second-order system characterized by the differential equation

$$\begin{bmatrix} \dot{x}_1 \\ \dot{x}_2 \end{bmatrix} = \begin{bmatrix} -1 & 0 \\ 0 & 2 \end{bmatrix} \begin{bmatrix} x_1 \\ x_2 \end{bmatrix} + \begin{bmatrix} f_1 \\ f_2 \end{bmatrix}, \quad \mathbf{x}(0) = \begin{bmatrix} 3 \\ 4 \end{bmatrix}$$

It is desired to find the interval T such that $\| \mathbf{x}(t) \| = [\mathbf{x}'(t)\mathbf{x}(t)]^{1/2} \leq C = 10$ when $\mathbf{f}_1$ and $\mathbf{f}_2$ are specified. Since this system is linear time-invariant, the problem can be solved exactly:

(i) if $f_1 = f_2 = 0$, then the system is short-time bounded for $T \leq 0.45$

(ii) if $f_1 = 0$, $f_2 = 4$, then the system is short-time bounded for $T \leq 0.32$

A solution is now found using Theorem 8.14. It is seen that $\lambda_M(t) = 2$ and from the specified initial conditions it is seen that

$$\| \mathbf{x}(0) \| = 5$$

Applying Theorem 8.14 with $\varepsilon_0 = 5$, $f_1 = f_2 = 0$, $(\varepsilon_f(t) = 0)$ and $C = 10$ results in (The kernel of the integral is positive. Therefore the upper limit can be taked as T.)

$$5 \exp \int_0^T 2 d\eta \leq 10$$

or

$$T \leq 0.347$$

For the case that $t_0 = 5$, $f_1 = 0$, $f_2 = 4$ $(\varepsilon_f(t) = 4)$, and $C = 10$,

$$5 \exp \int_0^T 2 d\eta + \int_0^T 4 \left[\exp \int_\tau^T 2 d\eta \right] d\tau \leq 10$$

or

$$T \leq 0.27$$

Thus it is seen that in both cases a valid solution is found.

Example 8.13. Consider the system

$$\begin{bmatrix} \dot{x}_1 \\ \dot{x}_2 \end{bmatrix} = \begin{bmatrix} -m/(T-t) & p - qt \\ -p + qt & -m/(T-t) \end{bmatrix} \begin{bmatrix} x_1 \\ x_2 \end{bmatrix} + \begin{bmatrix} \cos t \\ \sin t \end{bmatrix}$$

where m, p, and q are positive constants. It is desired to determine whether or not the initial conditions bounded in accordance with

$$(\mathbf{x}_0'\mathbf{x}_0)^{1/2} \leq \varepsilon_0$$

results in outputs bounded in accordance with

$$[\mathbf{x}'(t)\mathbf{x}(t)]^{1/2} \leq C$$

Applying Theorem 8.15 it is noted that since $-m/(T-t) < 0$ on $[0, T]$,

$$P(t) = 0$$

Also, since

$$\| f(t) \| = [\cos^2 t + \sin^2 t]^{1/2} = 1$$

one can take $\varepsilon_f(t) = 1$. Therefore (the kernels of integrals are positive and all upper limits can be taken as T)

$$\varepsilon_0 + \int_0^T d\tau \leq \frac{C}{\sqrt{2}}$$

or

$$\varepsilon_0 \leq \frac{C}{\sqrt{2}} - T$$

Thus given any C and T, an ε_0 providing a bound on the initial conditions can be determined that guarantees short-time boundedness.

Example 8.14. Consider the system characterized by the linear time-varying differential equation

$$\ddot{y}(t) - \left(\frac{1}{2} \sin^2 t\right) \dot{y}(t) + (\sin^2 t) y(t) = u_c$$

where u_c is a positive constant. A bound on u_c must be determined which guarantees that the phase-plane plot does not exceed 10 units during the interval $[0, T]$ with the initial conditions constrained by the inequality

$$[y^2(0) + \dot{y}^2(0)] \leq 2$$

Letting $x_1(t) \equiv y(t)$, $x_2(t) \equiv \dot{x}_1(t)$, and $\mathbf{x}(t) = [x_1(t), x_2(t)]'$ puts the system in the state-variable form of Eq. 8.151 where

$$\mathbf{A}(t) = \begin{bmatrix} 0 & 1 \\ -\sin^2 t & \frac{1}{2} \sin^2 t \end{bmatrix}$$

$$f(t) = \begin{bmatrix} 0 \\ u_c \end{bmatrix}$$

and

$$\mathbf{U}(t) = \begin{bmatrix} 0 & \frac{1}{2} \cos^2 t \\ \frac{1}{2} \cos^2 t & \frac{1}{2} \sin^2 t \end{bmatrix}$$

Clearly one can set

$$\varepsilon_f(t) = \| \mathbf{f}(t) \| = u_c$$

The maximum eigenvalue of $\mathbf{U}(t)$ is

$$\lambda_M(t) = \frac{1}{4} [\sin^2 t + (\sin^4 t + 4 \cos^4 t)^{1/2}]$$

Also, $P(t)$, as defined in Eq. 8.168, is given by

$$P(t) = \max\left[\frac{1}{2}(\sin^2 t + \cos^2 t), \frac{1}{2}\cos^2 t\right]$$
$$= \frac{1}{2}$$

The following inequalities result from Theorems 8.14a and 8.15 respectively:

$$2\exp\int_0^t \lambda_M(\xi)\,d\xi + u_c\int_0^t \exp\int_\tau^t \lambda(\xi)\,d\xi d\tau \leq 10$$
$$2\exp\int_0^t \frac{1}{2}\,d\xi + u_c\int_0^t \exp\int_\tau^t \frac{1}{2} d\xi d\tau \leq 10$$

A coarse comparison of Theorems 8.14a and Theorem 8.15 can be obtained by comparing $\lambda_M(t)$ and $P(t)$. It can be shown that

$$0.40 \leq \lambda_M(t) \leq 0.50$$
$$\text{avg}\,[\lambda_M(t)] = 0.458$$

Therefore in this case $\lambda_M(t) \leq P(t)$. Thus it is seen that Theorem 8.14a which uses $\lambda_M(t)$ will provide a somewhat better indication of the ranges of ε_0, $\varepsilon_f(t)$, $c(t)$, and T in which the system is short-time stable. Figure 8.4 shows a plot against T of the bounds $\varepsilon_{f\lambda}(T)$ and $\varepsilon_{p\lambda}(T)$ on u_c provided by Theorems 8.14a and 8.15 respectively. Clearly, in this case, although $\varepsilon_{f\lambda}(T)$ provides a larger bound on u_c than $\varepsilon_{fp}(T)$, they are comparable and in most situations the simplicity of obtaining $\varepsilon_{fp}(T)$ would make application of Theorem 8.15 preferable.

8.5. FREQUENCY-DOMAIN STABILITY CRITERIA [24]

The Nyquist stability criteria, applicable to single-loop, linear time-

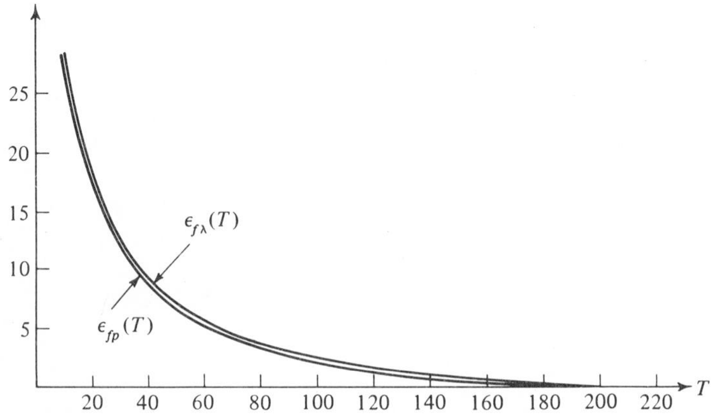

Fig. 8.4. Bounds on u_c, $\varepsilon_{f\lambda}(T)$ and $\varepsilon_{fp}(T)$, provided by Theorems 8.14a and 8.15, respectively.

invariant feedback systems, has been enjoying great popularity in analysis and design primarily because it is easy to use. Since it is an explicit frequency-domain technique, it provides more than just an indication of whether or not a system is stable: it also presents information in such a way as to aid the designer, working with components whose frequency characteristics he knows, in arriving at a suitable design. In addition, since well-known measurement procedures can be used to obtain the frequency characteristics of physical systems regardless of complexity, the criterion is useful even in cases in which accurate analysis of the system is not feasible because of either great complexity, unknown system equations, or unknown system parameters.

In this section, the Nyquist stability criterion is extended to feedback systems containing a single time-varying element[6]. The Nyquist criterion generalized to sush a time-varying system is referred to as the *circle criterion.*

The general *scalar* linear time-varying feedback system considered is shown in Fig. 8.5. The block marked $f(t)$ is a linear time-varying amplifier with gain $f(t)$ such that

$$\alpha \leq f(t) \leq \beta$$

The block marked $G(s)$ is a scalar linear *time-invariant* system with Laplace transfer function $G(s)$; the impulsive response of this system is denoted by $g(t)$. Thus for this system the output $y(t)$ can be expressed by

$$y(t) = \mathbf{C}\phi(t)\mathbf{x}_0 + \int_0^t g(t - \tau)\, d\tau \tag{8.187}$$

where $\phi(t - t_0)$ is the transition matrix of the time-invariant portion of the system, $\mathbf{C}$ is the matrix relating the output of the system to the states, i.e., $y(t) = \mathbf{C}\mathbf{x}(t)$, and $\mathbf{x}_0$ are the initial conditions on the states. For convenience define $w(t)$ by

$$w(t) \equiv -\mathbf{C}\phi(t)\mathbf{x}_0 \tag{8.188}$$

Thus $w(t)$ is the portion of the output due solely to the initial conditions of the time-invariant part of the system. Thus

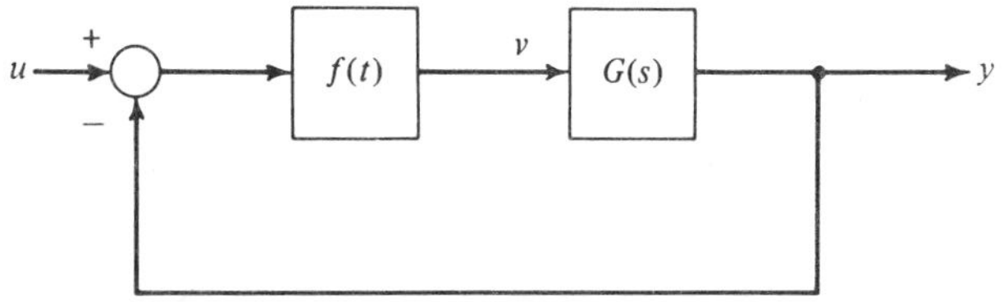

Fig. 8.5. Scalar linear time-varying feedback system.

[6]With only slight modifications the results obtained can be extended to feedback systems containing a single *nonlinear* time-varying element.

$$y(t) = \int_0^t g(t - \tau)v(\tau)\, d\tau - w(t) \tag{8.189}$$

Throughout the remainder of this section the following assumptions are made.

(i) The time-invariant portion of the system is stable:

$$\int_0^\infty |g(t)|\, dt < \infty \tag{8.190}$$

(ii) The initial conditions $\mathbf{x}_0$ are finite:

$$\int_0^\infty |w(t)^2|\, dt < \infty \tag{8.191}$$

(iii) All input functions $u(t)$ are such that

$$\int_0^\infty |u(t)|^2\, dt < \infty \tag{8.192}$$

(iv) The response $y(t)$ is well defined and satisfies the inequality

$$\int_0^t |y(\tau)|^2\, d\tau < \infty \tag{8.193}$$

for all *finite* $t > 0$.

Assumption (iv) is a trivial restriction in physical systems in view of assumptions (i), (ii), (iii). Essentially, it is assumed that the physical system does not contain components (the time-varying amplifier in particular) capable of delivering infinite energy during a finite time interval of time, i.e., the system contains no infinite power sources.

The sense in which the Nyquist criterion guarantees stability, although physically significant, is stronger than either the definition of stability or resonance given by Definitions 8.1 and 8.2.

Definition 8.7. The feedback system of Figure 8.5 is L_2-*stable* if and only if there exists a positive constant ρ with the property that the response $y(t)$ satisfies

$$\left[\int_0^\infty |y(t)|^2 dt\right]^{1/2} \leq \rho \left[\int_0^\infty |u(t) + w(t)|^2 dt\right]^{1/2} + \left[\int_0^\infty |w(t)|^2 dt\right]^{1/2} \tag{8.194}$$

for every initial condition function $w(t)$ satisfying inequality 8.191 and every input function $u(t)$ satisfying inequality 8.192.

In particular, if the system is L_2-stable, then the response is square-integrable whenever the input is square-integrable. It is shown [23] that the response $y(t)$ approaches zero as $t \to \infty$ for any square-integrable input $u(t)$ provided that the system is L_2-stable, $w(t) \to 0$ as $t \to \infty$ and inequality 8.190 is satisfied. In addition, it follows from the Schwarz inequality that the response $y(t)$ is uniformly bounded on $[0, \infty)$ for any square-integrable input $u(t)$, provided that the system is L_2-stable, $g(t)$ is uniformly bounded on $[0, \infty)$ and inequality 8.192 is satisfied.

The main result is now given.

Theorem 8.16. Let

$$G(i\omega) \equiv \int_0^\infty g(t)e^{-i\omega t}\, dt, \quad -\infty < \omega < \infty, \qquad i = \sqrt{-1} \tag{8.195}$$

The feedback system of Fig. 8.5 is L_2-stable if one of the following three conditions is satisfied:

1. $\alpha > 0$, and the locus of $G(i\omega)$ for $-\infty < \omega < \infty$ (a) lies outside of the circle C_1 of radius $\frac{1}{2}(\alpha^{-1} - \beta^{-1})$ centered on the real axis of the complex plane centered at $[-\frac{1}{2}(\alpha^{-1} + \beta^{-1}), 0]$, and (b) does not encircle C_1 (see Fig. 8.6).
2. $\alpha = 0$, and $R_e[G(i\omega)] > -\beta^{-1}$ for all real ω.
3. $\alpha < 0$, and the locus of $G(i\omega)$ for $-\infty < \omega < \infty$ is contained within the circle C_2 of radius $\frac{1}{2}(\alpha^{-1} - \beta^{-1})$ centered on the real axis of the complex plane at $[-\frac{1}{2}(\alpha^{-1} - \beta^{-1}), 0]$ (see Fig. 8.7).

Proof. The proof of Theorem 8.16 hinges on a result which is stated here as a lemma. The proof of the lemma, which can be found in Ref. 23, is intricate and lengthy and is omitted.

Lemma. If

$$z(t) = e(t) + \int_0^t g(t-\tau)f(\tau)e(\tau)\, d\tau \tag{8.196}$$

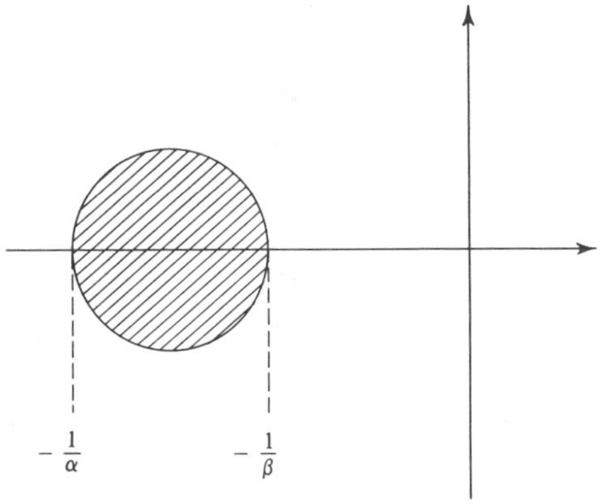

Fig. 8.6. Location of the "critical circle" C_1 in the complex plane ($\alpha > 0$). The feedback system is L_2-stable if the locus of $G(i\omega)$ for $-\infty < \omega < \infty$ lies outside C_1 and does not encircle C_1.

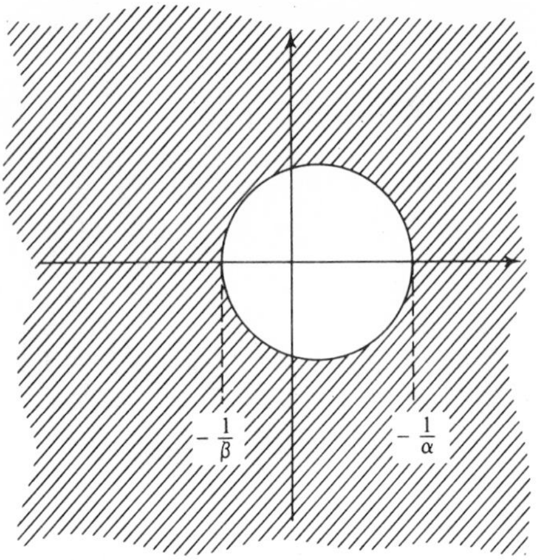

Fig. 8.7. Location of the "critical circle" C_2 in the complex plane ($\alpha < 0$). The feedback system is L_2-stable if the locus of $G(i\omega)$ for $-\infty < \omega < \infty$ is contained within C_2.

where

$$\text{(i)} \quad \int_0^\infty |g(t)|\,dt < \infty \tag{8.197}$$

$$\text{(ii)} \quad \int_0^t |e(t)|^2\,dt < \infty, \quad t \text{ finite} \tag{8.198}$$

$$\text{(iii)} \quad \int_0^\infty |z(t)|^2\,dt < \infty \tag{8.199}$$

$$\text{(iv)} \quad \alpha \leq f(t) \leq \beta \tag{8.200}$$

and

$$\text{I.} \quad 1 + \frac{1}{2}(\alpha + \beta)G(s) \neq 0 \quad \text{for} \quad \sigma \geq 0 \tag{8.201a}$$

$$\text{II.} \quad \frac{1}{2}(\beta - \alpha) \max_{-\infty<\omega<\infty} \left| G(i\omega)\left[1 + \frac{1}{2}(\alpha + \beta)G(i\omega)\right]^{-1} \right| < 1 \tag{8.201b}$$

where

$$G(s) = \int_0^\infty g(t)e^{-st}\,dt \tag{8.202}$$

and $\sigma \equiv Re[s]$, $\omega = Im[s]$, then

$$\int_0^\infty |e(t)|^2\,dt < \infty \tag{8.203}$$

The proof of Theorem 8.16 now follows. Since

$$v(t) = f(t)e(t) \tag{8.204}$$

and $\alpha \leq f(t) \leq \beta$, it follows that

$$\begin{aligned}\int_0^\infty v\,|(t)|^2\,dt &= \int_0^\infty |f(t)e(t)|^2\,dt \\ &\leq \int_0^\infty |f(t)|^2\,|e(t)|^2\,dt \\ &\leq \max(\beta^2, |\alpha|^2)\int_0^\infty |e(t)|^2\,dt\end{aligned} \tag{8.205}$$

A variable change easily establishes that

$$\int_0^t g(t-\tau)v(\tau)d\tau = \int_0^t g(\tau)v(t-\tau)\,d\tau \tag{8.206}$$

Therefore

$$\begin{aligned}\int_0^\infty \left|\int_0^t g(t-\tau)v(\tau)d\tau\right|^2 dt &= \int_0^\infty \left|\int_0^t g(\tau)v(t-\tau)d\tau\right|^2 dt \\ &\leq \int_0^\infty \left[\int_0^t |g(\tau)||v(t-\tau)|d\tau\right]\left[\int_0^t |g(\eta)||v(t-\eta)|\,d\eta\right] dt \\ &\leq \int_0^\infty |g(\tau)|\,d\tau \int_0^\infty |g(\eta)|\,d\eta \int_0^\infty |v(t-\tau)||v(t-\eta)|\,dt \\ &\leq \left[\int_0^\infty |g(t)|\,dt\right]^2 \left[\int_0^\infty |v(t)|^2\,dt\right]\end{aligned} \tag{8.207}$$

or

$$\int_0^\infty \left|\int_0^t g(t-\tau)v(\tau)\,d\tau\right|^2 dt \leq \left[\int_0^\infty |g(t)|\,dt\right]^2 \left[\int_0^\infty |v(t)|^2\,dt \right. \tag{8.208}$$

From Eq. 8.189 it follows that

$$\int_0^\infty |y(t)|^2\,dt = \int_0^\infty \left|\int_0^t g(t-\tau)v(\tau)\,d\tau - w(t)\right|^2 dt \tag{8.209}$$

Applying Minkowski's inequality gives

$$\left[\int_0^\infty |y(t)|^2\,dt\right]^{1/2} \leq \left[\int_0^\infty \left|\int_0^t g(t-\tau)v(\tau)\,d\tau\right|^2 dt\right]^{1/2} + \left[\int_0^\infty |w(t)|^2\,dt\right]^{1/2} \tag{8.210}$$

which, in conjunction with inequalities 8.205 and 8.208 gives

$$\begin{aligned}\left[\int_0^\infty |y(t)|^2\,dt\right]^{1/2} &\leq \max(\beta, |\alpha|)\left[\int_0^\infty |g(t)|\,dt\right]\left[\int_0^\infty |e(t)|^2\,dt\right]^{1/2} \\ &\quad + \left[\int_0^\infty |\omega(t)|^2\,dt\right]^{1/2}\end{aligned} \tag{8.211}$$

Use of inequalities 8.190 and 8.191 in 8.211 show that

$$\int_0^\infty |y(t)|^2\,dt < \infty \tag{8.212}$$

(i.e., the system is L_2-stable) if

$$\int_0^\infty |e(t)|^2 \, dt < \infty \tag{8.213}$$

Inequality 8.213 is easily established using the lemma just stated. From Fig, 8.5 it is readily shown that

$$u(t) + w(t) = e(t) + \int_0^t g(t - \tau)f(\tau)e(\tau) \, d\tau \tag{8.214}$$

Inequalities 8.191 and 8.192 verify that

$$\int_0^\infty |u(t) + w(t)|^2 \, dt < \infty \tag{8.215}$$

Again, assuming no infinite power sources,

$$\int_0^t |e(t)|^2 dt < \infty, \quad t \text{ finite} \tag{8.216}$$

Thus use of Eq. 8.214 and inequalities 8.186, 8.190, 8.215, and 8.216 in the lemma establishes inequality 8.213, and thus that system is L_2-stable.

Extending the ideas from complex variables used to establish the Nyquist criterion leads to:

(a) Condition I of the Lemma is satisfied if the polar plot of $G(i\omega)$ for $-\infty < \omega < \infty$ does not encircle or pass through the point $[-2(\alpha + \beta)^{-1}, 0]$.

(b) Condition II of the Lemma is satisfied if one of the following three conditions is satisfied:

  (i) $\alpha > 0$, and the locus of $G(i\omega)$ for $-\infty < \omega < \infty$ lies outside the circle C_1 of radius $\frac{1}{2}(\alpha^{-1} - \beta^{-1})$ centered in the complex plane at $[\frac{1}{2}(\alpha^{-1} - \beta^{-1}), 0]$.

  (ii) $\alpha = 0$, and $Re[G(i\omega)] > -\beta^{-1}$ for all real ω.

  (iii) $\alpha < 0$, and the locus of $G(i\omega)$ for $-\infty < \omega < \infty$ is contained within the circle C_2 of radius $\frac{1}{2}(\beta^{-1} - \alpha^{-1})$ centered in the complex plane at $[-\frac{1}{2}(\alpha^{-1} + \beta^{-1}), 0]$.

If $\alpha > 0$, the point $[-2(\alpha + \beta)^{-1}, 0]$ lies on the real-axis diameter of circle C_1, while $\alpha = 0$ or $\alpha < 0$, it is impossible for the polar plot of $G(i\omega)$ to encircle the point $[-2(\alpha + \beta)^{-1}, 0]$. Therefore, the conditions of the theorem guarantee that the feedback system is L_2-stable. Q.E.D.

Corollary 8.16. Let $q(s)$ and $p(s)$ be polynomials without common factors, and let

$$\begin{aligned} \dot{\mathbf{x}}(t) &= \mathbf{A}\mathbf{x}(t) + \mathbf{b}u(t) \\ y(t) &= \mathbf{c}'\mathbf{x}(t) \end{aligned} \tag{8.217}$$

be an irreducible representation of the Laplace transfer function

$$G(s) = \frac{q(s)}{p(s)}$$

and if $p(s)$ has no zeros in the half-plane $Re[s] > 0$, then

(i) all solutions of the zero-input system (see Fig. 8.8)

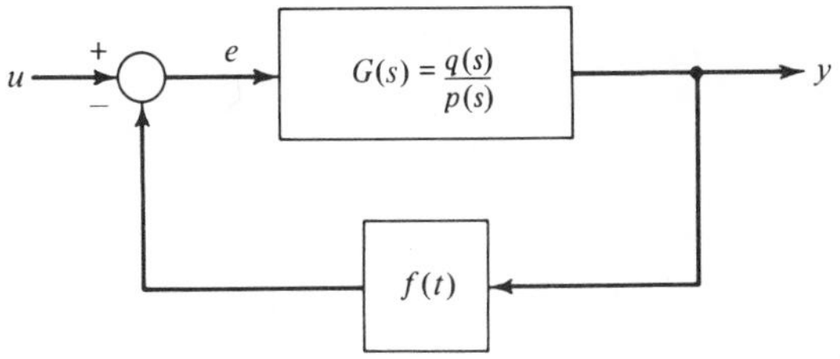

Fig. 8.8. Scalar linear time-varying system considered in Corollary 8.16.

$$\begin{aligned} \dot{\mathbf{x}}(t) &= \mathbf{A}\mathbf{x}(t) - \mathbf{b}f(t)y(t) \\ y(t) &= \mathbf{c}'\mathbf{x}(t) \end{aligned} \tag{8.219}$$

are bounded if

$$0 \leq \alpha \leq f(t) \leq \beta \tag{8.220}$$

and the Nyquist locus of $G(s)$ does not encircle or intersect the open disk which is centered on the negative real axis of the $G(s)$ plane and has as a diameter the segment of the negative real axis $(-\alpha^{-1}, -\beta^{-1})$.

(ii) all solutions of Eqs. 8.219 are bounded and go to zero at an exponential rate if there is some $\varepsilon > 0$ such that $0 \leq \alpha + \varepsilon \leq f(t) \leq \beta - \varepsilon$ and the Nyquist locus behaves as in (i). (Thus in this case, in accordance with Theorem 8.3, it is noted that all bounded inputs result in bounded outputs.)

The following eample illustrates the use of the circle criterion.

Example 8.15. It is desired to determine bounds on the function $f(t)$ which guarantee stability for the system characterized by the second-order differential equation

$$\frac{d^2x(t)}{dt^2} + 2\frac{dx}{dt} + f(t)x = 0$$

Note that the system shown in Fig. 8.9 is characterized by this equation.

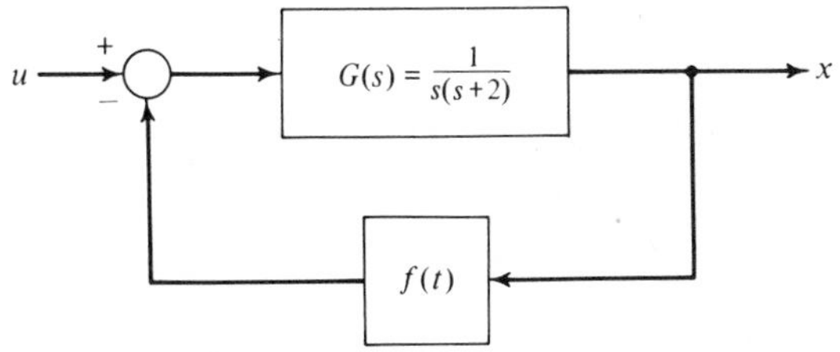

Fig. 8.9. Linear time-varying feedback system of Example 8.13.

Fig. 8.10 shows the Nyquist plot of $G(i\omega)$. It is seen from this plot that a reasonably large range of $f(t)$ (i.e., the greatest β assuring stability and providing a moderately low α) as determined from the circle criterion is

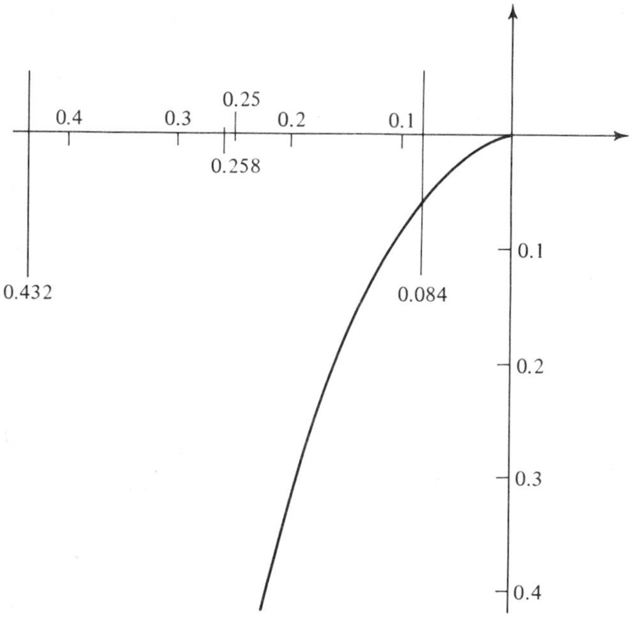

Fig. 8.10. Nyquist plot for $G(s) = \dfrac{1}{s(s+2)}$ to be used for "circle criterion" in Example 8.13.

$$2.31 < f(t) < 11.9$$

The largest range of $f(t)$ giving the smallest α is provided by

$$0 < f(t) < 4$$

It is interesting to note that the circle criterion does not predict stability for any positive finite ε such that

$$0 < f(t) < 4 + \varepsilon$$

However, it can be shown by other means that stability results even if

$$0 \leq f(t) \leq 11.6$$

thus pointing out that the circle criterion is generally quite conservative.

Since only the upper and lower bounds of the time-varying gain $f(t)$ are utilized in the circle criterion in determining whether or not the system is stable, it is not surprising that the sufficiency conditions can be so conservatve. One might expect that taking into account the variations of the gain $f(t)$, i.e., derivatives of $f(t)$, would provide a less conservative sufficient condition for stability. Such a consideration is introduced to advantage in Refs. [13], [20], [31], and [32]; the desirable frequency domain constructions are preserved in Refs. [20] and [32].

REFERENCES

[1] Bellman, R., "On an Application of a Banach-Steihauss Theorem to the Study of Boundedness of Solutions of Nonlinear Differential and Difference Equations," *Ann. Mathematics*, vol. 49, no. 3 (1948), pp. 515–522.

[2] Bellman, R., *Stability Theory of Differential Equations*, McGraw-Hill, New York, 1953, pp. 32–44.

[3] Bongiorno, J., "An Extension of the Nyquist-Barkhausen Stability Criterion to Linear Lumped-Parameter Systems with Time-Varying Elements," *IEEE Trans. on Automatic Control*, vol. AC-8 (1963), pp. 166–171.

[4] Bongiorno, J., "Real-Frequency Stability Criteria for Linear Time-varying Systems", *Proc. IEEE*, vol. 52, no. 7 (1964), pp. 832–841.

[5] Bridgland, T., "Stability of Linear Signal Transmission Systems," *SIAM Review*, vol. 5, no. 1 (1963), pp. 7–32.

[6] Brockett, R., and L. Forys, "On the Stability of Systems Containing a Time-Varying Gain", *Proceedings, Second Annual Allerton Conference on Circuit and System Theory*, September 1964, pp. 413–430.

[7] Brockett, R., and J. Willems, "Frequency Domain Stability Criteria—Parts I and II," *IEEE Trans. on Automatic Control*, vol. AC-10, nos. 3 and 4 (1965), pp. 255–261, 407–413.

[8] Brockett, R., "The Status of Stability Theory for Deterministic Systems," *IEEE Trans. on Automatic Control*, vol. AC-11, no. 3 (1966), pp. 596–606.

[9] Brockett, R., "Frequency-Domain Instability Criteria for Time-Varying and Nonlinear Systems," *Proc. IEEE*, vol. 55, no. 5 (1967), pp. 604–619.

[10] Cesari, L., *Asymptotic Behavior and Stability Problems in Ordinary Differential* Equations, Academic, New York, 1963.

[11] Desoer, C., "A Generalization of the Popov Criterion," *IEEE Transactions on Automatic Control*, vol. AC-10, no. 2 (1965), pp. 182–185.

[12] Dorato, P., "Short-Time Stability in Linear Time-Varying Systems," *IRE International Convention Record*, part 4 (1961), pp. 83–87.

[13] Gruber, M., and J. Willems, "On a Generalization of the Circle Criterion," *Proceedings, Fourth Annual Allerton Conference on Circuit and System Theory*, October 1966, pp. 827–835.

[14] LaSalle, J., and S. Lefschetz, *Stability by Liapunov's Direct Method*, Academic, New York, 1961.

[15] Kalman, R., "On the Stability of Time-Varying Linear Systems," *IRE Transactions on Circuit Theory*, vol. CT-9, 1962, pp. 420–422. Also, discussion by T. Bridgland and R. Kalman in vol. CT-10 (1963), pp. 539–542.

[16] Kaplan, W., *Operational Methods for Linear Systems*, Addison-Wesley, Reading, Mass., 1962, pp. 105–106, 503–511.

[17] Narendra, K., and R. Goldwyn, "A Geometrical Criterion for the Stability of Certain Nonlinear Nonautonomous Systems," *IEEE Trans. on* Circuit Theory, vol. CT-11 (1964), pp. 406–408.

[18] Popov, V., "Absolute Stability of Nonlinear Systems of Automatic Control," *Automation and Remote Control*, vol. 22, no. 8 (1961), pp. 857–875.

[19] Portasik, J. and H. D'Angelo, "Short-Time Stability of Forced Linear Time-Varying Systems," *Proceedings, Midwest Circuit Symposium*, May 1968.

[20] Rault, A., *Stability of Time-Varying Feedback Systems*, Thesis Department of Electrical Engineering, University of California, Berkeley, 1965.

[21] Rekasius, Z., "A Counter-Example for the Generalization of the Popov Criterion to Systems Containing a Single Time-Varying Element," *IEEE Trans. on Automatic Control*, vol. AC-11, no. 1 (1966), pp. 139–140.

[22] Rohrer, R., 'Stability of Linear Time-Varying Networks—Bounds on the Stored Energy," *Proceedings, National Electronics Conference*, 1963, pp. 107–114.

[23] Sandberg, I., "On the L_2-Boundedness of Solutions of Nonlinear Functional Equations," *Bell System Technical Journal*, vol. 43, (1964), pp. 1581–1599.

[24] Sandberg, I., "A Frequency- Domain Condition for the Stability of Feedback Systems Containing a Single Time-Varying Nonlinear Element," Bell System Technical Journal, vol. 43 (1964), pp. 1601–1608.

[25] Sandberg, I., "On the Stability of Solutions of Linear Differential Equations with Periodic Coefficients," *J. SIAM Applied Mathematics*, vol. 12, no. 2 (1964), pp. 487–496.

[26] Watson, J., and A. Stubbernd, "Stability of Systems Operating in a Finite Time Interval," *IEEE Trans. on Automatic Control*, vol. AC-12, 1967, p. 116.

[27] Weiss, L., and E. Infante, "Finite Time Stability Under Perturbating Forces and on Product Spaces," *IEEE Trans. on Automatic Control*, vol. AC-12, no. 1 (1967), pp. 54–59.

[28] Youla, D., "On the Stability of Linear Systems," *IEEE Trans. on Circuit Theory*, vol. CT-10 (1963), pp. 276–279.

[29] Zadeh, L., "On Stability of Linear Varying-Parameter Systems," *J. Appl. Physics*, vol. 22, no. 4 (1951), pp. 402–405.

[30] Zames, G., "On the Input-Output Stability of Time-Varying Nonlinear Feedback Systems—Part I: Conditions Derived Using Concepts of Loop Gain, Conicity, and Positivity; Part 2: Conditions Involving Circles in the Frequency Plane and Sector Nonlinearities," *IEEE Trans. on Automatic Control*, vol. AC-11, nos. 2 and 3 (1966), pp. 228–238, 465–476.

[31] Rekasius, Z., and J. Rowland, "A Stability Criterion for Feedback Systems Containing a Single Time-Varying Element," *IEEE Transactions on Automatic Control Theory*, vol. AC-10, no. 3 (1965), pp. 352–354.

[32] Bergen, A., "On the Stabilization of Time-Varying Feedback Systems," *Proceedings, First Asilomar Conference on Circuits and Systems*, Pacific Grove, California, November 1967.

[33] Gantmacher, F., *Matrix Theory*: *Volume I*, Chelsea, New York, 1959.

[34] Wazewski, T., "Sur la limitation der integrales des systèmes d'equations differentielles linéaires ordinaires," *Studia Math.*, vol. 10 (1958), p. 48–59.

PROBLEMS

8.1 Give examples, other than those given in the text, of linear systems that are:

(a) stable and nonresonant

(b) stable and resonant

8.2 Determine whether or not the systems characterized by the following equations are stable:

(a)

$$\begin{bmatrix} \dot{x}_1(t) \\ \dot{x}_2(t) \end{bmatrix} = \begin{bmatrix} -1 & e^{-t} \\ te^{-2t} & -2 \end{bmatrix} \begin{bmatrix} x_1(t) \\ x_2(t) \end{bmatrix}$$

(b)

$$\begin{bmatrix} \dot{x}_1(t) \\ \dot{x}_2(t) \end{bmatrix} = \begin{bmatrix} te^{-t}\sin t & 1 \\ -1 & 2 + \sin t \end{bmatrix} \begin{bmatrix} x_1(t) \\ x_2(t) \end{bmatrix}$$

8.3 Apply Theorems 8.10a, 8.11, 8.12, 8.14a, 8.15 to determine bounds on the initial condition $\mathbf{x}'(0)\mathbf{x}(0)$ so that $\mathbf{x}'(t)x(t) \leq 10$ on the time interval [0, 5] for the following systems. Compare results of each theorem.

(a)

$$\begin{bmatrix} \dot{x}_1(t) \\ \dot{x}_2(t) \end{bmatrix} = \begin{bmatrix} 2 & 5 \\ 1 & -2 \end{bmatrix} \begin{bmatrix} x_1(t) \\ x_2(t) \end{bmatrix}$$

(b)

$$\begin{bmatrix} \dot{x}_1(t) \\ \dot{x}_2(t) \end{bmatrix} = \begin{bmatrix} 1 & -3 \\ 2 & -4 \end{bmatrix} \begin{bmatrix} x_1(t) \\ x_2(t) \end{bmatrix}$$

(c)

$$\begin{bmatrix} \dot{x}_1(t) \\ \dot{x}_2(t) \end{bmatrix} = \begin{bmatrix} -1 & 2 \\ -2 & -2 \end{bmatrix} \begin{bmatrix} x_1(t) \\ x_2(t) \end{bmatrix}$$

(d)

$$\begin{bmatrix} \dot{x}_1(t) \\ \dot{x}_2(t) \end{bmatrix} = \begin{bmatrix} -1 & e^{-t} \\ 0 & -2 \end{bmatrix} \begin{bmatrix} x_1(t) \\ x_2(t) \end{bmatrix}$$

8.4 Apply Corollary 8.13 and Theorems 8.14a and 8.15 to determine bounds on $\|\mathbf{f}(t)\|$ to assure nonresonance, in the sense that $\|\mathbf{x}(t)\| \leq 10$, on the time interval [0, 5], for the following systems. Compare the three results in each case.

(a)

$$\begin{bmatrix} \dot{x}_1(t) \\ \dot{x}_2(t) \end{bmatrix} = \begin{bmatrix} 2 & 5 \\ 1 & -2 \end{bmatrix} \begin{bmatrix} x_1(t) \\ x_2(t) \end{bmatrix} + \begin{bmatrix} f_1(t) \\ f_2(t) \end{bmatrix}$$

(b)

$$\begin{bmatrix} \dot{x}_1(t) \\ \dot{x}_2(t) \end{bmatrix} = \begin{bmatrix} 1 & -3 \\ 2 & -4 \end{bmatrix} \begin{bmatrix} x_1(t) \\ x_2(t) \end{bmatrix} + \begin{bmatrix} f_1(t) \\ f_2(t) \end{bmatrix}$$

(c)

$$\begin{bmatrix} \dot{x}_1(t) \\ \dot{x}_2(t) \end{bmatrix} = \begin{bmatrix} -1 & 2 \\ -2 & -2 \end{bmatrix} \begin{bmatrix} x_1(t) \\ x_2(t) \end{bmatrix} + \begin{bmatrix} f_1(t) \\ f_2(t) \end{bmatrix}$$

8.5 Apply Theorems 8.14a and 8.15 to determine bounds on $\| f(t) \|$ to assure that $\| \mathbf{x}(t) \| \leq 10$ on the time interval [0, 5], for the following systems. Compare the results of the two theorems. In each case $x_1(0) = 3$, $x_2(0) = 4$.

(a)

$$\begin{bmatrix} \dot{x}_1(t) \\ \dot{x}_2(t) \end{bmatrix} = \begin{bmatrix} 2 & 5 \\ 1 & -2 \end{bmatrix} \begin{bmatrix} x_1(t) \\ x_2(t) \end{bmatrix} + \begin{bmatrix} f_1(t) \\ f_2(t) \end{bmatrix}$$

(b)

$$\begin{bmatrix} \dot{x}_1(t) \\ \dot{x}_2(t) \end{bmatrix} = \begin{bmatrix} 1 & -3 \\ 2 & -4 \end{bmatrix} \begin{bmatrix} x_1(t) \\ x_2(t) \end{bmatrix} + \begin{bmatrix} f_1(t) \\ f_2(t) \end{bmatrix}$$

(c)

$$\begin{bmatrix} \dot{x}_1(t) \\ \dot{x}_2(t) \end{bmatrix} = \begin{bmatrix} -1 & 2 \\ -2 & -2 \end{bmatrix} \begin{bmatrix} x_1(t) \\ x_2(t) \end{bmatrix} + \begin{bmatrix} f_1(t) \\ f_2(t) \end{bmatrix}$$

(d)

$$\begin{bmatrix} \dot{x}_1(t) \\ \dot{x}_2(t) \end{bmatrix} = \begin{bmatrix} -1 & e^{-t} \\ 0 & -2 \end{bmatrix} \begin{bmatrix} x_1(t) \\ x_2(t) \end{bmatrix} + \begin{bmatrix} f_1(t) \\ f_2(t) \end{bmatrix}$$

8.6 Prove Theorem 8.10b.

8.7 Prove Corollary 8.13.

8.8 Verify inequalities 8.165 and 8.166.

8.9 Prove Lemma 1b of Sec. 8.4.3.

8.10 Starting with inequality 8.172, prove Lemma 2 of Sec. 8.4.3.

8.11 Prove Theorem 8.14b.

8.12 Prove Theorem 8.15.

8.13 For systems characterized by Fig. 8.8, with time-varying gain $f(t)$, determine bounds α and β so that $\alpha \leq f(t) \leq \beta$ assuring stability and that

(i) $\beta - \alpha$ is as large as possible,

(ii) α is as small as possible,

(iii) β is as large as possible

for each of the following cases

(a) $G(s) = \dfrac{1}{s(s+1)(s+2)}$

(b) $G(s) = \dfrac{s+1}{s(s+2)}$

(c) $G(s) = \dfrac{(s+1)(s+3)}{s(s+2)(s+4)}$

9

Integral Transforms in the Analysis and Synthesis of Linear Time-Varying Systems

Integral transforms afford a means for the solution of boundary-value and initial-value problems in physics and engineering. In particular, use of the Laplace transform in the analysis and synthesis of time-invariant systems has proved particularly efficacious. The advantages and values stemming from use of the Laplace transform hinge on the fact that transformation of a linear differential equation with constant coefficients yields an tion of a linear differential equation with constant coefficients yields an algebraic equation (in the transform variables).

For time-varying linear systems, however, Laplace transformation of the characterizing linear differential equation (with time-varying coefficients)—when it can be effected—does not yield an algebraic equation, but generally another differential equation in the transform variables, s: thus usually no advantage attends Laplace transformation. If, however, different and *compatible* transformations can be effected (e.g., the Mellin transform is compatible with a system characterized by the Euler-Cauchy equation), then advantages and values result that parallel those of Laplace transformation for linear time-invariant systems.

9.1. THE GENERAL TRANSFORM METHOD FOR THE ANALYSIS OF LINEAR TIME-VARYING SYSTEMS

Consider the scalar linear time-varying system characterized by a linear differential equation with time-varying coefficients:

$$Lx(t) = a_0(t)\frac{d^n x(t)}{dt^n} + \cdots + a_n(t) = f(t) \tag{9.1}$$

In general, pursuant to certain conditions, a function $r(t)$ of a single real variable, t, is transformed into a function of the complex variable, $R(\lambda)$, by the following direct integral transform

$$\mathscr{L}[r(t)] \equiv R(\lambda) \equiv \int_a^b r(t)K(\lambda, t)\, dt \tag{9.2}$$

where $K(\lambda, t)$ is termed the *direct transform kernel* and a and b are limits of values hinging on the kernel $K(\lambda, t)$ and $\mathscr{L}$ denotes the integral transformation. An inverse of the integral transform is given by

$$\mathscr{L}^{-1}[R(\lambda)] = r(t) = \frac{1}{2\pi i}\int_C R(\lambda)k(t, \lambda)\, d\lambda \tag{9.3}$$

where $k(t, \lambda)$ is termed the *inverse transform kernel* C denotes an appropriately chosen contour in the λ-domain, and $\mathscr{L}^{-1}$ denotes the inverse of the integral transformation. For the case that $r(t)$ is the unit impulse applied at $t = \tau$, i.e.,

$$r(t) = \delta(t - \tau),\ a < \tau < b \tag{9.4}$$

it can be seen that

$$\begin{aligned} R(\lambda) &= \int_a^b \delta(t - \tau)K(\lambda, t)\, dt \\ &= K(\lambda, \tau) \end{aligned} \tag{9.5}$$

Thus taking the inverse transform of $R(\lambda) = K(\lambda, \tau)$ in accordance with Eq. 9.3 gives

$$\frac{1}{2\pi i}\int_C k(t, \lambda)K(\lambda, \tau)d\lambda = \delta(t - \tau) \tag{9.6}$$

Equation 9.6 provides the relation between the direct transform kernel $K(\lambda, t)$ and the inverse transform kernel $k(t, \lambda)$.

For the general scalar linear time-varying system characterized by Eq. 9.1, the *general system function*, $G(\lambda, t)$ is defined by

$$G(\lambda, t) \equiv \left.\frac{x(t)}{f(t)}\right|_{f(t)=k(t,\lambda)} \tag{9.7}$$

where $x(t) = G(\lambda, t)k(t, \lambda)$ is the response of the zero-state system for the case that the inverse transform kernel $k(t, \lambda)$ is taken as the input with the variable λ treated as a parameter. The zero-state output of the system is given by the superposition integral

$$y(t) = \int_{t_0}^{t} \Omega(t, \tau)u(\tau)\, d\tau \tag{9.8}$$

For the scalar system characterized by Eq. 9.1 this is written as

$$x(t) = \int_{t_0}^{t} \Omega(t, \tau)f(\tau)\, dt \tag{9.9a}$$

where $\Omega(t, \tau)$ is the impulsive response and $f(t)$ is the system input. Invoking causality for physical systems, i.e. $\Omega(t, \tau) = 0$ for $t < \tau$, Eq. 9.9a becomes

$$x(t) = \int_{t_0}^{\infty} \Omega(t, \tau)f(\tau)\, d\tau \tag{9.9b}$$

The superposition integral can be used to obtain the correct output for the case that the initial state at $t = t_0$ is not zero by changing the lower limit of the integral from t_0 to $-\infty$:

$$x(t) = \int_{-\infty}^{\infty} \Omega(t, \tau)f(\tau)\, d\tau \tag{9.9c}$$

In order to emphasize causality, the superposition integral is usually written as

$$x(t) = \int_{-\infty}^{t} \Omega(t, \tau)f(\tau)\, d\tau \tag{9.9d}$$

Thus for the case that the system input is $k(t, \lambda)$, it is seen that the system function $G(\lambda, t)$, defined in Eq. 9.7 can be written as

$$G(\lambda, t) = \frac{1}{k(t, \lambda)} \int_{-\infty}^{t} \Omega(t, \tau)k(\tau, \lambda)\, d\tau \tag{9.10}$$

An equation for the output $x(t)$ in terms of the system function $G(\lambda, t)$ is now obtained. Substitution for $f(\tau)$ by use of Eq. 9.3 in Eq. 9.9d gives

$$x(t) = \frac{1}{2\pi i} \int_{-\infty}^{t} \Omega(t, \tau) \left[\int_C F(\lambda)k(\tau, \lambda)d\lambda \right] d\tau \tag{9.11}$$

or, on interchanging integrals (assuming the necessary conditions for such to be permissible),

$$x(t) = \frac{1}{2\pi i} \int_C F(\lambda) \left[\int_{-\infty}^{t} \Omega(t, \tau)k(\lambda, \tau)d\tau \right] d\lambda \tag{9.12}$$

Substituting for the real integral in Eq. 9.12 from Eq. 9.10 gives

$$x(t) = \frac{1}{2\pi i} \int_C F(\lambda)G(\lambda, t)k(t, \lambda)\, d\lambda \tag{9.13}$$

Comparing Eq. 9.13 with Eq. 9.3 evidences the general advantage of introducing the system function: the system response is found by the inverse transform of the product of the transform of the input, $F(\lambda)$, and the system function, $G(\lambda, t)$, i.e.,

$$X(\lambda) = F(\lambda)G(\lambda, t) \tag{9.14}$$

For the very important case that $G(\lambda, t)$ is not a function of t, i.e.,

$$G(\lambda, t) = G(\lambda) \tag{9.15}$$

application of the integral transform reduces the differential equation to an algebraic equation in the one variable λ:

$$X(\lambda) = G(\lambda)F(\lambda) \tag{9.16}$$

When this is the case, the inverse transform kernel $k(t, \lambda)$ is the eigenfunction of the system and the inverse system function $G^{-1}(\lambda)$ is the eigenvalue, i.e.,

$$L[k(t, \lambda)] = G^{-1}(\lambda)k(t, \lambda) \tag{9.17}$$

Alternatively, the inverse transform kernel, $k(t, \lambda)$, is termed a *characteristic input*; the integral transform defined by Eqs. 9.2, 9.3, and 9.4 is termed a *compatible transform* with respect to the particular system of interest; and, the λ-domain is said to be the *compatible domain* with respect to the particular system of interest.

Most significant in the analysis and synthesis of complex physical systems is that the overall system function of combinations of compatible systems in parallel, series (cascade), or in feedback can be obtained by algebraic procedures involving the individual system functions.

9.2. DETERMINATION OF THE INVERSE TRANSFORM KERNEL, $k(t, \lambda)$, YIELDING A COMPATIBLE TRANSFORM

Taking the system input, $f(t)$, as the inverse transform kernel, $k(t, \lambda)$, the steady-state output is, by Eq. 9.7 the product $G(\lambda, t)k(t, \lambda)$, Thus the characterizing equation of the system, given by Eq. 9.1 can be written as

$$a_0(t)\frac{d^n}{dt^n}[G(\lambda, t)k(t, \lambda)] + \cdots + a_n(t)[G(\lambda, t)k(t, \lambda)] = k(t, \lambda) \tag{9.18}$$

For the case that $k(t, \lambda)$ is a characteristic input, i.e., a compatible transform is defined, Eq. 9.18 reduces to

$$a_0(t)\frac{d^n}{dt^n}[k(t, \lambda)] + \cdots + [\alpha_n(t) - G^{-1}(\lambda)]k(t, \lambda) = 0 \tag{9.19}$$

Obviously, success in use of the transform methods depends on solving the nth-order differential equation 9.19.

9.3. AN APPROACH FOR DETERMINING THE DIRECT TRANSFORM KERNEL $K(\lambda, t)$ YIELDING A COMPATIBLE TRANSFORM [1]

Some insight, and a useful result, is gained to the problem of determining the direct transform kernel $K(\lambda, t)$) which yields a compatible transform, by considering the relatively simple second-order linear differential equation

$$a_0(t)\frac{d^2x(t)}{dt^2} + a_1(t)\frac{dx(t)}{dt} + a_2(t)x(t) = f_1(t) \tag{9.20}$$

where $a_2(t)$ is not zero and all initial conditions are zero. Thus, the approach is to find the direct transform kernel of that integral transform which transforms the differential equation 9.20 to an algebraic equation in one variable.

Dividing each member of Eq. 9.20 by $a_2(t)$ yields an equation typified by

$$b_0(t)\frac{d^2x(t)}{dt^2} + b_1(t)\frac{dx(t)}{dt} + x(t) = f(t) \tag{9.21}$$

Therefore the problem is that of finding the direct transform kernel, $K(\lambda, t)$, of an integral transform of the form given in Eq. 9.2 for which the transform of Eq. 9.21 is a simple algebraic equation, i.e.,

$$\mathscr{L}[b_0(t)\ddot{x}(t) + b_1(t)\dot{x}(t) + x(t)] = \mathscr{L}[f(t)] \tag{9.22}$$

is to result in

$$m(\lambda)X(\lambda) + X(\lambda) = F(\lambda) \tag{9.23}$$

Thus the requirement that Eq. 9.23 exists is that

$$\mathscr{L}[b_0(t)\ddot{x}(t) + b_1(t)\dot{x}(t)] = m(\lambda)X(\lambda) \tag{9.24}$$

Including a factor $g(t)$ in the kernel $K(\lambda, t)$ gives

$$K(\lambda, t) = g(t)K_0(\lambda, t) \tag{9.25}$$

Define the derivative operator

$$L_2 \equiv g(t)b_0(t)\frac{d^2}{dt^2} + g(t)b_1(t)\frac{d}{dt} \equiv \frac{d}{dt}\,[p(t)\,\frac{d}{dt} \tag{9.26}$$

Thus

$$p(t) = g(t)b_0(t) \tag{9.27a}$$

$$\dot{p}(t) = g(t)b_1(t) \tag{9.27b}$$

The factor $g(t)$ is chosen so that the derivative operator L_2 is self-adjoint[1]:

[1]Let $\langle u, v\rangle$ denote the scalar product of the two real functions u and v given by

$$\langle u, v\rangle = \int_0^\infty uv\,dt \tag{9.27A}$$

If L is a derivative operator, the *adjoint operator* to L, designated by L^*, is obtained from the expression

$$\langle Lu, v\rangle = \langle u, L^*v\rangle \tag{9.27B}$$

If L is of the form

$$L \equiv a_0(t)\frac{d^n}{dt^n} + \cdots + a_{n-1}(t)\frac{d}{dt} + a_n(t) \tag{9.27C}$$

then it can be shown that

$$g(t)b_0(t)\frac{d^2x(t)}{dt^2} + g(t)b_1(t)\frac{dx(t)}{dt} = \frac{d^2}{dt^2}[g(t)b_0(t)x(t)] - \frac{d}{dt}[g(t)b_1(t)x(t)] \tag{9.28}$$

Equation 9.28, representing the condition for L_2 to be self-adjoint, is satisfied for

$$g(t) = \exp\left\{\int\left[\frac{b_1(t) - \dot{b}_0(t)}{b_0(t)}\right] dt\right\} \tag{9.29}$$

Carrying out the transformation indicated by Eq. 9.24 gives

$$\begin{aligned} m(\lambda)X(\lambda) &= \int_0^\infty [b_0\ddot{x}(t) + b_1(t)\dot{x}(t)]K(\lambda, t)\, dt \\ &= \int_0^\infty [g(t)b_0(t)\ddot{x}(t) + g(t)b_1(t)\dot{x}(t)]K_0(\lambda, t)\, dt \\ &= \int_0^\infty L_2[x(t)]K_0(\lambda, t)\, dt = \langle L_2x(t), K_0(\lambda, t)\rangle \end{aligned} \tag{9.30}$$

Since L_2 is defined as a self-adjoint operator it follows that

$$\langle L_2x(t), K_0(\lambda, t)\rangle = \langle x(t), L_2K_0(\lambda, t)\rangle \tag{9.31}$$

Thus Eq. 9.30 can be written as

$$m(\lambda)X(\lambda) = \int_0^\infty x(t)[L_2K_0(\lambda, t)]\, dt \tag{9.32}$$

By definition,

$$X(\lambda) = \int_0^\infty x(t)K(\lambda, t)\, dt = \int_0^\infty x(t)g(t)K_0(\lambda, t)\, dt \tag{9.33}$$

Substituting from Eq. 9.33 in Eq. 9.32 gives

$$m(\lambda)\int_0^\infty x(t)g(t)K_0(\lambda, t)\, dt = \int_0^\infty x(t)[L_2K_0(\lambda, t)]\, dt \tag{9.34}$$

$$L^* \equiv (-1)^n \frac{d^n}{dt^n}[a_0(t) + \cdots - \frac{d}{dt}[a_{n-1}(t) + a_n(t) \tag{9.27D}$$

When $L = L^*$, L is said to be self-adjoint. Note that a distinction is made between the adjoint of an *operator*, as defined here, and the adjoint of an *equation* as defined in Sec. 3.3. Recall that the adjoint of the matrix $\mathbf{A}(t)$ in obtaining the adjoint equation is $-\mathbf{A}'(t)$. Defining the scalar product for the n vectors $\mathbf{x}$ and $\mathbf{y}$ in the usual way,

$$\langle \mathbf{x}, \mathbf{y}\rangle = \sum_{i=1}^{n} x_i y_i$$

and taking the matrix $\mathbf{A}(t)$ as an operator, results in the adjoint of $\mathbf{A}(t)$ being $\mathbf{A}'(t)$. Thus it is seen that there is a difference of sign in the two adjoints and that they are therefore distinct.

A solution to Eq. 9.34 exists when

$$L_2K_0(\lambda, t) = m(\lambda)g(t)K_0(\lambda, t) \tag{9.35}$$

or simply, when

$$p(t)\frac{d^2K_0(\lambda, t)}{dt^2} + \dot{p}(t)\frac{dK_0(\lambda, t)}{dt} - m(\lambda)g(t)K_0(\lambda, t) = 0 \tag{9.36}$$

Substituting from Eqs. 9.27 in Eq. 9.36 gives

$$b_0(t)\frac{d^2K_0(\lambda, t)}{dt^2} + b_1(t)\frac{dK_0(\lambda, t)}{dt} - m(\lambda)K_0(\lambda, t) = 0 \tag{9.37}$$

Therefore the kernel $K(\lambda, t) = g(t)K_0(\lambda, t)$ can be found as the solution of the linear differential equation 9.37. As previously, Eq. 9.37 parallels in form the homogeneous equation associated with Eq. 9.21, which is the equation for which the solution is actually desired.

It is to be noted that a knowledge of the solution of a linear differential equation is essential for determining the desired kernel of the integral transform under which transformation of the differential equation of interest yields an algebraic equation. Transform methods are therefore advantageous in situations where the primary interest is in finding the responses of a single system (or particular type of system, e.g., the systems described by linear differential equations with constant coefficients) to a large variety of inputs. In these situations the kernel, once found as a result of solving Eq. 9.37, can be used repeatedly.

9.4. GENERAL BLOCK-DIAGRAM REDUCTION PROCEDURES IN THE COMPATIBLE DOMAIN

In this section general reduction procedures for obtaining the overall system function for systems combined in parallel, series, and feedback are developed. It is shown that if a common compatible domain exists for all the subsystem components, then conventional algebraic reduction procedures can be used to obtain the overall system function from the system functions of the components.

9.4.1. Parallel Connections. Figure 9.1 evidences that if the input $f(t)$, is $k(t, \lambda)$, the output $x(t)$ is

$$k(t, \lambda)G(\lambda, t) = k(t, \lambda)G_1(\lambda, t) + k(t, \lambda)G_2(\lambda, t) \tag{9.38}$$

Thus, after division by $k(t, \lambda)$,

$$G(\lambda, t) = G_1(\lambda, t) + G_2(\lambda, t) \tag{9.39}$$

If $k(t, \lambda)$ is the characteristic input for both individual blocks

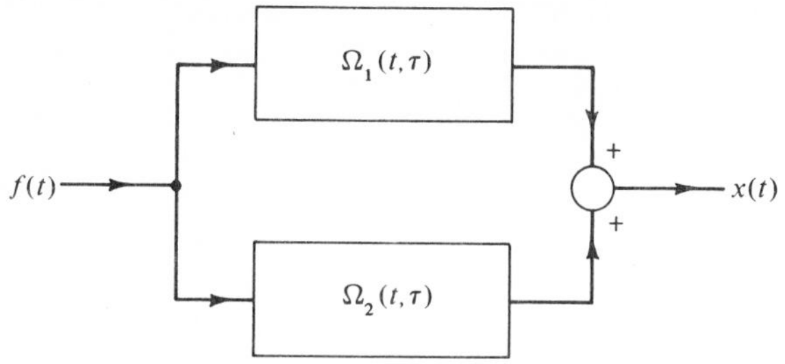

Fig. 9.1. Parallel connection of two linear time-varying systems having impulsive responses $\Omega_1(t, \tau)$ and $\Omega_2(t, \tau)$.

$$G(\lambda) = G_1(\lambda) + G_2(\lambda) \tag{9.40}$$

9.4.2. Series (Cascade) Connections. Figure 9.2 evidences that if the input, $f(t)$, is taken as $k(t, \lambda)$, the output of the first block is $k(t, \lambda)G_1(\lambda, t)$. The output of the second block, as determined by use of the superposition integral in Eq. 9.9d is

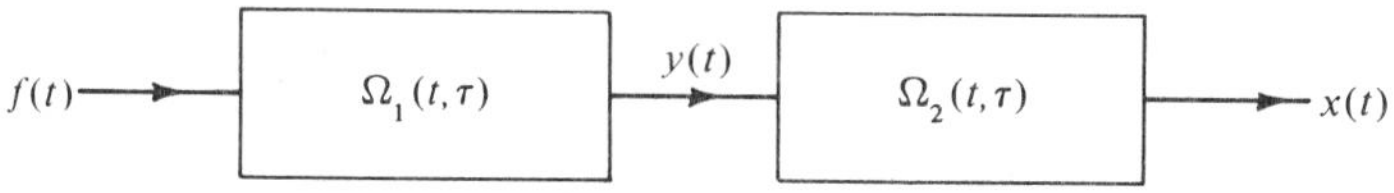

Fig. 9.2. Series connection of two linear time-varying systems having impulsive responses $\Omega_1(t, \tau)$ and $\Omega_2(t, \tau)$.

$$G(\lambda, t)k(t, \lambda) = \int_{-\infty}^{t} \Omega_2(t, \tau)G_1(\lambda, \tau)k(\tau, \lambda)\, d\tau \tag{9.41}$$

Thus, division by $k(t, \lambda)$ yields the overall system function as

$$G(\lambda, t) + \frac{1}{k(t, \lambda)} \int_{-\infty}^{t} \Omega_2(t,\tau)G_1(\lambda, \tau)k(\tau, \lambda)\, d\tau \tag{9.42}$$

If there exists a $k(t, \lambda)$ which is compatible for each of the cascaded subsystems, then $G_1(\lambda, t)$ is, in fact, not a function of t, i.e., $G_1(\lambda, t) = G_1(\lambda)$, and Eq. 9.42 can be written as

$$G(\lambda, t) = G_1(\lambda) \left\{ \frac{1}{k(t, \lambda)} \int_{-\infty}^{t} \Omega_2(t, \tau)k(\tau, \lambda)\, d\tau \right\} \tag{9.43}$$

Substituting from Eq. 9.10 in Eq. 9.43 gives, for series-connected compatible systems,

$$G(\lambda) = G_1(\lambda)G_2(\lambda) \tag{9.44}$$

9.4.3. Feedback Connections. If in Fig. 9.3 the input, $f(t)$, is taken as $k(t, \lambda)$, the output, $x(t)$, is $G(\lambda, t)k(t, \lambda)$. From Eq. 9.9d the output of the second block is

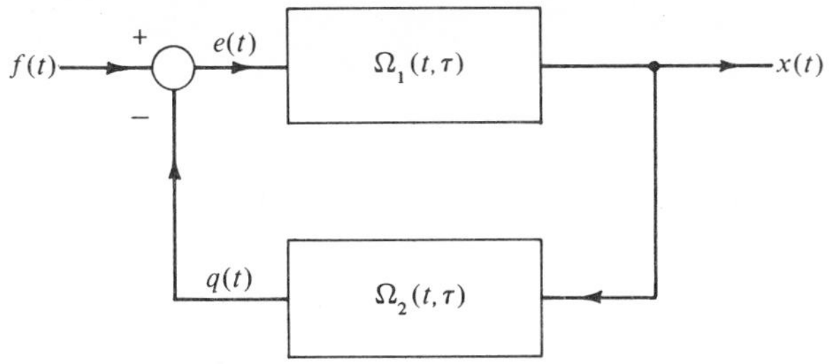

Fig. 9.3. Feedback connection of two linear time-varying systems having impulsive responses $\Omega_1(t, \tau)$ and $\Omega_2(t, \tau)$.

$$q(t) = \int_{-\infty}^{t} \Omega_2(t, \tau)G(\lambda, \tau)k(\tau, \lambda)\, d\tau \tag{9.45}$$

The input to the first block, $e(t)$, is $k(t, \lambda) - q(t)$. Thus from Eqs. 9.45 and 9.9d, as applied to the first block, the output is

$$G(\lambda, t)k(t, \lambda) = G_1(\lambda, t)k(t, \lambda) - \int_{-\infty}^{t} \Omega_1(t, \tau) \int_{-\infty}^{\tau} \Omega_2(\tau, \tau_1)G(\lambda, \tau_1)k(\tau_1, \lambda)\, d\tau_1\, d\tau \tag{9.46}$$

Thus determine the response of the overall system requires the solution of the integral equation 9.46 for $G(\lambda, t)$. If $k(t, \lambda)$ is a characteristic input for each of the subsystem blocks, Eq. 9.46 reduces to

$$G(\lambda)k(t, \lambda) = G_1(\lambda)k(t, \lambda) - G(\lambda)k(t, \lambda)\left\{\frac{1}{k(t, \lambda)} \int_{-\infty}^{t} \Omega_1(t, \tau)k(\tau, \lambda) \cdot \left[\frac{1}{k(\tau, \lambda)} \int_{-\infty}^{\tau} \Omega_2(\tau, \tau_1)k(\tau_1, \lambda)\, d\tau_1\right] d\tau\right\} \tag{9.47}$$

Substituting from Eq. 9.10 in Eq. 9.47 and dividing each member by $k(t, \lambda)$ gives

$$G(\lambda) = G_1(\lambda) - G(\lambda)G_1(\lambda)G_2(\lambda) \tag{9.48}$$

Solving Eq. 9.48 for $G(\lambda)$ gives for feedback-connected compatible systems

$$G(\lambda) = \frac{G_1(\lambda)}{1 + G_1(\lambda)G_2(\lambda)} \tag{9.49}$$

9.5 THE INVERSE RELATIONSHIP BETWEEN THE SYSTEM FUNCTION, $G(\lambda, t)$, AND THE IMPULSIVE RESPONSE, $\Omega(t, \tau)$

Let the direct transform of the unit impulse, $\delta(t - \tau)$, be defined, in accordance with Eq. 9.2, as

$$\Delta_\tau(\lambda) = \int_a^b \delta(t - \tau)K(\lambda, t)\, dt, \qquad a < \tau < b \tag{9.50}$$

Therefore

$$\Delta_\tau(\lambda) = K(\lambda, \tau) \tag{9.51}$$

If the input, $f(t)$, to a linear time-varying system is the unit impulse, $\delta(t - \tau)$, then the impulsive response, $\Omega(t, \tau)$, is, from Eq. 9.13,

$$\Omega(t, \tau) = \frac{1}{2\pi i} \int_C K(\lambda, \tau)k(t, \lambda)G(\lambda, t)\, d\lambda \tag{9.52}$$

where, as previously, $K(\lambda, t)$ denotes the kernel of the direct transform, $k(t, \lambda)$ the kernel of the inverse transform, and C a suitably chosen contour.

9.6. CLASSICAL EXAMPLES OF COMPATIBLE TRANSFORMS

It is instructive to note several kernels relative to the class of systems for which they are characteristic inputs and thus provide compatible transforms.

9.6.1. The Laplace Transform. The characteristic input for linear time-invariant systems is the well-known inverse transform kernel $e^{\lambda t}$ defining the Laplace transform. The transform equations are

$$R(\lambda) = \int_0^\infty r(t)e^{-\lambda t}\, dt \tag{9.53}$$

and

$$r(t) = \frac{1}{2\pi i} \int_{c-j\infty}^{c+j\infty} R(\lambda)e^{\lambda t} d\lambda \tag{9.54}$$

The Laplace transform is compatible with systems characterized by linear differential equations with constant coefficients, i.e., as typified by

$$\sum_{1=0}^{n} a_i \frac{d^i x(t)}{dt^i} = f(t) \tag{9.55}$$

9.6.2. The Mellin Transform. The inverse transform kernel corresponding to the Mellin transform is $t^{-\lambda}$. The transform equation are

$$R(\lambda) = \int_0^\infty r(t)t^{\lambda-1}\, dt \tag{9.56}$$

and

$$r(t) = \frac{1}{2\pi i} \int_{c-j\infty}^{c+j\infty} R(\lambda)t^{-\lambda}\, d\lambda \tag{9.57}$$

The Mellin transform is compatible with systems characterized by the Euler-Cauchy equations:

$$\sum_{j=0}^{n} a_j t^j \frac{d^j x(t)}{dt^j} = f(t) \tag{9.58}$$

9.6.3. The Hankel Transform. The inverse transform kernel of the Hankel transform is $\lambda J_n(\lambda t)$, correspondingly, the transform equation are

$$R_n(\lambda) = \int_0^\infty tJ_n(\lambda t)r(t)\,dt \tag{9.59}$$

and

$$r(t) = \int_0^\infty \lambda J_n(\lambda t)R_n(\lambda)\,d\lambda \tag{9.60}$$

The Hankel transform is compatible with systems characterized by the generalized Bessel equation:

$$\left[\frac{d^2}{dt^2} + \frac{1}{t}\frac{d}{dt} - \left(\frac{n^2}{t^2}\right) \pm a^2\right]^N x(t) = f(t) \tag{9.61}$$

9.7. SYNTHESIS OF LINEAR TIME-VARYING SYSTEMS AS EFFECTED THROUGH THE USE OF COMPATIBLE TRANSFORMS

In general, selection of a kernel which is compatible depends on the specific system of interest. However, a degree of generality is obtained by representing complex systems by a linear block diagram in terms of fundamental λ-domain building blocks. For example, if it is known that a system has a characteristic input, $k(t, \lambda)$, and a system function, $G(\lambda)$, in the compatible domain, other more complex compatible systems can be formed by combining systems whose system functions are constant multiples of $G(\lambda)$, $G^{-1}(\lambda)$, or 1. This result, although a seemingly trivial extension of the results in Sec. 9.4 on block-diagram reductions in a compatible λ-domain, implies that many results obtained in the analysis and synthesis of linear time-invariant systems can be used for classes of time-varying systems. Two examples are given.

9.71. Network Synthesis in the Compatible Domain [4]. In linear time-invariant network theory, there are a great many theorems relating the physical structure of a network to the functional form of impedance-type functions. In these theorems, the impedance $Z(s) = s$ is identified with an inductor, $Z(s) = \frac{1}{s}$ with a capacitor, and so on. Actually this identifies element types through the exponent of the basic operator associated with linear time-invariant networks, namely $\frac{d}{dt}$. This identification can be considered as the basic bridge between the physical specification of the network, and the mathematical specification of the impedance function of that network. It is suggested that any network theory which depends only on this identification of element types, and on the theory of analytic impedance functions, has a valid extension if translated into the appropriate generalized operator language.

Assume that an integral transform defined by specifying the inverse and direct transform kernels $k(t, \lambda)$ and $K(\lambda, t)$ is given. Further assume that a system has been found such that the defined transform is compatible to it: i.e., taking the transform of the system's characterizing differential equation

$$Lx(t) = f(t) \tag{9.62}$$

results in

$$X(\lambda) = G(\lambda)F(\lambda) \tag{9.63}$$

Clearly an *inverse system* can be defined by

$$L^{-1}x(t) = f(t) \tag{9.64}$$

or

$$x(t) = Lf(t) \tag{9.65}$$

Transforming Eq. 9.65 results in

$$X(\lambda) = G^{-1}(\lambda)F(\lambda) \tag{9.66}$$

Thus it is seen that the inverse system is compatible with the integral transform as defined. A system comprised of a constant time-invariant gain is compatible with respect to any integral transform. Therefore the set of fundamental components shown in Fig. 9.4 are compatible with respect to the integral transform defined.

Including an arbitrary gain in series with each of the fundamental components results in components that are also compatible with the defined

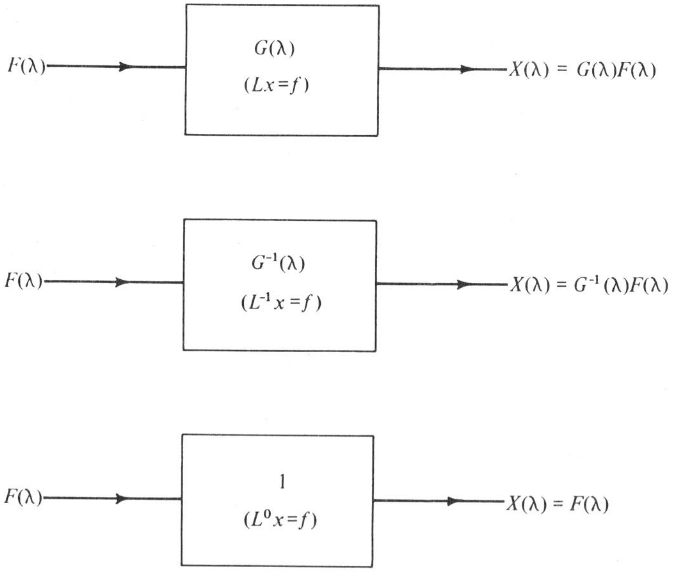

Fig. 9.4. A set of fundamentals components compatible with an integral transform.

integral transform. Thus the components shown in Fig. 9.5 also comprise a set of compatible fundamental components.

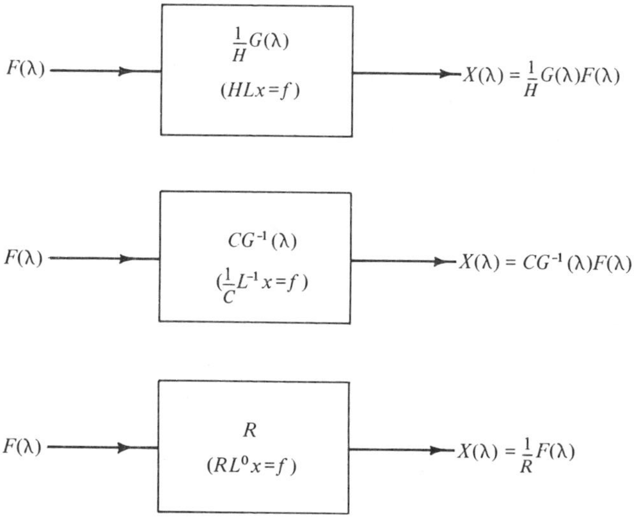

Fig. 9.5. A set of fundamental components compatible with an integral transform obtained by including constant gains $\frac{1}{H}$, C, R in series with the fundamental components of Fig. 9.4.

An example of a set of compatible fundamental components is comprised of the ordinary inductor, capacitor, and resistor shown in Fig. 9.6. This set is, of course, compatible with the Laplace transform.

The only two requirements in most of the present analysis and synthesis of networks utilizing the λ-domain are:

1. The existence of components satisfying the equations

$$f(t) = HL[x(t)]$$

$$f(t) = \frac{1}{C}L^{-1}[x(t)] \tag{9.67}$$

$$f(t) = \frac{1}{R}x(t)$$

2. The existence of a particular compatible transform enabling the transforming of Eqs. 9.67 to

$$X(\lambda) = \frac{1}{H}G(\lambda)F(\lambda)$$

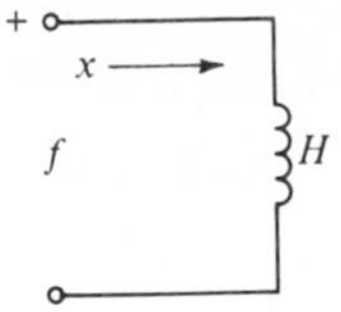

$$\begin{cases} f = HLx = H\frac{d}{dt}x, \; L = \frac{d}{dt} \\ X(\lambda) = \frac{1}{H}G(\lambda)F(\lambda) = \frac{1}{H}G(\lambda), \; G(\lambda) = \frac{1}{\lambda} \end{cases}$$

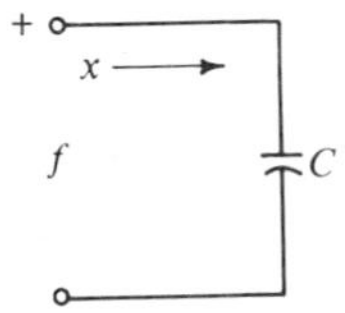

$$\begin{cases} f = \frac{1}{C}L^{-1}x = \frac{1}{C}\int_{-\infty}^{t} x\,dt, \; L^{-1} = \int_{-\infty}^{t} dt \\ X(\lambda) = CG^{-1}(\lambda)F(\lambda) = CF(\lambda), \; G^{-1}(\lambda) = \lambda \end{cases}$$

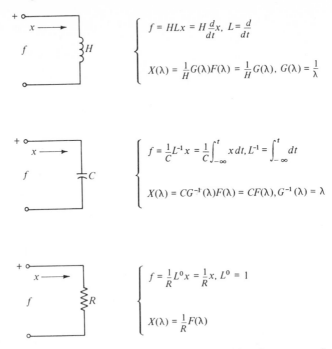

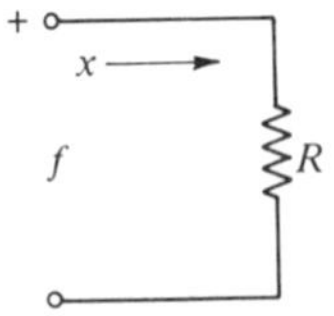

$$\begin{cases} f = \frac{1}{R}L^{0}x = \frac{1}{R}x, \; L^{0} = 1 \\ X(\lambda) = \frac{1}{R}F(\lambda) \end{cases}$$

Fig. 9.6. The ordinary inductor, capacitor and resistor comprise a set of fundamental components compatible with the Laplace transform.

$$X(\lambda) = CG^{-1}(\lambda)F(\lambda) \tag{9.68}$$

$$X(\lambda) = \frac{1}{R}F(\lambda)$$

That L has usually been taken as the simple derivative operator, and associated with use of the Laplace transform is incidental. It is, however, quite possible to define operational impedance functions, independently of time, for networks made up of the basic components defined by Eq. 9.67 for any linear operator L; the compatible kernel defining the transforms which yield Eqs. 9.68 must be known. In fact, the most significant theorem of network synthesis applies for an arbitrary linear operator, L [4]: "A necessary and sufficient condition than an analytic function of the complex parameter λ represent the impedance of some two-terminal network made up of the three types of elements, defined by Eqs. 9.67 and 9.68 is that this function be positive real; that is, that it be an analytic function which is real when λ is real, and whose real part is positive when the real part of λ is positive."

Example 9.1. A fundamental set of components, and the compatible transform, associated with the derivative operator

$$L = 1 + (1 + t)\frac{d}{dt} = \frac{d}{dt}[(1 + t)$$

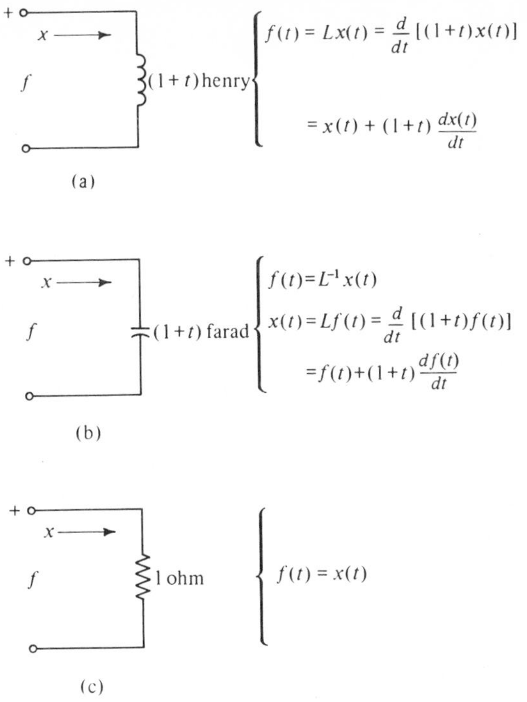

Fig. 9.7. A set of fundamental components corresponding to the derivative operator $L = \frac{d}{dt}[(1 + t)$.

is developed. A physical component realizing this operator is the time-varying inductor of $(1 + t)$ henrys as shown in Fig. 9.7a. A component realizing the inverse operator is the time-varying capacitor of $(1 + t)$ farads as shown in Fig. 9.7b. The constant resistor of 1 ohm shown in Fig. 9.7c completes the fundamental set of components. It is desirable to determine the integral transform such that transforming the differential equations characterizing the fundamental components results in the set of algebraic equations

$$X(\lambda) = \frac{1}{\lambda} F(\lambda) \qquad \text{inductor}$$

$$X(\lambda) = \lambda F(\lambda) \qquad \text{capacitor}$$

$$X(\lambda) = F(\lambda) \qquad \text{resistor}$$

The direct-transform kernel

$$K(\lambda, t) = (1 + t)^{-\lambda}$$

defines such an integral transform. In accordance with the definition of the integral transform given in Eq. 9.2

$$R(\lambda) = \int_a^b (1 + t)^{-\lambda} r(t)\, dt$$

Thus for the fundamental time-varying inductor

$$
\begin{aligned}
F(\lambda) &= \int_a^b (1+t)^{-\lambda} f(t)\, dt \\
&= \int_a^b (1+t)^{-\lambda} \frac{d}{dt}[(1+t)x(t)]\, dt \\
&= (1+t)^{1-\lambda} x(t)\Big|_a^b + \lambda \int_a^b (1+t)^{-\lambda} x(t)\, dt
\end{aligned}
$$

The quantities a and b are chosen such that the first term is $-\,x(0+)$. This is accomplished when $a = 0$, $b = \infty$ and $Re[\lambda] < 1$. Thus, by definition of the integral transform,

$$F(\lambda) = -\,x(0+) + \lambda X(\lambda)$$

and for the case that $x(0+) = 0$, the desired result is obtained:

$$X(\lambda) = \frac{1}{\lambda} F(\lambda) \qquad \text{inductor}$$

A similar analysis for the time-varying capacitor results in

$$X(\lambda) = \lambda F(\lambda) \qquad \text{capacitor}$$

Thus the integral transform compatible with the fundamental components of Fig. 9.7 is defined by

$$R(\lambda) = \int_0^\infty (1+t)^{-\lambda} r(t)\, dt$$

An illustration of the use of this fundamental set of components and the associated compatible transform is provided by detailing the procedure used for synthesizing a network from its impulsive response. It is specified that the current response of the desired network to a unit impulse $\delta(t)$ of voltage applied at $t = 0$ be

$$x(t)\big|_{f(t)=\delta(t)=\Omega(t,0)} = \frac{(1+t)^{\frac{1}{2}} + 2}{2(1+t)^{\frac{3}{2}}}$$

Thus

$$
\begin{aligned}
F(\lambda)\big|_{f(t)=\delta(t)} &= \int_0^\infty (1+t)^{-\lambda} \delta(t)\, dt \\
&= 1
\end{aligned}
$$

and

$$
\begin{aligned}
X(\lambda)\big|_{f(t)=\delta(t)} &= \int_0^\infty (1+t)^{-\lambda} \left[\frac{(1+t)^{\frac{1}{2}} + 2}{2(1+t)^{\frac{3}{2}}}\right] dt \\
&= \frac{1 + 6\lambda}{2\lambda + 4\lambda^2}
\end{aligned}
$$

Therefore, the *operational impedance*, obtained by taking the transform of the voltage input to the transform of the current output is

$$Z(\lambda) = \frac{E(\lambda)}{I(\lambda)} = \frac{2\lambda + 4\lambda^2}{1 + 6\lambda}$$

Expanding the admittance $Y(\lambda) = 1/Z(\lambda)$, in partial fractions gives

$$Y(\lambda) = \frac{1}{2\lambda} + \frac{1}{\frac{1}{2} + \lambda}$$

This admittance is readily realized by the network of Fig. 9.8.

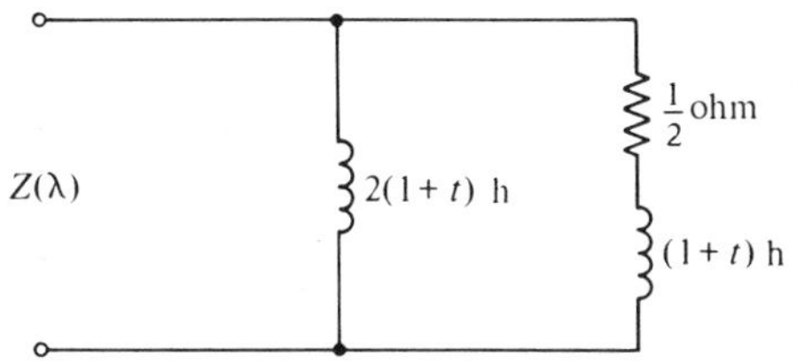

Fig. 9.8. Synthesized network having impulsive response given in Example 9.1.

9.7.2. The Fundamental Building Block Approach [9]. An approach used to obtain the compatible transforms for a large class of systems hinges on assuming a fixed structure for a *fundamental block* and then attempting to obtain an expression for the kernels of transformation $k(t, \lambda)$ and $K(\lambda, t)$ in terms of the general parameters of the assumed structure. A particularly useful structure, corresponding to a time-varying integrator, is shown in Fig. 9.9. It comprises a time-varying amplifier with gain $a(t)$ in cascade with an integrator (denoted by the operational notation $\left.\frac{1}{p}\right)$. The overall system is thus a variable-gain integrator. An explicit expression for a kernel compatible with this variable-gain integrator is developed.

Fig. 9.9. Fundamental time domain building block.

Consider $F(\lambda)$ and $X(\lambda)$ as transforms of the input and output. Let $G(\lambda)$ be the system function of the variable-gain integrator. Although, in general, the kernel may be any analytic function of λ, for simplicity let it be chosen such that

$$G(\lambda) = 1/\lambda \tag{9.69}$$

A general compatible inverse kernel for the variable-gain integrator is defined as any $k(t, \lambda)$ such that if $f(t) = k(t, \lambda)$, then $x(t) = G(\lambda)k(t, \lambda)$; i.e.,

$$\frac{1}{p}[k(t, \lambda)a(t)] = G(\lambda)k(t, \lambda) \tag{9.70}$$

Differentiating each member with respect to t and rearranging yields

$$\frac{dk(t, \lambda)}{k(t, \lambda)} = G^{-1}(\lambda)a(t)\,dt \tag{9.71}$$

Integrating Eq. 9.71 between 0 and t gives:

$$\ln k(t, \lambda) - \ln k(0, \lambda) = G^{-1}(\lambda)\int_0^t a(y)\,dy \tag{9.72}$$

Taking $k(0, \lambda) = 1$ results in

$$\ln k(t, \lambda) = G^{-1}(\lambda)\int_0^t a(y)\,dy \tag{9.73}$$

Thus

$$k(t, \lambda) = \exp\left[G^{-1}(\lambda)\int_0^t a(y)\,dy\right] \tag{9.74}$$

and, since $G(\lambda) = 1/\lambda$,

$$k(t, \lambda) = \exp\left[\lambda\int_0^t a(y)\,dy\right] \tag{9.75}$$

Example 9.2. Consider the case that $a(t) = 1$. Equation 9.75 then provides the compatible inverse kernel, i.e., $k(t, \lambda) = e^{\lambda t}$ which is recognized as the Laplace transform inverse kernel.

Example 9.3. Consider the case that $a(t) = -t^{-1}\delta^{(-1)}(t-1)$. Substituting in Eq. 9.75 gives for the compatible inverse kernel

$$k(t, \lambda) = \exp\left[-\lambda\int_0^t y^{-1}\delta^{(-1)}(y-1)\,dy\right]$$

$$= \exp\left[-\lambda\int_1^t y^{-1}dy\right] = \exp\left[-\lambda\ln t\right] = t^{-\lambda} \tag{9.76}$$

This is recognized to be the Mellin transform inverse kernel.

It is readily demonstrated that the inverse kernel of Eq. 9.75 is compatible with the inverse building block of Fig. 9.10.

Fig. 9.10. Inverse time-domain building block.

Since all kernels are characteristic inputs to constant amplifiers, the inverse kernel of Eq. 9.75 permits an algebraic analysis of any system that is a combination of the three compatible fundamental building blocks of Fig. 9.11.

The inverse kernel of Eq. 9.75 provides the inverse transform

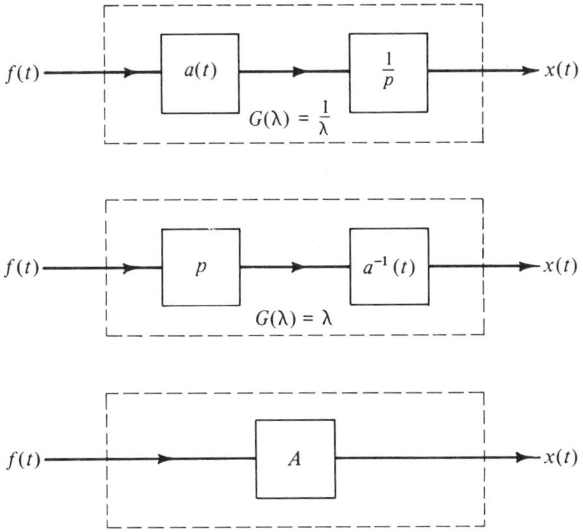

Fig. 9.11. Compatible fundamental building blocks.

$$r(t) = \frac{1}{2\pi i}\int_{c-j\infty}^{c+j\infty} R(\lambda) \exp\left[\lambda \int_0^t a(y)\,dy\right] d\lambda \tag{9.77}$$

where c is chosen such that $R(\lambda)$ exists over the path of integration. The kernel of the direct transform is obtained by a real change in the real variable. Thus let

$$u = \int_0^t a(y)dy,\ du = a(t)\,dt \tag{9.78}$$

implying that t is a function of u, i.e.,

$$t = q(u) \tag{9.79}$$

Substituting for u and t from Eqs. 9.78 and 9.79 in Eq. 9.77 gives

$$r[q(u)] = \frac{1}{2\pi i}\int_{c-j\infty}^{c+j\infty} R(\lambda)e^{\lambda u}\,d\lambda \tag{9.80}$$

recognizable as the inverse Laplace transform. Thus from the uniqueness of the Laplace transform it follows that

$$R(\lambda) = \int_0^\infty r[q(u)]e^{-\lambda u}\,du \tag{9.81}$$

Returning to the original variables by substituting for $u(t)$ and q from Eqs. 9.78 and 9.79 gives the direct transform as

$$R(\lambda) = \int_{q(0)}^{q(\infty)} x(t)a(t) \exp\left[-\lambda \int_0^t a(y)\,dy\right] dt \tag{9.82}$$

from which the direct kernel results:

$$K(\lambda, t) = a(t) \exp\left[-\lambda \int_0^t a(y)\,dy\right] \tag{9.83}$$

9.8. A NONCOMPATIBLE TRANSFORM: THE SYSTEM FUNCTION [17]

The Laplace transform, as a compatible transform, is a much-used modern operational technique for the analysis and synthesis of networks and control systems characterized by linear differential equations with *constant* coefficients. In an attempt to extend many of the accompanying advantages to linear time-varying parameter systems, an effort was made to develop a complete operational calculus for linear time-varying parameter systems by "extension" of Laplace transform theory. The transform thus proposed by Zadeh [17] is, except for time-invariant systems, a noncompatible transform. This extension has proved particularly useful as a tool for synthesis and as a vehicle for obtaining conceptual insight into a system's operation; it has found somewhat limited value in practice as a tool for analysis. Due to unwarranted high expectations that were initially held for this transform as a general purpose tool for the analysis and synthesis of all linear time-varying systems, it subsequently became the object of much negative reaction[2]. Both viewpoints were extreme and tended to promote misunderstanding and to hide the actual practical value of the transform. The major limitation of this operational method lies in the great difficulty, for all but very simple systems, of determining the *system function*. Zadeh's system function is a special case of the general system function defined by Eq. 9.7: namely, that

$$k(t, \lambda)|_{\lambda=s} \equiv \exp(st) \tag{9.84}$$

Thus in accordance with Eq. 9.10,

$$G(s, t) = \int_{-\infty}^{t} \Omega(t, \tau) e^{-s(t-\tau)}\,d\tau \tag{9.85}$$

[2]An example of some of the strong feelings existing toward Zadeh's system function is [9]:

> Although of academic interest, Zadeh's technique is of little practical use in that to obtain $G(s, t)$, or equivalently $\Omega(t, \tau)$, requires solving either the fundamental equation or a (similar) variation, for which no explict solution can be obtained. Also since the Laplace domain is non-compatible for variable systems, algebraic techniques cannot be used for signal-flow graph reduction. Instead complex integral or differential techniques must be used.

Statements such as this, although in a sense true, are, in the writer's opinion, overstrong. This is evidenced by the valuable, and practical, synthesis procedures based on having separable system functions advanced in Chapter 10.

where $\Omega(t, \tau)$ is the impulsive response of the scalar system. It is not surprising that the system function is difficult to determine. Obtaining it from Eq. 9.85 requires knowledge of the impulsive response which in general is quite difficult to determine.

The system function concept has proved, however, extremely useful in the synthesis of time-varying systems. This is especially true for the class of systems having separable system functions investigated in detail in Chapter 10. Therefore, preliminary to later use, a thorough discussion of the use of Zadeh's system function is now given.

It is revealing to compare Zadeh's system function as defined by Eq. 9.85 and the Laplace transfer function of a time-invariant system:

$$G(s) = \int_0^\infty g(\eta)e^{-s\eta}\, d\eta \tag{9.86}$$

where $g(t)$ is the system response to the unit impulse $\delta(t)$ applied at $t = 0$, $g(t - \alpha)$ is the system response to the unit impulse $\delta(t - \alpha)$ applied at $t = \alpha$. Thus by the real-translation theorem

$$e^{-s\alpha}G(s) = \int_\alpha^\infty g(\eta - \alpha)e^{-s\eta}\, d\eta \tag{9.87}$$

and

$$G(s) = \int_\tau^\infty g(\eta - \alpha)e^{-s(\eta-\alpha)}\, d\eta \tag{9.88}$$

Letting $\alpha = -t$ and $\eta = -\tau$ Eq. 9.88 results in

$$G(s) = \int_{-\infty}^t g(t - \tau)e^{-s(t-\tau)}\, d\tau \tag{9.89}$$

A comparison of Eqs. 9.85 and 9.89 shows that for the time-invariant case, Zadeh's system function is the Laplace transfer function.

Determining the system output for an arbitrary input is formally straightforward. If the Laplace transform of the system input is denoted by $F(s)$, the inverse is

$$f(\tau) = \frac{1}{2\pi i}\int_C F(s)e^{s\tau}\, ds \tag{9.90}$$

Substituting for $(f)\tau$ from Eq. 9.90 in Eq. 9.9d gives the output

$$x(t) = \frac{1}{2\pi i}\int_{-\infty}^t \Omega(t, \tau)\, d\tau \int_C F(s)e^{s\tau}\, ds \tag{9.91}$$

Inverting the order of integrations gives

$$x(t) = \frac{1}{2\pi i}\int_C F(s)\, ds \left[\int_{-\infty}^t \Omega(t, \tau)e^{s\tau}\, d\tau\right] \tag{9.92}$$

Substituting from Eq. 9.85 for the bracketed integral in Eq. 9.92 gives

$$x(t) = \frac{1}{2\pi i}\int_C F(s)G(s, t)e^{st}\, ds \tag{9.93}$$

This expression for the response parallels that for time-invariant systems

$$x(t) = \frac{1}{2\pi i}\int_C F(s)G(s)e^{st}\,ds \tag{9.94}$$

in that in both cases the transform of the response is the product of the transform of the input function and the system transfer function (system function), i.e., convolution in the time domain corresponds to multiplication in the transform variable domain. Of particular significance here is the important fact that the uniqueness holding between direct and inverse transforms for time-invariant systems does not hold for time-varying systems, i.e., although $x(t)$ is the inverse Laplace transform of $G(s, t)F(s)$, the direct Laplace transform of $x(t)$ is not $G(s, t)F(s)$.

Example 9.4. Consider the nonhomogeneous equation

$$t^2\frac{d^3x}{dt^3} + 6t\frac{d^2x}{dt^2} + 6\frac{dx}{dt} = f(t)$$

where the input $f(t)$ is taken to be the unit step applied at $t = 0$. This equation can be written in state-variable form as

$$\begin{bmatrix}\dot{x}_1(t)\\ \dot{x}_2(t)\\ \dot{x}_3(t)\end{bmatrix} = \begin{bmatrix}0 & 1 & 0\\ 0 & 0 & 1\\ 0 & -6t^{-2} & -6t^{-1}\end{bmatrix}\begin{bmatrix}x_1(t)\\ x_2(t)\\ x_3(t)\end{bmatrix} + \begin{bmatrix}0\\ 0\\ t_2\end{bmatrix}\delta^{(-1)}(t)$$

$$y(t) = [1 \quad 0 \quad 0]\begin{bmatrix}x_1(t)\\ x_2(t)\\ x_3(t)\end{bmatrix}$$

where $x_1(t) = x(t)$, $x_2(t) = \dot{x}(t)$, $x_3(t) = \ddot{x}(t)$.

The solution to this equation, with zero initial conditions, is found by first determining Zadeh's system function and then evaluating the complex inversion integral of Eq. 9.93.

The basis functions of the given equation are 1, t^{-1}, and t^{-2}. Thus the Wronskian matrix

$$\mathbf{W}(t) = \begin{bmatrix}1 & t^{-1} & t^{-2}\\ 0 & -t^{-2} & -t^{-3}\\ 0 & 2t^{-3} & 6t^{-4}\end{bmatrix}$$

is a fundamental matrix, and the transition matrix can be found from

$$\phi(t, \tau) = \mathbf{W}(t)\mathbf{W}^{-1}(\tau)$$

For the case that $\Omega(t, \tau)$ is a scalar, an expression for the system's impulsive response is

$$\Omega(t, \tau) = \mathbf{C}(t)\mathbf{W}(t)\mathbf{W}^{-1}(\tau)\mathbf{B}(\tau)$$

Therefore

$$\Omega(t, \tau) = \frac{1}{2}\left(\frac{\tau}{t} - 1\right)^2\delta^{(-1)}(t - t)$$

The system function is thus expressed by

$$G(s, t) = \int_{-\infty}^{t} \frac{1}{2} \left(\frac{\tau}{t} - 1\right)^2 \delta^{(-1)}(t - \tau)e^{-s(t-\tau)}\, dt$$

Letting $\tau = t - v$ gives

$$G(s, t) = \int_{0}^{\infty} \frac{1}{2} \frac{v^2}{t^2} \delta^{(-1)}(v)e^{-sv}\, dv = \frac{1}{s^3 t^2}$$

Thus the solution is

$$x(t) = \frac{1}{2\pi i} \int_C F(s)G(s, t)e^{st} ds = \frac{1}{t^2} \left[\frac{1}{2\pi i} \int_C \frac{1}{s^4} e^{st}\, ds \right] = \frac{t}{6}$$

9.8.1. Direct Determination of Zadeh's System Function. Of considerable interest in Zadeh's time-varying operational calculus is a technique for finding the system function directly from knowledge of the differential equation characterizing the system, thereby bypassing need for finding the basis functions or the impulsive response. A method of solution for this problem is as follows:

Since $e^{st}G(s, t)$ is, by definition, the response of the quiescent linear system to an input e^{st}, the system differential equation 9.1 can be written as

$$a_0(t) \frac{d^n[e^{st}G(s, t)]}{dt^n} + \cdots + a_n(t)[e^{st}G(s, t] = e^{st} \tag{9.95}$$

which is a nonhomogeneous linear equation of the form[3]

$$\alpha_n(t) \frac{d^n G(s, t)}{\partial t^n} + \cdots + \alpha_0(t)G(s, t) = 1 \tag{9.96}$$

wherein s is a complex constant (note that the subscripts of the coefficients, α, start with the highest derivative, contrary to the usual practice adhered to in this text).

[3]Equation 9.95 can be written in operational form as

$$A(p, t)\, [G(s, t)e^{st}] = e^{st} \tag{9.95A}$$

where $p \equiv d/dt$. Utilizing the identity [19]

$$F(p, t)\, [u, v] = uFv + \frac{du}{dt} F_p v + \frac{1}{2} \frac{d^2u}{dt^2} F_{pp}\, v + \cdots + \frac{1}{n!} \frac{d^n u}{dt^n} F_{p^n}\, v \tag{9.95B}$$

wherein

$$F_p \equiv \frac{\partial F(p, t)}{\partial p} \tag{9.95C}$$

yields the coefficients of Eq. 9.96 as

$$\alpha_r(t) = \frac{1}{r!} \left.\frac{\partial^r A(p, t)}{\partial p^r}\right|_{p=s}; \qquad r = 0, 1, \cdots, n \tag{9.95D}$$

In terms of the coefficients of the original differential equation,

$$A(p, t) = a_0(t)p^n + \cdots + a_{n-1}(t)p + a_n(t) \tag{9.95E}$$

The solution of Eq. 9.96 is the system function. Both the differential equation 9.96 and the associated original differential equation 9.1 are of order n, Sometimes it may be that Eq. 9.96 is easier to solve than is Eq. 9.b; but there is no *a priori* reason to think that such might be the case. Accordingly, solving Eq. 9,96 instead of Eq. 9.1 is advantageous ohly if a knowledge of the system function itself, as well as the output response of the system, is desired.

Obtaining a unique solution of Eq. 9.96 or any other nth-order differential equation, requires n specified boundary conditions. However, as a practical matter, in obtaining $G(s, t)$ from Eq. 9.96 this is not necessary. Recalling Eq. 9.85 stating that the product $G(s, t)e^{st}$ is the response of a quiescent system to an input e^{st} which is applied at $t = -\infty$ it is seen that only the "steady state" particular solution of Eq. 9.95 or 9.96 gives $G(s, t)$.

Example 9.5. Consider the linear differential equation

$$t^2 \frac{d^2x}{dt^2} + 4t \frac{dx}{dt} + 2x = f(t)$$

Zadeh's system function is obtained by solving the linear differential equation obtained by substitution in Eq. 9.95:

$$t^2 \frac{d^2}{dt^2} [G(s, t)e^{st}] + 4t \frac{d}{dt} [G(s, t)e^{st}] + 2G(s, t)e^{st} = e^{st}$$

or in the form of Eq. 9.96:

$$t^2 \frac{d^2G(s, t)}{dt^2} + (2st^2 + 4t)\frac{dG(s, t)}{dt} + (t^2s^2 + 4ts + 2)G(s, t) = 1$$

It is noted that this equation is not easier to solve than the original differential equation. In fact, due to the fact that a solution is required in terms of coefficients that are functions of *two* variables, t and s, the differential equation for $G(s, t)$ is generally more difficult to solve than the original differential equation. Substitution verifies that

$$G(s, t) = \frac{1}{t^2s^2}$$

9.8.2. Determination of the Differential Equation from the System Function $G(s, t)$. The constant-coefficient linear differential equation characterizing a system having Laplace transfer function $G(s)$, input $f(t)$ and output $x(t)$ is easily determined from

$$x(t) = G(p)f(t) \tag{9.97}$$

where $p \equiv d/dt$.

Example 9.6. A system having a transfer function

$$G(s) = \frac{1}{s^2 + 2s + 3}$$

is characterized by the input-output relation

$$x(t) = \frac{f(t)}{p^2 + 2p + 3}$$

Thus multiplying by $p^2 + 2p + 3$ gives

$$\frac{d^2x(t)}{dt^2} + 2\frac{dx(t)}{dt} + 3x(t) = f(t)$$

The time-variant linear differential equation characterizing a system function $G(s, t)$ can also be determined from

$$x(t) = G(p, t)f(t) \tag{9.98}$$

Example 9.7. A system having a system function

$$G(s, t) = \frac{1}{s^3t^2}$$

is characterized by the input-output relation

$$x(t) = \frac{1}{p^3t^2}f(t)$$

Multiplying by p^3t^2 gives

$$p^3t^2x(t) = f(t)$$

Carrying out the operation $p^3 = d^3/dt^3$ on the product $t^2x(t)$ gives the final result

$$t^2\frac{d^3x(t)}{dt^3} + 6t\frac{d^2x(t)}{dt^2} + 6\frac{dx}{dt} = f(t)$$

which is in agreement with the example in Sec. 9.8.

It should be noted, however, that had the system function been written as

$$G(s, t) = \frac{1}{t^2s^3}$$

the procedure indicated would have resulted in the differential equation

$$t^2\frac{dx^3(t)}{dt^3} = f(t)$$

which is erroneous in that this differential equation's system function is not $1/t^2s^3$. Therefore, the manner in which the system function is written is critical in determining the differential equation. Algorithmic procedures are available [20] for determining the differential equation from the system function. The significant point to be made here is that, under proper conditions, the operational equation

$$x(t) = G(p, t)f(t)$$

does characterize the system differential equation.

9.8.3. Zadeh's Block-Diagram Algebra. For linear time-invariant systems the basic ombinatorial relations that are very useful in obtaining the transfer function of a complex system are summarized in Table 9.1. The set of corresponding relationships for combining time-varying blocks is derived here.

Parallel Connections. From Fig. 9.12 it follows that

$$\Omega(t, \tau) = \Omega_1(t, \tau) + \Omega_2(t, \tau) \tag{9.99}$$

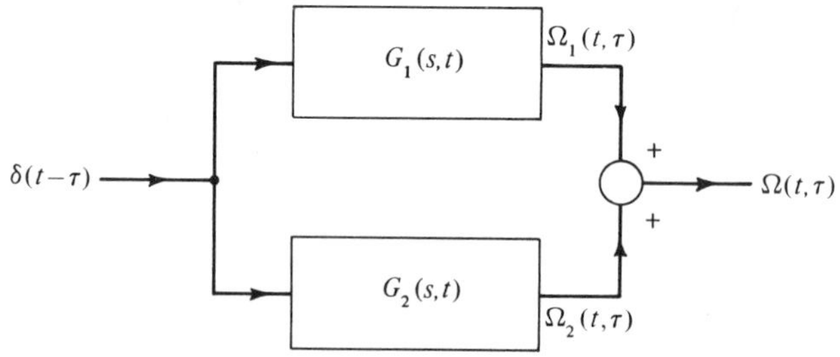

Fig. 9.12. Parallel connection of two linear time-varying systems having system functions $G_1(s, t)$ and $G_2(s, t)$: impulsive input.

Transforming Eq. 9.99 by use of Eq. 9.85 results in

$$G(s, t) = G_1(s, t) + G_2(s, t) \tag{9.100}$$

which parallels that relationship for combining parallel-connected time-invariant systems (Table 9.1).

Series Connections. Analysis of the second block of Fig. 9.13 gives

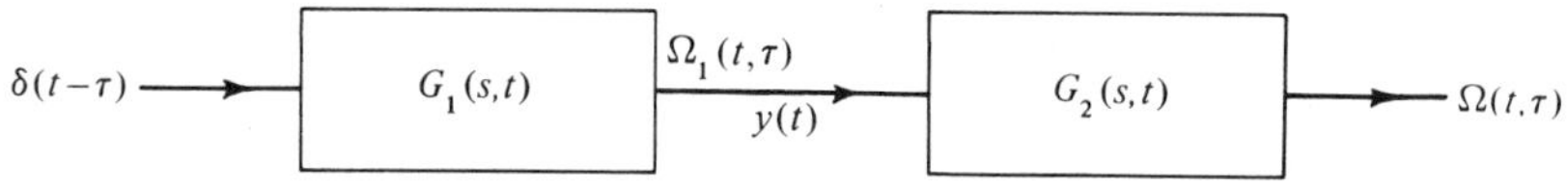

Fig. 9.13. Series connection of two linear time-varying systems having system functions $G_1(s, t)$ and $G_2(s, t)$: impulsive input.

$$\Omega(t, \tau) = \int_{-\infty}^{t} \Omega_2(t, \tau_0)y(\tau_0)\, d\tau_0 = \int_{\tau}^{t} \Omega_2(t, \tau_0)\Omega_1(\tau_0, \tau)\, d\tau_0 \tag{9.101}$$

Thus the overall system response of two series-connected systems is determined by evaluation of the integral of Eq. 9.101.

The overall system function $G(s, t)$ of series-connected systems can be expressed in terms of the system functions of each of the cascaded sys-

Table 9.1. Basic combinations of time-invariant blocks.

(1) Parallel

$$\Omega_3(t) = \Omega_1(t) + \Omega_2(t)$$

$$G_3(s) = G_1(s) + G_2(s)$$

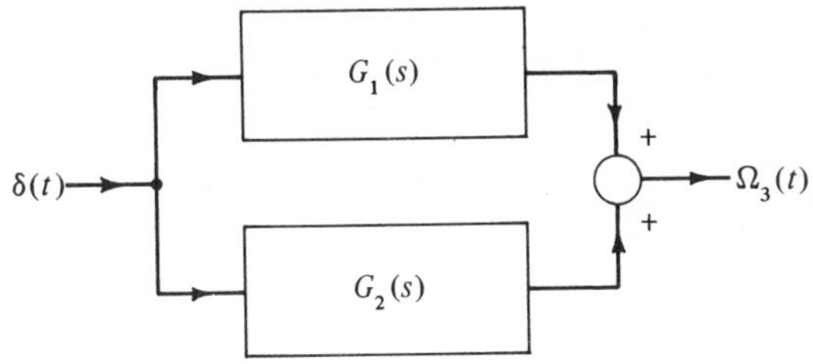

(2) Series

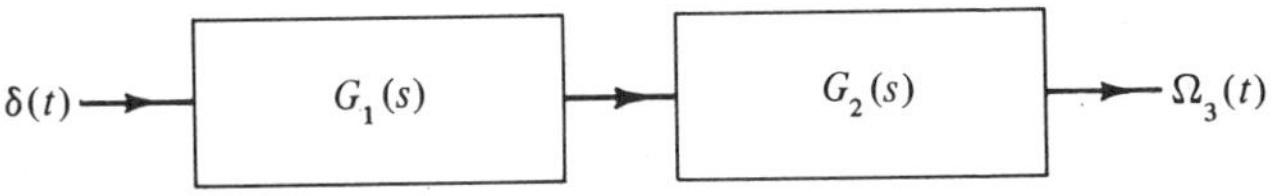

$$\Omega_3(t) = \int_0^t \Omega_2(t-\tau)\,\Omega_1(\tau)\,d\tau$$

$$G_3(s) = G_2(s)\,G_1(s)$$

(3) Feedback

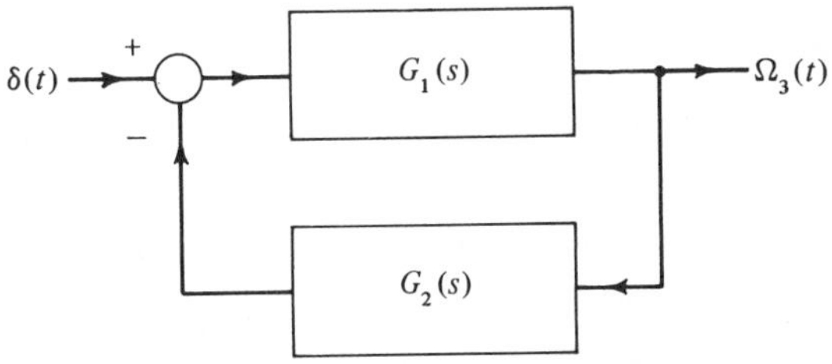

$$\Omega_3(t) = \int_0^t \Omega_1(t-\tau)[\delta(t) - \int_0^\tau \Omega_2(\tau-\tau_0)\,\Omega_3(\tau_0)\,d\tau_0]\,d\tau$$

$$G_3(s) = \frac{G_1(s)}{1 + G_1(s)\,G_2(s)}$$

tems. In Sec. 9.8 it is demonstrated that the differential equation characterizing a system having function $G(s, t)$ can be represented by

$$x(t) = G(p, t)f(t) \tag{9.102}$$

where $p \equiv \dfrac{d}{dt}$. Thus with reference to Fig. 9.14, the output of each of the cascaded systems can be written operationally as

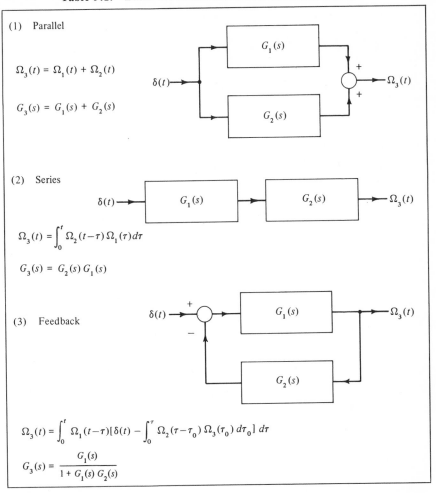

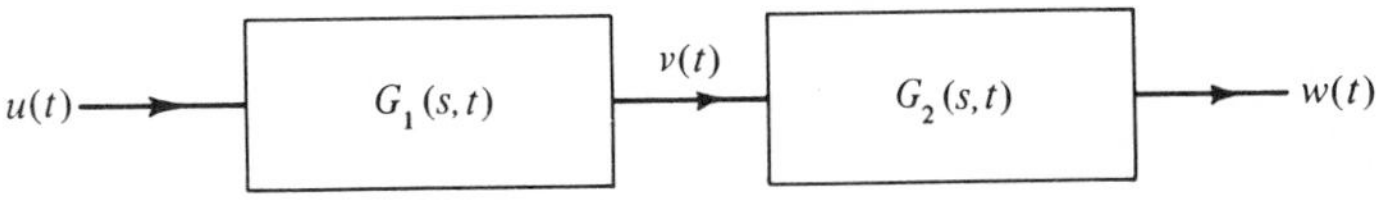

Fig. 9.14. Series connection of two linear time-varying systems having system functions $G_1(s, t)$ and $G_2(s, t)$: arbitrary input.

$$v(t) = G_1(p, t)u(t) \tag{9.103a}$$

$$w(t) = G_2(p, t)v(t) \tag{9.103b}$$

Combining Eqs. 9.103a and 9.103b gives

$$w(t) = G_2(p, t)[G_1(p, t)u(t)] \tag{9.104}$$

Defining the overall system function of the cascaded systems as $G(s, t)$ gives the overall relation

$$w(t) = G(p, t)u(t) \tag{9.105}$$

Comparing Eqs. 9.103 and 9.105 results in

$$G(p, t)u(t) = G_2(p, t)[G_1(p, t)u(t)] \tag{9.106}$$

Let $u(t) \equiv e^{st}$ in Eq. 9.106:

$$G(p, t)e^{st} = G_2(p, t)[G_1(p, t)e^{st}] \tag{9.107}$$

By definition of the system function, a system having a system function $G(s, t)$ and input e^{st} has an output $G(s, t)e^{st}$. However, according to Eq. 9.105 the output to an input e^{st} is also $G(p, t)e^{st}$. Thus

$$G(p, t)e^{st} = G(s, t)e^{st} \tag{9.108}$$

Use of the relation 9.108 in Eq. 9.107 results in

$$G(s, t)e^{st} = G_2(p, t)[G_1(s, t)e^{st}] \tag{9.109}$$

It is seen in Sec. 9.8.1 that the differential equation characterizing the system, when the forcing function is $F(t) = e^{st}$, can be written as

$$A(p, t)[G(s, t)e^{st}] = e^{st} \tag{9.110}$$

and is reducible to the form

$$e^{st}\left[\alpha_n(t)\frac{\partial^n G(s, t)}{\partial t^n} + \cdots + \alpha_0(t)G(s, t)\right] = e^{st} \tag{9.111}$$

where

$$\alpha_r(t) = \frac{1}{r!}\frac{\partial^r A(s, t)}{\partial s^r} \tag{9.112}$$

Comparing the right-hand side of Eq. 9.109 with Eqs. 9.110, 9.111, and 9.112, results in

$$G(s, t) = \beta_m(t)\frac{\partial^n G_1(s, t)}{\partial t^n} + \cdots + \beta_0(t)G_1(s, t) \tag{9.113}$$

where

$$\beta_r(t) = \frac{1}{r!}\frac{\partial^r G_2(s, t)}{\partial s^r} \tag{9.114}$$

Substituting from Eq. 9.114 in Eq. 9.113 gives

$$G(s, t) = \frac{1}{n!} \frac{\partial^n G_2(s, t)}{\partial s^n} \frac{\partial^n G_1(s, t)}{\partial t^n} + \cdots + G_2(s, t)G_1(s, t) \tag{9.115}$$

where n denotes the order of the system characterized by $G_2(s, t)$. Thus Eq. 9.115, involving differentiation only, gives a straightforward approach to determining the overall system function of two series-connected systems.

A relation that is somewhat simpler to remember is now obtained. Let $G_2(p, t)$ be expressed as the infinite series

$$G_2(p, t) = a_0(t) + a_1(t)p + a_2(t)p^2 + \cdots \tag{9.116}$$

Substituting from Eq. 9.116 in Eq. 9.109 gives

$$\begin{aligned} G(s, t)e^{st} &= [a_0(t) + a_1(t)p + a_2(t)p^2 + \cdots][G_1(s, t)e^{st}] \\ &= a_0(t)G_1(s, t)e^{st} + a_1(t)\left[\frac{\partial G_1(s, t)}{\partial t} + sG_1(s, t)\right] e^{st} \\ &+ a_2(t)\left[\frac{\partial^2 G_1(s, t)}{\partial t^2} + 2s\frac{\partial G_1(s, t)}{\partial t} + s^2 G_1(s, t)\right] e^{st} \\ &+ a_3(t)\left[\frac{\partial^3 G_1(s, t)}{\partial t^3} + 3s^2 \frac{\partial^2 G_1(s, t)}{\partial t^2} + 3s^2 \frac{\partial G_1(s, t)}{\partial t} \right. \\ &\left. + s^3 G_1(s, t)\right] e^{st} + \cdots \end{aligned} \tag{9.117}$$

Equation 9.117 can be written in operational form as

$$\begin{aligned} G(s, t) = [&a_0(t) + a_1(t)(p + s) + a_2(t)(p + s)^2 \\ &+ a_3(t)(p + s)^3 + \cdots]G_1(s, t) \end{aligned} \tag{9.118}$$

Comparing the bracketed infinite series in Eq. 9.118 with the infinite series defined in Eq. 9.116 results in

$$G(s, t) = G_2(p + s, t)G_1(s, t) \tag{9.119}$$

In this relation the t in $G_2(p + s, t)$ is treated as a constant parameter, and $G_1(s, t)$ is treated as a function of time with s as a parameter. Comparing Eqs. 9.101 and 9.119 with the time-invariant counterparts in Table 9.1 shows a significant difference; multiplication of system functions does not correspond in general to convolution in the time domain. Symbolically, Eq. 9.119 is written as

$$G(s, t) = G_2(s, t)*G_1(s, t) \tag{9.120}$$

where, in general, the $*$ operation is noncommutative.

In working with combinations of time-varying systems the notion of an *inverse system function* is particularly useful. Two system functions $G_1(s, t)$ and $G_2(s, t)$ are said to be inverses of each other if and only if

$$G_1(s, t)*G_2(s, t) = G_2(s, t)*G_1(s, t) = 1 \tag{9.121}$$

Symbolizing the inverse of $G(s, t)$ as $G^{-1}(s, t)$ enables writing Eq. 9.121 as

$$G(s, t)*G^{-1}(s, t) = G^{-1}(s, t)*G(s, t) = 1 \tag{9.122}$$

This equation shows that the impulsive response of two series-connected blocks which are inverses of each other is an impulse. Correspondingly, for series-connected inverse blocks Eq. 9.101 becomes

$$\delta(t - \tau) = \int_{\tau}^{t} \Omega(t, \tau_0)\Omega^{-1}(\tau_0, \tau)\, d\tau_0 \tag{9.123}$$

Feedback Connections. Analysis of the feedback block diagram of Fig. 9.15 gives

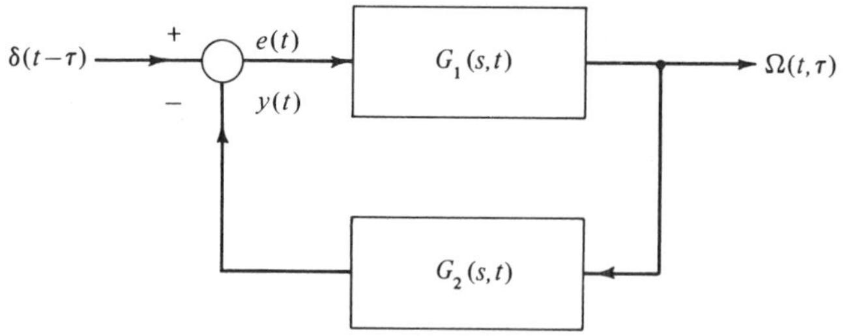

Fig. 9.15. Feedback connection of two linear time-varying systems having system functions $G_1(s, t)$ and $G_2(s, t)$: impulsive input.

$$y(t) = \int_{-\infty}^{t} \Omega_2(t, \tau)\Omega(t, \tau)\, d\tau \tag{9.124}$$

and

$$\Omega(t, \tau) = \int_{0}^{t} \Omega_1(t, \tau_2)e(\tau_2)\, d\tau_2 \tag{9.125}$$

But as

$$e(t) = \delta(t - \tau) - y(t) \tag{9.126}$$

combining Eqs. 9.124, 9.125, and 9.126 gives

$$\Omega(t, \tau) = \int_{\tau}^{t} \Omega_1(t, \tau_2)\left[\delta(\tau_2 - \tau) - \int_{\tau}^{\tau_2} \Omega_2(\tau_2, \tau_1)\Omega(\tau_1, \tau)\, d\tau_1\right] d\tau_2 \tag{9.127}$$

which reduces to

$$\Omega(t, \tau) = \Omega_1(t, \tau) - \int_{\tau}^{t} \Omega_1(t, \tau_2)\left[\int_{\tau}^{\tau_2} \Omega_2(\tau_2, \tau_1)\Omega(\tau_1, \tau)\, d\tau_1\right] d\tau_2 \tag{9.128}$$

For unity feedback case, Eq. 9.128 gives

$$\Omega(t, \tau) = \Omega_1(t, \tau) - \int_{\tau}^{t} \Omega_1(t, \tau_2)\Omega(\tau_2, \tau)\, d\tau_2 \tag{9.129}$$

The overall system function, $G(s, t)$ is now expressed in terms of the system functions of the two feedback-connected blocks. With reference to Fig. 9.16, the outputs of the two systems connected in feedback, are

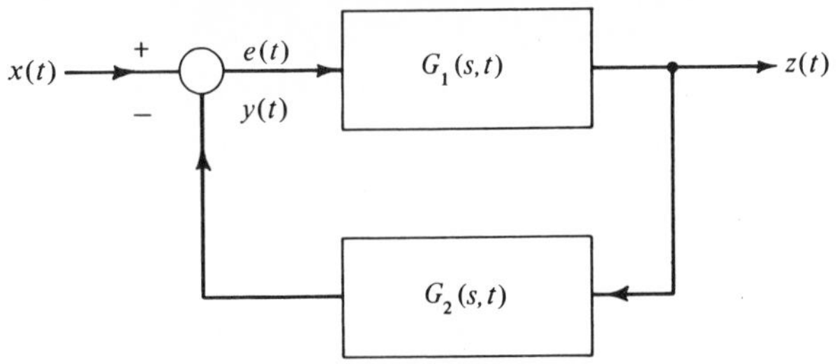

Fig. 9.16. Feedback connection of two linear time-varying systems having system functions $G_1(s, t)$ and $G_2(s, t)$: arbitrary input.

$$z(t) = G_1(p, t)e(t) \tag{9.130a}$$

$$y(t) = G_2(p, t)z(t) \tag{9.130b}$$

where

$$e(t) = x(t) - y(t) \tag{9.131}$$

Combining Eqs. 9.130a, 9.130b, and 9.131 results in

$$z(t) = G_1(p, t)x(t) - G_1(p, t)[G_2(p, t)z(t)] \tag{9.132}$$

Using the series notation of Eq. 9.120 gives

$$z(t) = G_1(p, t)x(t) - G_1(p, t)*G_2(p, t)z(t) \tag{9.133}$$

Rearranging equation gives

$$[1 + G_1(p, t)*G_2(p, t)]z(t) = G_1(p, t)x(t) \tag{9.134}$$

Defining the overall system function of the feedback system as $G(s, t)$ implies that

$$z(t) = G(p, t)x(t) \tag{9.135}$$

Substituting from Eq. 9.135 in Eq. 9.134 and rearranging gives the desired result

$$G(s, t) = [1 + G_1(s, t)*G_2(s, t)]^{-1}G_1(s, t) \tag{9.136}$$

where the $*$ operation and the $[\ ]^{-1}$ operation denote the series-connected and inverse operations defined in Eqs. 9.120 and 9.122. Comparing Eq. 9.136 with the corresponding time-invariant counterpart in Table 9.1 evidences a close resemblance, if multiplication and the taking of reciprocals for time-invariant systems are considered as special cases of the * and inversion operations defined for time-varying systems.

Thus it follows that the block-diagram algebra of time-varying systems bears a strong formal resemblance to the block-diagram algebra of time-invariant systems. Unfortunately, this formal resemblance is of little advantage in practice when the actual system function for a complex system is desired. The amount of work in performing the $*$ and the $[\ ]^{-1}$ operation is, in many cases, excessive.

REFERENCES

[1] Aseltine, J., "A Transform Method for Linear Time-Varying Systems," *J. Appl. Physics*, vol. 25 (1954), pp. 761–764.

[2] Balasubramian, R., and B. Deekshatulu, "Forced Response of Linear Time-Varying Systems," *IEEE Trans. on Automatic Control*, vol. AC-10, no. 4 (1965), pp. 485–486.

[3] Brikker, I. N., "The Frequency Analysis of Linear Variable-Parameter Systems," *Automation and Remote Control*, vol. 27, no. 8 (1966), pp. 1375–1388.

[4] Davis, H., "The Analysis and Synthesis of a Class of Linear Time-Varying Networks", *IEEE Trans. on Applications and Industry*, vol. 82 (1963), pp. 325–330.

[5] Davis, H., and E. C. Ho, "Generalized Operational Calculus for Time-Varying Networks," *Report No. 54-71*, Department of Engineering, University of California at Los Angeles, California, July 1954.

[6] DeClaris, N., and N. Liskov, "A Synthesis Method for Linear Time-Varying Systems," *Proceedings*, National Electronics Conference, 1965, pp. 599–604.

[7] Gerardi, F. R., "Application of Mellin and Hankel Transforms to Networks with Time-Varying Parameters," *IRE Trans. on Circuit Theory*, vol. CT-6 (1959), pp. 197–207.

[8] Gersho, A., "Characterization of Time-Varying Linear Systems," *Proc. IEEE*, vol. 51 (1963), p. 238.

[9] Johnson, G., and F. Kilmer, "Integral Transforms for Algebraic Analysis and Synthesis of a Class of Linear-Variable and Adaptive Systems," *IRE Trans. on Automatic Control*, vol. AC-7 (1962), pp. 97–106.

[10] Kaplan, W., *Operational Methods for Linear Systems*, Addison-Wesley, Reading, Mass., 1962.

[11] Klafter, R., "A Compatible Transform for a Class of Linear Time-Varying Discrete Systems," *IEEE Trans. on Circuit Theory*, vol. CT-14, no. 1 (1967), pp. 103–104.

[12] McMahon, L., "Impulse Response Synthesis for a Class of Time-Varying Networks," *IEEE Trans. on Circuit Theory*, vol. CT-10 (1963), pp. 460–461.

[13] Tranter, C., *Integral Transforms in Mathematical Physics*, Wiley, New York, 1951.

[14] Wattenburg, W., "Transform Methods and Time-Varying Systems," *Report No. 321*, Electronics Research Laboratory, University of California at Berkeley, California, September 1960.

[15] Weiss, L., "Integral Transforms and Time-Varying Systems," *Report on Representation and Analysis of Signals, Part XI*, The John Hopkins University, Baltimore, Md., May 1962.

[16] Weiss, L., "On System Functions with the Separability Property," *International Journal of Control*, vol. 1, no. 5 (1965), pp. 487–496.

[17] Zadeh, L., "Frequency Analysis of Variable Networks," *IRE Proc.*, vol. 38 (1950), pp. 291–299.
[18] Zadeh, L., "General Input-Output Relations for Linear Networks," *IRE Proc.*, vol. 40 (1952), p. 103.
[19] Graham, D., E. Brunelle, W. Johnson, and Passmore, H., "Engineering Analysis Methods for Linear Time-Varying Systems," *Technical Documentary Report ASD-TDR-62-362*, Astia, January 1963.
[20] Rudnitskii, B., "The Synthesis of Systems with Variable Parameters," *Automation and Remote Control*, vol. 26, no. 2 (1965), pp. 206–213.

PROBLEMS

9.1 Show that the well-known Laplace transform complies with the condition of Eq. 9.6 relating the direct and inverse transform kernels.

9.2 The RC network of Fig. P9.2 represents three networks:

(i) $C(t) = 1$ farad
(ii) $C(t) - \sin t$ farads
(iii) $C(t) = t$ farads

(a) Determine the general function $G(\lambda, t)$ with respect to the inverse transform kernel $k(t, \lambda) = e^{\lambda t}$.
(b) Repeat part *a* with respect to the inverse transform kernel $k(t, \lambda) = t^{-\lambda}$.
(c) Determine the compatible direct and inverse transform kernels for each of the three networks.

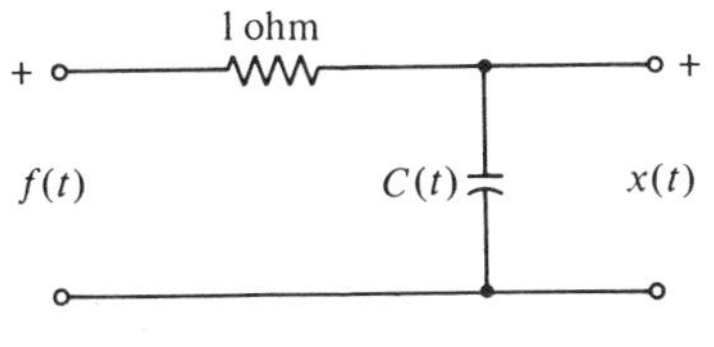

Fig. P9.2. Network for Prob. 9.2.

9.3 (a) Find *RL* networks that are compatible with the *RC* networks of Prob. 9.2.
(b) Using isolating amplifiers combine the compatible *RL* and *RC* networks in a parallel, series, and feedback configuration and determine the overall system function for each combination.

9.4 (a) Using the basic definitions of the adjoint and self-adjoint operators, as given in footnote 1, verify Eq. 9.28.
(b) Show that the expression for $g(t)$ as given in Eq. 9.29 satisfies Eq. 9.28.

9.5 Using a method of analysis similar to that of Sec. 9.2 or Sec. 9.3 determine the direct transform kernel compatible with the differential operator

$$L = (1 + t)\frac{d}{dt} + 1$$

Compare your result with the result in Example 9.1.

9.6 (a) What property must the impulsive-response function of a network have to insure that its operational impedance, with respect to a particular integral transform, is a rational function of only the transform variable λ?.

(b) Give two examples of impulsive-response functions, and their associated networks, which are compatible with the integral transform defined in Example 9.1.

9.7 Show that the system represented by the block diagram of Fig. 9.10 is compatible with the inverse transform kernel of Eq. 9.75.

9.8 In the system considered in Example 9.4, show that the Laplace transform of $x(t)$ is not $G(s, t)F(s)$.

9.9 (a) Determine the Zadeh system function $G(s, t)$ for the networks defined in Prob. 9.2.

(b) Using the system functions determined in part *a*, determine the response of the networks to

(i) $f(t) = \delta^{(-1)}(t)$

(ii) $f(t) = e^{-2t}\delta^{(-1)}(t)$

10

Separability

If a function of two variables is the sum of a finite number of products of two functions, each of which is a function of one of the single independent variables, it is termed *separable*, i.e., $Q(x, y)$ is separable if

$$Q(x, y) = q_1(x)q_2(y) \tag{10.1}$$

or, more generally, if

$$Q(x, y) = \sum_{i=1}^{n} q_{1i}(x)q_{2i}(y) \tag{10.2}$$

for finite n. Many operations on a function of two variables simplify considerably if the function is separable. In this chapter the mathematical and physical simplifications associated with both the separable scalar impulsive response $\Omega(t, \tau)$ and the separable system function $G(s, t)$ are investigated. It is important to note, and it is shown, that a separable $\Omega(t, \tau)$ does not necessarily imply that $G(s, t)$ is separable; similarly, a separable $G(s, t)$ does not imply that $\Omega(t, \tau)$ is separable.

10.1. SEPARABLE IMPULSIVE RESPONSE, $\Omega(t, \tau)$

As estalished by Theorem 5.1 *all* impulsive responses of linear systems characterized by the scalar linear time-varying differential equation $Lx(t) = f(t)$ are separable, i.e.,

$$\Omega(t, \tau) = \sum_{i=1}^{n} p_i(t)q_i(\tau), \; t \geq \tau \tag{10.3}$$

Further, the $p_i(t)$ are the basis functions of the homogeneous differential equation $Lx(t) = 0$ and the $q_i(\tau)$ are the basis functions of the adjoint homogeneous dfferential equation $L^*x(t) = 0$. That this is indeed the case is easily verified.

Consider the system characterized by the linear differential equation

$$Lx(t) \equiv a_0(t)\frac{d^n x(t)}{dt^m} + \cdots + a_n(t)x(t) = f(t) \tag{10.4}$$

By definition of the impulsive response, if the input $f(t)$, to the quiescent system, is the unit impulse $\delta(t - \tau)$, the output $x(t)$ is the impulsive response $\Omega(t, \tau)$—i.e.,

$$L\Omega(t, \tau) = \delta(t - \tau) \text{ for zero initial condititions} \tag{10.5}$$

Equation 10.5, in accordance with Sec. 4.1.4, can be written as a homogeneous equation with nonzero initial conditions:

$$L\Omega(t, \tau) = 0; \begin{cases} \left.\dfrac{\partial^i \Omega(t, \tau)}{\partial t^i}\right|_{t=\tau} = 0; \ i = 0, \cdots, n-2 \\ \left.\dfrac{\partial^{n-1}\Omega(t, \tau)}{\partial t^{n-1}}\right|_{t=\tau} = \dfrac{1}{a_n(\tau)} \end{cases} \tag{10.6}$$

The adjoint system is characterized by the adjoint linear differential equation[1]

$$L^*x(t) = (-1)^n \frac{d^n}{dt^n} \lfloor a_0(t)x(t)] + \cdots + a_n(t)x(t) = f(t) \tag{10.7}$$

Thus if $f(t)$ is the unit impulse $\delta(t - \tau)$

$$L^*\Omega^*(t, \tau) = \delta(t - \tau); \qquad \text{zero initial conditions} \tag{10.8}$$

where $\Omega^*(t, \tau)$ is defined as the impulsive response of the quiescent adjoint system. Rewriting Eq. 10.8 as a homogeneous equation with nonzero initial conditions gives

$$L^*\Omega^*(t, \tau) = 0; \begin{cases} \left.\dfrac{\partial^i \Omega^*(t, \tau)}{\partial t^i}\right|_{t=\tau} = 0, \ i = 0, \cdots, n-2 \\ \left.\dfrac{\partial^{n-1}\Omega^*(t, \tau)}{\partial t^{n-1}}\right|_{t=\tau} = \dfrac{1}{(-1)^n a_n(\tau)} \end{cases} \tag{10.9}$$

From the definition of an adjoint it is easily shown[2] that

[1]See footnote 1, Sec. 9.3.

[2]In footnote 1, Sec. 9.3 the adjoint is defined by the relation

$$\langle Lx, y\rangle = \langle x, L^*y\rangle \tag{10.10A}$$

where, for the case of real variables,

$$\langle u, v\rangle \equiv \int_0^\infty uv\, dt \tag{10.10B}$$

Equation 10.10A can be written as

$$\int_0^\infty y(t)\, Lx(t)\, dt = \int_0^\infty x(t)L^*y(t)\, dt \tag{10.10C}$$

$$\Omega^*(t, \tau) = \Omega(\tau, t) \tag{10.10}$$

Assume now that the impulsive response has the form

$$\Omega(t, \tau) = \sum_{i=1}^{n} p_i(t)q_i(\tau), \ t \geq \tau \tag{10.11}$$

Substituting from Eq. 10.11 in Eq. 10.6 gives

$$L\left[\sum_{i=1}^{n} p_i(t)q_i(\tau)\right] = 0 \tag{10.12}$$

Thus if the $p_i(t)$ are the basis functions of the homogeneous equation, Eq. 10.12 is satisfied. The $q_i(t)$ could be determined from a consideration of the initial conditions

$$\begin{aligned} \left.\frac{\partial^i \Omega(t, \tau)}{\partial t^i}\right|_{t=\tau} &= 0; \ i = 0, \cdots, n-2 \\ \left.\frac{\partial^{n-1} \Omega(t, \tau)}{\partial t^{n-1}}\right|_{t=\tau} &= \frac{1}{a_n(\tau)} \end{aligned} \tag{10.13}$$

However, the $q_i(t)$ can be determined from consideration of the adjoint system and its impulsive response. Equations 10.10 and 10.11 lead to the assumed form of the adjoint impulsive response as

$$\Omega^*(t, \tau) = \Omega(\tau, t) = \sum_{i=1}^{n} p_i(\tau)q_i(t) \tag{10.14}$$

Substituting from Eq. 10.14 in Eq. 10.9 gives

$$L^*\left[\sum_{i=1}^{n} p_i(\tau)q_i(t)\right] = 0 \tag{10.15}$$

Thus it is seen that the $q_i(t)$ are the basis functions of the adjoint system. Therefore, corroborating Theorem 5.1, the *separable* form for the impulsive response given by Eq. 10.11 is valid. However, for the scalar case the $p_i(t)$ and the $q_i(t)$ are basis functions of the system and its adjoint respectively.

Emphasis of separable impulsive responses suggests the existence of nonseparable impulsive responses: but as noted, these are nonexistent for

---

Therefore

$$\langle L\Omega(t, s), \Omega^*(t, \xi)\rangle = \langle \Omega(t, s), L^*\Omega^*(t, \xi)\rangle \tag{10.10D}$$

or

$$\int_0^\infty \Omega^*(t, \xi)L\Omega(t, s)\,dt = \int_0^\infty (\Omega t, s)L^*\Omega^*(t, \xi)\,dt \tag{10.10E}$$

Substituting from Eqs. 10.5 and 10.8 in 10.10E gives

$$\int_0^\infty \Omega^*(t, \xi)\delta(t - s)\,dt = \int_0^\infty \Omega(t, s)\delta(t - \xi)\,dt \tag{10.10F}$$

Thus

$$\Omega^*(s, \xi) = \Omega(\xi, s) \tag{10.10G}$$

linear systems characterized by ordinary differential equations. Accordingly discussion of separable impulsive responses appears to entail all linear systems of interest here. Unfortunately, the impulsive response is seldom available in the form of Eq. 10.3, or, for that matter, any other form. Rather, only an approximation to the impulsive response is usually available or can be found—and this may or may not be separable. It is in this thought that separable impulsive responses are discussed.

Several simplifications that arise as a result of having a separable impulsive response available in analysis and synthesis are now discussed.

10.1.1. Evaluating the Superposition Integral. For a separable impulsive response the superposition integral is

$$x(t) = \sum_{i=1}^{n} p_i(t) \int_{t_0}^{t} q_i(\tau) f(\tau)\, d\tau \tag{10.16}$$

When arbitrariness in selection of approimations to the $q_i(t)$ exists, they should be so chosen that the N integrations of Eq. 10.16 can be effected as straightforwardly as possible.

10.1.2. Evaluating the System Function, $G(s, t)$. For separable impulsive response Eq. 9.85 yields

$$G(s, t) = \sum_{i=1}^{n} p_i(t) e^{-st} \int_{-\infty}^{t} q_i(\tau) e^{s\tau}\, d\tau \tag{10.17}$$

or simply

$$G(s, t) = \sum_{i=1}^{n} p_i(t) e^{-st} Q_i(-s, t) \tag{10.18}$$

where $Q_i(-s, t)$ denotes the two-sided Laplace transform of $q_i(\tau)u(t - \tau)$. Equation 10.18 shows that a separable impulsive response does not imply necessarily a separable system function. Obviously, appropriate choice of the $q_i(t)$ simplifies evaluation of the n integrals of Eq. 10.17. It is of special interest to note that if $q_i(t) = c_i e^{a_i t}$, the system function is both separable and easily evaluated; this is demonstrated in Sec. 10.2.

10.1.3. Synthesizing the System. A system with impulsive response of the form of Eq. 10.4 can be synthesized by the configuration of Fig. 10.1. This realization utilizes amplifiers with time-varying gain (or signal generators and multipliers), integrators, and a summer.

10.1.4. Determination of the Differential Equation from the Impulsive Response. In accordance with Theorem 5.1, the separable property of the impulsive response enables a straightforward determination of the system's characterizing differential equation when the impulsive response is

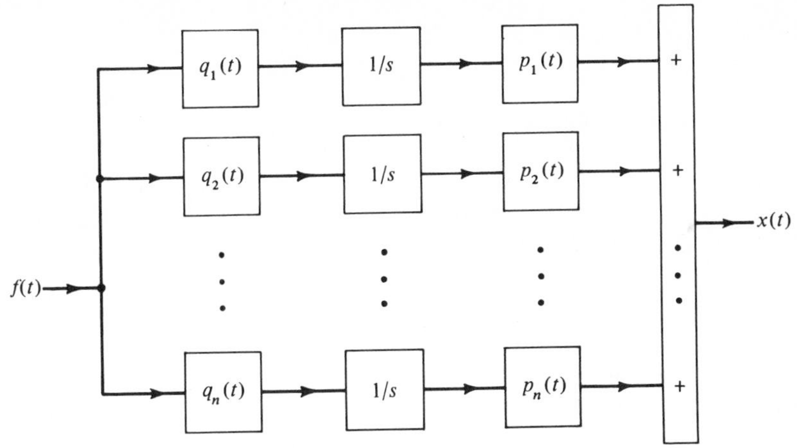

Fig. 10.1. Simulation of linear time-varying system having a separable impulsive response, $\Omega(t, \tau)$, as given in Eq. 10.15.

known. Consider the system characterized by the linear differential equation

$$a_0(t)\frac{d^n x(t)}{dt^n} + \cdots + a_n(t)x(t) = 0 \tag{10.19}$$

having the set of basis functions $x_1(t), \cdots, x_n(t)$. It is thus possible to write the solution to the homogeneous linear differential equation, and its first n derivatives, in terms of the basis functions and n arbitrary constants depending on initial conditions:

$$\begin{bmatrix} x(t) \\ \vdots \\ x^{(n)}(t) \end{bmatrix} = \begin{bmatrix} x_1(t) & \cdots & x_n(t) \\ \vdots & & \vdots \\ x_1^{(n)}(t) & \cdots & x_n^{(n)}(t) \end{bmatrix} \begin{bmatrix} C_1 \\ \vdots \\ C_n \end{bmatrix} \tag{10.20}$$

Due to the linear dependency of $x(t)$ on the basis functions $x_1(t), \cdots, x_n(t)$

$$\det \begin{bmatrix} x_1(t) & & x_n(t) & x(t) \\ \vdots & & \vdots & \vdots \\ x_1^{(n)}(t) & \cdots & x_n^{(n)}(t) & x^{(n)}(t) \end{bmatrix} = 0 \tag{10.21}$$

Evaluation of the determinant of Eq. 10.21 results in a differential equation of the form

$$b_0(t)\frac{d^n x(t)}{dt^n} + \cdots + b_n(t)x(t) = 0 \tag{10.22}$$

Comparison of Eqs. 10.19 and 10.22 shows that the determinant of Eq. 10.21, involving the basis functions gives the system differential equation. However, this determinant can also be used to obtain the differential equation when the impulsive response is given. Since the impulsive response is assumed to be given in the separable form

$$\Omega(t, \tau) = \sum_{i=1}^{n} p_i(t)q_i(\tau) \tag{10.23}$$

the basis functions can be determined from the impulsive response by inspection.

Example 10.1. Find the homogeneous differential equation characterizing the system with impulsive response

$$\Omega(t, \tau) = \frac{1}{5}(t^{-2}\tau^3 - t^3\tau^{-2})$$

Because of the separability of the impulsive response in the form of Eq. 10.23, the basis functions are determined by inspection

$$x_1(t) = t^{-2},\ x_2(t) = t^3$$

Thus in accordance with Eq. 10.21, the characterizing differential equation is determined by

$$\det \begin{bmatrix} t^{-2} & t^3 & x(t) \\ -2t^{-3} & 3t^2 & \dot{x}(t) \\ 6t^{-4} & 6t & \ddot{x}(t) \end{bmatrix} = 0$$

which, upon expansion and simplification, becomes

$$\frac{d^2x}{dt^2} - 6t^{-2}x = 0$$

10.2. SEPARABLE SYSTEM FUNCTION, $G(s, t)$

In general, if a linear system is said to be separable, it is implied that the system function, $G(s, t)$, is separable [1, 5, 6, 11]; i.e.,

$$G(s, t) = \sum_{i=1}^{m} b_i(t)H_i(s) \tag{10.24}$$

It is useful to determine the nature of the impulsive-response function of a system possessing a separable system function.

Zadeh's system function, as given by Eq. 9.85 is

$$G(s, t) = \int_{-\infty}^{t} \Omega(t, \tau)e^{-s(t-\tau)}\,d\tau$$

Since, according to Eq. 10.3, all impulsive responses of finite linear lymped systems are separable,

$$G(s, t) = \sum_{i=1}^{n} p_i(t)\int_{-\infty}^{t} q_i(\tau)e^{-s(t-\tau)}\,d\tau \tag{10.25}$$

Making the variable substitution in the integrand $\xi = t - \tau$ gives

$$G(s, t) = \sum_{i=1}^{n} p_i(t) \int_0^\infty q_i(t - \xi) e^{-s\xi} \, d\xi \tag{10.26}$$

or, interchanging the order of summation and integration,

$$G(s, t) = \int_0^\infty \Omega(t, t - \xi) e^{-s\xi} \, d\xi \tag{10.27}$$

where

$$\Omega(t, t - \xi) = \sum_{i=1}^{n} p_i(t) q_i(t - \xi) \tag{10.28}$$

It is noted in Eq. 10.26 that $G(s, t)$ is separable when $q_i(t - \xi)$ is of the form

$$q_i(t - \xi) = \sum_{k=1}^{m} \beta_{ik}(t) \gamma_{ik}(\xi) \tag{10.29}$$

Substitution from Eq. 10.29 in Eq. 10.26 results in

$$G(s, t) = \sum_{i=1}^{n} p_i(t) \sum_{k=1}^{m} \beta_{ik}(t) \int_0^\infty \gamma_{ik}(\xi) e^{-s\xi} \, d\xi \tag{10.30}$$

or, rearranging, gives $G(s, t)$ in the *separable* form

$$G(s, t) = \sum_{i=1}^{n} \sum_{k=1}^{m} p_i(t) \beta_{ik}(t) \Gamma_{ik}(s) \tag{10.31}$$

where

$$\Gamma_{ik}(s) = \int_0^\infty \gamma_{ik}(\xi) e^{-s\xi} = \text{Laplace transform of } \gamma_{ik}(\xi) \tag{10.32}$$

The only function[3] having the property defined by Eq. 10.29 is an exponential, or a linear combination of exponentials. Thus

$$q_i(t) = \sum_{k=1}^{n} c_{ik} e^{\alpha_{ik} t} \tag{10.33}$$

[3]Actually, the most general function having the property defined by Eq. 10.29 is of the type

$$q_i(t) = \sum_{k=1}^{n} c_{ik} t^m e^{\alpha_{ik} t} \tag{10.33A}$$

which corresponds to m repeated roots in the s-domain. For simplicity this generalization will not be considered here. However all results obtained for the case $m = 0$ are easily generalized to the case $m \neq 0$.

and

$$q_i(t-\xi) = \sum_{k=1}^{n} c_{ik} e^{\alpha_{ik} t} e^{-\alpha_{ik}\xi} \tag{10.34}$$

Comparing Eqs. 10.29 and 10.3 shows that

$$\beta_{ik}(t) = c_{ik} e^{\alpha_{ik} t} \tag{10.35a}$$

$$\gamma_{ik}(\xi) = e^{-\alpha_{ik}\xi} \tag{10.35b}$$

Equation 10.35b shows that the form of $Q_{ik}(s)$ is

$$\Gamma_{ik}(s) = \text{Laplace Transform } e^{-\alpha_{ik}\xi} = \frac{1}{s+\alpha_{ik}} \tag{10.36}$$

Substituting from Eq. 10.36 in Eq. 10.31 gives

$$G(s, t) = \sum_{i=1}^{n} \sum_{k=1}^{m} p_i(t) c_{ik} e^{\alpha_{ik} t} \left(\frac{1}{s+\alpha_{ik}}\right) \tag{10.37}$$

Thus the form of the impulsive response which results in a separable system function is

$$\Omega(t, \tau) = \sum_{i=1}^{n} p_i(t) \sum_{k=1}^{m} c_{ik} \exp(\alpha_{ik}\tau)\delta^{(-1)}(t-\tau) \tag{10.38}$$

Equation 10.38 can be written as

$$\Omega(t, \tau) = \sum_{i=1}^{n} p_i(t) v_i(\tau) \delta^{(-1)}(t-\tau) \tag{10.39}$$

where the $v_i(\tau)$, denoting linear combinations of exponentials; the $p_i(t)$ are the basis functions of the homogeneous differential equation characterizing the linear system with impulsive response $\Omega(t, \tau)$. Another useful form is

$$\Omega(t, \tau) = \sum_{i=1}^{m} d_i(t) \exp(\alpha_i\tau)\delta^{(-1)}(t-\tau) \tag{10.40}$$

where the set of $d_i(t)$ do not necessarily comprise a set of basis functions of the characterizing differential equation.

$\Omega_\xi(t, \xi)$ is defined as $\Omega(t, \tau)$ with the variable change $\xi = t - \tau$:

$$\Omega_\xi(t, \xi) \equiv \Omega(t, t-\xi) \tag{10.41}$$

Thus $\Omega_\xi(t, \xi)$ denotes the impulsive response at time t to an impulse applied at time $t - \xi$. Therefore, in accordance with Eq. 10.27, if $\Omega_\xi(t, \xi)$ is separable in t and ξ, i.e., if

$$\Omega_\xi(t, \xi) = \sum_{i=1}^{m} b_i(t) h_i(\xi) \tag{10.42}$$

then substitution for $\Omega(t, t-\xi) \equiv \Omega_\xi(t, \xi)$ in Eq. 10.28 shows that the system function is separable and given by

$$G(s, t) = \sum_{i=1}^{m} b_i(t) \int_0^\infty h_i(\xi) e^{-s\xi}\, d\xi \tag{10.43}$$

Comparing Eq. 10.23 and 10.43 evidences that $H_i(s)$ is the Laplace transform of $h_i(\xi)$.

Several simplilcations occurring when a function is separable are now discussed.

10.2.1. Determination of the System Responses. For separable $G(s, t)$ Eq. 9.93 is written as

$$x(t) = \sum_{i=1}^{m} b_i(t) \frac{1}{2\pi i} \int_C F(s) H_i(s) e^{st}\, ds \tag{10.44}$$

or simply

$$x(t) = \sum_{i=1}^{m} b_i(t) \mathscr{L}^{-1}[F(s) H_i(s)] \tag{10.45}$$

where $\mathscr{L}^{-1}$ denotes the inverse Laplace transform.

10.2.2. Synthesizing the System. Zadeh [12] notes that a separable system function is of particular physical significance in that it can be synthesized by appropriately interconnecting a linear time-invariant system with time-varying amplifiers. Although Zadeh in discussing the "expansion of variable networks" considers only systems with periodically varying parameters, his insight into the synthesis of these networks provides the groundwork for the expansion, and subsequent synthesis, of networks with nonperiodic parameter variations.

The system function of a periodically varying system can be expressed as a Fourier series by

$$\begin{aligned} G(s, t) = G_0(s) &+ G_1'(s) \cos \omega_0 t + G_1''(s) \sin \omega_0 t + \cdots \\ &+ G_2'(s) \cos 2\omega_0(t) + G_2'' \sin 2\omega_0 t + \cdots \end{aligned} \tag{10.46}$$

Truncation of the right-hand member of Eq. 10.46 yields an approximation to the system function in separable form. Physically interpreted, Eq. 10.46 evidences that the system can be realized as a parallel-series combination of a number of time-invariant systems having sinusoidally varying gains, as in Fig. 10.2.

A system with system function given by Eq. 10.43 is to be synthesized in a similar fashion, as in Fig. 10.3.

Due to the *physical* separation of the time-varying portion from the time-invariant portion that can be achieved in synthesizing a system with a separable system function, these systems are termed *separable systems*

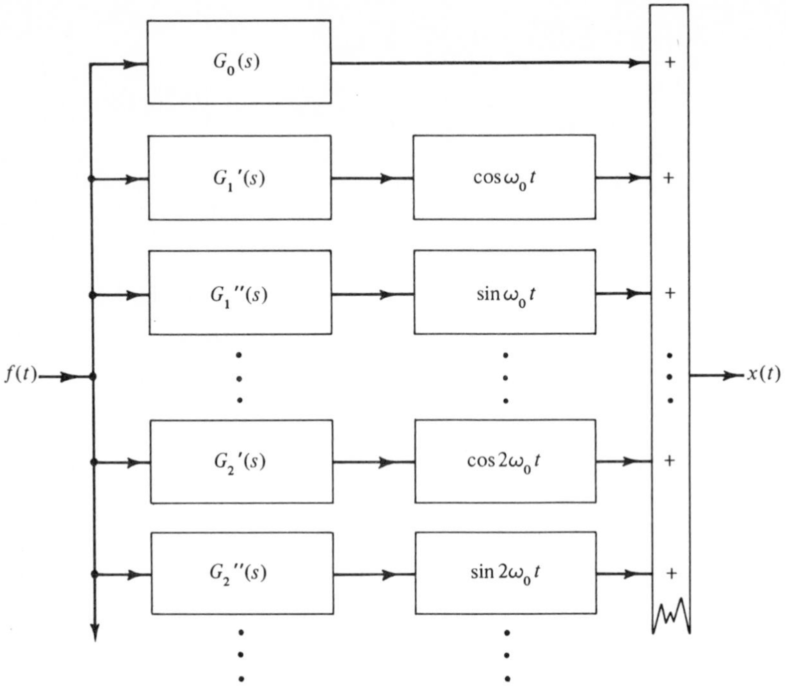

Fig. 10.2. Simulation of linear periodically time-varying system having a separable system function, $G(s, t)$, as given in Eq. 10.46.

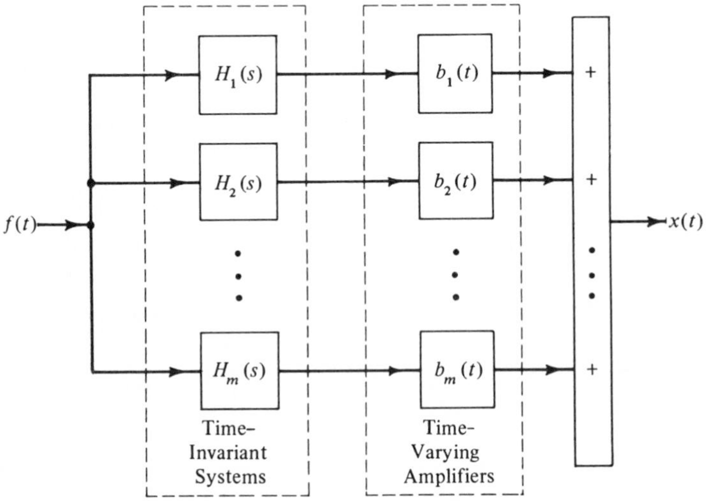

Fig. 10.3. Simulation of general linear time-varying system having a separable system function, $G(s, t)$, as given by Eq. 10.23.

(recall that a system with a separable impulsive response is not necessarily a separable system).

10.2.3. "Time-Varying Poles". The expansion of Eq. 10.23 evidences that any system function that is separable has no time-varying singularities ("time-varying poles"); for such singularities result solely from the time-varying part of the system; gain is the only variable in these systems. In fact, a system function characterizing *any* stable linear time-varying system has no time-varying singularities [3]. This is now established.

Zadeh's system function, as defined in Eq. 9.85 is repeated here:

$$G(s, t) = \int_{-\infty}^{t} \Omega(t, \tau)e^{-s(t-\tau)}\, d\tau \tag{10.47}$$

Substituting the separable form of the impulsive response from Eq. 10.15 in Eq. 10.47, and rearranging, gives

$$G(s, t) = \sum_{i=1}^{n} p_i(t)e^{-st} \int_{-\infty}^{t} q_i(\tau)e^{s\tau}\, d\tau \tag{10.48}$$

Equation 10.48 reveals that the singularities of the system function $G(s, t)$ in the finite s-plane are necessarily the singularities of the integral

$$F_i(s, t) = \int_{-\infty}^{t} q_i(\tau)e^{s\tau}\, d\tau \tag{10.49}$$

Breaking the interval of integration into two subintervals yields

$$F_i(s, t) = \int_{-\infty}^{0} q_i(\tau)e^{s\tau}\, d\tau + \int_{0}^{t} q_i(\tau)e^{s\tau}\, d\tau \tag{10.50}$$

It is noted that the first integral of Eq. 10.50 is independent of t, thus any singularities due to this integral are independent of t. Thus any "time-varying singularities" that $G(s, t)$ may have are due solely to the second integral of Eq. 10.50. Setting $s = x + iy$ the second integral can be written as

$$\begin{aligned} f(s, y) &= \int_{0}^{t} q_i(\tau)e^{x\tau} \cos y\tau\, d\tau + i\int_{0}^{t} q_i(\tau)e^{x\tau} \sin y\tau\, d\tau \\ &= u + iv \end{aligned} \tag{10.51}$$

Applying the Cauchy-Riemann conditions for analyticity to Eq. 10.51 gives

$$\frac{\partial u}{\partial x} = \int_{0}^{t} q_i(\tau)\tau e^{x\tau} \cos y\tau\, d\tau \tag{10.52a}$$

$$\frac{\partial u}{\partial y} = -\int_{0}^{t} q_i(\tau)e^{x\tau}\tau \sin y\tau\, d\tau \tag{10.52b}$$

$$\frac{\partial v}{\partial x} = \int_{0}^{t} q_i(\tau)\tau e^{x\tau} \sin y\tau\, d\tau \tag{10.52c}$$

$$\frac{\partial v}{\partial y} = \int_{0}^{t} q_i(\tau)e^{x\tau}\tau \cos y\tau\, d\tau \tag{10.52d}$$

Thus

$$\frac{\partial u}{\partial x} = \frac{\partial v}{\partial y}, \quad \frac{\partial u}{\partial y} = -\frac{\partial v}{\partial x} \tag{10.53}$$

and the Cauchy-Riemann conditions are satisfied provided that $q_i(t)$ is integrable. Thus, the second integral of Eq. 10.50 is analytic in the interval $(0, t)$ provided that $q_i(t)$ is integrable. If it is assumed that the linear system in question is nonresonant, then

$$\int_{-\infty}^{\infty} |\Omega(t, \tau)|\, d\tau = \int_{-\infty}^{\infty} \left| \sum_{i=1}^{n} p_i(t) q_i(\tau) \delta^{(-1)}(t - \tau) \right| d\tau < \infty \tag{10.54}$$

and the $q_i(\tau)$ are integrable. Hence [3]

Theorem 10.1. If the input and output variables of a nonresonant system are related by a linear differential equation, then the system cannot have time-varying singularities[4].

10.2.4. Implications of Separability of $\Omega(t, \tau)$ and $G(s, t)$. In the preceding it is established that all linear lumped finite-order systems having impulsive-response functions $\Omega(t, \tau)$ are separable, i.e., $\Omega(t, \tau)$ is of the form of Eq. 10.3 with n finite. Conversely, a linear system having a nonseparable impulsive-response function (i.e., separation in the form of Eq. 10.3 is possible only with infinite n) implies that the system cannot be realized with a finite number of lumped components but, rather, that the realization requires *distributed-parameter* components.

The implications of separability of the system function $G(s, t)$ are, however, quite different. If $G(s, t)$ is separable, i.e., of the form of Eq. 10.23, then the system can be realized in terms of a proper combination of time-invariant dynamical systems and time-varying amplifiers (see Fig.

[4]Cruz further states [3]:

In particular, time-varying poles cannot be associated with stable linear differential systems. The concept of a time-varying pole may be useful in approximate analysis of slowly time-varying linear systems, but it has no place in the synthesis of linear differential systems.

Weiss lends additional insight to tųe situation [11]:

If a system function $G(s, t)$ derivable from a linear differential system is rational in s; i.e., if $G(s, t)$ can be represented as a finite sum of partial fractions, viz.

$$G(s, t) = \sum_{k=1}^{m} \frac{A_k(t)}{s + s_k(t)}$$

then the s_k must be constants. In other words, a rational system function must be separable. . . . If $G(s, t)$ is not rational in s, in that it consists of an infinite sum of partial fractions, but it corresponds to an ordinary finite-order, linear differential system, then the infinite sum of partial fractions must be a *representation* of the basic system function which of necessity consists of a finite number of terms.

10.3). Clearly, the time-invariant portions of the system can be either finite or infinite dimensional. Thus, whether or not a system with separable system function $G(s, t) = \sum_{i=1}^{m} b_i(t)H_i(s)$, with m finite, can be realized as a finite order system is determined by whether or not the $H_i(s)$ are rational functions of s.

10.3. OBTAINING SEPARABLE APPROXIMATIONS TO FUNCTIONS OF TWO VARIABLES

If a nonseparable function $\Omega(t, \tau)$ is available as a representation of the impulsive response of a linear system, it may be desirable to find an approximation to this impulsive function so that the approximation is either separable in t and τ or the system function derivable from the approximation is separable in t and s. The implication for a separable approximation to the impulsive response is

$$\Omega(t, \tau) \cong \Omega_a(t, \tau) = \sum_{i=1}^{n} p_i(t)q_i(\tau)\delta^{(-1)}(t - \tau) \tag{10.55}$$

The implication for a separable approximation to the system function is

$$\Omega(t, t - \xi) \cong \Omega_\xi(t, \xi) = \sum_{i=1}^{m} b_i(t)h_i(\xi)\delta^{(-1)}(\xi) \tag{10.56}$$

Accordingly, the problem of finding a separable approximation to the system function can be formulated as that of finding a separable approximation to the impulsive response; in both cases it is assumed that the impulsive response, or an adequate approximation to it, is available.

The general problem may thus be stated as:

Given the real fuction $\Omega(t, \tau)$ of the two real variables t and τ, find the separable approximation

$$\Omega_a(t, \tau) = \sum_{i=1}^{n} p_i(t)q_i(\tau)\delta^{(-1)}(t - \tau) \tag{10.57}$$

Usually the functions $q_i(\tau)$ are chosen quite arbitrarily before evaluation of the approximate representation is begun. This choice is influenced by various factors: by the accuracy desired of an approximation with a specific number of terms; by desire to simplify the determination of the $p_i(t)$; by desire to simplify analysis in which the resulting $\Omega_a(t, \tau)$ is to be used. Several approaches to obtaining $\Omega_a(t, \tau)$ are now given.

10.3.1. Train of Impulse Planes [2]. This approach to obtaining an approximation to an impulsive-response function which corresponds to a separable system function stems from consideration that the impulsive response is of interest insofar as it can aid in characterizing the system: i.e., enabling the determination of the system output for a given input. Accordingly, the ultimate criterion by which the approximation $\Omega_a(t, \tau)$ to the actual impulsive response, $\Omega(t, \tau)$ is to be judged is by the relative agreement of the outputs $x_a(t)$ and $x(t)$, obtained by use of $\Omega_a(t, \tau)$ and $\Omega(t, \tau)$ respectively, for some general input $f(t)$ of interest. The fact that $\Omega_a(t, \tau)$ and $\Omega(t, \tau)$ are themselves apparently grossly dissimilar should not, in itself, cause concern. With this in mind, it is suggested that the function $\Omega(t, \tau)$ be approximated with a train, or series, of impulse planes such that

$$\Omega(t, \tau) \cong \Omega_a(t, \tau) = \sum_{i=0}^{n} (\alpha_{i+1} - \alpha_i) b_i(t) \delta(t - \tau - \alpha_i) \qquad (10.58)$$

Note that the system function corresponding to $\Omega_a(t, \tau)$ is separable. However, $\Omega_a(t, \tau)$ is not separable and thus cannot be realized by a finite-order system.

Taking $\Omega(t, \tau)$ as the impulsive response to an impulse applied at $t = \tau$, causality requires

$$\Omega(t, \tau) = 0; \; t < \tau \qquad (10.59)$$

A plot of $\Omega(t, \tau)$ as a function of t and τ comprises a three-dimensional representation. Consider a sequence of planes parallel to the plane $t - \tau = 0$; i.e.,

$$t - \tau - \alpha_i = 0; \; i = 0, 1, \cdots, N \qquad (10.60)$$

where $\{\alpha_i\}$ denotes a finite sequence of real numbers. The intercepts of the planes with the $\Omega(t, \tau)$ surface are denoted by the $b_i(t)$'s shown shaded in Fig. 10.4. For a fixed τ, the series of Eq. 10.58 is the usual impulse train; for variable τ, it may be termed an impulse-plane train or simply a *train of impulse planes*.

Using the impulsive response of Eq. 10.58 in the superposition integral yields the desired input-output relation

$$x_a(t) = \sum_{i=1}^{N} a_i(t) f(t - \alpha_i) \qquad (10.61)$$

where

$$p_i(t) = (\alpha_{i+1} - \alpha_i) b_i(t) \qquad (10.62)$$

A system with impulsive response as in Eq. 10.58 can be physically realized by a tapped delay line (a pure delay is realized by an infinite-dimension system: i.e., a distributed parameter system such as a transmission line), a set of time-varying amplifiers and a summing amplifier, as shown in Fig. 10.5.

The minimum number of taps that can be used for a simulation depends on the allowable error in $x(t)$; but in general, the more rapid the

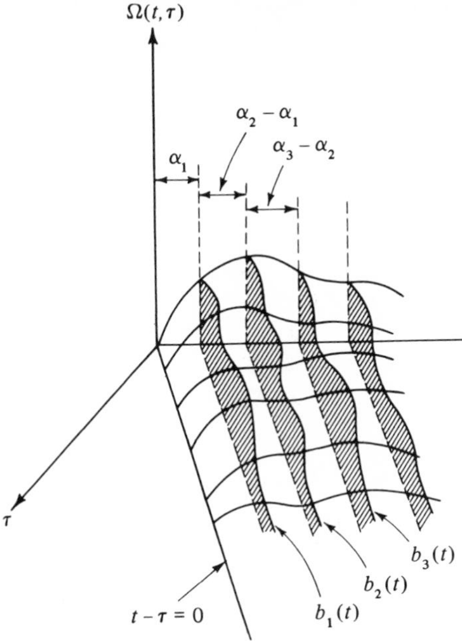

Fig. 10.4. Graphical three-dimensional representation of train of impulse planes.

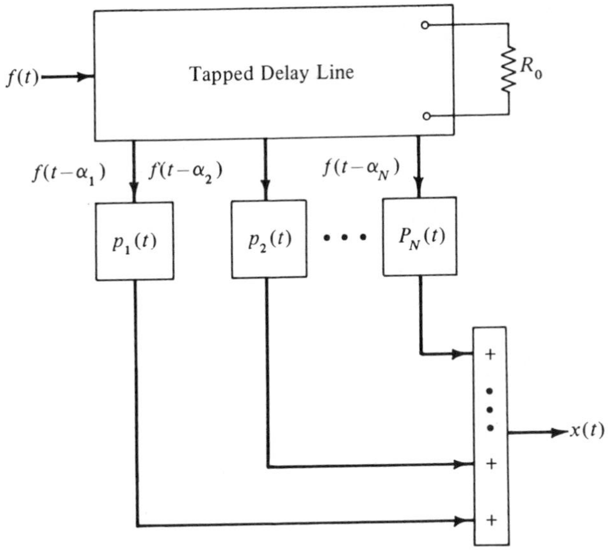

Fig. 10.5. Simulation of system having impulsive response, $\Omega(t, \tau)$, given by Eq. 10.58; i.e., a train of impulse planes.

oscillatory nature of $f(t)$, the more taps are required. Obviously, this simulation is particularly useful for relatively smooth $f(t)$.

Example 10.2. Determine a separable approximation to the impulsive-response function

$$\Omega(t, \tau) \exp [-\alpha(t - \tau)(1 + \zeta \cos \omega_0(t)]\delta^{(-1)}(t - \tau)$$

Using an approximation in the form of a train of impulse planes gives

$$\Omega_a(t, \tau) = \sum_{i=1}^{n} (\alpha_{i+1} - \alpha_i)b_i(t)\delta(t - \tau - \alpha_i)$$

where the $b_i(t)$ are determined as the intersection of the plane

$$t - \tau - \alpha_i = 0$$

and the surface $\Omega(t, \tau)$. Thus

$$b_i(t) = \exp [- \alpha\alpha_i(1 + \zeta \cos \omega_0 t)]\delta^{(-1)}(\alpha_i)$$

By letting

$$\alpha_{i+1} - \alpha_i = \alpha_{j+1} - \alpha_j = \sigma;\ i, j=1, \cdots, N$$

that is, by choosing uniform delays, $b_i(t)$ can be written as

$$b_i(t) = \exp [- i\alpha\, \sigma(1 + \zeta \cos \omega_0 t)]\delta^{(-1)}(i\sigma)$$

Thus

$$\Omega_a(t, \tau) = \sum_{i=1}^{n} \sigma \exp [- i\alpha\, \sigma(1 + \zeta \cos \omega_0 t]\delta^{(-1)}(i\sigma)\delta(t - \tau - i\sigma)$$

10.3.2. The General Orthonormal Expansion [6]. A convenient choice for the $q_i(\tau)$ of Eq. 10.57 is a set of orthonormal functions; i.e., a set of functions having the property that

$$\int_{-\infty}^{\infty} q_k(\tau)q_j(\tau)d\tau = \delta_{jk} \tag{10.63}$$

where δ_{jk} is the Kronecker delta. The use of orthonormal functions for the $q_i(t)$ is of great value when $\Omega(t, \tau)$ is to be determined so that

$$E(t) = \int_{-\infty}^{\infty} [\Omega(t, \tau) - \Omega_a(t, \tau)]^2\, d\tau \tag{10.64}$$

is minimized. For orthonormal $q_i(\tau)$, minimization of $E(t)$ gives[5]

$$p_i(t) = \int_{-\infty}^{\infty} \Omega(t, \tau)q_i(\tau)\, d\tau \tag{10.65}$$

and

$$E_{\min}(t) = \int_{-\infty}^{\infty} \Omega^2(t, \tau)\, d\tau - \sum_{i=1}^{N} p_i^2(t) \tag{10.66}$$

In most instances those $q_i(\tau)$ whose Laplace transforms $Q_i(s)$ are rational in s provide the best overall compromise in the sense of minimizing: (1) the labor in evaluating the $p_i(t)$; (2) the labor in evaluating the system output $x(t)$; (3) the number of terms N for a given approximation accuracy. However, a notable exception—orthogonal functions $q_i(\tau)$ having nonrational $Q_i(s)$ and offering convenient representations—is the nonoverlapping functions of τ evidenced in Cruz's train of impulse planes described in the preceding section. An appropriate set of nonoverlapping pulses may provide a better approximation to $\Omega(t, \tau)$ than does the train of impulse planes. Although the labor of calculation in this case is greater, it is not prohibitive.

Example 10.3 [4]. Determine an approximation $\Omega_a(t, \tau)$, in terms of an orthonormal expansion, to the impulsive response

$$\Omega(t, \tau) = \exp[-\alpha(t - \tau)(1 - \zeta \cos \omega_0 t)]\delta^{(-1)}(t - \tau)$$

so that the system function

$$G_a(s, t) = \int_{-\infty}^{t} \Omega_a(t, \tau) e^{-s(t-\tau)}\, dt$$

is separable.

Making the substitution $\xi = t - \tau$ results in

$$\Omega(t, t - \xi) = \Omega_\xi(t, \xi) = \exp[-\alpha\xi(1 - \zeta \cos \omega_0 t)]\delta^{(-1)}(\xi)$$

Thus, in accordance with Sec. 10.2, $G_a(s, t)$ is separable if $\Omega_\xi(t, \xi)$ is separable. Choose the arbitrary[6] functions

$$f_1(\xi) = e^{-\alpha\xi}\delta^{(-1)}(\xi)$$
$$f_2(\xi) = e^{-\alpha(1-\zeta)\xi}\delta^{(-1)}(\xi)$$

so that

$$\Omega_{a\xi}(t, \xi) = A_1(t)f_1(\xi) + A_2(t)f_2(\xi)$$

Obtain the orthonormal basis $q_1(\xi)$, $q_2(\xi)$ that spans the same function space spanned by the basis $f_1(\xi)$, $f_2(\xi)$:

$$q_1(\xi) = a_{11}f_1(\xi) = a_{11}e^{-\alpha\xi}\delta^{(-1)}(\xi)$$
$$q_2(\xi) = a_{21}f_1(\xi) + a_{22}f_2(\xi)$$
$$= a_{21}e^{-\alpha\xi}\delta^{(-1)}(\xi) + a_{22}e^{-\alpha(1-\zeta)\xi}\delta^{(-1)}(\xi)$$

[5]It must be assumed that $\int_{-\infty}^{\infty} \Omega^2(t, \tau)\, d\tau$ exists, a requirement which is satisfied if the approximated system is nonresonant $\left(\int_{-\infty}^{\infty} |\Omega(t, \tau)|\, d\tau < M_s < \infty\right)$, and has a uniformly bounded impulsive response ($|\Omega(t, \tau)| < M_h < \infty$). These conditions are satisfied in most problems in practice, at least for the range of t which must be considered.

[6]Note that electrical networks with responses $f_1(t - \tau)$ and $f_2(t - \tau)$ are physically realizable by combinations of resistors and capacitors.

where

$$\int_0^\infty q_1^2(\xi)d\xi = \int_0^\infty q_2^2(\xi)d\xi = 1$$

$$\int_0^\infty q_1(\xi)q_2(\xi)\, d\xi = 0$$

Thus

$$a_{11} = \sqrt{2\alpha}$$

$$a_{21} = \frac{2}{\zeta}\sqrt{2\alpha(1-\zeta)}$$

$$a_{22} = \left(\frac{-2+\zeta}{\zeta}\right)\sqrt{2\alpha(1-\zeta)}$$

It is necessary that

$$\Omega_{a\xi}(t, \xi) = p_1(t)q_1(\xi) + p_2(t)q_2(\xi)$$

be the best approximation, in the least-mean-square sense to $\Omega_\xi(t, \xi)$. Thus

$$p_1(t) = \int_0^\infty \Omega_\xi(t, \xi)q_1(\xi)\, d\xi = \frac{\sqrt{2\alpha}}{2\alpha - \alpha\zeta \cos \omega_0 t}$$

$$p_2(t) = \int_0^\infty \Omega_\xi(t, \xi)q_2(\xi)\, d\xi$$

$$= \frac{2}{\zeta}\sqrt{2\alpha(1-\zeta)}\, \frac{1}{2\alpha - \alpha\zeta\cos\omega_0 t} + \frac{\left(\frac{-2+\zeta}{\zeta}\right)\sqrt{2\alpha(1-\zeta)}}{2\alpha - \alpha\zeta(1+\cos\omega_0 t)}$$

Since

$$\Omega_{a\xi}(t, \xi) = p_1(t)q_1(\xi) + p_2(t)q_2(\xi) = A_1(t)f_1(\xi) + A_2(t)f_2(\xi)$$

it can be determined that

$$A_1(t) = \frac{2}{(2 - \zeta\cos\omega_0 t)}\left[\frac{(2-\zeta)(1-\cos\omega_0 t)}{2 - \zeta(1+\cos\omega_0 t)}\right]$$

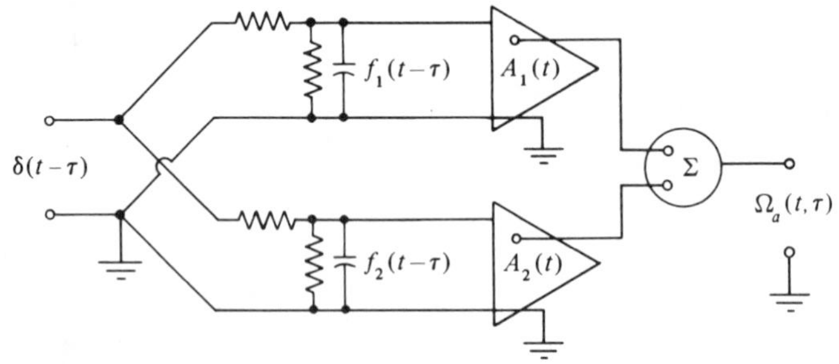

Fig. 10.6. Simulation of system having impulsive response $\Omega_a(t, \tau) = A_1(t)f_1(t-\tau) + A_2(t)f_2(t-\tau)$.

$$A_2(t) = \frac{2}{(2 - \zeta \cos \omega_0 t)} \left\{ \frac{(4 - 2\zeta)(1 - \zeta) \cos \omega_0 t}{(2 - \zeta \cos \omega_0 t)[2 - \zeta(1 + \cos \omega_0 t)]} \right\}$$

A simulation of a system with impulsive response $\Omega_a(t, \tau)$ is shown in Fig. 10.6 In Fig. 10.7 are comparative plots of $\Omega(t, \tau)$ and its approximation $\Omega_{a\xi}(t, \tau)$ for $\alpha t = 0, 1, 10$ and $\zeta = 0.5$.

10.3.3. Determination of Impulsive Response in Separable Form From The System Specifications [9]. Two relatively simple methods are advanced for approximating a system's impulsive response, in separable form, when the specifications are given. The first method requires that the output and input be specified, and that the input be given as a polynomial; the second method requires that only the very critical information about the system's response be given; e.g., final value, peak overshoot, etc. In that these two methods allow the construction of an impulsive-response function $\Omega(t, \tau)$, in separable form directly from the specifications, they differ from the train of impulsive planes of Sec. 10.3.1 and the orthonormal expansion

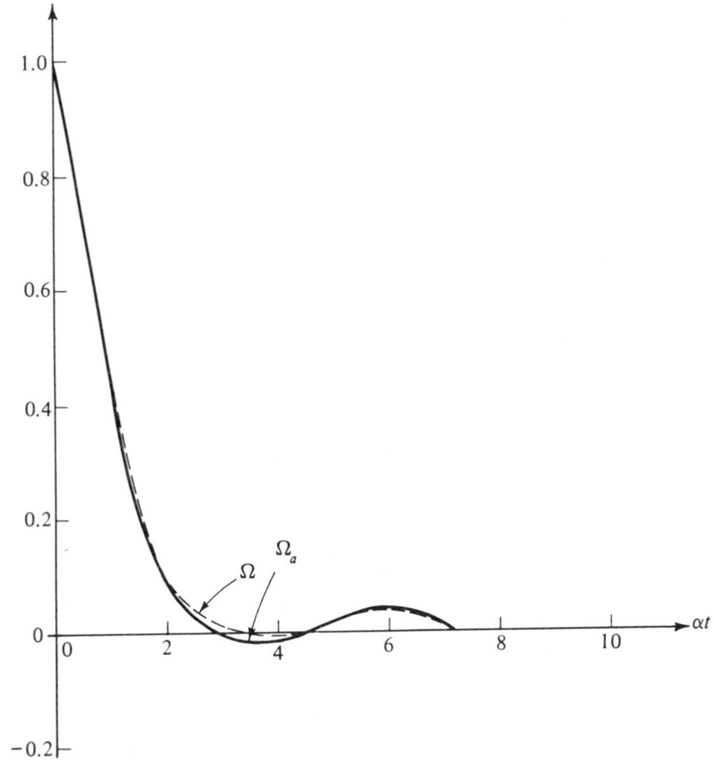

Fig. 10.7a. Example 10.3: approximation to impulsive response ($\alpha\tau = 0$, $\zeta = 0.5$).

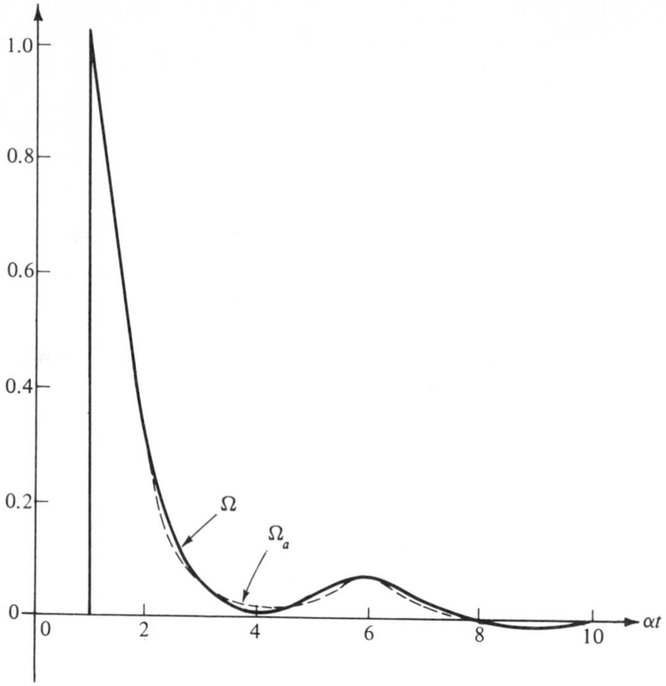

Fig. 10.7b. Example 10.3: approximation to impulsive response ($\alpha\tau = 1.0$, $\zeta = 0.5$).

method of Sec. 10.3.2, both of which require that a function $\Omega(t, \tau)$ be known before a separable approximation to it can be effected.

Approximation of Impulsive Response of Systems with Polynomial Inputs. Consider a linear system that is specified by its polynomial input

$$f(t) = f(t - \tau) = \sum_{n=0}^{N} C_n(t - \tau)^n \delta^{(-1)}(t - \tau) \tag{10.67}$$

and its corresponding output $x(t, \tau)$. A method is now proposed [9] for determing the impulsive response of this system in the general separable form

$$\Omega(t, \tau) = \sum_{i=1}^{r} p_i(t)q_i(\tau)\delta^{(-1)}(t - \tau) + b_r(t)\delta(t - \tau) \tag{10.68}$$

where the term $b_r(t)\delta(t - \tau)$ is included to allow for the possibility of a time-varying amplifier with gain $b_r(t)$ being in parallel with the rest of the system, i.e., $b_r(t)\delta(t - \tau)$ represents the nondynamical portion of the system.

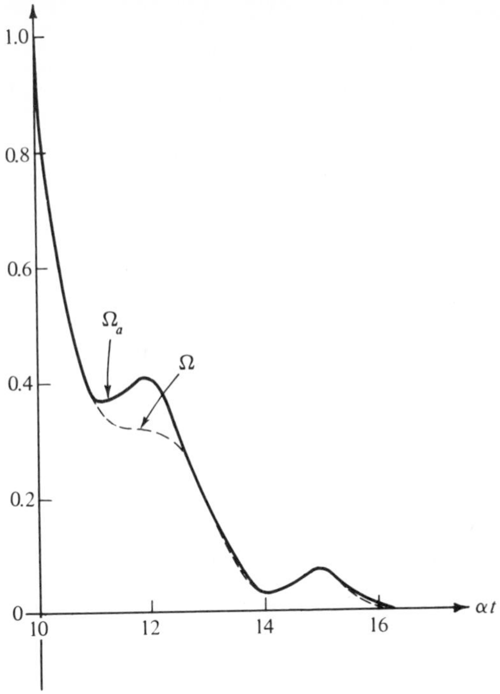

Fig. 10.7c. Example 10.3: approximation to impulsive response ($\alpha\tau = 10.0$, $\zeta = 0.5$).

In accordance with the superposition integral, the response of the system is given by

$$x(t, \tau) = \int_{-\infty}^{t} \Omega(t, \xi) f(\xi - \tau)\, d\xi \tag{10.69}$$

Substituting from Eq. 10.67 in Eq. 10.69 gives

$$x(t, \tau) = \int_{-\infty}^{t} \Omega(t, \xi) \sum_{n=0}^{N} C_n(\xi - \tau)^n \delta^{(-1)}(\xi - \tau)\, d\xi \tag{10.70}$$

which, upon interchange of the integral and summation becomes

$$x(t, \tau) = \sum_{n=0}^{\infty} C_n \int_{\tau}^{t} \Omega(t, \xi)(\xi - \tau)^n\, d\xi \tag{10.71}$$

Substituting from Eq. 10.68 in Eq. 10.71 gives

$$x(t, \tau) = \sum_{n=0}^{N} C_n \int_{\tau}^{t} (\xi - \tau)^n \left[\sum_{i=1}^{r} p_i(t) q_i(\xi) + b_r(t)\delta(t - \xi) \right] d\xi \tag{10.72}$$

Defining

$$\Omega_1(t, \xi) \equiv \sum_{i=1}^{r} p_i(t)q_i(\xi) \tag{10.73}$$

gives

$$x(t, \tau) = \sum_{n=0}^{N} C_n \int_\tau^t (\xi - \tau)^n \Omega_1(t, \xi)d\xi + b_r(t) \sum_{n=0}^{N} C_n(t - \tau)^n \tag{10.74}$$

The problem of determining $\Omega(t, \tau)$, as given by Eq. 10.68 is broken into two parts: that of finding $b_r(t)$ and that of finding $\Omega_1(t, \tau)$. To determine $b_r(t)$ assume that k is the lowest subscript of the nonzero C_n's. Thus

$$x(t, \tau) = \sum_{n=k}^{N} C_n \int_\tau^t \Omega_1(t, \xi)(\xi - \tau)^n d\xi + b_r(t) \sum_{n=k}^{N} C_n(t - \tau)^n \tag{10.75}$$

Taking the k_{th} partial derivative of $x(t, \tau)$ with respect to τ gives

$$\begin{aligned} \frac{\partial^k x(t, \tau)}{\partial \tau^k} &= \sum_{n=k}^{N} C_n \int_\tau^t \Omega_1(t, \xi)(-1)^k(n)(n-1)\cdots(n-k+1)(\xi - \tau)^{n-k}\, d\xi \\ &+ b_r(t) \sum_{n=k}^{N} C_n(-1)^k n(n-1)\cdots(n-k+1)(t-\tau)^{n-k} \end{aligned} \tag{10.76}$$

In the limit, as $\tau \to t$, Eq. 10.76 results in

$$\lim_{\tau \to t} \left[\frac{\partial^k x(t, \tau)}{\partial \tau^k}\right] = b_r(t)c_k(-1)^k k! \tag{10.77}$$

Thus solving Eq. 10.77 for $b_r(t)$ gives the desired result

$$b_r(t) = \frac{(-1)^k}{k!C_k} \lim_{\tau \to t} \left[\frac{\partial^k x(t, \tau)}{\partial \tau^k}\right]; \qquad k = \text{lowest subscript of the nonzero } C_n\text{'s} \tag{10.78}$$

To determine $\Omega_1(t, \tau)$, define

$$x'(t, \tau) \equiv x(t, \tau) - b_r(t) \sum_{n=0}^{N} C_n(t - \tau)^n \tag{10.79}$$

Comparison of Eqs. 10.75 and 10.79 shows that

$$x'(t, \tau) = \sum_{n=0}^{N} C_n \int_\tau^t \Omega_1(t, \xi)(\xi - \tau)^n\, d\xi \tag{10.80}$$

Taking the first $N + 1$ derivatives of $x'(t, \tau)$ with respect to τ gives

$$\frac{\partial x'(t, \tau)}{\partial \tau} = \sum_{n=0}^{N} C_n \int_\tau^t \Omega_1(t, \xi)(-1)n(\xi - \tau)^{n-1}\, d\xi - C_0\Omega_1(t, \tau) \tag{10.81a}$$

$$\vdots$$

$$\vdots$$

$$\frac{\partial^k x'(t, \tau)}{\partial \tau^k} = \sum_{n=0}^{N} C_n \int_{\tau}^{t} \Omega_1(t, \xi)(-1)^k(n)(n-1)\cdots(n-k+1)(\xi-\tau)^{n-k}\, d\xi$$
$$+ \sum_{j=0}^{k-1} C_j \frac{\partial^{k-1-j}\Omega_1(t, \tau)}{\partial \tau^{k-1-j}}(-1)^j(j!) \qquad (10.81\text{b})$$

$$\vdots$$

$$\frac{\partial^{N+1} x'(t, \tau)}{\partial \tau^{N+1}} = \sum_{j=0}^{N} (-1)^{j+1}(j!)C_j \frac{\partial^{N-j}\Omega_1(t, \tau)}{\partial \tau^{N-j}} \qquad (10.81\text{c})$$

The last Eq. 16.81c of the set of $(N + 1)$ derivatives of $x'(t, \tau)$ is a linear *time-invariant* equation whose solution is $\Omega_1(t, \tau)$. As it is an N_{th}-order differential equation, N boundary conditions are necessary in order to obtain a unique solution. The N necessary boundary conditions are obtained from the first N derivatives of $x'(t, \tau)$, given by Eq. 10.81, by taking their limits as $\tau \to t$:

$$\lim_{\tau \to t}\left[\frac{\partial^k x'(t, \tau)}{\partial \tau^k}\right] = \sum_{j=0}^{k=1} (-1)^{j+1}(j!)C_j \left.\frac{\partial^{k-1-j}\Omega_1(t, \tau)}{\partial \tau^{k-1-j}}\right|_{\tau \to t}$$
$$k = 1, 2, \cdots, N \qquad (10.82)$$

Thus the following recursive equation for the boundary values is obtained:

$$\left.\frac{\partial^{k-1}\Omega_1(t, \tau)}{\partial \tau^{k-1}}\right|_{\tau \to t} = \frac{1}{C_0}\left.\frac{\partial^k x'(t, \tau)}{\partial \tau^k}\right|_{\tau \to t}$$
$$- \sum_{j=1}^{k-1} (-1)^{j+1}(j!)C_j \left.\frac{\partial^{k-1-j}\Omega_1(t, \tau)}{\partial \tau^{k-1-j}}\right|_{\tau \to t}; \qquad k = 1, 2, \cdots, N \qquad (10.83)$$

As the differential equation 10.81c for $\Omega_1(t, \tau)$ is with respect to τ, the boundary values determined by Eq. 10.83 as $\tau \to t$ are actually *final* values. By making the substitution

$$\tau = t - z \qquad (10.84)$$

it is observed that as $\tau \to t$, $z \to 0$. Thus this substitution changes the final-value differential equation for $\Omega_1(t, \tau)$ with respect to τ, to an initial-value differential equation for $\Omega_1(t, t - z)$ with respect to z.

Example 10.4. It is specified that a system be synthesized so that an input

$$f(t - \tau) = [2 + (t - \tau) - 2(t - \tau)^2]\delta^{(-1)}(t - \tau)$$

produces an output

$$x(t, \tau) = -\frac{7}{6}t^5 + t^4\left[\frac{5}{6} + \frac{10}{3}\tau\right] + t^3\left[1 - \frac{3}{2}\tau - 3\tau^2\right]$$
$$+ t^2\left[2\tau + \frac{1}{2}\tau^2 + \frac{2}{3}\tau^3 + 1\right]$$
$$+ t\left[2 - \tau - 3\tau^2 + \frac{1}{6}\tau^3 + \frac{1}{6}\tau^4\right]$$

Determine the impulsive response $\Omega(t, \tau)$ that satisfies these specifications.

Comparison of the specified $f(t - \tau)$ with Eq. 10.67 shows that $N = 2$, $C_0 = 2$, $C_1 = 1$, $C_2 = -2$; the first nonzero C_n is $C_0 = 2$. Thus use of Eq. 10.78 with $k = 0$ results in

$$b_r(t) = \frac{1}{C_0}\lim_{\tau\to t}[x(t, \tau)] = t$$

Substitution of $b_r(t) = t$ in Eq. 10.74 results in

$$x(t, \tau) = \sum_{n=0}^{N} C_n \int_{\tau}^{t} \Omega_1(t, \xi)(\xi - \tau)^n \, d\xi + [2t + t(t - \tau) - 2t(t - \tau)^2]$$

Thus in accordance with Eq. 10.79,

$$x'(t, \tau) = t^3\left(3 - \frac{3}{2}\tau - 3\tau^2\right) + t^2\left(-2\tau + \frac{1}{2}\tau^2 + \frac{2}{3}\tau^3\right)$$
$$+ t^4\left(\frac{5}{6} - \frac{10}{3}\tau\right) + t\left(-\tau^2 + \frac{1}{6}\tau^3 + \frac{1}{6}\tau^4\right) - \frac{7}{6}t^5$$

Taking the first three derivatives with respect to τ gives

$$\frac{\partial x'(t, \tau)}{\partial \tau} = t^3\left(-\frac{3}{2} - 6\tau\right) + t^2(-2 + \tau + 2\tau^2) - \frac{10}{3}t^4$$
$$+ t^4\left(-2\tau + \frac{1}{2}\tau^2 + \frac{2}{3}\tau^3\right)$$

$$\frac{\partial^2 x'(t, \tau)}{\partial \tau^2} = -6t^3 + t^2(1 + 4\tau) + t(-2 + \tau + 2\tau^2)$$

$$\frac{\partial^3 x'(t, \tau)}{\partial \tau^3} = 4t^2 + t(1 + 4\tau)$$

Substituting from above in Eq. 10.81c, with $N = 2$, results in the linear time-invariant differential equation for $\Omega_1(t, \tau)$.

$$4t^2 + t(1 + 4\tau) = 4\Omega_1(t, \tau) + \frac{\partial \Omega_1(t, \tau)}{\partial \tau} - 2\frac{\partial^2 \Omega_1(t, \tau)}{\partial \tau^2}$$

with the final values obtained from the recursive equation 10.83:

$$\Omega_1(t, t) = -\frac{1}{C_0}\left\{\frac{\partial x'(t, \tau)}{\partial \tau}\bigg|_{\tau\to t}\right\} = 2t^2$$

$$\frac{\partial \Omega_1(t, \tau)}{\partial \tau}\bigg|_{\tau\to t} = -\frac{1}{C_0}\left\{\frac{\partial^2 x'(t, \tau)}{\partial \tau^2}\bigg|_{\tau\to t} - C_1\Omega_1(t, t)\right\} = t$$

Changing to an initial value problem by the variable substitution $\tau = t - z$ and simplifying the algebraic manipulations by letting

$$k_1 \equiv 4t^2 + \frac{t}{2}$$
$$k_2 \equiv 2t$$
$$f(z) \equiv \Omega_1(t, t - z)$$

Thus

$$\frac{d^2f(z)}{dz^2} + \frac{1}{2}\frac{df(z)}{dz} - 2f(z) = k_2 z - k_1;\ f(0) = 2t^2,\ f^1(0) = -t$$

Solving and changing variables back to the original results in

$$\Omega(t, \tau) = t^2 + t\tau + t\delta(t - \tau)$$

Approximation of Impulsive Response of Systems Whose Specifications Do not Include Equations of Input and Output Functions. An alternate procedure, for approximating the impulsive response of a system described by specifications which do not include equations describing the system's input and corresponding output, is now advanced [9]. By use of the Pade approximation it allows construction of the impulsive-response function $\Omega(t, \tau)$, in separable form, directly from the specifications.

In illustration of this method, consider the problem of approximating the impulsive response $\Omega(t, \tau)$ in the particular region of interest $0 \leq \tau \leq T_s$ under the condition that the system, in response to a unit-step[7] input applied at some time $t = T < T_s$, settle to within n percent of its final steady-state value (unity) at the time $t = T_s$, where $T_s > T$. This problem is one typical of the design of a final-value controller.

[7]Synthesis procedures that require that the impulsive response be known can still be used as the impulsive response $\Omega(t, \tau)$ is related to the unit-step response $H(t, \tau)$ by

$$\Omega(t, \tau) = -\frac{\partial H(t, \tau)}{\partial t} \tag{10.85A}$$

The proof is straightforward. By the superposition integral the response of a system to an arbitrary forcing function $f(t)$ is

$$x(t) = \int_0^t \Omega(t, \xi) f(\xi)\, d\xi \tag{10.85B}$$

Considering a unit-step forcing function $\delta^{(-1)}(t - \tau)$, the unit-step response $H(t, \tau)$ is

$$H(t, \tau) = \int_0^t \Omega(t, \xi)\delta^{(-1)}(\xi - \tau)\, d\xi = \int_\tau^t \Omega(t, \xi)\, d\xi \tag{10.85C}$$

Let $\dfrac{\partial H_0(t, \xi)}{\partial \xi} = \Omega(t, \xi)$. Thus

$$H(t, \tau) = H_0(t, t) - H_0(t, \tau) \tag{10.85D}$$

Taking the derivative with respect to τ gives the desired result

$$\frac{\partial H(t, \tau)}{\partial \tau} = -\frac{\partial H_0(t, \tau)}{\partial \tau} = -\Omega(t, \tau) \tag{10.85E}$$

Figure 10.8, in which the τ axis is taken perpendicular to the plane of the paper, gives a two-dimensional view of the unit-step reponse $H(t, \tau)$; the planes defined by the curves $H(t, 0)$ and $H(t, T)$ bound the region of interest of $H(t, \tau)$.

Choosing $H(t, 0)$ and $H(t, T)$ of the forms

$$H(t, 0) = 1 - \exp(-a_1 t) \tag{10.86a}$$

and

$$H(t, T) = 1 - \exp[-a_2(t - T)] \tag{10.86b}$$

a_1 and a_2 are chosen so that

$$H(T_s, 0) = H(T_s, T) = 1 - \frac{n}{100} \tag{10.87}$$

Thus $H(t, \tau)$ meets the specifications for $\tau = 0$ and $\tau = T$. The unit-step response, $H(t, \tau)$, could be fixed for more than two values of τ, providing a better approximation. However, the number of values of τ for which $H(t, \tau)$ is fixed is generally equal to the number of terms in the final separable function. Thus the better the desired approximation, the higher the order of the resulting synthesized system.

As a first approximation, satisfying exactly the restrictions provided by Eqs. 10.86 and 10.87, $H(t, \tau)$ can be taken as the discontinuous function

$$H(t, \tau) = H(t, 0) + [H(t, T) - H(t, 0)]\delta^{(-1)}(\tau - T) \tag{10.88}$$

where $\delta^{(-1)}(\tau - T)$ denotes the unit-step function occurring at $\tau = T$. This is illustrated in the region of interest, $0 \leq \tau \leq T$, by Fig. 10.9.

It is possible now, using a Pade approximation, to approximate the surface described by Eq. 10.88 by a smooth continuous surface; a smooth continuous $H(t, \tau)$ is generally simplest insofar as a physical realization is concerned. Laplace transforming Eq. 10.88, with τ as the transformed variable, gives

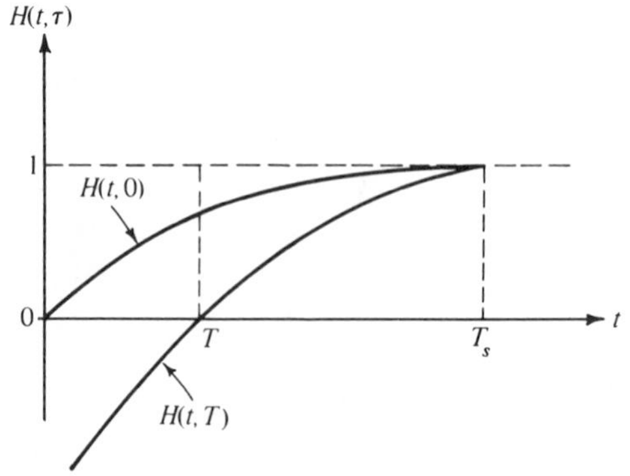

Fig. 10.8. Two-dimensional view of planes cutting unit-step response function, $H(t, \tau)$, at $\tau = 0$ and $\tau = T$.

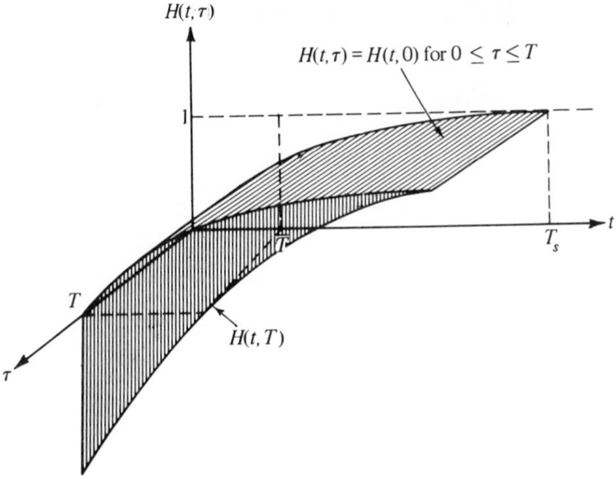

Fig. 10.9. Three-dimensional representation of discontinuous approximation to impulsive response function, $H(t, \tau)$, valid in region of interest $0 < \tau < T$.

$$\bar{H}(t, s) = \frac{1}{s}\{H(t, 0) + [H(t, T) - H(t, 0)]e^{-sT}\} \tag{10.89}$$

Approximating e^{-sT}/s by the Pade approximation[8]: i.e.,

$$e^{-sT}/s = \frac{-2(s - 3T)}{Ts(s^2 + 4s/T + 6/T^2)} \tag{10.90}$$

and substituting from Eq. 10.90 in Eq. 10.89 gives

$$\bar{H}(t, s) = \bar{H}_a(t, s) = \frac{1}{s} H(t, 0) + [H(t, T) - H(t, 0)]\left[\frac{2(s - 3/T)}{Ts(s^2 + 4s/T + 6/T^2}\right] \tag{10.91}$$

[8]*Pade Approximation* [10]. Suppose it is desired to approximate the function e^{-x} by the function $(1 - ax)/(1 + bx + cx^2)$. Taking the Taylor series of these two functions gives

$$e^{-x} = 1 - x + \frac{x^2}{2!} - \frac{x^3}{3!} + \cdots \tag{10.90A}$$

$$\frac{1 - ax}{1 + bx + cx^2} = 1 + (a - b)x - [c - b(a - b)]x^2 + \{c(a - b) - b[c + b(a - b)]\}x^3 + \cdots \tag{10.90B}$$

Equating coefficients of like powers of x up to x^3 results in $a = -1/3$, $b = 2/3$, $c = 1/6$. Therefore

$$e^{-x} \cong \frac{1 - \frac{1}{3}x}{1 + \frac{2}{3}x + \frac{1}{6}x^2} \tag{10.90C}$$

Inverse Laplace-transforming $H_a(t. s)$ gives the final approximaton as

$$H_a(t, \tau) = \{H(t, 0)[\exp(-2\tau/T) \sin(\sqrt{2}\,\tau/T + \psi) + H(t, T)[1 - 3\exp(-2\tau/T) \sin(\sqrt{2}\,\tau/T + \psi)]\}\delta^{(-1)}(t - \tau) \quad (10.92)$$

where $\psi = \sin^{-1}(1/3)$ and $H(t, 0)$ and $H(t, T)$ are given in Eqs. 10.86 and 10.87.

Note that other Pade approximations can be used for e^{sT}/s in Eq. 10.89 and that a better approximation is obtained if a higher-order polynomial is used. The particular approximation used was chosen because of its relative simplicity and because the numerator polynomial is of lesser degree than the denominator polynomial.

Two variations of this procedure that provide better accuracy are:

1. Fix $H(t, \tau)$, according to the problem specifications, at more than the two points in the region of interest, $0 \leq \tau \leq T$, used in Eqs. 10.86 and 10.87. Then the first discontinuous approximation to $H(t, \tau)$, comparable to Eq. 10.89, involves a series of steps.

2. Approximate a higher *derivative* of $H(t, \tau)$ as a series of step functions in the τ direction and integrate this function, after smoothing by a Pade approximation, an appropriate number of times to obtain $H(t, \tau)$.

10.4. REDUCTION OF A TIME-VARYING LINEAR DIFFERENTIAL OPERATOR TO A SUM OF STATIONARY OPERATORS [8]

A linear differential equation with time-varying coefficients can be written in operator form as

$$A(t, p)x(t) = f(t) \quad (10.93)$$

where $p \equiv \dfrac{d}{dt}$ and

$$A(t, p) = \sum_{k=0}^{n} A_k(t)p^k \quad (10.94)$$

$A(t, p)$ is referred to as the time-varying operator or the *nonstationary* operator. In some cases the determination of the solution to Eq. 10.93, or its impulsive response, is simplified by transforming Eq. 10.93 to the form

$$\sum_{j=1}^{m} S_j(p)[s_j(t)x(t)] = f(t) \quad (10.95)$$

where $S_j(p)$ is a stationary operator and $s_j(t)$ is a known function of time which is referred to as the *kernel* of the operator.

For the case $m = 1$ the solution of Eq. 10.95 is obtained by solving the linear constant-coefficient differential equation for $X(t) = s_1(t)x(t)$.

In some cases when $m > 1$ the impulsive response may be obtained straightforwardly by using the Laplace transform; in other cases one gets a differential equation in s of lower order, and no apparent advantage in obtaining a solution results. However, even in instances where form 10.95 does not lead to a simpler analytic solution, it often proves useful in effecting an analog representation of the equation (particularly in the case that $m \leq n$; see Fig. 10.10), or possibly helps in analyzing the structure from which the original equation derives.

An important application of such a reduction arises in the use of Boxer and Thaler's z-form [13] and Halijak's trapezoidal convolution [14] which require that the differential equation to be in the form of Eq. 10.95.

An algorithm is now introduced [8] whereby a nonstationary differential operator $A(t, p)$, representable as a finite power series in terms of the differential operator p (i.e., $A(t, p)$ as shown in Eq. 10.94 with the $A_k(t)$ differentiable for $k = 0, 1, \ldots, n$), is reduced to a sum of stationary operators with suitable kernels; e.g.,

$$A(t, p) = \sum_{j=1}^{m} S_j(p)[s_j(t) \tag{10.96}$$

The algorithm is such that the nonstationary operator $A(t, p)$ reduces to the desirable single stationary operator case of $m = 1$ whenever this reduction is possible. This is not to say, however, that Eq. 10.96 has, in general, the fewest number of terms possible.

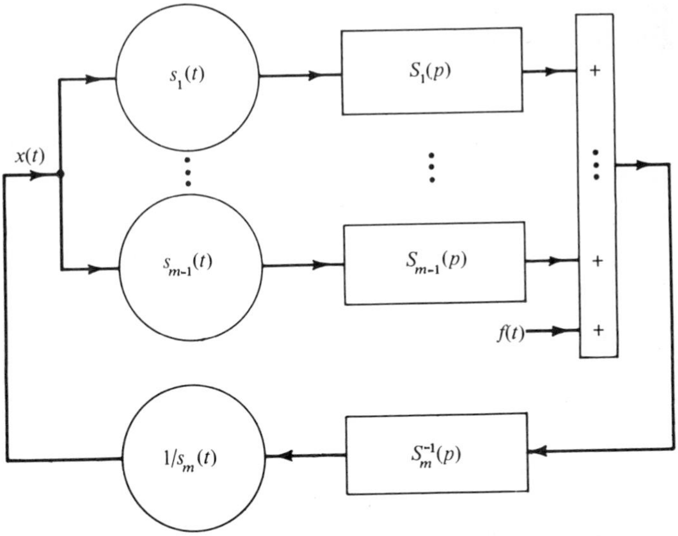

Fig. 10.10. Simulation of linear differential equation having a differential nonstationary operator, $A(t, p)$, expressable as a sum of stationary operators.

An important condition in itself, and the one on which Sklyarevich's algorithm is based, is that under which $A(t, p)$ can be reduced to a *single* operator $S_1(p)$ with the kernel $s_1(t)$. This condition is found form the formula [8]

$$S_1(p)[s_1(t)x(t)] = s_1(t+q)S_1(p)x(t) = A(t, p)x(t) \tag{10.97}$$

where

$$q \equiv \frac{\partial}{\partial p} \tag{10.98}$$

Expanding $s_1(t+q)$ in a Taylor series with respect to the operator q about the point $q = 0$ gives

$$s_1(t+q) = \sum_{j=0}^{\infty} \frac{1}{j!} s_1^{(j)}(t) q^j \tag{10.99}$$

where $s_1^{(j)}(t)$ denotes the jth derivative of $s_1(t)$ with respect to t. Substituting for $s_1(t+q)$ from Eq. 10.99 in Eq. 10.97 results in

$$A(t, p) = \sum_{j=0}^{\infty} \frac{1}{j!} s_1^{(j)}(t) S_1^{(j)}(p) \tag{10.100}$$

where $S_1^{(j)}(p)$ denotes the jth derivative of $S_1(p)$ with respect to p.

Accordingly, if there exist functions $s_1(t)$ and $S_1(p)$ such that Eq. 10.100 is satisfied, the nonstationary operator $A(p, t)$ reduces to the form of a single stationary operator $S_1(p)$ with the kernel $A_1(t)$.

Since the form of Eq. 10.94 indicates a lumped nth-order system, it is reasonable to assume that

$$S_1(p) = \sum_{i=0}^{n} a_i p^i \tag{10.101}$$

where the a_i do not depend on t since $S_1(p)$ is stationary. Differentiating Eq. 10.101 gives

$$S_1^{(j)}(p) = \begin{cases} \displaystyle\sum_{i=j}^{n} \frac{i!}{(i-j)!} a_i p^{i-j} & j \leq n \\ 0 & j > n \end{cases} \tag{10.102}$$

Substituting for $S_1^{(j)}(p)$ from Eq. 10.102 in Eq. 10.100 results in

$$A(t, p) = \sum_{j=0}^{n} \sum_{i=j}^{n} \frac{i!}{j!(i-j)!} a_i s_1^{(j)}(t) p^{i-j} \tag{10.103}$$

and setting $k = i - j$ gives

$$A(t, p) = \sum_{j=0}^{n} \sum_{k=0}^{n-j} \frac{(k+j)!}{j!k!} a_{k+j} s_1^{(j)}(t) p^k \tag{10.104}$$

Interchanging summations with respect to j and k and comparing Eqs. 10.104 and 10.94 shows that

$$A_k(t) = \sum_{j=0}^{n-k} \frac{(k+j)!}{j!k!} a_{k+j} s_1^{(j)}(t) \qquad k = 0, 1, \cdots, n \tag{10.105}$$

Setting $a_n = 1$ (with no loss of generality) in Eq. 10.105 yields a system of $n + 1$ equations in n unknown constants, $a_j (j = 0, 1, \cdots, n - 1)$, and one unknown function $s_1(t)$.

$$A_0(t) = \sum_{j=0}^{n} a_j s_1^{(j)}(t) \tag{10.106a}$$

$$\vdots$$

$$A_{n-1}(t) = \sum_{j=0}^{1} \frac{(n-1+j)!}{j!(n-1)!} a_{n-1+j} s_1^{(j)}(t)$$

$$A_n(t) = s_1(t) \tag{10.106b}$$

Thus the system of n equations for $A_0(t), \cdots, A_{n-1}(t)$, given by Eqs. 10.106a, can be solved for $a_0, \cdots, a_{n-1}$ once $s_1(t)$ is known to be equal to $A_n(t)$ by Eq. 10.106b. Solution of this system of equations yields

$$a_i s_1(t) = \sum_{j=0}^{n-i} \frac{(-1)^j (i+j)!}{i!j!} A_{i+j}^{(j)}(t) \tag{10.107}$$

Thus Eqs. 10.101, 10.106b, and 10.107 enable complete determination of the stationary operator $S_1(p)$ and its kernel $s_1(t)$, whenever the nonstationary operator $A(t, p)$ is reducible to a single stationary operator.

It is now necessary to establish whether or not such a reduction is possible. Introduce the functions

$$r_i(t) \equiv \sum_{j=0}^{n-i} \frac{(-1)^j (i+j)!}{i!j!} A_{i+j}^{(j)}(t) \tag{10.108}$$

Therefore

$$r_n(t) = A_n(t) \tag{10.109}$$

Note that when the nonstationary operator can be reduced to a single stationary operator,

$$r_i(t) = a_i s_1(t) = a_i A_n(t); \; i = 0, 1, \cdots, n \tag{10.110}$$

showing that all the functions $r_i(t)$ are linearly dependent of each other. Equivalently, if all the functions $r_i(t)$, as defined in Eq. 10.108, are pairwise linearly dependent, the nonstationary operator $A(t, p)$ is reducible to the stationary operator $S_1(p)$ with the kernel $s_1(t) = r_n(t)$. The coefficients of the stationary operator of Eq. 10.101 are then furnished by

$$a_i = \frac{r_i(t)}{r_n(t)} \tag{10.111}$$

In general, some of the functions $r_i(t)$ are linearly independent and it is not possible to reduce $A(t, p)$ to a single stationary operator. In this case Sklyarevich's algorithm proceeds as follows:

1. Choose $r_n(t) = A_n(t)$ to be the first kernel $s_1(t)$.
2. Select a_{1i} arbitrarily except for $a_{1n} = 1$ and form the arbitrary stationary operator

$$S_1(p) = \sum_{i=0}^{n} a_{1i} p^i \tag{10.112}$$

3. Define the nonstationary operator

$$F_2(p, t) = A(p, t) - S_1(p)[s_1(t) \tag{10.113}$$

The effect of this substraction can be seen by writing

$$S_1(p)[s_1(t) = \sum_{k=0}^{n} A_{1k}(t) p^k \tag{10.114}$$

where the $A_{1k}(t)$ are expressed in terms of $S_1(p)$ and $s_1(t)$ through use of Eq. 10.105. When $k = n$

$$A_{1n}(t) = A_n(t) = s_1(t) \tag{10.115}$$

Therefore

$$F_2(p, t) = \sum_{k=0}^{n} A_k(t) p^k - \sum_{k=0}^{n} A_{1k}(t) p^k \tag{10.116}$$

becomes

$$F_2(p, t) = \sum_{k=0}^{n-1} [A_k(t) - A_{1k}(t)] p^k \tag{10.117}$$

evidencing that the operator $F_2(p, t)$ is of a lower order than $A(p, t)$.

4. Repeat the algorithm for $F_2(p, t)$, obtaining

$$F_3(p, t) = F_2(p, t) - S_2(p)[s_2(t) \tag{10.118}$$

The process is repeated successively until an operator

$$F_h(p, t) = s_m(t) \tag{10.119}$$

is obtained, independent of the differential operator p. The nonstationary operator $A(t, p)$ then can be written as the sum of nonstationary operators by use of Eq. 10.96.

As the a_{ji} are not uniquely determined, there are various ways of representing a nonstationary operator as a sum of stationary operators. A procedure that is easily applied is to choose the $a_{ji} = 0$ (except for $a_{jn} = 1$). This gives $S_j(p) = p^j$ and $s_j(t) = r_j(t)$, yielding the general result

$$A(t, p)x(t) = \sum_{j=0}^{n} p^j[r_j(t)x(t)] \tag{10.120}$$

which, however, usually is not the simplest reduction.

Example 10.5. Determine $A(t, p)$ as a sum of stationary operators when

$$A(t, p) = t^3p^2 + t^2p + 1$$

Using of Sklyarevich's algorithm:

1. Choose

$$r_2(t) = A_2(t) = s_1(t) = t^3$$

2. Select $a_{12} = 1$, $a_{10} = a_{11} = 0$. Thus

$$S_1(p) = \sum_{i=0}^{2} a_{1i}p^i = p^2$$

3. Define

$$\begin{aligned} F_2(p, t) &= (t^3p^2 + t^2p + 1) - p^2t^3 \\ &= (t^3p^2 + t^2p + 1) - (t^3p^2 - 6t^2p + 6t) \\ &= -\,5t^2p - 6t + 1 \end{aligned}$$

Choose

$$r_1(t) = -\,5t^2 = s_2(t)$$

4. Select $a_{21} = 1$, $a_{20} = 0$. Thus

$$S_2(p) = \sum_{i=0}^{1} a_{21}p^i = p$$

5. Define

$$\begin{aligned} F_3(p, t) &= (-\,5t^2p - 6t + 1) + 5pt^2 \\ &= (-\,5t^2p - 6t + 1) - (-\,5t^2p - 10t) \\ &= 4t + 1 \end{aligned}$$

Choose

$$r_0(t) = 4t + 1 = s_3(t)$$

6. Select $a_{31} = 1$. Thus

$$S_3(p) = 1$$

7. Define

$$F_4(p, t) = (4t + 1) - (4t + 1) = 0$$

Therefore

$$A(t, p) = \sum_{i=1}^{3} S_i(p)s_1(t)$$
$$= p^2t^3 - 5pt^2 + 4t + 1$$

Example 10.6. Determine $A(t, p)$ as a sum of stationary operators when

$$A(t, p) = \sin \omega t p^2 + 2\omega \cos \omega t p - \omega^2 \sin \omega t$$

Using Sklyarevich's algorithm,

1. Choose

$$r_2(t) = A_2(t) = s_1(t) = \sin \omega t$$

2. Select

$$S_1(p) = p^2$$

3. Define

$$F_2(p, t) = (\sin \omega t p^2 + 2\omega \cos \omega t p - \omega^2 \sin \omega t) - p^2 \sin \omega t = 0$$

Therefore

$$A(t, p) = p^2 \sin \omega t$$

Thus the differential equation

$$\sin \omega t \frac{d^2x(t)}{dt^2} + 2\omega \cos \omega t \frac{dx(t)}{dt} - \omega^2 \sin \omega t x(t) = \delta(t)$$

can be written as

$$\frac{d^2}{dt^2}[x(t) \sin \omega t] = \delta(t)$$

Solving for $x(t) \sin \omega t$ with $x(0) = \dot{x}(0) = 0$ results in

$$x(t) \sin \omega t = t$$

Thus

$$x(t) = t/\sin \omega t$$

REFERENCES

[1] Bendat, J., "Exact Integral Equation Solutions and Synthesis for a Large Class of Optimum Time-Variable Linear Filters," *IRE Trans. on Information Theory*, vol. IT-3 (1957).

[2] Cruz, J., "A Generalization of the Impulsive Train Approimation for Time-Varying Linear System in the Time-Domain," *IRE Trans. on Circuit Theory*, vol. CT-6 (1959), pp. 393–394.

[3] Cruz, J., "On the Realizability of Linear Differential Systems," *IRE Trans. on Circuit Theory*, vol. CT-7 (1960), pp. 347–348.

[4] Cruz, J., "On the Synthesis of Time-Varying Linear Systems," *Technical Note No. 9*, Circuit Theory Group, Engineering Experiment Station, University of Illinois, Urbana, Ill., August 1959.

[5] Cruz, J., and M. Van Valkenberg, "The Synthesis of Models for Time-Varying Linear Systems," *Proceedings*, Symposium on Active Networks and Feedback Systems, Polytechnic Press, Polytechnic Institute of Brooklyn, N. Y., 1960, pp. 621–623.

[6] Gilbert, E., "An Approximate Method for Analytically Evaluating the Response of Time-Variable Linear Systems," *IRE Trans. on Circuit Theory*, vol. CT-8 (1961), pp. 289–295.

[7] Mal'chikov, S., "On the Synthesis of Linear Automatic Control Systems with Variable Parameters," *Automation and Remote Control*, vol. 20 (1959), pp. 1543–1549.

[8] Sklyarevich, A., "Representing Nonstationary Linear Differential Polynomial Operators in the Form of Sums of Stationary Operators," *Automation and Remote Control*, vol. 22 (1961), pp. 255–262.

[9] Stubberud, A., "A Technique for the Synthesis of Linear Nonstationary Feedback System—Part I: The Approvination Problem," *IEEE Transactions on Applications in Industry*, vol. 67 (July 1963), pp. 192–196.

[10] Truxal, J., *Control Systems Synthesis*, McGraw-Hill, New York, 1955.

[11] Weiss, L., "Time-Varying Systems with Separable System Functions," *Report on Representation and Analysis of Signals,* Part XIV, John Hopkins University, Baltimore, Md.

[12] Zadeh, L., "Frequency Analysis of Variable Networks," *IRE Proc.*, vol. 38 (1950), pp. 291–299.

[13] Boxer, R. and Thaler, S., "An Operational Calculus for Numerical Analysis," *IRE International Convention Record*, part 2 (1956), pp. 100–105.

[14] Halijak, C., "Digital Approximation of the Solutions of Differential Equations Using Trapezoidal Convolution," *Bendix Systems Document ITM-64*, Bendix Systems Division, Ann Arbor, Mich., August 1960.

[15] Weiss, L., "On System Functions with the Separability Property," *International Journal of Control*, vol. 1, no. 5 (1965), pp. 487–496.

PROBLEMS

10.1 (a) Give an example of a physical linear time-varying system with separable impulsive-response $\Omega(t, \tau)$ and a nonseparable system function $G(s, t)$.

(b) Repeat for the case that both the impulsive response and the system function are separable.

(c) Repeat for the case that neither the impulsive response nor the system function are separable.

(d) Repeat for the case that the impulsive response is nonseparable and the system function is separable.

10.2 Use Theorem 5.1 and the results of Sec. 6.3 to determine the state-variable equations in phase-variable form of a system having the impulsive response

$$\Omega(t, \tau) = \frac{1}{5}(t^{-2}\tau^{3} - t^{3}\tau^{-2})$$

Compare your results with those obtained in Example 10.1.

10.3 Give an example of a physical linear time-varying system that can be effectively analyzed using the notion of "time-varying poles." Carefully justify such an analysis, stating the conditions under which the analysis is proper.

10.4 (a) Determine separable approximations to the following impulsive-response functions using both the train of impulse planes method (Sec. 10.3.1) and the orthonormal expansion method (Sec. 10.3.2)

(i) $\Omega(t, \tau) = e^{t\tau}\delta^{(-1)}(t - \tau)$

(ii) $\Omega(t, \tau) = \sin[\cos(t - \tau)]\delta^{(-1)}(t - \tau)$

(b) Synthesize systems corresponding to each of the approximations obtained in part *a*. Insofar as a physical realization is concerned, which of these two methods is of greater practical use? Why?

(c) Compare the response of the actual systems to that of the approximate systems for unit-step inputs applied at various times $t \geq 0$.

10.5 Synthesize a system which when excited by the input

$$f(t - \tau) = [1 + (t - \tau) + (t - \tau)^2]\delta^{(-1)}(t - \tau)$$

produces the output

$$x(t, \tau) = t^5 - t^4(1 + \tau) + t^3(1 + \tau + \tau^2) - t^2(1 + \tau + \tau^2 + \tau^3) + t(1 + \tau + \tau^2 + \tau^3 + \tau^4)$$

10.6 Determine $A(t, p)$ as a sum of stationary operators for each of the following cases

(i) $A(t, p) = t \sin tp^2 + 2(\sin t + t\cos t)p + 2\cos t - t\sin t$

(ii) $A(t, p) = tp^2 + t^3p + t^2$

INDEX